CW00923770

MATH
ECONOMICS

A COMPANION TO MANKIW AND TAYLOR ECONOMICS

KEN HEATHER AND
SIMKA STEFANOVA

$\sum_{T}^{M} 4^e$

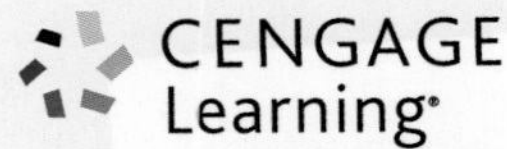

Maths For Economics:
A Companion to Mankiw and Taylor Economics
Ken Heather and Simka Stefanova

Publisher: Annabel Ainscow
Commissioning Editor: Abbie Coppin
Content Project Manager: Sue Povey
Manufacturing Manager: Eyvett Davis
Marketing Manager: Vicky Pavlicic
Typesetter: diacriTech, India
Cover design: Simon Levy Associates

© 2017, Cengage Learning EMEA

ALL RIGHTS RESERVED. No part of this work covered by the copyright herein may be reproduced or distributed in any form or by any means, except as permitted by U.S. copyright law, without the prior written permission of the copyright owner.

While the publisher has taken all reasonable care in the preparation of this book, the publisher makes no representation, express or implied, with regard to the accuracy of the information contained in this book and cannot accept any legal responsibility or liability for any errors or omissions from the book or the consequences thereof.

Products and services that are referred to in this book may be either trademarks and/or registered trademarks of their respective owners. The publishers and author/s make no claim to these trademarks. The publisher does not endorse, and accepts no responsibility or liability for, incorrect or defamatory content contained in hyperlinked material.

All the URLs in this book are correct at the time of going to press; however the Publisher accepts no responsibility for the content and continued availability of third party websites.

For product information and technology assistance, contact **emea.info@cengage.com**.

For permission to use material from this text or product, and for permission queries, email **emea.permissions@cengage.com**.

British Library Cataloguing-in-Publication Data
A catalogue record for this book is available from the British Library.

ISBN: 978-1-4737-2542-3

Cengage Learning EMEA
Cheriton House, North Way, Andover, Hampshire, SP10 5BE
United Kingdom

Cengage Learning products are represented in Canada by Nelson Education Ltd.

For your lifelong learning solutions, visit **www.cengage.co.uk**

Purchase your next print book, e-book or e-chapter at **www.cengagebrain.com**

Printed in China by RR Donnelley
Print Run 01 Print Year 2017

BRIEF CONTENTS

CONTENTS

PART 11 THE REAL ECONOMY IN THE LONG RUN 261

PART 12 INTEREST RATES, MONEY AND PRICES IN THE LONG RUN 279

PART 13 THE MACROECONOMICS OF OPEN ECONOMIES 323

PART 14 SHORT-RUN ECONOMIC FLUCTUATIONS 347

PART 15 INTERNATIONAL MACROECONOMICS 403

ABOUT THE AUTHORS

KEN HEATHER is an experienced academic who has a passion for teaching. He has spent a lifetime in higher education, mostly in the UK, teaching a wide range of courses in economics and statistics at both undergraduate and post-graduate level. He has been an editor of an economics journal and is the author of several books. He has also made several series of educational films in economics, mathematics and statistics, for which he received a Special Commendation from the UK's Economics Network. Currently he is a visiting teaching fellow at the Varna University of Management in Sofia, Bulgaria.

SIMKA STEFANOVA has a background in marketing as well as economics and mathematics. She has taught in a number of institutions of higher education in her native Bulgaria but she has also lectured in several European countries including the UK, where she did her master's degree. Her research interest has focused on rationality and decision-making, on which she has published. She also has wide experience outside of higher education; this has included managing the production of educational films and being deputy editor of a national newspaper. She currently teaches at the American College in Sofia and is also a visiting lecturer at the Varna University of Management in Sofia.

INTRODUCTION

A fruit seller has a basket of oranges. A customer buys half of what he has, plus half an orange. A second customer buys half of what is then left, plus half an orange. A third customer then purchases half of what is then left, plus half an orange. Now the fruit seller has none left. He had not broken or cut any of the oranges. How many did he have to start with?

You might, or might not, find this an interesting problem, but you may also think it an irrelevant one unless you happen to be a fruit vendor. Generations of students have reacted in much the same way with regard to problems found in maths for economics. They may, or may not, have felt that such problems are interesting but felt that they say nothing about the world around them. If you feel like this we hope this book will make you change your mind. The world is a fascinating place and grappling with mathematical problems will significantly increase your understanding of it.

We assume very little by way of previous understanding of maths beyond what you would have met at school by the time you were 16. Not everything will be easy but it will be quite within your grasp with some effort. It is not a conventional textbook on maths for economics. Here, you will find mathematics in context. The maths illuminates the economics you are learning. Each chapter relates closely to the economics of the corresponding chapter of Mankiw and Taylor, 4th edition, although this book can be used alongside almost any introductory economics text. That you are learning the maths in context should make it easier and certainly more relevant. Most people find that learning in the abstract is harder than learning in a specific context. Here you will be engaged in contextual learning.

Do not expect this book to be a complete course in mathematics. You will be learning what is necessary to understand the economics you are studying. One outcome of this approach is that the chapters vary considerably in length. Nevertheless, the time you give to any of the chapters will repay you richly.

As part of your study, at the end of each chapter we have included some problems for you to try to solve. The answers to many of them are available online but you should resist looking until you have made a serious attempt at the problems first. The answers can be found on the student companion website for Mankiw and Taylor Economics, 4th edition. This can be accessed through cengagebrain.co.uk.

The answer to the problem about the orange seller, and how to go about solving it, can be found at the back of the book, in the appendix. However, as with the problems at the end of the chapters, we think you should resist looking at the answer until you have spent some time trying to work it out for yourself.

Writing this book has proved demanding but it has been an enjoyable task that has proved very stimulating. We hope that reading it will have the same outcome for you.

ACKNOWLEDGEMENTS

Many people have helped us with the writing of this book. We would especially like to thank the following:

Dr Martin Greenhow, who spent many hours reading all that we wrote. He willingly gave us so much thoughtful feedback that is reflected throughout the book.

Dr Peter Andrew, who provided the material for Chapter 26, which enables an understanding of the mathematics of the financial crisis. Peter also provided valuable insights into several other chapters.

Many people have kindly commented on parts of this book and in particular we would like to thank Dr James Heather, Rossitsa Stefanova, Lazar Kunchev, Dr David Bibby and David Cawthorne.

Dr Carine Drapier provided feedback on earlier drafts and Professor Erich Ruppert wrote the questions at the end of each chapter. Erich also provided many valuable suggestions for improvements to the main text.

Our thanks go also to Dr Yuting Bai, Dr Daryna Grechyna, James Johnston, Paul Lovejoy, Dr Claire Lines and Dr Silvia Szilagyiova.

We would also like to thank Dr Andrew Ashwin, who suggested that we write this book and also gave us feedback on draft chapters.

Thank you too to Abbie Coppin, who has been very patient in dealing with the many editorial issues.

We had no idea how hard it would be to write the book but we think it has been very worthwhile.

Of course, we take full responsibility for any errors that remain.

Turn the light on with MindTap

MindTap represents a new approach to online learning. A fully online learning solution, MindTap combines all of your learning tools, readings, multimedia, activities and assessments, into a singular Learning Path that guides you through your course.

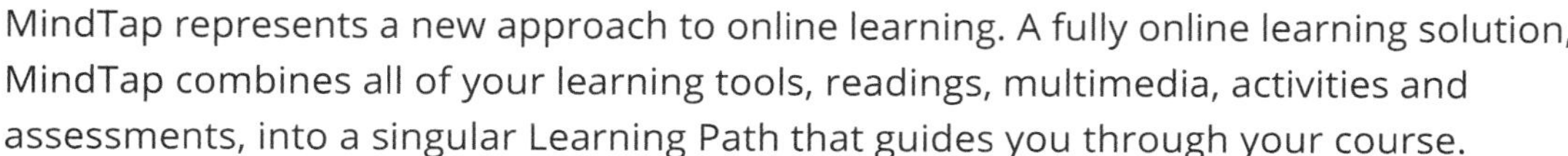

Lecturers can easily personalize the experience by customizing the presentation of these learning tools and content to their students so that they have access to course content exactly when they need it.

MindTap can be fully integrated into most Learning Management Systems giving you a seamless experience. You will also have a dedicated team of Digital Course Support professionals to make your use of MindTap a success.

To find out more students can go to **login.cengagebrain.com** and instructors can go to **login.cengage.com** or speak to their local Cengage Learning EMEA representative.

MindTap is available with some of our bestselling titles across multiple disciplines including Accounting, Economics, Management, Psychology, Engineering and Chemistry

ENGAGED WITH YOU | **www.cengage.com/mindtap**

PART 1 INTRODUCTION TO ECONOMICS

1 WHAT IS ECONOMICS?

In this chapter, we discuss the importance of an understanding of mathematics and statistics as an essential aid to studying economics. We want you to be sure that you know why it is worth giving time to the understanding of some maths and statistics and why it will make you a better student of economics. Here we present ten reasons why you need to study maths and statistics for an understanding of the subject.

INTRODUCTION

In this chapter we outline ten principles of mathematics and statistics for economics. Our purpose in doing so is not to introduce to you the key mathematical ideas you will need. We leave that until Chapter 2 where we will give you our preview of coming attractions in your study of mathematics and statistics for economics. In this chapter we will show that, although you can understand some economic ideas without very much maths, your understanding will always be limited. Whole books have been written giving some real insights into economic relationships using nothing but words, but the knowledge conveyed is often partial and incomplete.

Let's take an example. One of the early ideas that you will be introduced to in studying economics is the Law of Demand. This says that when the price of a good is decreased, all other things being equal, more of it will be purchased. It's perfectly clear what this means. Who needs mathematics or statistics to understand that? But to what extent will lower prices lead to a higher amount being bought? How do we quantify it? This requires some basic mathematics. A firm needs to have a clear idea of the relationship between its prices and its likely sales if it is to survive in business. Governments need to be able to quantify the effects of changes in prices on demand when changing taxes, for example. When governments pass legislation requiring firms to pay higher wages to their workforce, they may decide that they cannot afford to do so and then they will make some people unemployed. Without some maths it is difficult to establish outcomes of these sorts of issues. For example, what has happened in the past when minimum wage laws have been introduced? Has unemployment resulted? If so, what is the extent of the unemployment? We need some mathematics and statistics to answer this so that we have a fuller picture of the effects that are otherwise only described in general terms. Without that fuller picture our understanding is partial and businesses and governments are unable to weigh up the possible costs and benefits of changes in prices, taxes or laws.

Although you need to understand some ideas in basic maths and statistics this is not a textbook in those subjects. The ideas developed in this book are all set in a particular context. You are learning these mathematical and statistical procedures because you are understanding economics. You learn some maths but as you learn it you learn why you are doing it.

People face trade-offs. To get one thing we like we usually have to give up another thing we also like. Studying for a degree has an opportunity cost: there is less time for something else. Costs are opportunity costs and it is valuable to be able to quantify the costs and benefits to help inform decision-making. This equally applies to studying mathematics to help with understanding economics. Is studying maths and statistics alongside economics worth that opportunity cost? The answer is that it definitely is.

Here, then, are ten very good reasons why the benefits of studying maths and statistics far outweigh the costs. Don't treat each reason in isolation, each one is a benefit to you. But when all ten are taken together the case is overwhelming.

Mathematics Stimulates Curiosity

If you have decided to do a degree then surely you must have some curiosity about your chosen subject. Mathematics will excite that curiosity.

You may have heard of the Fibonacci sequence. If you haven't met this sequence in a study of maths you may have come across it because it forms part of the plot in 'The Da Vinci Code', a very popular detective story by the famous novelist Dan Brown.[1] The name that the sequence bears is the name of an Italian mathematician best known by the name of Fibonacci but who was actually born Leonardo da Pisa. Among many other things he set the following problem:

A new born pair of rabbits needs one month to mature and by the end of the second month and in every subsequent month reproduce themselves. How many pairs of rabbits will there be at the end of any one-month period?

The answer is a sequence of 'Fibonacci' numbers that begins as follows:

0, 1, 1, 2, 3, 5, 8, 13, 21, 34, 55, 89, 144, 233, 377......

(Can you see how to add more numbers to the sequence? You just add the last two numbers together.) There is something strange about this sequence of numbers. As you move along this sequence, dividing each number by the one before it, it produces a ratio that gets ever closer to 1.618, sometimes known as phi, or the golden ratio. We will demonstrate this with some of the early numbers in the sequence. We do it in Table 1.1.

Now this seems like a problem that only a handful of slightly strange people might be interested in. Unless you are interested in the possibility of rabbits overrunning the world it seems a pretty dry and meaningless problem. In fact, it turns out that to have a property that is truly quite remarkable. The number forms a pattern that you see over and again in nature. This golden ratio is present everywhere.

TABLE 1.1 **Fibonacci Sequence and the Golden Ratio**

Sequence	0	1	1	2	3	5	8	13	21	34	55	89	144	233	377	610	987
Division by previous number	–	–	1	2	1.5	1.666	1.600	1.625	1.615	1.619	1.618	1.618	1.618	1.618	1.618	1.618	1.618

Take a minute from reading this and get a tape measure. Measure your height and then divide the result by the distance from your tummy button to the floor. The answer will be close to 1.618. Now measure the distance from your shoulders to your finger tips and divide the result by the distance from your elbow to your fingertips. The answer will be close to 1.618. Now look at the length of your fingers in turn, measuring from the tip of the base to the wrist. Each is larger than the preceding one by … yes, this same golden ratio.

It is a ratio observed in sea shells, pinecones, hurricanes and the human face. Remarkably, the DNA molecule is 34 angstroms long by 21 angstroms wide for each full cycle of the double helix spiral. These two numbers, 34 and 21, appear in the Fibonacci series shown in Table 1.1, and their ratio is very close to 1.618.

So a curiosity about an aspect of mathematics led to a remarkable discovery. In the same way, mathematical curiosity has proved very beneficial to an understanding of economics. The insights that have followed from the

[1] Dan Brown (2003) *The Da Vinci Code*. Doubleday.

mathematical curiosity of economists have led to all kinds of insights into the way that society operates. One of the best known examples is that of the work of John Nash, an Economics Nobel Prize winner, whose life was portrayed in the book and film 'A Beautiful Mind', released in 2001. If you haven't seen it do watch it.

The movie suggested that Nash began seeing a kind of mathematical pattern of behaviour in the way that men competed for the attentions of women. From these observations came mathematical insights into how, among other things, companies set prices, advertising budgets are determined and why oil prices are what they are. The Sveriges Riksbank Prize in Economic Sciences in memory of Alfred Nobel, often referred to as the Nobel Prize, was awarded for this work on what is known as game theory. You will get to study this topic later for no study of economics can be complete without these insights. Mathematical curiosity led to highly significant discoveries.

Mathematics, then, isn't a dry set of rules to be drilled into your brain. It's a way of looking at the world in general and economics in particular that stimulates curiosity and leads to a more fruitful understanding of the subject. There is no guarantee that you will become a Nobel Laureate but as you study mathematics it will further excite your curiosity to see what else you can discover.

Maths is an Important Part of Logical Reasoning

Mathematics is great training for the mind. If you are to study economics you need to think in a rigorous way. Economics isn't a loose collection of thoughts about the economy, it's about having a systematic understanding of the way in which the economy and its component parts operate. In our study of economics we generally begin with a series of observations about some part of the economy and reason through to meaningful conclusions. This means training your mind to think logically.

Descriptive economics can only take you so far. You might read about, for example, a proposed merger between two companies. In five years' time the issue may no longer be of any relevance or interest. However, if you have studied the links between firms, costs, markets and so on in order to understand that particular merger, you will find in years to come that you can analyze *any* merger issue because you have thought through the underlying processes of merger activity. Mathematics is a powerful way of training the mind to think in that reasoned way about such economic issues.

You will discover this also when you come to read the literature about the subject. Almost all of the textbooks on any economic subject will require rigorous thinking but most of them will also require you to think with mathematical reasoning. This will become more evident as you pursue your studies. Indeed at some point it will be impossible to read the literature in economics without some mathematical understanding. So now is the time to begin to deal with some basic mathematical reasoning.

Many people, you may be one of them, find maths hard, and because of that are scared of it. Don't worry. Others have been there before you and you may be surprised to know who some of them are.

'When I started doing statistics at university yes it was hard. But I think that's true of anything worth doing. You have to go through the challenge of understanding how it works.' [2]

These are the words of John Pullinger, who is the UK National Statistician, Head of the Government Statistical Service (GSS) and Chief Executive of the UK Statistics Authority!

Be assured, it becomes easier with practice. Think of mathematics as a language. You probably learned a foreign language at school or college. At first you couldn't recall the simplest verbs or how to put a sentence together but with effort you obtained at least some measure of competence. You may not have become fluent. You may not be a master linguist but some proficiency in language is certainly possible with effort. This is equally true of the language of mathematics. As Sir Robert Worcester, the founder of MORI Polling and Research and The Chancellor of the University of Kent, has said:

'You don't have to be a statistician but you have to understand the basics.' [3]

Maths and Statistics are Powerful Analytical Tools

Maths and statistics enable us to interpret data. We are constantly bombarded with sets of numbers, data, graphs and tables. Often this data is presented as a way of supporting a particular point of view. But is the argument that the data claims to support actually true? Does the data really support the argument or has it been presented in a way that

---

[2] John Pullinger, CB, UK National Statistician, Head of the Government Statistical Service and Chief Executive of the UK Statistics Authority: www.economicsnetwork.ac.uk/statistics/videos/1_interpreting_and_using_data

[3] Sir Robert Worcester, KBE, DL, Founder of MORI Polling and Research, Chancellor of the University of Kent: *ibid.*

misleads the reader? Let's take a simple example. There is much evidence to suggest that people tend to be happier when their income is higher. (We will examine this topic in more detail in a later chapter.) As J.K. Galbraith famously wrote:

'Wealth is not without its advantages and the case to the contrary, although it has often been made, has never proved widely persuasive.'[4]

It is often noted that one country has a higher average income than another and is often accompanied by some data. Imagine that there are two countries in the world, where they each have only three citizens. Now look at Table 1.2 which shows the weekly incomes received by each of these people in their respective societies.

TABLE 1.2 Income Levels in Two Hypothetical Societies (euros per week)

	Society A	Society B
Sam	120	40
Brenda	6	40
Johann	6	40

It could quite rightly be stated that Society A has a higher average income. In society A there is an average income of:

$$(120 + 6 + 6)/3 = €44 \text{ per week}$$

In Society B there is an average income of:

$$(40 + 40 + 40)/3 = €40 \text{ per week}$$

Society A's average income is in fact 10 per cent higher than Society B's.

But most of the population of Society A is living at a comparatively miserable level of income. In many ways the claim would be misleading. In a later chapter we will be able to give a clearer picture of which society of the two represented in the table is likely to be happier. But it will involve a little mathematics.

It is often the case that once we have analyzed the data we can make sensible predictions about the future. If we know how people have behaved in the past with regard to price changes, wage rises, changes in the cost of foreign goods, etc. we can make reasonable predictions about what they might do in the future. We won't always get it right but we will get it right far more often than we would otherwise.

There are objections raised regarding the predictions that can be made about human behaviour at this point. People aren't statistics and it is not always possible to reduce people's complex and sometimes irrational behaviour to a series of equations. It is entirely true that we cannot predict with any certainty an individual's behaviour but we can generally predict how the great majority of a large number will behave.

Students can find it frustrating that economists build their understanding of the world by making assumptions that are perceived as invalid. Take the assumption that firms wish to maximize profits and that they know precisely how much it costs to produce their output that we often make in examining business behaviour. We also often assume they know precisely how much they will sell at every possible price. We then produce a mathematical model of these relationships. This all seems so unreal. Fritz Machlup,[5] an American economist, once used a powerful illustration to help with this perceived difficulty. Imagine a two-lane road, i.e. a single carriageway in each direction. Now imagine trying to model the decision of a motorist attempting to overtake. It would be hugely complex. One would need to consider, among other things, vehicle speed, lighting and weather conditions, the gradient of the road and the assumptions about the behaviour of other drivers. You might reasonably conclude that it is too complex for a driver ever to take a decision to overtake. Yet millions of such decisions are taken every day, almost all of them correct. Similarly, economists will sometimes model a firm's behaviour using mathematical precision and assuming that its cost and revenue conditions are perfectly known. In practice they are not. Does that necessarily mean that the profit-maximizing model is invalid and of little use in understanding economic behaviour? It does not. As with the driver on the road, so the manager of a firm takes decisions as if all the many variables affecting the decision are precisely known. As with drivers so it is with businesses. Business people often make the correct decisions; that's how they survive in business. So examining decisions on the basis of unreal assumptions can often effectively and accurately predict economic behaviour.

[4] J.K Galbraith (1958) *The Affluent Society*. Houghton Mifflin, p.1.

[5] F. Machlup (1946) 'Marginal Analysis and Empirical Research.' *American Economic Review*, vol. 36, September, pp. 519–54.

We must point out here that although we may start our consideration of the economy with many unrealistic simplifying assumptions we nevertheless later drop some of those key assumptions that economists sometimes make, in order to be more realistic. Thus, for example, we do later consider the possibility that managers do not seek to maximize profits. We also use some mathematics to consider behaviour when a firm's demand conditions are not well known. Unrealistic assumptions need not lead to unrealistic conclusions.

We often use language that is unfamiliar to those whose behaviour we are describing. Decisions of consumers, for example, may be described in terms of mathematical reasoning. Few people shopping in a supermarket would use such terminology about their purchases, yet the precision of language of consumer behaviour enables clear thinking that reaches important conclusions about consumer demand. You may have watched a leading snooker or pool player score a large number of points. A physicist may describe such behaviour in terms of kinetic energy, forces and angles. The snooker player may not fully understand the physics of playing shots but is likely to be a much better player than a physicist. Similarly, an economist may use language unfamiliar to consumers but it can still accurately describe behaviour and helps us towards the clear thinking that enables insights to be made into consumer choices.

'The best ideas often come from some insight into the way the world works and understanding the way the world works comes from understanding numbers.' [6]

Mathematics Enables Precision

It is often better to be precise than to be merely roughly right. Maths is an important tool in making precision possible. Let's take an example. There are various ways in which you can measure the relationship between a firm's output and its costs of production. We will study them in a forthcoming chapter. However, the most precise and accurate ways are those which use some mathematics. A little more precision can be bought with a little more maths.

Of course, there is a problem here. You can be precise but you can be precisely wrong. However, this is why statistical methods are so valuable. Economic reflection produces theories that are testable. We can see whether our precise argument fits the facts. We shall do this on a number of occasions throughout the book. One illustration of this principle will suffice now. Working out the demand for, say, cars is quite tricky. Demand depends, among other things, upon their price, the price of petrol, the price of other forms of transport and peoples' incomes. How much will each of these factors contribute to the overall demand? Firms need to know. However, to separate out these different factors requires precise mathematical reasoning. It also needs some statistical analysis. We shall begin to see how this analysis is done in the next chapter.

Does all this mean that all economists agree about everything? An impression given by the popular press is that economists disagree among themselves on nearly everything. In fact the great majority of economists agree on the great majority of topics. Certainly they disagree with each other nowhere near as much as they disagree with members of public. And yes that statement has been tested and found to be so! [7]

Mathematical and statistical reasoning can help to avoid what is often called the *post hoc ergo propter hoc* fallacy. (Latin for 'after this, therefore because of this'.) For seaside towns it has been shown that where there are more ice cream sales there are higher numbers of accidents by drowning in the sea. The conclusion is inescapable: Ban ice cream sales to save lives. How do we show that such an argument is false? Because two things occur in sequence, or possibly together, it doesn't follow that the first causes the second. It isn't ice cream sales that *cause* drowning. It is hot weather that causes more people to go to the beach, which increases the likelihood of drowning whilst at the same time increasing ice cream sales.

If you think this is an easy mistake to spot you would be wrong. Scientific studies are full of such errors. Let's consider one.

Did you know that the night air was responsible for malaria? Of course it isn't but it was once thought to be. It was noticed that often those who went out at night suffered from malaria. Therefore night air causes malaria. It took some time before scientists discovered that this was a classic *post hoc* fallacy. Malaria was caused by mosquito bites and mosquitoes preferred the night.

Now let's take a specific, but tricky, economics example. Here is an argument made during a period of rapid house price increases. 'We know that house prices will continue rising in the near future because the increase in land prices has yet to be fully reflected in the price of houses.' Does that sound convincing? It's quite wrong. When demand for housing increases house prices increase and since land is needed for houses to be built, the increased demand for

[6] John Pullinger, *op cit.*

[7] *The Economist* (2014) Economics for the masses, 20 August.

houses increases demand for land causing land prices to rise. Rises in land prices are a result of house price increases, not the other way around.

Errors of this kind are difficult to avoid. But mathematical and statistical reasoning can separate out cause from effect.

Through Maths and Statistics Differences of Viewpoint can be Resolved

When economists disagree their difference can often be resolved by a little maths and statistics. To see this it will help to make an important distinction between normative and positive economics. Briefly, normative statements are those requiring a value judgement, for example: 'What ought to be done …'; 'What should happen …'; 'The minimum wage rate should be higher'; 'Firms ought to do more to protect the environment'; 'The rich should be taxed more heavily than the poor'; and 'Accountants are more boring than mathematicians.'

No matter what information is examined, it need not change your view for or against it because the statement rests on value judgements and people have different values.

On the other hand positive statements are those free of value judgements; 'If the minimum wage rate was £2 per hour higher, an extra half million workers would be unemployed.'

'If advertising alcohol was banned, demand for alcoholic products would fall by 10 per cent.'

Such positive statements imply and include no moral judgment of good or bad, right or wrong.

These statements may be true or false but over time evidence becomes available to prove or disprove the accuracy of these positive statements provided the evidence is correctly analyzed using appropriate statistical methods. Normative statements cannot be disproved in this way. We need to be careful to distinguish the kind of statement being made.

However, maths and stats plays an important role even in the area of normative statements. Take the normative statement: 'The rich should pay more tax.' If we correctly analyze the evidence we may find out the extent to which poorer people declare themselves to be less happy and the extent to which poorer people are undernourished and commit more crimes or not. We can discover the extent to which higher income earners are discouraged from working by higher taxes. When all this evidence is assembled we may find some people changing their minds because they are better able to assess the costs and benefits of higher taxes on the rich.

Even some normative issues, then, may be at least partly resolved through an understanding of mathematics and statistics. And a word of warning: you may find that you are the one who is wrong. No one is infallible. It seems that the famous economist J. M. Keynes said in answer to a comment that he had previously said something different: 'When someone persuades me that I am wrong, I change my mind. What do you do?'

Maths and Statistics Help with the Law of Unintended Consequences

When you listen to arguments or make your own this may well involve policy recommendations of some kind. Often it will take the form of arguing that governments should or should not do a particular thing. Here it is essential to think through all the consequences of any action you may recommend. Sometimes an action can do more harm than good because of the unintended consequences.

Here is a claimed illustration of the law. You can decide for yourself whether it is a believable example. If cities make helmets compulsory in bike-hire schemes, then it seems clear that there will be a benefit. Those who cycle will have protection in accidents. However, people may simply ride bikes less if they don't like helmets. And if people don't ride bikes so much, and take the car instead, then they are less fit and that means that more of them die of heart-attacks. A law attempting to improve people's health may make it worse! How could you use statistical evidence to check this?

Be very careful not to propose a solution to a problem until you have thought through *all* the consequences. Let's look at an example. It concerns international relationships. The US government has sometimes limited imports of steel, often by taxing imports, in order to protect the American steel industry. Its proponents argue that it protects American jobs, but it has an unintended consequence: steel prices are higher than they would otherwise be. This adds to costs and therefore raises prices in many industries including the car industry. Demand in these industries is reduced … creating unemployment! It seems that the imposition of controls on steel imports to protect American jobs has sometimes had the unintended consequence of increasing US unemployment.

With sufficient mathematics and statistics the evidence is available to suggest that this would be a possible outcome. An understanding of maths and statistics can contribute to avoiding unintended consequences.

Maths Helps us to Reach Counter-Intuitive Conclusions

What do we mean by counter-intuitive? A counterintuitive is something that goes against what seems common sense or logical. Many things have been discovered that are counter-intuitive.

You probably know that for water to freeze, it needs to reach a temperature of 32 degrees Fahrenheit, or 0 degrees centigrade. For water to boil, it needs to reach 212 degrees Fahrenheit, or 100 degrees centigrade. So which will freeze faster: some amount of water at room temperature or the same amount of boiling water? It is clearly logical, just common sense that the water at room temperature will freeze faster. It begins much closer to freezing point. This is often not the case. Boiling water will often freeze faster than lukewarm water because of what is known as the Mpemba effect. Careful analysis leads us to the correct but counter-intuitive conclusion.

Now let's take an example from economics. Suppose a government is concerned about unemployment. It decides to help by boosting government spending by one million euros. To pay for this expenditure it raises taxes by the same amount. It is clearly common sense that the overall level of spending in the economy will be unchanged. The boost to the economy from increased government spending is exactly offset by the reduction in spending caused by the increase in taxation. We explore this in detail in Chapter 31 but the conclusion is obvious, common sense … and wrong. It's hard to explain why in words although attempts have been made. Later in the book it will become clear why this is an example of the counter-intuitive, but it requires some simple algebra.

Economists have argued that to reduce drug addiction it should be de-criminalized. The Swiss model is to provide trained nurses to inject heroin addicts so that they don't catch HIV. This reduces crime and therefore benefits not only the addict but society at large. The Swiss model is counter-intuitive, but such conclusions have been reached only as a result of careful statistical analysis.

Maths and statistics help us to reach correct but counter-intuitive conclusions.

Maths Requires Practice

Earlier we drew a parallel between learning maths and learning a foreign language. There is also a parallel between learning maths and learning to play a musical instrument. It requires a lot of practice. At times in the early days it can seem a bit dull and repetitive but as your confidence grows it becomes increasingly enjoyable. You experiment. You try things. And your confidence grows further.

Talent and natural ability can play a part. Some are more naturally gifted and it comes more easily to those fortunate few. But almost anyone can reach a level of competence with the required determination. That is why as part of your studies you will have some problems to work through. Whatever happens, it will be good for you to spend time on these problems. To the extent that you can't do some of them it will tell you what you need to work at. To the extent that you are able to do them it will give you confidence that you are making progress.

There are people who can play the music of Beethoven well, giving pleasure to themselves and others. There were times when these same people struggled to master their basic scales. They find that so easy now but they can look back and remember how challenging it was at the time. It will be the same for you with mathematics once you practice and develop confidence and competence.

You may not ever get to be the mathematical equivalent of a concert pianist but you can certainly attain the necessary skills to become a successful economist. Remember, maths requires practice.

Maths Makes your Grades Better

You haven't just begun a course of study to scrape through it with a bare pass. You want to do well. Your proficiency in mathematics will make your exam and coursework answers more powerful. You will be demonstrating a deeper and fuller knowledge of the subject. You will also find that your exam answers can be more concise. You can answer questions more quickly. This gives you precious extra time and space to give a fuller answer than would otherwise be possible.

Your study of maths will also help you with related subjects that you may be studying. You will need these principles there too. Accounting and finance for example uses some of the same mathematical concepts that you will study for economics.

Even seemingly maths free subjects like sociology and politics need mathematics and statistics. You are learning to understand people and as Sir Robert Worcester says:

'You can't understand people in any depth, on any aggregate basis, without a reasonable understanding of statistics.'[8]

---

[8] Sir Robert Worcester, *op cit.*

Maths and Statistics are Important for your Longer-Term Future

The years of study pass very quickly. You may have little idea what you will do with your life after those years have gone. But one thing is sure: almost whatever you decide to do, your prospects will be enhanced by a good grasp of mathematics and statistics.

You may choose to go further in your study of economics, perhaps a masters' degree or a PhD. You will certainly need some mathematics to cope with such programmes so now is a good time to start learning some basic concepts. The literature that you will need to read will be such that an understanding of maths is essential.

You may be involved in a job requiring some maths and statistics. You will either not get such a job or feel uncomfortable in it unless your mathematical competence is reasonably good. But you may finish up in a job that seems to involve little mathematics. You may be a specialist in some area of business where the input of maths is small. But still your knowledge of maths will be important. Imagine going to the specialist with a pain in your kidney. You have a specific problem that you want solved. The doctor has an ability to help, partly because he/she has specialized in dealing with problems of the kind you have. However, that ability is partly determined by a more general medical training in which the doctor has seen your problem as part of your overall health. Studying how healthy bodies work enables an appreciation of what happens when things go wrong. It is this general perspective which is crucial for understanding your particular medical problem. Similarly, if you are to focus on almost any business problems you will be much better able to do so if you have an overview of economics. You will have that if you have a good grasp of maths.

You are also quite probably interested in the amount of income you will be earning. Soon you will learn that a restricted supply means a higher price. This applies to goods but also to labour markets. Good economists with a background in basic maths are a scarce commodity and you will be able to obtain a premium price for your labour services. In other words you will get a higher salary. The best firms are not interested in mediocre students, even students of economics. Don't be mediocre but make the most of your studies. Make sure you get your money's worth by attending everything, reading all you can and questioning everything too.

Almost whatever you do, maths and statistics are important for your longer term future.

Summary

We hope that, having thought through these ten principles, you no longer think that economics students are made to study maths just to drive you mad with frustration. You *need* maths and statistics.

The number of techniques you will require is not very large. For an investment of time and effort now you will gain a tremendous return.

PROBLEMS AND APPLICATIONS

1 Some people pride themselves with not knowing maths. And some of them even have become very rich. Give three good reasons why you should not follow their example with respect to maths.

2 Stephanie has been promoted to become the general manager of a medium-sized firm because she has made several very profitable decisions for the firm over the last couple of months and she's also very good at negotiating with suppliers, customers and employees. However, she claimed that she has not used any of these complicated formula that she learned in her advanced maths classes in 10 years. Do you think her training in maths did not help her in any way to be successful?

3 After talking to a couple of market players you tell your boss that introducing a new product into the market will probably increase the firm's revenues. He tells you that this answer is not good enough and sends you back to do some more work. Why?

4 Create an example of false causation or the *post hoc* fallacy.

5 There are always discussions about normative issues in politics. Which possible uses do statistics have in such a discussion?

2 THINKING LIKE AN ECONOMIST

We begin this chapter by introducing graphing techniques. Then we extend your knowledge as we introduce you to a further eight mathematical and statistical tools that you will find valuable in your study of economics. They are as follows: measures of central tendency, variance and the standard deviation, probability, logarithms, correlation, regression, differentiation and integration.

A basic understanding of these is essential so that you can follow the mathematical and statistical ideas that you will meet in the first year of a study of economics in general and of this book in particular. These will enable you to understand how economists formulate their ideas, how they test these ideas to see if they are correct, and how they use these ideas to make predictions.

GRAPHING

Many of the concepts that economists study can be expressed with numbers – the price of bananas, the quantity of bananas sold, the cost of growing bananas and so on. These numbers often represent variables – things that can change. Economists are interested in these variables and in particular are interested in how variables are related to each other. When the price of bananas rises, for example, people buy fewer bananas. Does this mean that there is a relationship between the price variable and the demand variable? If there is sufficient proof that not only are the two variables related but that there is a strong relationship between the two then this may help in predicting a more general relationship between two variables. Economists will use maths to represent such relationships and also through graphs.

Functions

In economics a lot of use is made of functions. Demand and supply equations are two examples of functions. Typically, functions are expressed as:

$$y = f(x)$$

or simply $f(x)$.

This means that the value of y is dependent on the value of the terms in the bracket – in our example above there is only one value, x, so the value of y is dependent on the value of x.

In the example above, the value of y is dependent on the value of a single variable x. However, it is quite possible that the value of y could be dependent on a range of different variables. This can also be represented in the form of a function which would look like:

$$y = f(x_1 \dots \dots \dots x_n)$$

Where $x_1 \dots \dots \dots x_n$ represents a range of variables.

A function is defined by its 'domain', as well as by what it does. The domain is the set of values for which the function is defined. Functions generally act on a domain which is taken as the whole set of real numbers unless otherwise stated or somehow impossible.

Let's take an example. What is the domain of the function $y = \frac{1}{x+1}$?

The function is not defined where $x + 1 = 0$, because we cannot divide a number by zero. Hence it is not defined at $x = -1$ so that's not part of its 'natural domain'. We can say that the domain of this function is all real numbers, excluding -1, that is, all $x \neq -1$.

Linear Equations

During your course it is likely that you will have to work with linear equations – equations which are represented graphically as straight lines. A linear equation typically looks like:

$$y = a + bx$$

In this equation, y = the value plotted on the vertical axis (the dependent variable) and x is the value on the horizontal axis (the independent variable).

a is a constant and represents the point where the line cuts the y axis and b is the slope of the line or its gradient. We can plot a linear equation as a graph by assigning different values to x and using the equation to establish the value of y in each case. This is represented in the table for Figure 2.1 for the linear equation $y = 5 + 2x$.

FIGURE 2.1

Values of *x* and *y* for the linear equation $y = 5 + 2x$ between $x = 0$ and $x = 10$ when

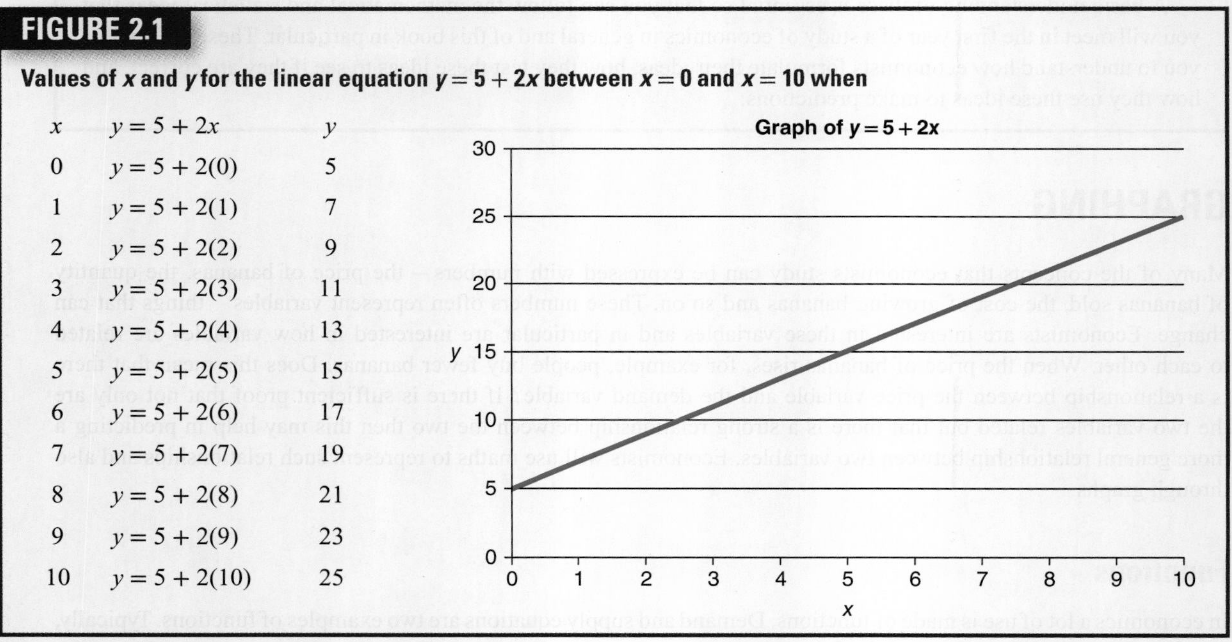

x	$y = 5 + 2x$	y
0	$y = 5 + 2(0)$	5
1	$y = 5 + 2(1)$	7
2	$y = 5 + 2(2)$	9
3	$y = 5 + 2(3)$	11
4	$y = 5 + 2(4)$	13
5	$y = 5 + 2(5)$	15
6	$y = 5 + 2(6)$	17
7	$y = 5 + 2(7)$	19
8	$y = 5 + 2(8)$	21
9	$y = 5 + 2(9)$	23
10	$y = 5 + 2(10)$	25

Notice that the line intersects the vertical axis where $x = 0$. The value of the constant a in this equation is 5 and represents the vertical intercept, the point where the equation of the line cuts the vertical axis. The next thing to notice is that as we give different values for x we see that the value of y rises by 2 for each increase of x by 1. In the equation, the constant b is 2 and is the slope or gradient of the line.

Types of Graphs

The line graph we generated from the equation is one example of a graph that you will use in your study of economics. There are a number of others.

Why use graphs at all? Graphs serve two purposes. First, when developing economic theories, graphs offer a way to express visually ideas that might be less clear if described with equations or words. Secondly, when analyzing economic data, graphs provide a way of finding how variables are in fact related in the world. Whether we are working with theory or with data, graphs provide a means by which we can see patterns and relationships. Choosing the appropriate graphical method is important – the aim is to make the information we are trying to view as clear as possible. An effective economist chooses the type of graph that best suits the purpose at hand.

FIGURE 2.2

Types of Graph

The pie chart in panel (a1) shows the proportion of GDP accounted for by agriculture, industry (that is, industrial production and construction) and services in Sweden. Notice how large the service sector is in this advanced economy. The pie chart in panel (a2) shows the same information but for Sierra Leone. Notice that for this relatively less developed economy the agricultural sector is much bigger than for Sweden. The bar graph in panel (b) shows the interest rate set by the European Central Bank, the ECB. The time-series graph in panel (c) shows the unemployment rate for the 28 European Union countries from 2005–14. Panel (d) shows the same information as panel (c) but uses a different scale for the vertical axis.

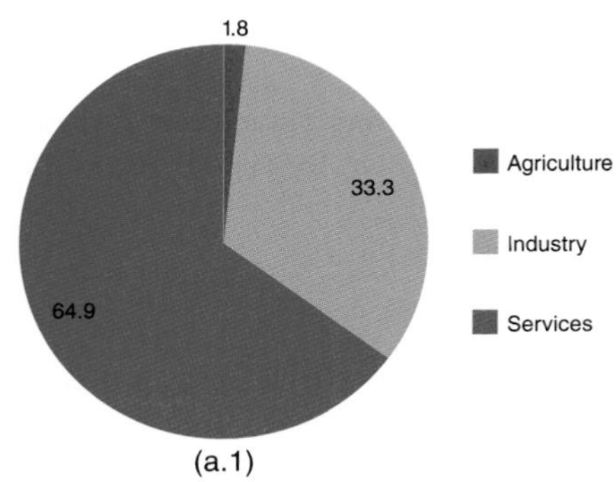

(a.1)

Source of data: CIA World Factbook

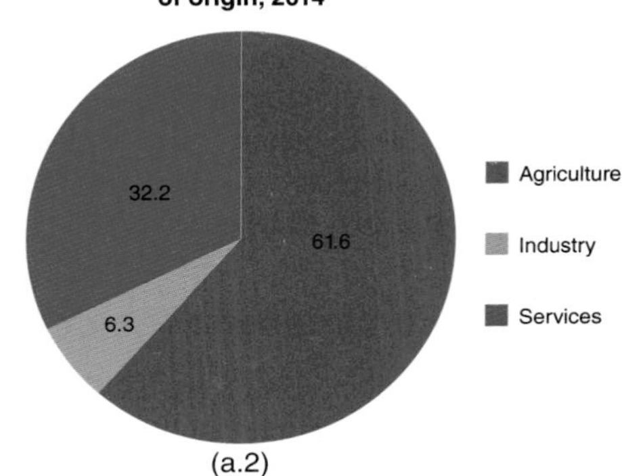

(a.2)

Source of data: CIA World Factbook

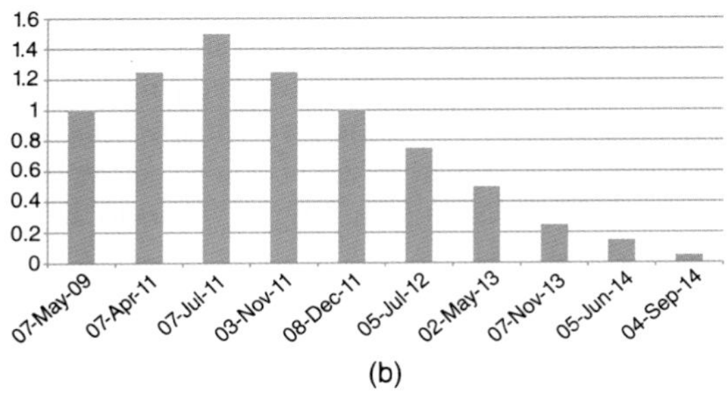

(b)

Source of data: Eurostat

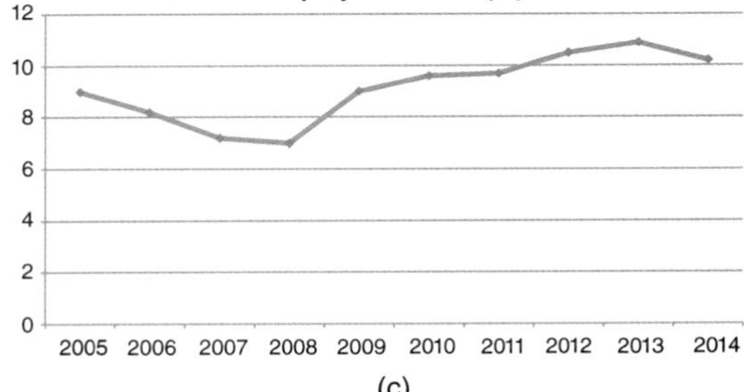

(c)

Source of data: Eurostat

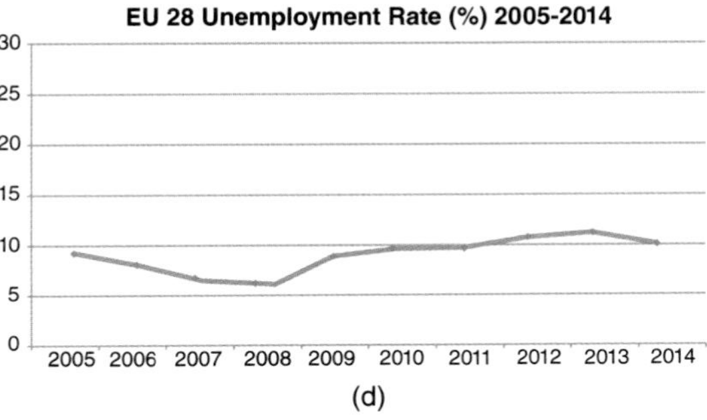

(d)

Source of data: Eurostat

Interpreting Line Graphs

Look at the line graph in panel (c) of Figure 2.2. The unemployment rate starts off at about 9 per cent in 2005, falls to around 7 per cent in 2008 before rising to about 10.9 per cent in 2013. Thereafter it begins to fall again. The difference between the unemployment rate in 2008 and 2009 is about 2 per cent – a relatively large rise – which is represented by a relatively steep upward sloping line. From 2013 to 2014, the unemployment rate falls by about 0.7 per cent – a relatively small fall. This is represented by a relatively flat line.

Looking at the shallowness or steepness of a line graph can tell us a great deal about the rate of change – whether our variable is changing quickly or slowly. However, we must take care in ensuring that we take note of the scale of the graph we are using. Look at the graph in panel (d). This shows exactly the same information as that in panel (c) but the scale on the vertical axis has been changed. If you look at the vertical axis you will notice that in panel (c) the data for the unemployment rate covers the range from 0 to 12 per cent. In panel (d) the range is from 0 to 30 per cent.

The change in the unemployment rate does not look anything like as dramatic in panel (d) and the line appears to be relatively flat. This is a reminder that if we are comparing information on two different line graphs we have to make sure that we take note of the scale before drawing any conclusions.

Don't just look at the picture, then, but look at the scales, units, etc. When examining a graph check whether the scales are the same. Do they start at (0,0)? They may not, and there can be good reasons for this so long as it's clear why they don't. It is easy to be deceived.

Graphs of Two Variables: The Coordinate System

Although the three graphs in Figure 2.2 (b), (c) and (d) are useful in showing how a variable changes over time or across individuals, such graphs are limited in how much they can tell us. These graphs display information only on a single variable. Economists are often concerned with the relationships between variables. Thus, they need to be able to display two variables on a single graph. The *coordinate system* makes this possible.

Suppose you want to examine the relationship between study time and examination marks for students attending economics lectures. You could record a pair of numbers: hours per week spent studying and marks obtained in the final course examination. These numbers could then be placed in parentheses as an *ordered pair* and appear as a single point on the graph. Albert, for instance, is represented by the ordered pair (25 hours/week, 70 per cent examination mark), while his classmate Alfred is represented by the ordered pair (5 hours/week, 40 per cent examination mark).

We can graph these ordered pairs on a two-dimensional grid. The first number in each ordered pair, called the *x-coordinate,* tells us the horizontal location of the point. The second number, called the *y-coordinate,* tells us the vertical location of the point. The point with both an x-coordinate and a y-coordinate of zero is known as the *origin.* The two coordinates in the ordered pair tell us where the point is located in relation to the origin: x units to the right of the origin and y units above it.

Figure 2.3 graphs examination marks against study time for Albert, Alfred and the rest of the students who attended the course. This type of graph is called a *scatterplot* because it plots scattered points. Looking at this graph,

FIGURE 2.3

Using the Coordinate System

Final examination mark is measured on the vertical axis and study time on the horizontal axis. Albert, Alfred and the other students on their course are represented by various points. We can see from the graph that students who spend more hours studying tend to get higher marks.

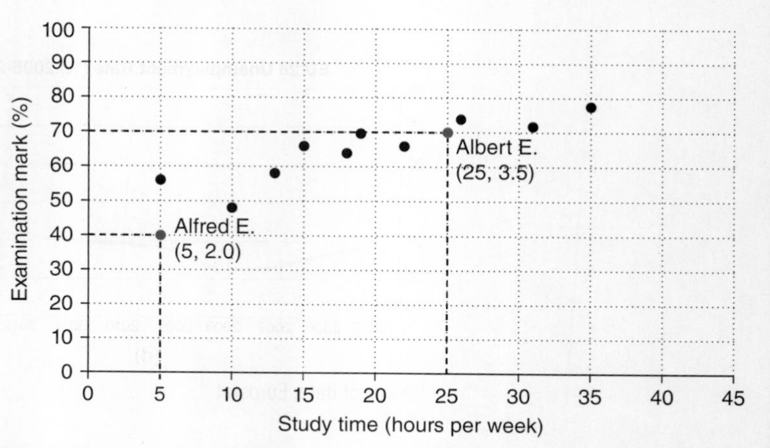

we immediately notice that points further to the right (indicating more study time) also tend to be higher (indicating a better examination result). Because study time and examination mark typically move in the same direction, we say that these two variables have a *positive correlation.* By contrast, if we were to graph time spent partying per week and examination marks, we would probably find that higher party time is associated with lower marks; because these variables typically move in opposite directions, we would call this a *negative correlation.* In either case, the coordinate system makes the correlation between the two variables easy to see.

Limitations of Scatter Plot Graphs

Looking at the scatter plot in Figure 2.3, it seems intuitively sensible that more time devoted to study is associated with higher marks. But just because two variables appear to have a relationship does not mean we can simply accept the data at face value. As economists we have to be critical – we have to question what we see. The following example highlights this issue.

Assume that data are released in a particular area which we shall call Region X, which shows a rise in the number of newborn babies over a period of time. At the same time, it is observed that the stork population in Region X has also risen over the same period of time. There is a 'theory' that storks bring babies. This 'theory' comes from the belief that storks are a fertility symbol. Storks live in and around marsh and wetland areas. There was also an ancient belief that the souls of unborn babies lived in water and that storks carried these souls to mothers – hence the belief that storks bring babies.

Looking at the scatter plot in Figure 2.4 it seems clear that there is a correlation between the two variables and one might be drawn to the conclusion that storks do indeed bring babies. However, common sense and biology tell us that what we are seeing is simply a coincidence – two variables which seem to have some correlation but where the correlation is due to chance. To determine whether there is a relationship between variables and the extent to which any relationship is due to chance can be identified by the use of different statistical tests. If the appropriate tests were carried out on this data it is likely to tell us that there is a significant correlation and the extent to which the correlation is due to chance. This example serves as another reminder that economists must always question and never simply accept things at face value.

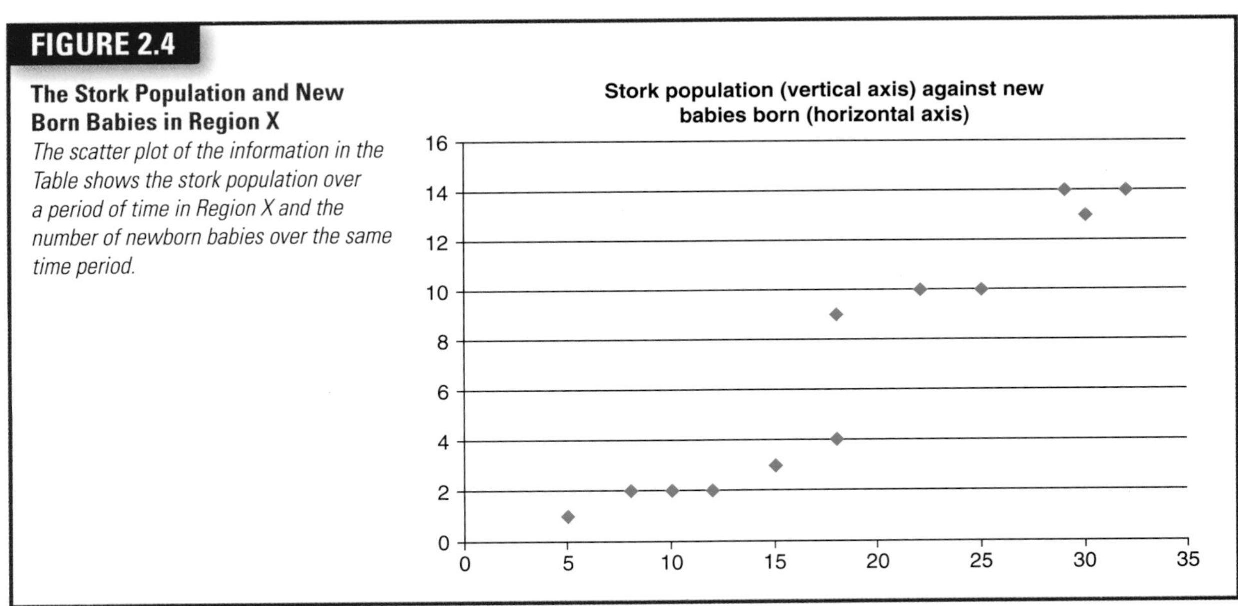

FIGURE 2.4

The Stork Population and New Born Babies in Region X

The scatter plot of the information in the Table shows the stork population over a period of time in Region X and the number of newborn babies over the same time period.

Curves in the Coordinate System

Students who study more do tend to get higher marks, but other factors also influence a student's marks. Previous preparation is an important factor, for instance, as are talent, attention from teachers and even eating a good breakfast. A scatter plot like Figure 2.3 does not attempt to isolate the effect that study has on grades from the effects of other variables. Often, however, economists prefer looking at how one variable affects another while holding everything else constant. The principle used here is referred to as *ceteris paribus*, a Latin phrase which roughly translated means 'other things being equal'. Economists analyze problems which they fully understand have multiple factors which could be affecting outcomes being investigated. In order to try and isolate the factors which are the most significant ones, the principle of *ceteris paribus* is used. It enables us to look at how changes in one variable affect outcomes assuming other variables that we know might have an effect are held constant. We can then look at the other variables in turn and build a more complete picture of the effect of changes in variables.

To see how this is done, let's consider one of the most important graphs in economics – the *demand curve.* The demand curve traces out the effect of a good's price on the quantity of the good consumers want to buy. Before showing a demand curve, however, consider Table 2.1, which shows how the number of novels that Maria buys depends on her income and on the price of novels. When novels are cheap, Maria buys them in large quantities. As they become more expensive, she borrows books from the library instead of buying them or chooses to go to the cinema instead of reading. Similarly, at any given price, Maria buys more novels when she has a higher income. That is, when her income increases, she spends part of the additional income on novels and part on other goods.

TABLE 2.1 **Novels Purchased by Maria**

This table shows the number of novels Maria buys at various incomes and prices. For any given level of income, the data on price and quantity demanded can be graphed to produce Maria's demand curve for novels, as shown in Figures 2.5 and 2.6.

	Number of Novels Bought at Different Income Levels		
Price (€)	€20 000	€30 000	€40 000
10	2 novels	5 novels	8 novels
9	6	9	12
8	10	13	16
7	14	17	20
6	18	21	24
5	22	25	28
	Demand curve, D_3	Demand curve, D_1	Demand curve, D_2

We now have three variables – the price of novels, income and the number of novels purchased – which is more than we can represent in two dimensions. To put the information from Table 2.1 in graphical form, we need to hold one of the three variables constant and trace out the relationship between the other two. Because the demand curve represents the relationship between price and quantity demanded, we hold Maria's income constant and show how the number of novels she buys varies with the price of novels.

Suppose that Maria's income is €30 000 per year. If we place the number of novels Maria purchases on the *x*-axis and the price of novels on the *y*-axis, we can graphically represent the middle column of Table 2.1. When the points that represent these entries from the table – (5 novels, €10), (9 novels, €9) and so on – are connected, they form a line. This line, pictured in Figure 2.5, is known as Maria's demand curve for novels; it tells us how many novels Maria purchases at any given price. The demand curve is downward sloping, indicating that a higher price reduces the quantity of novels demanded. Because the quantity of novels demanded and the price move in opposite directions, we say that the two variables are *negatively or inversely related.* (Conversely, when two variables move in the same direction, the curve relating them is upward sloping, and we say the variables are *positively related.*)

Now suppose that Maria's income rises to €40 000 per year. At any given price, Maria will purchase more novels than she did at her previous level of income. Just as earlier we drew Maria's demand curve for novels using the entries from the middle column of Table 2.1, we now draw a new demand curve using the entries from the right-hand column of the table. This new demand curve (curve D_2) is pictured alongside the old one (curve D_1) in Figure 2.6; the new curve is a similar line drawn farther to the right. Economists therefore say that Maria's demand curve for novels *shifts* to the right when her income increases. Likewise, if Maria's income were to fall to €20 000 per year, she would buy fewer novels at any given price and we say that her demand curve would shift to the left (to curve D_3). Although we often say that the curve has shifted to the right or to the left, we might, as an alternative, say that it has shifted upwards or downwards. We shall explore this alternative expression in Chapter 3.

In economics, it is important to distinguish between *movements along a curve* and *shifts of a curve.* As we can see from Figure 2.5, if Maria earns 30 000 per year and novels are priced at 8 apiece, she will purchase 13 novels per year. If the price of novels falls to 7, Maria will increase her purchases of novels to 17 per year. The demand curve,

FIGURE 2.5

Demand Curve

The line D_1 shows how Maria's purchases of novels depend on the price of novels when her income is held constant. Because the price and the quantity demanded are negatively related, the demand curve slopes downward.

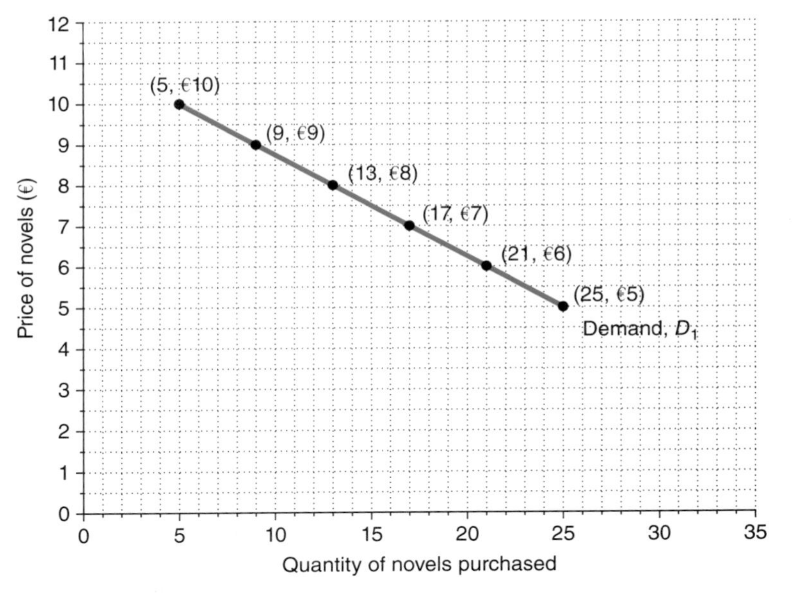

FIGURE 2.6

Shifting Demand Curves

The location of Maria's demand curve for novels depends on how much income she earns. The more she earns, the more novels she will purchase at any given price, and the further to the right her demand curve will lie. Curve D_1 represents Maria's original demand curve when her income is €30 000 per year. If her income rises to €40 000 per year, her demand curve shifts to D_2. If her income falls to €20 000 per year, her demand curve shifts to D_3.

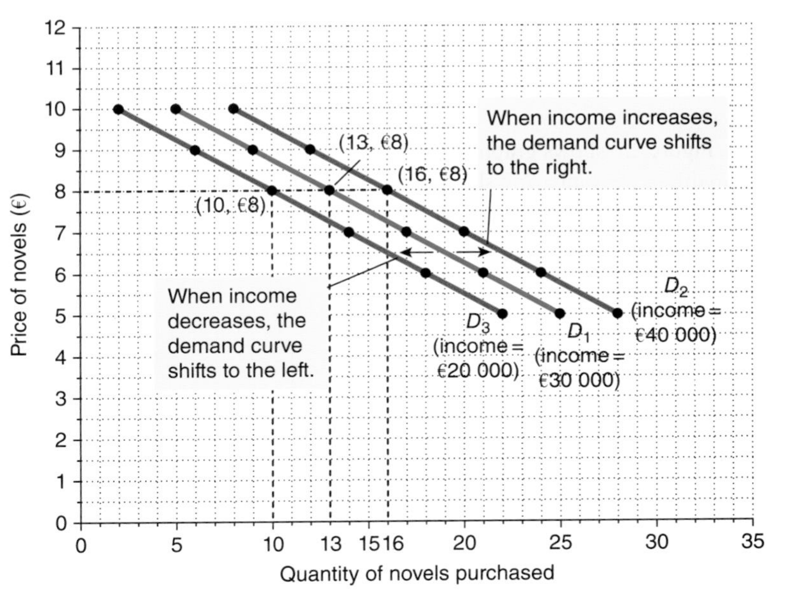

however, stays fixed in the same place. Maria still buys the same number of novels *at each price*, but as the price falls she moves along her demand curve from left to right. By contrast, if the price of novels remains fixed at 8 but her income rises to €40 000, Maria increases her purchases of novels from 13 to 16 per year. Because Maria buys more novels *at each price*, her demand curve shifts out, as shown in Figure 2.6.

There is a simple way to tell when it is necessary to shift a curve. When a variable that is not named on either axis changes, the curve shifts. Income is on neither the *x*-axis nor the *y*-axis of the graph, so when Maria's income changes, her demand curve must shift. Any change that affects Maria's purchasing habits, besides a change in the price of novels, will result in a shift in her demand curve. If, for instance, the public library closes and Maria must buy all the books she wants to read, she will demand more novels at each price, and her demand curve will shift to the right.

Or, if the price of going to the cinema falls and Maria spends more time at the movies and less time reading, she will demand fewer novels at each price, and her demand curve will shift to the left. By contrast, when a variable on an axis of the graph changes, the curve does not shift. We read the change as a movement along the curve.

Slope

One question we might want to ask about Maria is how much her purchasing habits respond to price. Look at the demand curve D_2 pictured in Figure 2.7. This curve is very steep, Maria purchases nearly the same number of novels regardless of whether they are cheap or expensive. The demand curve D_1 is much flatter, Maria purchases fewer novels when the price rises. To answer questions about how much one variable responds to changes in another variable, we can use the concept of *slope*.

The slope of a line is the ratio of the vertical distance covered to the horizontal distance covered as we move along the line. This definition is usually written out in mathematical symbols as follows:

$$slope = \frac{\Delta y}{\Delta x}$$

where the Greek letter Δ (delta) stands for the change in a variable. In other words, the slope of a line is equal to the 'rise' (change in y) divided by the 'run' (change in x). The slope will be a small positive number for a fairly flat upward sloping line, a large positive number for a steep upward sloping line and a negative number for a downward sloping line. A horizontal line has a slope of zero because in this case the y-variable never changes; a vertical line is said to have an infinite slope because the y-variable can take any value without the x-variable changing at all.

What is the slope of Maria's demand curve for novels? First of all, because the curve slopes down, we know the slope will be negative. To calculate a numerical value for the slope, we must choose two points on the line. With Maria's income at 30 000, she will purchase 21 novels at a price of 6 or 13 novels at a price of 8. When we apply the slope formula, we are concerned with the change between these two points; in other words, we are concerned with the difference between them, which lets us know that we will have to subtract one set of values from the other, as follows:

$$slope = \frac{\Delta y}{\Delta x} = \frac{\text{first } y\text{-coordinate} - \text{second } y\text{-coordinate}}{\text{first } x\text{-coordinate} - \text{second } x\text{-coordinate}} = \frac{6-8}{21-13} = \frac{-2}{8} = \frac{-1}{4}$$

Figure 2.7 shows graphically how this calculation works. Try computing the slope of Maria's demand curve using two different points. You should get exactly the same result, −1/4. One of the properties of a straight line is that it has the same slope everywhere. This is not true of other types of curves, which are steeper in some places than in others.

FIGURE 2.7

Calculating the Slope of a Line

To calculate the slope of the demand curve, we can look at the changes in the y- and x-coordinates as we move from one point (21 novels, €6) to another point (13 novels, €8). The slope of the line is the ratio of the change in the y-coordinate (−2) to the change in the x-coordinate (+8), which equals -¼.

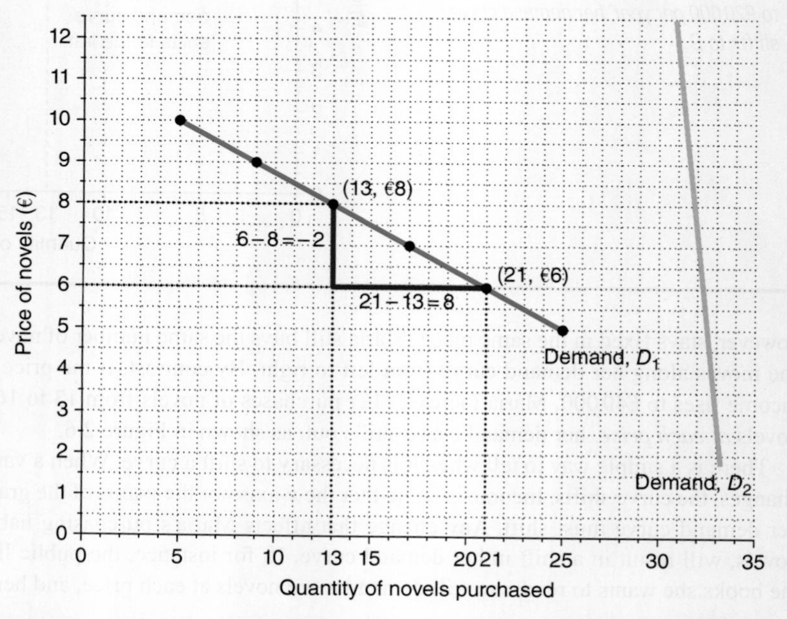

The slope of Maria's demand curve tells us something about how responsive her purchases are to changes in the price. A small slope (a number close to zero) means that Maria's demand curve is relatively flat; in this case, she adjusts the number of novels she buys substantially in response to a price change. A larger slope (a number further from zero) means that Maria's demand curve is relatively steep; in this case she adjusts the number of novels she buys only slightly in response to a price change.

Cause and Effect

Economists often use graphs to advance an argument about how the economy works. In other words, they use graphs to argue about how one set of events *causes* another set of events. With a graph like the demand curve, there is no doubt about cause and effect. Because we are varying price and holding all other variables constant, we know that changes in the price of novels cause changes in the quantity Maria demands. Remember, however, that our demand curve came from a hypothetical example. When graphing data from the real world, it is often more difficult to establish how one variable affects another.

The first problem is that it is difficult to hold everything else constant when measuring how one variable affects another. If we are not able to hold variables constant, we might decide that one variable on our graph is causing changes in the other variable when actually those changes are caused by a third *omitted variable* not pictured on the graph. Even if we have correctly identified the two variables to look at, we might run into a second problem – *reverse causality.* In other words, we might decide that A causes B when in fact B causes A. The omitted variable and reverse causality traps require us to proceed with caution when using graphs to draw conclusions about causes and effects.

Omitted Variables

To see how omitting a variable can lead to a deceptive graph, let's consider an example. Imagine that the government, spurred by public concern about the large number of deaths from cancer, commissions an exhaustive study from Big Brother Statistical Services. Big Brother examines many of the items found in people's homes to see which of them are associated with the risk of cancer. Big Brother reports a strong relationship between two variables: the number of cigarette lighters that a household owns and the probability that someone in the household will develop cancer. Figure 2.8 shows this relationship.

FIGURE 2.8

Graph with an Omitted Variable

The upward sloping curve shows that members of households with more cigarette lighters are more likely to develop cancer. Yet we should not conclude that ownership of lighters causes cancer, because the graph does not take into account the number of cigarettes smoked.

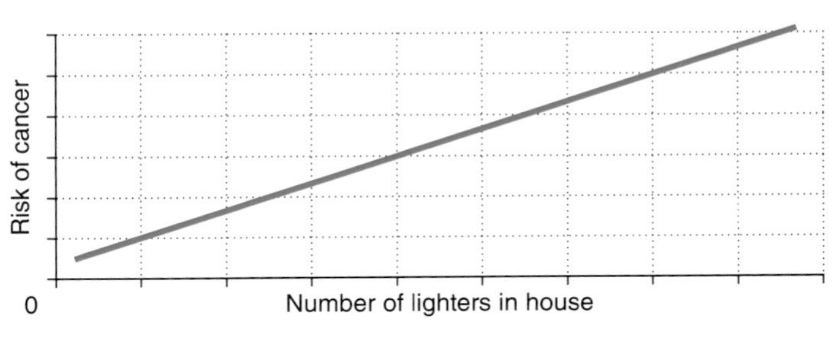

What should we make of this result? Big Brother advises a quick policy response. It recommends that the government discourages the ownership of cigarette lighters by taxing their sale. It also recommends that the government requires warning labels: 'Big Brother has determined that this lighter is dangerous to your health.'

In judging the validity of Big Brother's analysis, one question is paramount: has Big Brother held constant every relevant variable except the one under consideration? If the answer is no, the results are suspect. An easy explanation for Figure 2.8 is that people who own more cigarette lighters are more likely to smoke cigarettes and that cigarettes, not lighters, cause cancer. If Figure 2.8 does not hold constant the amount of smoking, it does not tell us the true effect of owning a cigarette lighter.[1]

This story illustrates an important principle: when you see a graph being used to support an argument about cause and effect, it is important to ask whether the movements of an omitted variable could explain the results you see.

[1] Half of young British adults that smoke will die of smoking-related diseases. Most young smokers appear to believe that the figure is much lower.

Reverse Causality

Economists can also make mistakes about causality by misreading its direction. To see how this is possible, suppose the Association of European Anarchists commissions a study of crime in Eurovia and arrives at Figure 2.9, which plots the number of violent crimes per 1000 people in major Eurovian cities against the number of police officers per 1000 people. The anarchists note the curve's upward slope and argue that because police increase rather than decrease the amount of urban violence, law enforcement should be abolished.

If we could run a controlled experiment, we would avoid the danger of reverse causality. To run an experiment, we would set the number of police officers in different cities randomly and then examine the correlation between police and crime. Figure 2.9, however, is not based on such an experiment. We simply observe that more dangerous cities have more police officers. The explanation for this may be that more dangerous cities hire more police. In other words, rather than police causing crime, crime may cause police. Nothing in the graph itself allows us to establish the direction of causality.

It might seem that an easy way to determine the direction of causality is to examine which variable moves first. If we see crime increase and then the police force expand, we reach one conclusion. If we see the police force expand and then crime increase, we reach the other. Yet there is also a flaw with this approach: often people change their behaviour not in response to a change in their present conditions but in response to a change in their *expectations* of future conditions. A city that expects a major crime wave in the future, for instance, might well hire more police now. This problem is even easier to see in the case of babies and baby cots. Couples often buy a baby cot in anticipation of the birth of a child. The cot comes before the baby, but we wouldn't want to conclude that the sale of cots causes the population to grow!

FIGURE 2.9

Graph Suggesting Reverse Causality

The upward sloping curve shows that Eurovian cities with a higher concentration of police are more dangerous. Yet the graph does not tell us whether police cause crime or crime-plagued cities hire more police.

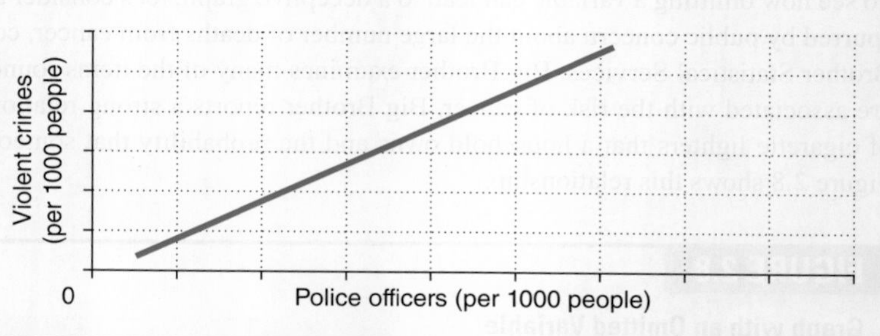

There is no complete set of rules that says when it is appropriate to draw causal conclusions from graphs. Yet just keeping in mind that cigarette lighters don't cause cancer (omitted variable) and baby cots do not cause larger families (reverse causality) will keep you from falling for many faulty economic arguments.

Constrained Optimization

Throughout this book we will look at situations where consumers, firms and governments are assumed to exhibit maximizing or minimizing behaviour. Consumers might be assumed to want to maximize the satisfaction (utility) they get from consumption, firms might be assumed to want to maximize profits but minimize costs, and governments might want to maximize tax revenue, for example. In most cases, there will be factors which will limit the extent to which this maximizing or minimizing behaviour can be carried out such as time, income and resources. In the case of consumers, the ability to maximize utility will be subject to a constraint – their income. Firms might want to minimize costs but subject to the constraint of their income (revenue) or the factor inputs that they have at their disposal.

Economists will often carry out analysis under conditions of constrained optimization. Typically this might take the form: maximize x subject to the existence of y constraint. Usually, the constraint is assumed to be fixed and so a calculation can be made which shows the optimizing (maximum or minimum) behaviour given the constraint which exists. We can then change the constraint to see how behaviour would differ and what the outcome would be. You will probably learn some of the mathematical techniques for solving constrained optimization problems in the quantitative methods modules that you will take alongside your Principles of Economics module.

Real versus Nominal Values

Economists deal with numbers but it is important to have some understanding of the numbers we might happen to be working with. Distinguishing between real and nominal values is extremely important. A simple way to understand the difference between nominal and real values is to remember that nominal values are expressed in money terms whereas real values are expressed as quantities. Typically, we will look at values which are affected by price movements over time. For example, if a firm was to tell you that it had sold €1 million worth of extra products over the last year (2014) what does that tell you? The answer is: not very much! If the firm sold 10 million worth of goods the year before (2013) you might be tempted to think that now selling 11 million worth is a 'good' thing and indeed, it might be.

Now assume that you know a little bit more about the situation of the firm in our example. Assume that the firm sold 10 million units in 2013, each priced at 1. Making a judgement on the performance of the firm in 2014 requires we know a little bit more about the extra 1 million worth of sales – the nominal value. If the price of the goods sold in 2014 stayed at 1, then we know that the firm sold an extra 1 million units that year – a 10 per cent increase in sales volumes, which we might conclude is a creditable performance. However, would you come to the same conclusion if you discovered that the price they sold their products at in 2014 was 10, meaning they only sold an extra 100 000 units in that year? Now the increase in sales is only 1 per cent – not such a good performance. The performance of the firm is largely due to the change in price not the amount of goods sold. In this case, nominal sales rose by 1 million but real sales rose by 100 000 units.

Real values, therefore, take into account price changes over time or the adjusting factors such as the seasons, whereas nominal values don't take account of these adjusting factors. For this reason you might see nominal values referred to as *current prices* whereas real values might be referred to as *constant prices.*

MEASURES OF CENTRAL TENDENCY

A measure of central tendency is a summary measure used to describe how a set of data is clustered around a central value. For example, what is the average level of income in EU countries? How does the average salary vary between different jobs? How does the average tax level in Europe compare with that in the United States (US)? During the last year what was the average value of the euro against the pound sterling? What is the level of inflation in Europe, on average? Given the frequent use of the concept it is important to be clear what it means, otherwise misunderstanding and misinterpretation can arise.

There are three measures of central tendency that are most commonly used: the mean, the median and the mode.

The Mean

Imagine that you are having a game of darts with some friends. You throw seven darts and score, from worst to best, 3, 5, 5, 5, 7, 10, and 14. (It looks like you are not very good at darts). The mean or the average score is simply the sum of the scores (or values) divided by the number of scores (or observations):

$$3 + 5 + 5 + 5 + 7 + 10 + 14 = 49/7$$

gives a mean score of 7.

Formally we could write the mean as:

$$\overline{X} = \frac{\sum X}{N}$$

Where:

$\overline{X}$ (say X bar) is the mean

$\sum$ (this is the Greek capital letter *sigma,* commonly used to mean 'the sum of')

X is the symbol for the scores

N is the number of scores

You will frequently think about the mean average in the context of your studies – what is your average mark?

Assume you are studying five modules, each of which is assessed by a piece of coursework. So far you have handed in four pieces of coursework which have been returned to you with the following marks. In ascending order they are:

56, 65, 73 and 82.

You have set yourself a goal of getting an average mark of 70. How many marks will you need in your final piece of coursework to achieve your goal?

Let's call the score you need, the unknown score, x. Your goal, your desired average is:

$$70 = \frac{(56 + 65 + 73 + 82 + x)}{5}$$

If we now multiply through by 5 and simplify, we have:

$$(56 + 65 + 73 + 82 + x) = 350$$
$$276 + x = 350$$
$$x = 74$$

Your current average is: $\frac{(56 + 65 + 73 + 82)}{4} = 69$

Your current average score is slightly lower than your desired goal and in order to push up your average to 70, you need to get at least 74 in your final coursework.

In studying economics you will frequently meet the concept of the mean average. A firm wishes to know the mean average cost of producing a certain number of units of output. A government wants to know the mean average amount of people's incomes that is saved. They may well want to know also the mean average amount of their incomes they take in tax, perhaps comparing that average with a figure for other countries. The mean average is a very useful measure in economics; however, it doesn't tell us everything and may even hide information if we use it thoughtlessly.

Let's take an example to show how it can be misleading. According to the US Census Bureau in September 2014, the average income in the United States was $51 939. It might be concluded that that citizens in the US enjoy a relatively wealthy existence but this figure masks a considerable gap between rich and poor. There are a large number of people in the US who live in considerable poverty with an income far lower than the average whereas there are some who enjoy a living standard far above this mean average.

Consider the UK. Imagine that everyone in the country is given a height that reflects their income (before tax and before any payments of state handouts). So an average income person is averagely tall. High income people are taller, very low income people are reduced in height proportionately. Now imagine that everyone is lined up in a parade with the shortest at the front and the tallest at the back. Now the parade passes by us at a great speed so everyone has passed by in one hour. How long before the mean average height (average income) person appears in front of you? The answer is that this person doesn't appear until around the 49th minute. This means that if you live in the UK with just an average income you are better off than over three-quarters of the population. Such is the effect of considering just the mean average in the context of income distribution.

The reasons for such disparities and their possible effects have always been of great interest to economists and we shall reflect on this issue in a later chapter. The mean average is a good starting point for looking at these questions but we need to be able to measure the degree of disparity and for that we need some further statistical techniques. We will be looking at one or two shortly and others later in the book.

The Median

The median is the middle value when we rank a set of observations in ascending order. Recall your scores in 7 throws in a game of darts. Ranking them from worst to best you scored:

3, 5, 5, 5, 7, 10 and 14.

The middle value of your seven scores is the 4th number, 5. This is the median score. The median is the middle number. If there is an even number of observations, we take an average of the two middle values. So in the case of your four coursework marks we have:

$$56, 65, 73, 82$$

We take the mean average of the two middle values:

$$\frac{(65 + 73)}{2} = 69$$

Your median average coursework mark is 69.

Note that if you had been good enough to hit the treble 20 with one of your throws instead of the 14, the mean average would be higher (13.57) but it would make no difference to the median score.

The Mode

The third type of average typically used is the mode. This is the value which occurs most frequently in a series of observations. In the example of our run of darts scores, the most common score is 5, that is, it is the value which occurs with the greatest frequency. If all the numbers in the series appear only once each, there is no mode.

Note, if your best dart had been a triple 20 instead of the 14 and thus had a higher mean average it would have made no difference to the modal score.

Summary

- Mean average: The most commonly used meaning of average.
- Median: The middle value of a series.
- Mode: The most often occurring value in a series.

Keep in mind, then, that instances of the term average will most likely be referring to the mean average. Keep in mind also that this mean average number may be very enlightening. But on its own it may not be.

VARIANCE AND THE STANDARD DEVIATION

We begin our understanding of the terms variance and standard deviation by referring back to our darts example. There we saw that the seven scores were:

$$3 + 5 + 5 + 5 + 7 + 10 + 14$$

and the mean average score was 7.

Now assume that your playing partner also throws seven darts but she scored seven with every throw. Her mean average score will also be 7, but she is considerably more consistent in her throwing. Similarly, when looking at the coursework scores of 56 + 65 + 73 + 82, we found the mean average score to be 69. Assume you have a friend on the course who had gained marks of 68 for two pieces and 70 for the other two. Your friends mean average will be:

$$\frac{(68 + 68 + 70 + 70)}{4} = 69$$

In this example, you both have the same average mark but, again, your performance seems considerably more variable in comparison to your friend.

Now look at Table 2.2 which shows the annual starting salary levels for graduates in two different companies. Each company takes on ten new graduates a year. Both companies have the same average starting salary but their policy towards graduates' starting salary is clearly very different. The salaries in Company B are clustered around the mean much more than in Company A. In each of our examples the mean tells only part of the story.

TABLE 2.2 **Graduate Annual Starting Salaries in Two Companies, 000s Euros**

Graduate Employee	Company A	Company B
1	18	28
2	20	29
3	20	29
4	20	29
5	26	30
6	30	30
7	32	30
8	40	30
9	40	32
10	54	33

To give us a fuller picture of what the mean average is telling us, we need to have some measure of how variable is the performance of a dart player, a student's coursework and the starting salaries of companies (in our examples). It is the standard deviation that will tell us this degree of variability.

The standard deviation is a statistical measure of dispersion or variation in the value of a set of data around the mean. The more spread out the data, the higher the standard deviation. Your darts companion data shows no variation at all. Your fellow student's marks show little variation compared with yours. He is more consistent with coursework than you are. Let's see how to calculate the standard deviation for a given set of data, using the example of the graduate starting salaries from Table 2.2.

We will start by working out the standard deviation of starting salaries for Company A, which is detailed in Table 2.3.

TABLE 2.3 **Computing the Standard Deviation of Graduate Starting Salary in Company A**

Individual Salary, (x)	Mean Salary, $(\bar{x})$	Difference, $(x - \bar{x})$	Square of Difference, $(x - \bar{x})^2$
18	30	−12	144
20	30	−10	100
20	30	−10	100
20	30	−10	100
26	30	−4	16
30	30	0	0
32	30	2	4
40	30	10	100
40	30	10	100
54	30	24	576

The first step is to find the mean average, $(\bar{x})$. We do this by summing all the salaries and dividing by the number of starting employees.

$$\frac{(18 + 20 + 20 + 20 + 26 + 30 + 32 + 40 + 40 + 54)}{10} = 30$$

We have recorded the mean average in column two.

The second step is to work out the difference between each of the observations and the mean. This difference we have labelled Difference, $(x - \bar{x})$. For the first recorded new employee the starting salary was 18, the average for all starting employees was 30, so $(x - \bar{x}) = -12$. We have done this for all new employees and recorded the result in column 3. Now we have to square these differences[2] to get the Square of Difference, $(x - \bar{x})^2$. So for the first employee:

$$-12 \times -12 = 144$$

[2] It is necessary to square the differences. If we do not do so, then the sum of the differences, the sum of the numbers in Column 3, will be zero. By squaring the differences all the numbers become positive. Then, after the summing the squared differences we can take the square root of this sum.

We have repeated the calculation for all ten observations and entered the results in column 4. If we now sum the values in column 4 we get 1240.

The mean average of the sum of the squared differences is called the variance. That is, the variance is:

$$\frac{\sum (x - \bar{x})^2}{n}$$

Where:

Σ is used as a summation sign to mean 'sum all of'

n = the number of observations, in our case 10.

$$\frac{1240}{10} = 124$$

We have one last step. We take the square root of the variance to get the standard deviation, which we will call S.

$$S = \sqrt{\frac{\sum (x - \bar{x})^2}{n}}$$

The square root of 124 = 11.14

If you undertake the same procedure with Company B you will find that the standard deviation is 1.41. This indicates that the degree of variability in the salaries in Company B is smaller than that for Company A.

There is one further consideration about the standard deviation which can be important under some circumstances. A larger standard deviation may reflect not larger variations but larger numbers. Let's illustrate this by thinking about the monthly variations in output over a year by two manufacturing companies.

Consider a light bulb manufacturer which produces, on average, 8000 bulbs per day. Differences in demand and availability of raw materials means that there are variations around this mean. Using the same formula that we have just used we find the standard deviation of output turns out to be about 1000 light bulbs.

By contrast a truck assembly plant puts together a mean average of 16 trucks per month. The availability of parts and fluctuations in demand means that the standard deviation of its output is 3.

The standard deviation for the light bulb manufacturer is 1000. For the truck assembly plant, it is 3. Does this tell us that variations around the mean are much greater for the light bulb maker? Not necessarily. Variations in light bulb production are bound to be absolutely greater because the numbers are so much higher. It's the proportionate variations that are important, not the absolute number. Fortunately, we can deal with the problem and calculate the proportionate variations very easily by calculating a coefficient of variation.

The coefficient of variation is given as:

$$\frac{\textit{Standard deviation } (s)}{\textit{Mean } (\bar{x})}$$

The coefficient of variation for the light bulb manufacturer is:

$$\frac{1000}{8000} = 0.125$$

For the truck assembly plant it is:

$$\frac{3}{16} = 0.186$$

This tells us that the proportionate variations in production are higher for the truck assembly plant.

In our example we have found the standard deviation of all the observations, that is, of the whole 'population'. Sometimes we only know about a sample of the population. Then we must make our calculations using the sample that we have. This is known as the sample standard deviation.

Summary

We have explored why just looking at the mean average of a set of data can give limited insight, or worse still, misleading information. The use of the standard deviation and the coefficient of variation can help to avoid these problems. This will be true not only of light bulbs and truck manufacturing but of a wide range of economic data, including variations in income levels and inflation rates.

Understanding these issues will prove particularly useful when we consider the important subject of finance.

PROBABILITY

When you study economics you will often find that some simplifications of reality have been made in order to make it easier to analyze what is going on. For example, we will study how a consumer behaves and will begin by assuming that our consumer knows exactly what something is worth to them before they buy it. But this is not always the case. When you buy a holiday you don't know how much you will enjoy the experience. Life is so often uncertain. As we develop our understanding of economics we will want to look at situations where an outcome isn't certain at all. A firm may invest in some new machinery hoping to make a profit but it may sell less than it hoped and make a loss.

It is sometimes more realistic, therefore, to think of an event having a variety of possible outcomes, some more likely than others. Studying probability will help discover the likelihood of something happening. Let us look at a few rules of probability that will help in studying economic situations where the outcome isn't certain.

The Probability of a Single Event

The starting point of understanding probability is to see that the probability of any event, *P*, is given as:

$$P = \frac{\textit{Number of ways an event can happen}}{\textit{Total number of possible outcomes}}$$

For example, if you have a set of playing cards what is the chance you will draw a red card when pulling one card from the pack? There are 52 playing cards in a pack (excluding the joker) so the denominator is 52. There are 13 red diamonds in the pack, 13 red hearts, 13 black spades and 13 black clubs. So there are 26 red cards in the pack, and subsequently 26 ways in which this event can occur. The probability of pulling a red card from a pack is:

$$P = \frac{26}{52}$$

We can find an equivalent fraction by dividing the number on the top line, the numerator, by the same amount as number on the bottom line, the denominator. Here we can divide both numbers by 26 to give:

$$P = \frac{1}{2} \textit{ or } 0.5 \textit{ or } 50\%$$

The probability of any event occurring can be expressed as a decimal value between 0 and 1. The more likely an event, the closer the probability of its occurring is to one. Unlikely events will take a value closer to zero. If an event is impossible, the probability is zero. If it is certain, the probability is one.

Suppose ten people apply for a job, four of whom are women and six are men. Assume all are equally able and the human resources (HR) department has no sexual bias. What are the chances that a woman will be appointed? Let's call the appointment of the woman a favourable outcome.

To calculate this probability the formula becomes:

$$P = \frac{\textit{Number of favourable outcomes}}{\textit{Total number of all possible outcomes}}$$

In our example:

$$P = \frac{\textit{Number of women applicants}}{\textit{Total number of all applicants}}$$
$$= \frac{4}{10}$$
$$= \frac{2}{5}$$

Or in decimals, 0.4. We can also express the outcome as a percentage and state that the probability of a woman being appointed is 40 per cent.

Suppose two of the candidates are called Zoe. What is the probability of a woman called Zoe getting the job? The number of possible outcomes is now 2 (there are two applicants called Zoe) and the total number of applicants is still 10. The probability, therefore is 2/10 = 0.2 *or* 20 per cent.

All the possible outcomes of an event are referred to as the **sample space**. Each probability is a fraction of the sample space, so the sum of the probabilities of all the possible outcomes must add up to one.

We can use this knowledge to calculate what the probability is of the job going to a man?

The probability must be 1 – the probability of a woman being selected. Here it is:

$$P = 1 - \frac{2}{5}$$

$$P = \frac{3}{5} \textit{ or } 0.6 \textit{ or } 60\%$$

What is the probability of the job going to a person whose name is not Zoe? The answer is:

$$P = 1 - \frac{1}{5}$$

$$P = \frac{4}{5} \textit{ or } 0.8 \textit{ or } 80\%$$

Recall that the probability of the job going to someone whose name is Zoe was 0.2. We can check that our answer of 0.8 above is correct because the principle is that the sum of all possibilities = 1.

The Probability of Two Events

Now let's imagine we have two events. After a candidate has been selected the HR department will appoint a second person from the remaining group. What is the probability that a man will be appointed second if a woman has been appointed first?

The probability of a woman being appointed first was 4/10 or 0.4. But now the sample space changes. There are only nine candidates left for the second appointment. Six are male so the probability of a male being appointed to the second post is 6/9 *or* 2/3 *or* 0.67.

Finally let's make things just a little more complicated. What are the odds of the two women being appointed? This is trickier than it might at first seem. We have to treat these two appointments as separate occasions. We have already seen that there is a 4/10 chance that a woman secures the first job. In the second round there are three woman and six men. So this time there is a 3/9 chance a woman will be appointed, or a 1/3 chance.

To find the chance that two women will be appointed we must multiply the chances together.

$$\frac{4}{10} \times \frac{1}{3} = \frac{4}{30} \textit{ or } 0.13 \ (\textit{2 decimal places}) \textit{or } 13\%$$

We can check that by considering the other three possibilities, namely:

a. two men being appointed,
b. a man followed by a woman,
c. a woman followed by a man

Consider possibility a)

In the first round there is a 6/10 chance and in round two a 5/9 chance.

$$P = \frac{6}{10} \times \frac{5}{9} = \frac{1}{3} \text{ or } 33\%$$

Now consider possibility b)
In the first round there is 6/10 chance and in round two a 4/9 chance:

$$P = \frac{6}{10} \times \frac{4}{9} = \frac{3}{5} \times \frac{4}{9} = 0.27 \text{ or } 27\%$$

Now finally consider possibility c)
In the first round there is 4/10 chance and in round two a 6/9 chance:

$$P = \frac{4}{10} \times \frac{6}{9} = \frac{2}{5} \times \frac{2}{3} = 0.27 \text{ or } 27\%$$

Now add all the possibilities that make up the sample space:

$$0.13 + 0.33 + 0.27 + 0.27 = 1$$

Summary

We have spent some time looking at some basic rules of probability because life is uncertain, and because in economics, as well as in other spheres of life, we shall meet a number of problems where such probability calculations will aid our understanding of the issues.

LOGARITHMS

You may have noticed that economic data and diagrams are often presented in a 'log' form. 'Log' here stands for 'logarithm'. In this section we will explain what logarithms are and why they are so widely used in economics.

Most simply put, a logarithm is a different way of looking at an exponent. An exponential expression is one where a number is raised to a given power in order to get another number, e.g.:

$$2^3 = 8(2 \times 2 \times 2)$$
$$3^4 = 81(3 \times 3 \times 3 \times 3)$$
$$4^2 = 16(4 \times 4)$$

Let's take one of these examples: $3^4 = 81$. What have we done here? We have repeatedly multiplied 3 by itself by the number of times as the power to which we are raising it. So:

$$3^4 = 3 \times 3 \times 3 \times 3 = 81$$

A slightly different way of looking at this expression is to ask to what power we need to raise 3 by in order to get 81:

$$3^x = 81 \quad (1)$$

How much is x? We already know the answer: $x = 4$.

A logarithm is the power to which we need to raise a number to get another number. We write this in the following way:

$$\log_3 81 = x \quad (2)$$

We know how much x is in this case, so we can write:

$$\log_3 81 = 4$$

We read this as: 'logarithm (or log, as is often said for brevity) base three of eighty-one equals four'.

Notice that even though they are written differently, expressions (1) and (2) say absolutely the same thing. We are looking at the power we have to raise 3 to in order to get 81.

Let's try a few more examples:

$$\log_5 125 = y$$

We want to find the power (y) we need to raise 5 to in order to get 125. 5 to the first power (5^1) is 5, 5 to the second power (5^2) is 25, 25 multiplied by 5 is 125. So the answer is 3.

$$\log_5 125 = 3$$

What about this one:

$\log_2 64 =$? What power do we need to raise 2 to in order to get 64?

2 to the first power = 2, 2 to the second power is 4, 2 to the third power is 8, $8 \times 2 = 16$, $16 \times 2 = 32$, $32 \times 2 = 64$. So that comes to the sixth power.

$$\log_2 64 = 6$$

Having arrived at this answer, can we say what is $\log_{64} 2$, that is, to what power do we have to raise 64 to in order to get 2? If $\log_2 64 = 6$, in order to do the opposite, we need to reverse the exponent (the power to which we are raising). That would mean that $\log_{64} 2 = \frac{1}{6}$. Raising 64 to the 1/6th power gives us 2.

Let's have one more example. What is $\log_2 \frac{1}{64}$? Here we still have base 2 but instead of looking to raise it to a power to give 64, we want to obtain 1/64, which is the reciprocal of 64. In this case we will need to raise 2 to the negative 6th power. So:

$$\log_2 \frac{1}{64} = -6.$$

Use of Logs in Economics

Logarithms have many interesting and useful properties but they are beyond the purposes of this book. So what we are going to do here is explain why, and the significance of using logs in economics rather than any other form of recording and presenting information.

First of all, you need to be acquainted with two special kinds of logs, as these are the ones that you will encounter in the great majority of cases in your study of economics.

The first one is $\log_{10}$ of any number. The $\log_{10}$ of 1000 is the power to which 10 must be raised to get 1000 (3). The log base 10 is so common that most calculators will calculate log base 10 of any number when you are asking for a log. They are set like that by default.

The second one is the so-called natural logarithm. This is simply a log, which has a base e. 'e' is a natural constant, like the number π, and is approximately equal to 2.71. Log_e of 100 is approximately 4.6 (or written in exponential form, $e^{\sim 4.6} = 100$). The number e appears everywhere in nature, but it also appears in finance. The log base e is very commonly used in economics, in finance, in fact so often than some publications don't even bother to specify that it is the natural log they are using and simply denote it 'log'. It is however called the natural logarithm and it is usually denoted by ln. ln is the same thing as $\log_e$ but is the accepted, correct way to write it. $\ln(x)$ is only defined for $x > 0$: we can only find the natural log of positive numbers.

One of the main reasons why logs are used in economics is that if you have a variable growing at a constant percentage rate with time, as for example population or sales, the log of that variable will grow as a linear function of time. The variable itself will have an exponential growth, which means it will change in a non-linear way, depending on the power of its function. However the log of the variable will change as a linear function. This allows for neat and comprehensive diagrams that clearly show the change with time. Moreover, as the relationship is nearly linear but not perfect, any deviations from it are meaningful – they come to show a significant drop or rise of the variable in a given period, which is not the case with non-linear relationships. We shall illustrate this shortly with an example taken from the growth of a country's population.

Another very useful property of logs is that they are not defined for non-positive numbers. This makes using the log of a variable in regressions, instead of the level of this variable, very convenient whenever you are interested in a variable that cannot be negative, like GDP or years of schooling. (We will look at regression in the next section of this chapter.)

In order to see fully the significance of the use of logs in economics, you need to understand the logarithmic scale. It is very different from an ordinary linear scale in one crucial aspect.

On the standard linear scale that you are probably most familiar with, when you move a fixed distance either to the right or to the left, you are adding or subtracting the same amount. So if you have chosen a fixed distance of 1, if you move once to the right, you are adding 1. If you move once to the left, you are subtracting 1. For instance, if you start at zero and move once to the right, you are now at 1. If you move again, you are at 2, a third time and you are at 3. If you now move once to the left, you will be at 2, and if you move 3 times to the left, you will be at −1. You can also choose to move any fraction of your chosen fixed distance, for example ½. So if you start at one and move ½ of the fixed distance, you will be at 1.5. You can choose any fixed distance. If you start at zero and choose 10, that will take you to $0 + 10 = 10$. If you do it again, you will get to $10 + 10 = 20$.

However, things are different with a logarithmic scale because when you move to the right at your chosen fixed distance, let's say 10, you are not adding ten, you are ***multiplying*** by ten. And when you move to the right again, you are ***multiplying*** by ten again, etc. Conversely, if you move to the left you ***divide*** by ten. This implies that on a logarithmic scale, it doesn't make sense to start at zero, as any number multiplied by zero is zero. So, if you start from one and move ten to the right, you will be at $1 \times 10 = 10$. But then if you move to the right once more you will be at $10 \times 10 = 100$ and so on. Every time you move to the right at your fixed distance, you multiply by ten. If you start from one and move the distance to the left, you must divide by ten and that will take you to 1/10. You can also move fractions of the fixed distance, but you do that by logs. For instance, if you want to find where 2 is on your scale, you need to find $\log_{10} 2$. The number that you get is the fraction of 10 that you need to move from your starting point 1, in order to get to 2. In this case $\log_{10} 2 = 0.301$, so you need to move about one third of the way between 1 and 10 to be at 2.

Although this sounds complicated and messy, it is actually an excellent way of presenting data meaningfully. First, it allows you to present a much broader range of data, starting from very small numbers like 1/1000 and rapidly but neatly going to very large numbers, like 1 000 000. This would not be possible with a linear scale. Second, and even more important, with each movement along the number line (or the axis) you are not adding or subtracting, you are scaling up or down, multiplying and dividing. This means that you are representing ***proportionate*** changes in the variable that you are interested in not ***nominal*** ones. On a linear scale, a change from say, 10 to 20 is a 100 per cent increase, but a move from 20 to 30 is 50 per cent, and a movement from 30 to 40 is 33 per cent or a third. On a log scale each fixed distance movement has to represent the same proportionate change. So if 10 to 20 is a 100 per cent increase, the next move should take us to 40, which is 100 per cent more than 20. The next one takes us to 80 which is a 100 per cent increase from 40. This is especially useful in economics, when looking at changes in prices, elasticity of demand and supply, changes in income, etc. as you will see in chapters to come; however, we will illustrate with one example now.

Figure 2.10 panel a) shows a population increase for a country over a long period of time. While the data is only for illustrative purposes it is typical of many countries. Now, of course, the size of the population is not only increasing but accelerating. There are occasions, however, when this gives a false impression of what is happening. The acceleration may not be due to a higher birth rate or a lower death rate. It may be attributable simply to the fact that there are more people having children. We may wish to know what is happening over time to the proportionate increase in the population. Panel b) of figure 2.10 tells us. Population is increasing but the rate of change is constant. How did we represent this? The vertical axis has a log scale. The increase in population from, say 5 to 10 millions is shown as the same distance as the increase from 10 to 20 millions, because in each case it represents a doubling of population. Panel b) of the graph gives a different impression of population growth. Which is the correct representation? Both are. Both add to our understanding provided that we look carefully at the axes and know how to interpret the use of logs.

FIGURE 2.10

Illustrative Population Increase over Time

Both graphs show the same information. Panel (a) plots population growth over time. Panel (b) shows the same information but the vertical axis uses a log scale. This enables us to see proportionate changes in population over time.

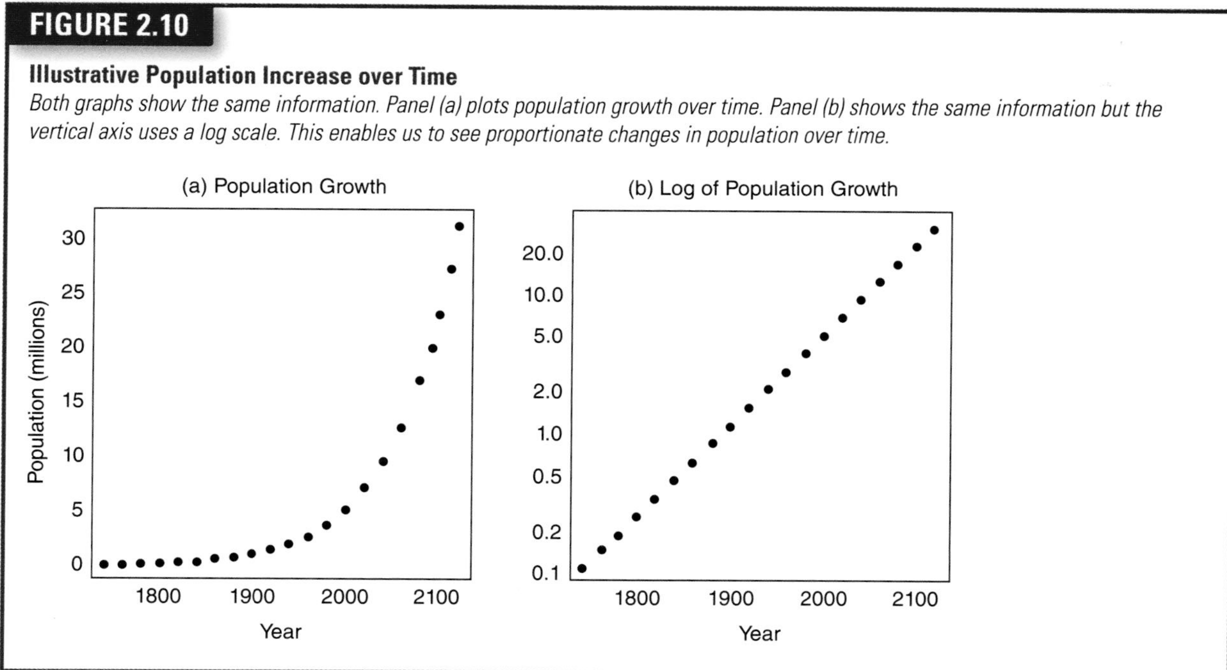

CORRELATION

Economists are often concerned with the strength of relationship between two variables. How closely are two variables related? The extent to which they go together we call correlation. Look at the following examples of two variables that relate in an obvious way:

- As the temperature rises, ice cream sales increase.
- As people's income rise they tend to spend more.
- A student's exam performance tends to rise with class attendance.

In each case as one variable increases, so does the other. This is called positive correlation.

Now think about these examples:

- As the temperature increases, hot chocolate sales decrease.
- As alcohol consumption rises, judgment tends to decrease.
- The more cigarettes people smoke, the shorter their lives.

In these cases as one variable increases the other decreases. These are examples of negative correlation.

Not all variables are related in this way. Consider the relationship between the number of car accidents in Copenhagen and electricity consumption in London. We would not expect any correlation at all. As one variable increases the other doesn't change at all or if it does, there is no cause and effect between the two variables. This is an example of what is called zero correlation. Let's consider just one other kind of correlation.

- As a farmer adds fertiliser to a field, the crop yield goes up at first but will fall with even bigger applications.

This is an example of a non-linear correlation, that is, a relationship exists but it is a relationship that doesn't tend to form a straight line.

Plotting these relationships in the form of a diagram we would have one of the four relationships shown in Figure 2.11, sometimes called a scatter plot for obvious reasons.

FIGURE 2.11

Some Possible Relationships between *x* and *y*

When x and y tend to increase together we have a positive correlation. This is shown in panel (a). When y tends to decrease as x increases this is a negative correlation. We show this in panel (b). If x and y are unrelated there is no correlation. This is shown in panel (c). Sometimes x and y are related but in a non-linear way. One such relationship is shown in panel (d).

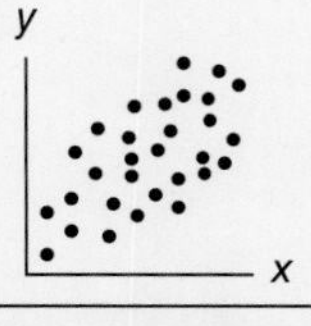

Panel (a) A positive relationship

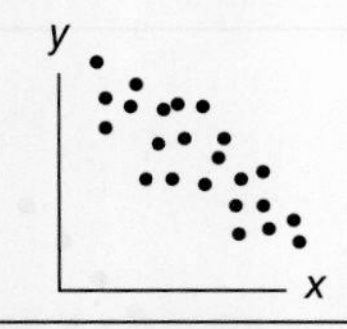

Panel (b) A negative relationship

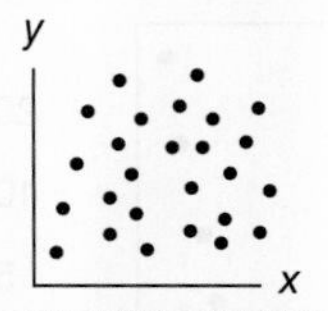

Panel (c) No relationship

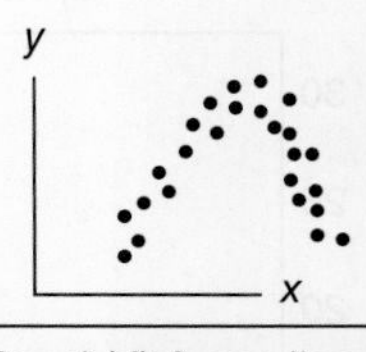

Panel (d) A non-linear relationship

If two variables changed in exactly the same way as each other in a direct relation to each other, the correlation would be 'perfect' and equal to 1. If there is no correlation between the two variables, the number would be zero. In reality, the fit between two variables will lie somewhere between 0 and 1; the closer to 1, the stronger the correlation and the closer to 0 the weaker the correlation. We can measure the strength of the correlation or closeness of fit in several ways. However we shall do so by using a statistical formula called the Spearman Rank Correlation Coefficient.[3] The formula looks complicated but work through it with us step by step in the following example and you will see that it isn't really. Generally, you won't need to know how to calculate the closeness of fit. It can be done electronically through the use of statistical packages like Excel or SPSS, but doing it manually once is very useful because you get to see what the formula is doing and you then know how to interpret the result of a calculation – which is really the bit we are interested in.

The formula for Spearman Rank Correlation Coefficient is as follows:

$$\rho = 1 - \frac{6\sum d_i^2}{n(n^2 - 1)}$$

The value of the coefficient is often denoted by the Greek letter ρ (rho)

We shall explain what d is as we work through the example.

The term 'i' means each one in turn. If you are not familiar with this you will see how we use this shortly.

Example

The Organisation for Economic Cooperation and Development (OECD) has produced some data regarding the housework done by men and by women. We have the top ten countries ranked by the amount of housework done. The first three columns in Table 2.4, shows that Indian women do more housework than the women in any other country. South African women come second and so on. In column two we take the ranking order of men for those ten countries. So for example, Indian men are ranked 10th because of those ten countries represented they do less housework than men in any of the other nine. Of these ten countries French men do the most so they have a rank of one.

Now compare these two columns. Is there any correlation? If there is, is it negative or positive? It isn't easy to tell, but our formula will reveal the answer.

[3] An ordinal scale is used where the order matters but not the difference between the values. You might, for example, ask someone to express the degree to which they enjoy a lecture on a scale of 1 to 10. A score of 8 suggests more enjoyment than a score of 6. But the difference between the 8 and the 6 may not be the same as that between 6 and 4. The values simply express an order. By contrast, an interval scale is used as a measure when the difference between two values is meaningful. The difference between a temperature of 10 degrees Celsius and 20 degrees Celsius is the same difference as between 20 degrees Celsius and 30 degrees Celsius. The formula we use here to illustrate correlation is suitable for use with an ordinal scale.

TABLE 2.4 **Housework done by men and women in ten countries (minutes per week)**

Country	Women	Men	d	d^2
India	1	10	−9	81
South Africa	2	7	−5	25
Germany	3	3	0	0
France	4	1	3	9
Netherlands	5	4	1	1
Finland	6	2	4	16
UK	7	8	−1	1
USA	8	5	3	9
Norway	9	9	0	0
Sweden	10	6	4	16

We begin our calculation by computing the differences in the rankings (d). We do this in column 4. If we summed each of these differences it would come to zero. We square the differences, (d squared, column 5) and sum these. That way we turn negative numbers into positive ones which give us the absolute size of difference in ranking and this is what we are interested in.

Summing column 5 ($\sum d^2$) gives:

$$81 + 25 + 0 + 9 + 1 + 16 + 1 + 9 + 0 + 16 = 158$$

Now look at our formula and we can calculate the correlation coefficient.

$$\rho = 1 - \frac{6\sum d_i^2}{n(n^2 - 1)}$$

We worked out d^2 and i simply means 'each of them in turn'. So in this case i means each of the d^2s. The term n is the number of observations we have. In our case we have ten of them in turn. So this all gives:

$$\rho = 1 - \frac{6 \times 158}{10(100 - 1)}$$

$$= 1 - \left(\frac{948}{990}\right)$$

$$= 0.042$$

The number is positive but only just above zero, so there is almost no correlation at all between the ranking of men and women on this issue.

The result we have found is of limited value because a number of factors are at work. In particular there are both cultural differences between countries and differences in the total time spent on housework between countries. Whilst the result is interesting it is not very surprising nor very revealing. One would need more sophisticated tools of analysis to investigate further.

Suppose now that there had been a positive correlation. Would that have proved that there was a causal link? No. Correlation is just that. It says nothing about causality, whatever the value we obtain. For example, looking at figures of ice cream sales and accidents by drowning in the sea might show a strong correlation. Because two things are correlated it doesn't follow that the first causes the second. It isn't ice cream sales that cause drowning. The hot weather encourages more people to go to the beach and more people on the beach is likely to increase the number of people who go in the sea which leads to an increase in the number susceptible to drowning. What is also happening is that as more people visit the seaside in the hot weather, they are likely to buy ice creams and this results in higher ice cream sales. There is a link but it is not a causal one. Correlation does not imply causation, but another technique called regression may help us with the problem of causality. Discovering whether a link exists between two sets of data is an important part of the economist's toolbox.

REGRESSION

Regression is used in economics because it has significant advantages over correlation. First, while correlation doesn't imply causality, regression may enable us to determine whether there is a causal relationship between variables and to see what causes what. For example, it will help us to know whether additional spending on the police service reduces crime. Will increased investment in education raise people out of poverty? We need to know not just whether there is a correlation between these pairs of variables, we need to know the causality. Discerning the causality may be attempted with regression analysis.

Second, regression allows us to look at multiple variables. Let's take an example. The demand for a product is dependent on incomes, but a number of other factors too, such as the level of wealth, expectations about the future and so on. Multiple regression techniques help us to identify this multiple causality. Furthermore it enables us to understand the extent of the causality. Just how much does an extra €1000 a year in tax rebates to the population cause increases in spending? To what extent does an increase in interest rates of 2 per cent reduce the level of consumption?

To illustrate let's take a look at the problem of trying to determine how much a firm might choose to invest in production capacity in a country. Governments collect data on the volume of investment and we also know the level of interest rates at any one time in a country. We might also hypothesize that the level of investment will depend on firms' expectations about profits.

First, let's try to see if investment depends upon interest rates. If we assume the relationship between investment and interest rates is linear, our equation might look like this:

$$I = a + \beta x \tag{1}$$

On the left-hand side is I, our dependent variable, in our case investment (because we believe that investment is dependent on the level of interest rates). On the right-hand side is a, some constant (or intercept), and β, our coefficient (or slope) multiplied by x, our independent (or explanatory) variable. In this example, the independent or explanatory variable, x, is interest rates. The regression is a single regression in that investment depends only on one variable, interest rates. We have no other explanatory variables. It is also a linear relationship.

However, the world is more complex and we hypothesize that a number of variables are at work on investment levels.

In this case, we would run a multiple regression:

$$I = a + \beta_1 x_1 + \beta_2 x_2 + \beta_n x_n \tag{2}$$

We have several variables to help explain investment, interest rates, expectations about profits, and could include any other factors we might think important. The β coefficients measure the size of the impact of each of these variables. We labelled them β_1, β_2, etc. because the size of the impact will probably be different for different variables.

If we now plug in our data for some time period and run regression (1) through the computer we might get something like this.

If we again call investment I and interest rates r:

$$I = 100 - 1.2r$$

The β coefficient of −1.2 (note it is negative) tells us that investment will fall by 1.2 times the change in interest rates. If interest rates rise by 1 per cent, investment will fall by 1.2 times. If interest rates fell by 1 per cent, investment would rise by 1.2 per cent. The constant, 100, indicates that there will be some amount, say €100 million worth of investment, regardless of the level of interest rates.

If we now run a regression for equation (2) put in expectations of profits, so that we are looking to see if investment is a function of expected profits and interest rates too, we might get:

$$I = 100 - 1.2r + 0.05\,EP$$

Where:

EP = expected profits

This time, higher expected profits cause more investment. The coefficient ($\beta = 0.05$) is positive. Notice that adding a variable may change the perceived impact of the other variables. In our case we still find interest rates affect investment but to a different degree.

You will also find that the regression gives you other information relating to the accuracy and reliability of the results. One statistic we mention briefly is called the R^2. Its value will be between 0 and 1 and will tell you the extent to which the dependent variable is explained by the independent variables. For example an R^2 of 0.2 suggests that only 20 per cent of the variations in our investment data are explained by the explanatory variables we have put in. It looks like there are some important explanatory variables missing. The higher the R^2, the more confidence we will have that we have found the appropriate causal influences we were looking for.

Remember, the purpose of this section has not been to teach you all there is to know about regression. It is to help you interpret results of regressions that you find that have been performed on economic data.

DIFFERENTIATION

Differentiation is one part of a branch of maths called calculus. It is used to find the rate of change of a curve or function. Although there is a lot one could know about differentiation, what you will need in order to handle this introductory course is quite straightforward and, importantly, becomes even more straightforward with practice.

Differentiation means the process of taking the derivative. The derivative measures how fast something is changing. Figure 2.12 has been drawn to represent a hill. Imagine that you are driving up the hill. The slope of the hill is changing as you go. It's steeper in some parts than others. How steep the hill is depends upon where you are. It's steeper at point A than at point B. We have shown this by drawing a tangent to the curve at each of points A and B. A tangent is a straight line passing through a point on a curve so that it just touches it. Differentiation is a way of measuring the slope of the hill at any point.

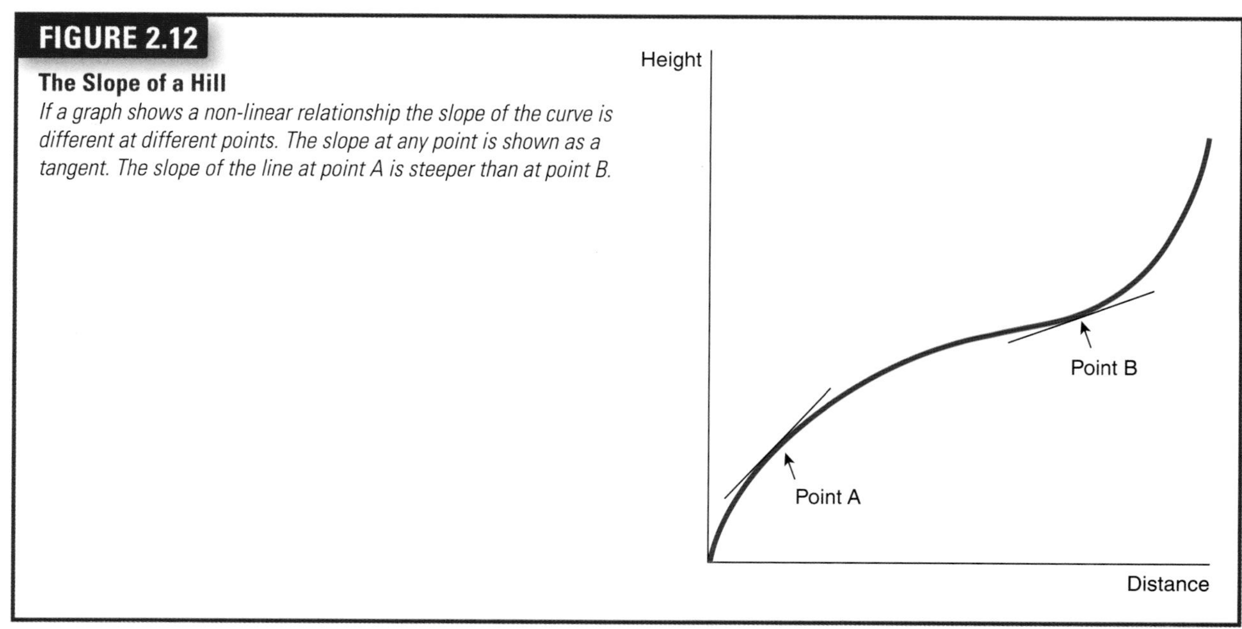

FIGURE 2.12

The Slope of a Hill

If a graph shows a non-linear relationship the slope of the curve is different at different points. The slope at any point is shown as a tangent. The slope of the line at point A is steeper than at point B.

Suppose that the line is a vertical one. A vertical line is said to have an infinite slope because the y-variable can take any value without the x-variable changing at all. A line that is almost vertical is said to have an almost infinite slope because the y-variable changes by a large amount even for a small change in x.

Now imagine that a hill that varies in slope is a curve that represents the relationship between a firm's output and the costs of producing it. If the firm produces 5 units per week, the total cost is €340 and if it produces 10 units a week it costs €2315. There is a mathematical formula, or function, which will describe this kind of relationship so that we can work out the cost for any level of output. One formula of the shape of a cost curve you will meet later in the book might be described as:

$$C(x) = 15 + 3x^2 + 2x^3$$

Where:
C = cost
x = nos of units of output per week

We can write $C(x)$ to remind ourselves that the cost, C, is dependent upon the number of units of output per week, x.

If the firm decides to produce 5 units of output per week we can find out what that will cost by replacing x with 5:

$$\begin{aligned} C(x) &= 15 + 3x^2 + 2x^3 \\ &= 15 + 3(5 \times 5) + 2(5 \times 5 \times 5) \\ &= 15 + 75 + 250 \\ &= 340 \end{aligned}$$

At 10 units of output per week costs are:

$$\begin{aligned} C(x) &= 15 + 3x^2 + 2x^3 \\ &= 15 + 300 + 2000 \\ &= 2315 \end{aligned}$$

Now we are ready to differentiate this function to find how steep the hill is at any point, or, in our case, how fast costs are changing at any level of output. There are two forms of notation to represent differentiating a function to find its slope. Sometimes a function is written as $f(x)$. You can read it as 'f of x'. Then the derivative is written as $f'(x)$. You can read this as 'f dashed of x'. This derivative $f'(x)$, when we put in a value for x, will tell us how quickly the original function $f(x)$ is changing at that particular value. We shall illustrate this in a moment.

There are some basic rules which we can follow to differentiate a function and find the slope of a curve at any point. These are not all the rules of differentiation but are the ones we will use in this book. We don't attempt to explain the proof, which is beyond the scope of this book. Should you want to find this out you can consult any good mathematics text.

Constant Function Rule

By a constant, we mean a function which always takes the same value regardless of the inputted value. The derivative of a constant is zero and the reason for this is that if something is constant, then the rate at which it is changing must be zero; in other words, it isn't changing at all. For example, our illustrative function was:

$$C(x) = 15 + 3x^2 + 2x^3$$

Suppose it had been just:

$$C(x) = 15$$

We have the value 15 regardless of the level of x. The derivative of the term 15 is 0. In general, given a function:

$$\begin{aligned} f(x) &= k \\ f'(x) &= 0 \end{aligned}$$

Power Rule

Now we consider the derivative when there is a power term in a function. Any power of the form x^n is differentiated in the following way. You bring the power, n, down to the front, leave x where it is and reduce the power by one. So if we differentiate the term x^2, we get $2x^1$, or more simply, $2x$. If we differentiate the term $2x^3$, we have $3 \times 2 = 6$ so we have $6x^2$. We can us this principle for any power. If we had a term $5x^4$, we could differentiate it in the same way. It would give us $20x^3$.

Notice that the derivative of x^2 is $2x$ but so is the derivative of x^2+10, or x^2+50, or indeed x^2 plus any constant. If this isn't clear then you can try plotting these. You will find that they are parallel curves. That is, x^2 is displaced vertically by, for example, 10 or 50. Thus the slopes are the same at any given value of x.

The following general form can help in remembering the power rule:

$$f'(x^n) = nx^{(n-1)}$$

Sum Rule

The derivative of the sum of two functions is the sum of the individual derivatives of those functions. The sum rule allows us to take the derivative of each term separately and add them together.

So what is the derivative of our function? If we were using x and y as the terms we would write:

$$\frac{dy}{dx}$$

(say dee y by dee x)

But here we use C for costs so we can write:

$$\frac{dC}{dx} = 6x + 6x^2$$

The slope of our cost function at any point is $6x + 6x^2$

The Benefits of Using Differentiation in Economics

Economists, as you will discover, are often interested in small, marginal changes. For example, we might want to know how much extra it costs to make one additional unit. That is, what is the marginal cost of that unit? We are thus interested in the slope of the total cost function at a particular output level. We can get an approximate answer by working out costs at, say, 15 units and costs at 16 units of output per period and calculating the difference. But if we need absolute precision in finding the cost of the 16th unit, we need to differentiate.

There are many examples in economics of the need to look at marginal changes. We will therefore use these rules of differentiation on a number of occasions throughout the book.

INTEGRATION

Integration can be a complex topic but for the purpose of following this book we need only to grasp the basic idea. Integration is a technique that can be used to find many things but its commonest use in economics is in finding areas – in particular, finding an area under a curve. It would be straightforward to do this without the need to integrate if the curve was linear but we may need to find the area under the curve of a function that is non-linear, such as area A, the area under the curve shown in Figure 2.13.

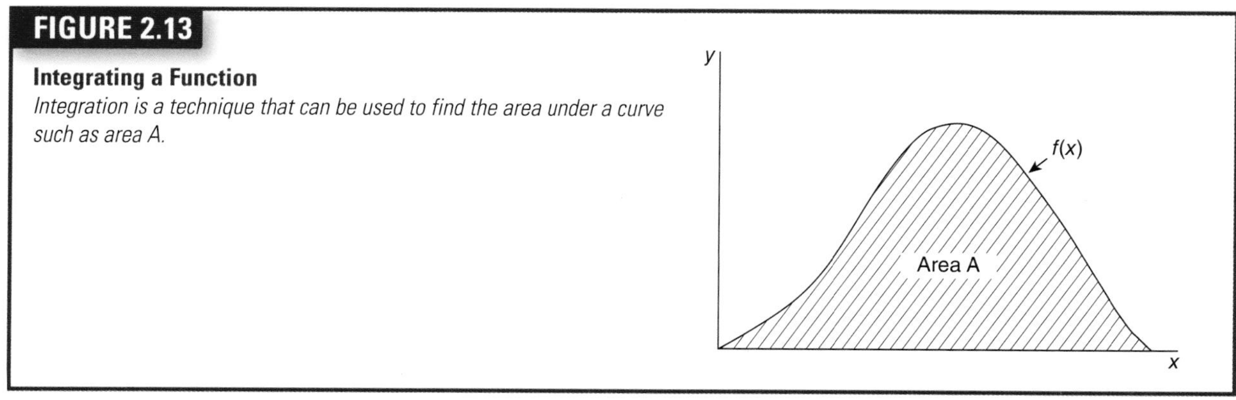

FIGURE 2.13

Integrating a Function

Integration is a technique that can be used to find the area under a curve such as area A.

Finding an integral is effectively the reverse of finding a derivative, which we did in the previous section. For example, using the principles we developed for differential calculus, we know that the derivative of x^2 is $2x$. The integral of $2x$ is x^2. The derivative of $4x^3$ is $12x^2$ and the integral of $12x^2$ is $4x^3$.

How do we do this? Let's take an example. We want to integrate that term $12x^2$. First, we work out the new power by increasing the existing power by one. So in our case our new power has been increased from 2 to 3 to give us $12x^3$. Second, we divide this number, this coefficient, by the new power, 3.

$$\frac{12x^3}{3} = 4x^3$$

The notation for an integral is an elongated S (∫.) Following this integral symbol we have the function of which we want to find the integral ($2x$ in our example). This is called the integrand. Finally we write dx to make clear that we are integrating with respect to x (whatever x represents). So if we are integrating $2x$ the problem to solve would be written as:

$$\int 2x \, dx$$

The answer would be written like this:

$$\int 2x\,dx = x^2 + c$$

We have explained all the elements of the answer except the c term at the end. This c is called the Constant of Integration. We put it there because there are many functions whose derivative is $2x$.

As we have seen, the derivative of x^2 is $2x$ but so is the derivative of $2x + 10$ or $2x + 50$, or $2x$ plus any constant. Remember that, as we explained in the previous section, the derivative of a constant is zero. So when we take a function and find the derivative we cannot know all of the reverse of the operation. We only know part of it, in this case, $2x$, but there may well have been a constant of some value. So we write $+ c$ to finish. Whist we always write it as $+ c$, remember that c might easily take a negative value.

The general form for integrating a power function[4] is:

$$\int x^n dx = \frac{x^{n+1}}{n+1} + c$$

What if we have more than one term in the function we wish to integrate? Just as with differentiation we can work out the answer for each part of the function and add them together.

We said that the derivative of x^2 is $2x$ and the integral of $2x$ is x^2. We said that the derivative of $4x^3$ is $12x^2$ and the integral of $12x^2$ is $4x^3$. So if we wanted to find the integral of the function:

$$Y = 2x + 12x^2$$

The integral of the first term is x^2 and the integral of the second term is $4x^3$ so we just add the terms together and write:

$$\int 2x + 12x^2 = x^2 + 4x^3 + c$$

Summary

You can now see how closely linked are the concepts of differentiation and integration. Differentiation and integration can be used to consider more complex functions than the ones we have been considering in this chapter but these are beyond the scope of our needs for this book.

[4] The formula works except in the special case where n = −1. If n = −1 the expression reduces to $\frac{x^0}{0}$, which is indeterminate. We will not meet such a case in this book.

PROBLEMS AND APPLICATIONS

In your job later on you will frequently have a large number of observations or data points from which you need to calculate an average. If you do this with pencil and paper or even your pocket calculator you are unlikely to keep your job for very long. Nowadays we typically use a computer with a standard spreadsheet software or even a statistical software package to solve these problems. However, it is extremely helpful for your understanding if you do this the slow way.

1 Calculate the average study time of the five students listed below.

Observation number	Study time per week [minutes]
1	70
2	120
3	30
4	60
5	90

2 You are observing the behaviour of 32 students. Five of them study for 30 minutes a week and three 120 minutes weekly. You can read this and the study intensity of the other 24 students from the table below, where the entry in the

column 'number of observations' tells you how many students study for how many minutes. Calculate the average study time.

Number of observations	Study time per week
5	30
3	60
9	70
12	90
3	120

Calculate the median for the two problems given above.

3 Identify the mode of study time from the table in Problems 1 and 2.

4 You and seven of your friends check your wallets before going out. The table below lists how much cash each student is carrying. Calculate the variance and the standard deviation of the amount of cash. Also calculate the coefficient of variation.

Observation number	Cash in wallet
Student 1	€ 12.80
Student 2	€ 76.20
Student 3	€ 21.60
Student 4	€ 24.10
Student 5	€ 7.65
Student 6	€ 38.50
Student 7	€ 49.30
Student 8	€ 9.85

5 Why do you need to work with probabilities in economics?

6 Imagine yourself working in a car dealership for higher class cars. There are 15 people milling around in the showroom. Three people have called ahead because they have already made a decision and would like to sign a contract. You would like to earn the bonus, but you do not personally know the customers, yet. What is the probability that you approach one of the people that will actually buy a car? After you are in a discussion with your random pick in the showroom when one of your colleagues approaches another person. What is the probability of finding one of the people that has come to sign a contract?

7 Calculate the logarithms of the values in the list below

a. $x = \ln 100$
b. $x = \log 100$
c. $x = \ln 1000000$
d. $x = \ln 1$
e. $x = \log 1$
f. $x = \ln 0.7$
g. $x = \log 0.7$

8 Are people more reluctant to show their wallet to friends if they have little money in it? Might this be different among students, since they do not want their peers to perceive them as 'rich'? When you were collecting the data on how much cash your friends carry with them, you also noted in which sequence they showed and counted out their money. The results are given in the table below. Calculate the coefficient of correlation between the rank of the amount of cash carried and the sequence in which it was presented. Which of the above hypotheses would this support?

Observation number	Cash in wallet	Sequence of showing
Student 1	€ 12.80	6
Student 2	€ 76.20	3
Student 3	€ 21.60	5
Student 4	€ 24.10	2
Student 5	€ 7.65	7
Student 6	€ 38.50	1
Student 7	€ 49.30	4
Student 8	€ 9.85	8

9 The cost for a firm to produce the output quantity x is given by $C(x) = 0.25x^3 + 5x^2 + 25x + 187.5$. Calculate the first derivative of the cost function $C(x)$.

10 You have analyzed a very large sample data set of 257 158 income tax returns in Germany. For the income tax due on these returns you have calculated an average mean of €32 999, the mode turned out to be €0.00 and the median €3275. The lowest tax payment in your sample was €0.00 the highest, however, was €21 753 706. Describe and interpret these figures.

11 The tax laws in your sample data set make a distinction between total earnings and taxable income. Some parts of your earnings are exempted from taxation and there are also certain deductibles that are subtracted from your earnings to calculate the taxable income. Your analysis provides the following statistics:

	Mean	Median	Mode	Variance	Standard deviation	Coefficient of variation	Number of observations
Total earnings	€33 802.54	€25 974.00	€ 0.00	8 303 325 282	€91 122.58	2.70	268 573
Taxable income	€28 837.27	€21 388.00	€ 0.00	7 599 201 487	€87 173.40	3.02	265 995

Describe and interpret the results.

12 Car producers and dealers advertise a single value for the average fuel consumption per 100 km of a particular make and model. Which other key statistics on fuel consumption would you like to ask for to get a better picture?

13 The fact that a constant growth process with a rate of 'a' per cent is leading to an exponential development of the variable in question (Y) can formally be written as $Y_t = (1 + a)^t$ where t denotes the time period since the start of the growth process.

Because $log_b\ Y_t = log_b\ ((1 + a)^t) = t \times log_b\ (1 + a)$ you could write for example $ln\ Y_t = t \times ln\ (1 + a)$. How many years will it take for a given value of Y to double if the growth rate is $a = 0.02 = 2$ per cent and how many years will it take for a doubling at a growth rate of $a = 0.05 = 5$ per cent?

PART 2 SUPPLY AND DEMAND: HOW MARKETS WORK

3 THE MARKET FORCES OF SUPPLY AND DEMAND

In this chapter we review the basic mathematics of supply and demand using linear equations and examining the concept of inverse demand and supply functions. In doing so we introduce the idea of a choke price. Then we examine the mathematics of shifting the demand curve and finally look at non-linear functions, finding equilibrium in markets using the mathematics of quadratic equations.

BASIC MATHEMATICS OF SUPPLY AND DEMAND

In a perfectly competitive market, it is assumed that an individual firm cannot influence the price P, but only the quantity, Q, of the good that it produces. Mathematically, this is represented in the form of a function which states that the value of one variable (quantity purchased for example) is a function of (or is dependent on) another set of variables, one of which may be price. In such a function, Q (the dependent variable) is a function of P (the independent variable). The simplest kind of model of the demand curve has the following form:

$$Q_D = a - bP$$

Where:
Q_D = quantity demanded of some good per period
P = the price of the good
a and b, are coefficients (numbers which define the dependency between the variables). These are positive constants.

The simplest kind of model of the supply curve has the following form:

$$Q_S = c + dP$$

Where:
Q_S = quantity supplied of some good per period
P = the price of the good
c and d, are coefficients and are positive constants.

The demand curve can also depend on other variables such as consumer income, denoted by Y (not I, which we use to stand for investment) and the price of alternative goods, say P_j.

As an example, our demand function might look like this:

$$Q_D = a - bP + eY + fP_j$$

If the coefficient of Y, for example, was $e = 5$ and we are told that $Y = 300$, then $eY = 1500$.

Similarly, the supply curve can also depend on other variables such as wage costs, W, and material costs, M. Then our supply function might look like this:

$$Q_S = 30 + \tfrac{1}{2}P - gW - hM$$

Notice we have used different letters for the coefficients in the demand and supply functions. For demand we used a, b, e and f as constants and for supply, c, d, g and h. This is to indicate that, although they are constants, they may well take different values. There are no set rules for what letters or symbols are used to indicate the coefficient but it is important to ensure it is clear where one coefficient may take on different values to another.

Later we will consider supply and demand functions with more than one variable but here we examine the simplest form where demand and supply are a function of price only.

Market equilibrium occurs when $Q_D = Q_S$. We can find this equilibrium using algebra or by plotting supply and demand curves and finding the intersection of the curves graphically. To do this we need to understand the idea of an inverse demand curve and an inverse supply curve.

Inverse Demand and Supply Curves

Instead of making Q the subject of a demand or supply equation we can make P the subject. This seems odd at first because it suggests that P is a function of Q_D and of Q_S, whereas Q_D and Q_S are functions of P. Quantity demanded is determined by price, not vice versa. The same applies to quantity supplied. Although it seems strange to present information in this inverse form there are good reasons for doing so. Some we shall see later but one we can see immediately.

One of the reasons for preferring the inverse form is that diagrammatically it is customary to show the price on the vertical axis and quantity on the horizontal axis. This means in effect that the demand curve is a visual representation of the inverse demand curve and the supply curve is a visual representation of the inverse supply curve. Let's first develop this idea in the context of the demand curve.

The Demand Function

A demand curve can be thought of as a visual representation of a set of plans in the minds of consumers – plans with regard to the amount they wish to buy at different possible prices. Suppose our demand curve is given as:

$$P = 20 - Q_D$$

Where P = price in euros, and Q_D = quantity per period of time demanded, say tonnes per week.

How do we represent this diagrammatically? We do this in Figure 3.1.

There are no non-linear terms in this kind of equation. It's an equation of a straight line (a linear equation). If we can find two points on the curve we can connect them and we have our demand curve.

Two possibilities are to find the quantity demanded when the price is zero, and the price at which quantity demanded drops to zero.

First, how much is demanded at a zero price? We can discover this by setting $P = 0$.

$$P = 20 - Q_D$$
$$0 = 20 - Q_D$$
$$Q_D = 20$$

These coordinates are plotted in Figure 3.1 as point A. Next, at what price does quantity demanded become zero? This is known as the choke price, the price at which all demand is choked off. No consumer is willing to purchase. We can discover this choke price by setting $Q = 0$.

$$P = 20 - Q_D$$
$$P = 20 - 0$$
$$P = 20$$

FIGURE 3.1

An Illustrative Demand Curve

If the demand function is of the form $P = 20 - Q_D$, then quantity demanded, Q_D, at a zero price is 20. At a price, P, of €20 the quantity demanded is zero. If $P = 10$, quantity demanded is 10.

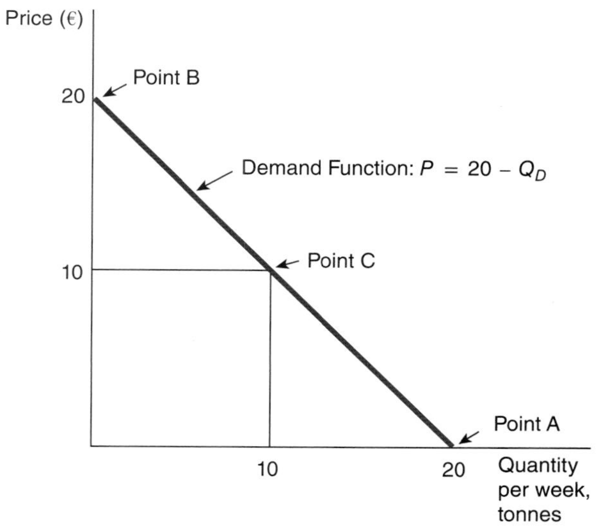

These coordinates are plotted as point B in Figure 3.1. We have then drawn a straight line connecting the two points. We can now use this demand curve to find different paired values for the relationship between price and quantity demanded for the equation $P = 20 - Q_D$.

For example if $P = 10$,

$$10 = 20 - Q_D$$
$$Q_D = 10$$

This is plotted as point C on Figure 3.1.

We have now represented the set of plans in the minds of consumers both diagrammatically and mathematically.

The Supply Function

A supply curve can be thought of as a visual representation of a set of plans in the minds of suppliers – plans with regard to the amount they wish to sell at different possible prices. Suppose our supply curve is given as:

$$P = 8 + 2Q_S$$

Where P = price in euros, and Q_s = quantity (say tonnes per week) supplied.

This equation is also a linear equation and if we follow the same process as we did for graphing the demand curve we can draw the supply curve for this equation. We do this in Figure 3.2.

First we find the vertical intercept of the supply curve, so we set $Q_S = 0$.

$$P = 8 + 2Q_S$$
$$P = 8 + 2 \times 0$$
$$P = 8$$

We show this as point A in, Figure 3.2. Now let's find another point. How much will suppliers offer for sale at a price of, say, 16?

$$P = 8 + 2Q_S$$
$$16 = 8 + 2Q_S$$
$$2Q_S = 8$$
$$Q_S = 4$$

This is shown as point B in Figure 3.2. Connecting these two points with a straight line gives us the supply curve for this equation. As with the demand curve this is an equation that will be true for many values. For example if $P = 20$, $Q_S = 6$ (point C in Figure 3.2).

FIGURE 3.2

An Illustrative Supply Curve

Given the supply function $P = 8 + 2Q_{S,}$ quantity supplied is zero at a price, P, of 8 or less. At a price, P, of €20 quantity supplied is 6.

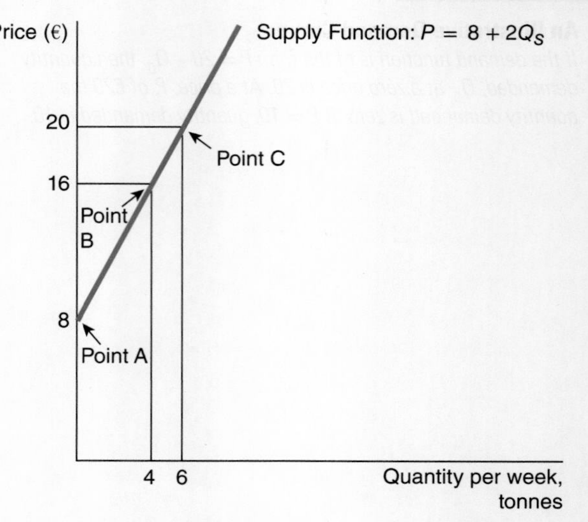

Note that when we picked two points to establish the position of the demand curve, we used the horizontal and vertical intercepts, $P = 0$ and $Q_D = 0$. But a supply curve will probably only meet one intercept so we choose another, random point $P = 16$ to specify the location of the supply curve.

We have now represented the set of plans in the minds of suppliers both diagrammatically and mathematically.

Solving for Equilibrium Price and Quantity

As we have already said, market equilibrium occurs where $Q_D = Q_S$. This can be done using algebra or by finding the intersection of the supply and demand curves graphically. Here we show several ways of finding equilibrium price and quantity algebraically using our two equations above.

Equating the Equations

This involves setting the two equations equal to one another and then solving for the unknown value. In our example we have:

$$P = 20 - Q_D$$

And:

$$P = 8 + 2Q_S$$

Then in equilibrium:

$$20 - Q_D = 8 + 2Q_S$$

Rearranging to bring all the Q terms on one side we have:

$$3Q = 12$$
$$Q = 4$$

Having solved for Q we can now find the value of P by substituting $Q = 4$ into either the demand or supply equation. Take the demand equation:

$$P = 20 - Q_D$$
$$P = 20 - 4$$
$$P = 16$$

Had we used the supply curve we would have obtained the same result:

$$P = 8 + 2Q_S$$
$$P = 8 + 8$$
$$P = 16$$

Substitution Method

An alternative, but entirely equivalent, method is to substitute into one of the equations the value of one of the unknowns from the other equation. We then solve for the remaining unknown. Here:

$$P = 20 - Q_D$$
$$P = 8 + 2Q_S$$

We can substitute into the supply equation $20 - Q_D$ for P:

$$20 - Q_S = 8 + 2Q_S$$

Rearranging to bring the Q terms onto the left hand side:

$$3Q = 12$$
$$Q = 4$$

We can now substitute this value back into either of the equations in order to solve for P. If we use the demand equation we get:

$$P = 20 - Q_D$$
$$P = 20 - 4$$
$$P = 16$$

The intersection of the demand and supply curves is therefore at (16, 4) as can be seen in Figure 3.3.

FIGURE 3.3

Market Equilibrium

Market equilibrium is where quantity supplied is equal to quantity demanded. Given the supply and demand functions, the equilibrium price in this case is €16 and the equilibrium quantity supplied and demanded is 4 units.

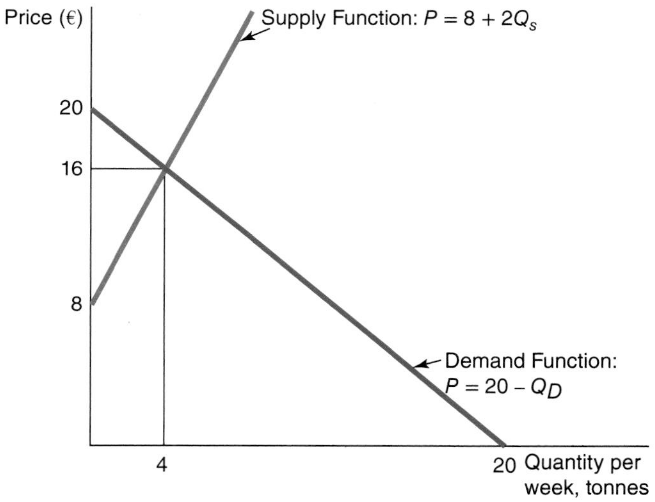

Row Operation

There is one further way to solve for the intersection point of any two linear equations, sometimes called the row operation method. This involves multiplying or dividing one equation so that the coefficient of one of the unknowns is the same in each of the equations. This enables us to eliminate one of the unknowns by subtracting one equation from the other.

We will show this method with a different example.

Suppose we have two linear equations as follows:

$$5x + 2y = 100 \quad (1)$$

$$20x + 4y = 300 \quad (2)$$

To solve we might multiply equation (1) by 4 to give:

$$20x + 8y = 400 \quad (3)$$

Now we can subtract equation (2) from equation (3):

$$20x + 8y = 400$$
$$20x + 4y = 300$$
$$0 + 4y = 100$$
$$y = 25$$

We can now find the value of the other unknown, x, by substituting the now known value of y into either of the equations. Using equation (1):

$$5x + 2y = 100$$
$$5x + 50 = 100$$
$$x = 10$$

As a check we could substitute $y = 25$ into equation (2):

$$20x + 4y = 300$$
$$20x + 100 = 300$$
$$20x = 200$$
$$x = 10$$

Shifts in the Curves

A change in price is shown as a movement along the demand curve but a change in any other relevant variable shifts the whole curve. We can demonstrate this mathematically.

Up to this point we have been working with a linear demand curve with one independent variable. However, demand for goods is determined by a number of variables. When we include these other variables we have what is called a multi-variate function. Let's assume that quantity demanded of good x, Q_{Dx} is a function of its own price, P_x the price of another good, good y, P_y and income which we will call Y. So let's assume our demand function is given as:

$$Q_{Dx} = -\frac{1}{2}P_x - P_y + 4Y$$

To plot the demand curve we need to know the coefficients of P_y and Y. Let's assume $P_y = 30$ and $Y = 20$. So:

$$Q_{Dx} = -\frac{1}{2}P_x - 30 + 4(20)$$

$$Q_{Dx} = -\frac{1}{2}P_x + 50$$

This is our demand function. But to plot the demand curve we must now find the inverse demand curve.

$$Q_{Dx} = -\frac{1}{2}P_x + 50$$

$$-\frac{1}{2}P_x = Q_{DX} - 50$$

$$\frac{1}{2}P_x = 50 - Q_{DX}$$

$$P_x = 100 - 2Q_{DX}$$

We can now plot this inverse demand curve. As before we can establish two points and join them together by a straight line. We are still working with linear curves.

When $P_x = 0$ we have:

$$0 = 100 - 2Q_{Dx}$$
$$2Q_{Dx} = 100$$
$$Q_{Dx} = 50$$

This is plotted as point A in Figure 3.4.

When $Q_{Dx} = 0$ we have:

$$P_x = 100 - 2(0)$$
$$P_x = 100$$

This is plotted as point B in Figure 3.4 and the two points, A and B have established the position of the demand curve. Now we will see what happens if something changes other than price. To illustrate, we assume that there is an increase in income, e.g. Y increases from 20 to 30.

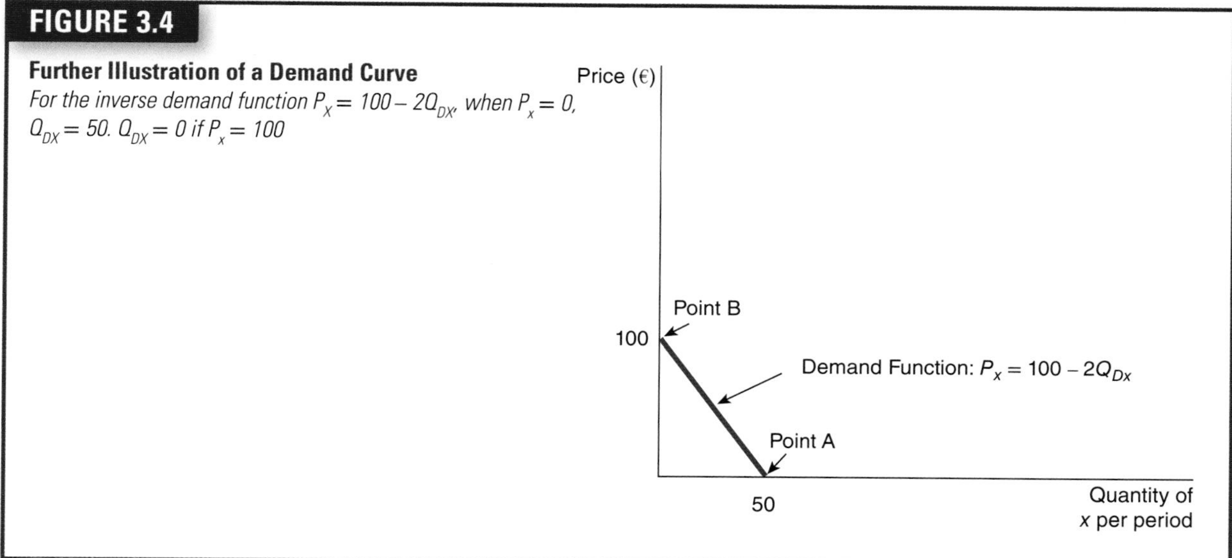

FIGURE 3.4

Further Illustration of a Demand Curve

For the inverse demand function $P_X = 100 - 2Q_{DX}$, when $P_x = 0$, $Q_{DX} = 50$. $Q_{DX} = 0$ if $P_x = 100$

The demand function is:

$$Q_{Dx} = -\frac{1}{2}P_x - P_y + 4Y$$

Plugging in the new values, (nothing changes except income, *Y*):

$$Q_{Dx} = -\frac{1}{2}P_x - 30 + 4(30)$$
$$= -\frac{1}{2}P_x + 90$$

This is the new demand function. Now we can find the inverse demand function:

$$Q_{Dx} = -\frac{1}{2}P_x + 90$$
$$-\frac{1}{2}P_x = Q_{Dx} - 90$$
$$\frac{1}{2}P_x = 90 - Q_{Dx}$$
$$P_x = 180 - 2Q_{Dx}$$

As before we can find two convenient spots on the demand curve and plot the whole curve by joining them together. As before the two spots we will find will be were $P = 0$ and where $Q_{Dx} = 0$. When $P_x = 0$ we have:

$$0 = 180 - 2Q_{Dx}$$
$$2Q_{Dx} = 180$$
$$Q_{Dx} = 90$$

This can be plotted as point C on the new demand curve shown in Figure 3.5.

To find our second point, when $Q_{Dx} = 0$ we have:

$$P_x = 180 - 2Q_{Dx}$$
$$P_x = 180 - 2(0)$$
$$P_x = 180$$

This is plotted as point D in Figure 3.5 and connecting points C and D gives us the new demand curve when income has risen from 20 to 30.

Figure 3.5 shows the new demand curve and shows the original demand curve from Figure 3.4.

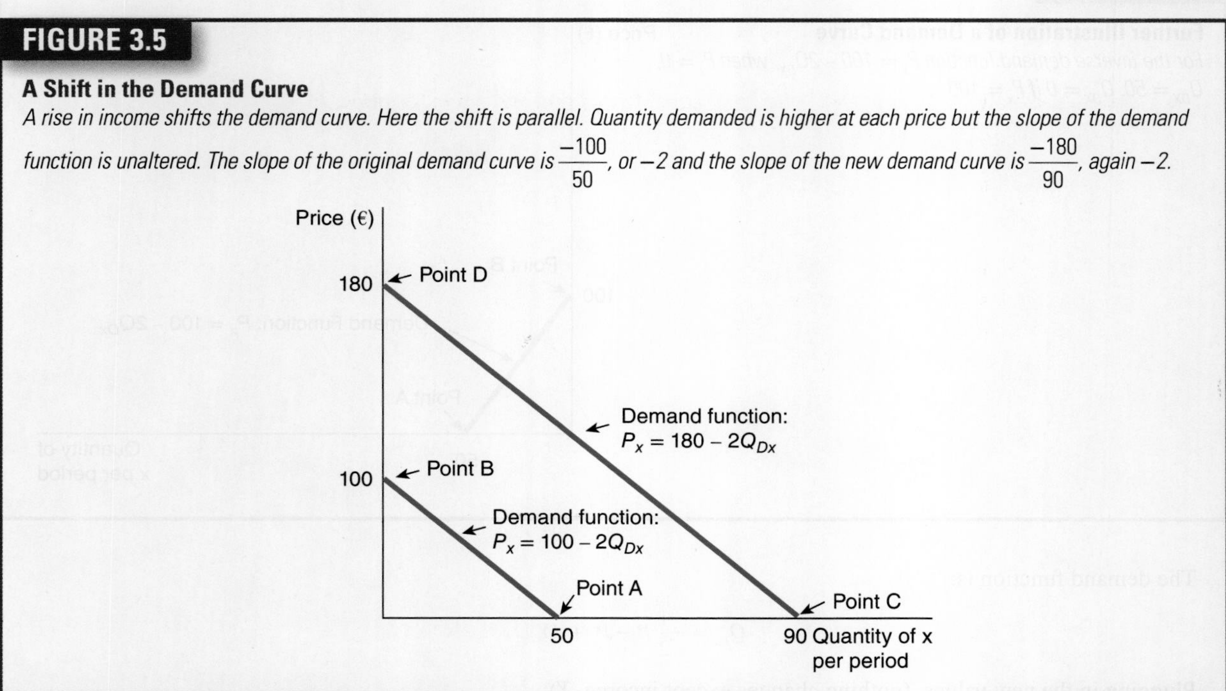

FIGURE 3.5

A Shift in the Demand Curve

A rise in income shifts the demand curve. Here the shift is parallel. Quantity demanded is higher at each price but the slope of the demand function is unaltered. The slope of the original demand curve is $\frac{-100}{50}$*, or −2 and the slope of the new demand curve is* $\frac{-180}{90}$*, again −2.*

Two things are especially worthy of note. When the price of a good changes, but all other variables remain the same, then we are looking at a different quantity demanded (or supplied) on the same demand (or supply) curve. Any change in one of the other variables shifts the whole demand (or supply) curve. Here a rise in income shifts the demand curve. At every price, quantity demanded is now higher. If the only factor that has changed is price then we say '*ceteris paribus*' which means 'all other things remaining the same'. If price changes, then, *ceteris paribus*, the position of the demand curve has not altered.

Notice also that the two demand curves are parallel. There is no change in the slope of the curve. The slope of a curve is the rise divided by the run. From Figure 3.5 we can see that the slope of the original curve is $\frac{-100}{50}$, or −2 and the slope of the new demand curve is $\frac{-180}{90}$, again −2.

Let's summarize what we have learned so far. We have:

- Created inverse supply and demand functions from supply and demand functions.
- Found market equilibrium using our supply and demand equations.
- Seen how changes in a demand function can be represented as a new demand curve.

Non-Linear Functions

All of our discussion so far has assumed that the demand and supply functions are linear. There is no reason to think that this will always be so. We may have a non-linear demand or supply curve (or indeed both). Then the process of solving for a market equilibrium price must be modified. We will demonstrate this now assuming a linear demand curve but a non-linear supply curve represented as a 'quadratic equation'. A quadratic equation has the form $y = a + bx + cx^2$.

Our functions will still show the quantity supplied of the commodity increasing with price and the quantity demanded for the commodity decreasing with price. As before, the market for the commodity is in equilibrium when supply is equal to demand.

In our example both supply and demand are functions only of price.

The supply function is a quadratic equation:

$$Q_S = 2P + 4P^2$$

The demand function is a linear function:

$$Q_D = 80 - 20P$$

To find equilibrium in our market we set supply equal to demand and solve for price, P.

$$2P + 4P^2 = 80 - 20P$$

Rearranging the terms we get a quadratic equation:

$$80 - 22P - 4P^2 = 0$$

Now we can solve the equation by means of the quadratic formula[1] from the general form given above, such that $a = 80$, $b = -22$, and $c = -4$.

Using the standard formula, the value of x is given by:

$$\begin{aligned} x &= \frac{-b \pm \sqrt{b^2 - 4ac}}{2a} \\ &= \frac{-(-22) \pm \sqrt{(-22)^2 - 4(80)(-4)}}{2(-4)} \\ &= \frac{22 \pm \sqrt{484 + 1280}}{-8} \\ &= \frac{22 \pm \sqrt{1764}}{-8} \\ &= \text{either } \frac{64}{-8} = -8 \\ &= \text{or } \frac{-20}{-8} = 2.5 \end{aligned}$$

We can eliminate from our consideration the negative value. Price has to be positive. A negative value for price would have no economic meaning. Then we are left with a single meaningful value of 2.5. Now that we have found the equilibrium price, we can find the equilibrium quantity. We substitute in the demand curve equation:

$$\begin{aligned} Q_D &= 80 - 20P \\ Q_D &= 80 - 20(2.5) \\ Q_D &= 30 \end{aligned}$$

Since this is the equilibrium quantity, we can check whether we get the same answer if use the supply function:

$$\begin{aligned} Q_S &= 2P + 4P^2 \\ Q_S &= 2(2.5) + 4(2.5)^2 \\ Q_S &= 5 + 4(6.25) \\ Q_S &= 30 \end{aligned}$$

We have now used the mathematics of quadratic equations to find market equilibrium when we do not have a linear demand and linear supply function. In this example, price is 2.5 and quantity is 30.

[1] An alternative method of solving this equation is factorization, but we will not be using this method in this book.

To the Right or Upwards?

When there is a change in price we show this graphically as a movement along the demand curve. However when there is a change in some other factor that affects demand, then the whole demand curve shifts. For example, as we have seen, an increase in income is one factor that will normally shift the demand curve such that more is demanded at every price. In this case economists will usually say that it shifts the demand curve to the right. An alternative way of looking at this is to say that the demand curve shifts *upwards*.

Instead of thinking that more will be demanded at each price we could think of it in this way. As a result of the rise in income any given quantity can now fetch a higher price. This is actually what is being plotted when we plot P (the dependent variable plotted along the vertical axis) as a function of Q (the independent variable plotted along the horizontal axis). So it all depends on what you consider to be the independent and dependent variables. For example, suppose to begin with we have a demand curve:

$$Q = 10 - P/2$$

Here Q depends on P and would be plotted vertically, with P horizontally.

Now suppose a rise in income means that we have a new demand function of:

$$Q = 15 - P/2$$

This is a shift up of 5 for Q. Q increases by 5 for any given price. If we are plotting this in the usual way, that is with Q on the x axis and P on the y axis then the inverse relation or function (sometimes called the reverted relation or function) we have:

$$P = 20 - Q$$

for the old inverse demand function and:

$$P = 30 - Q$$

for the new inverse demand function.

So P is now shifted up by 10 for any given quantity Q. It may look as though the line moves to the right by 5 and so that is what economists say, but it is really an optical illusion for linear functions only. A shift up in P by 10 is mathematically correct. This is illustrated diagrammatically in Figure 3.6.

FIGURE 3.6

Shifting the Demand Curve: To the Right or Upwards?

The new inverse demand curve can be seen as one that has shifted to the right by 5 since at each price quantity demanded has increased by 5. Alternatively we can say that it has shifted upwards by 10 since any given quantity can be sold at a price which is ten higher than before the rise in income. Mathematically, seeing it as an upward shift is correct, but economists still prefer to think of it as a shift right because they usually want to focus on the quantity demanded for any given price.

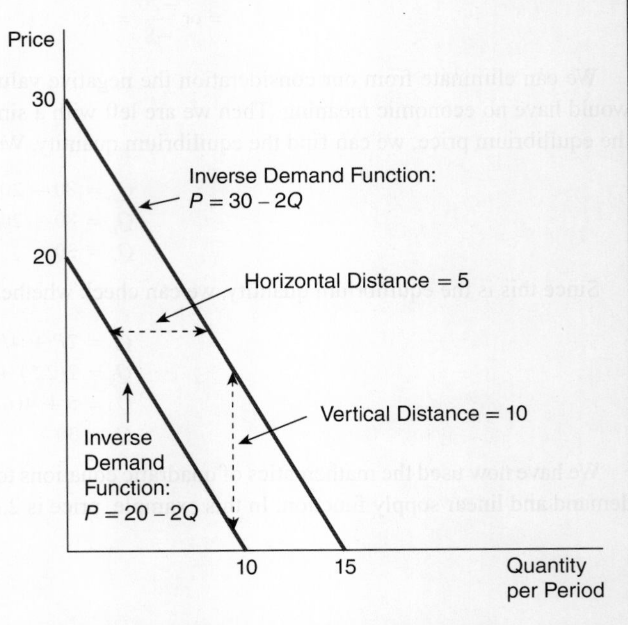

The difference is apparent with nonlinear functions. Here we choose a quadratic $g(Q)$ although what follows is true for all nonlinear functions. Let's suppose that originally:

$$P = 20 - 2Q^2 = g(Q)$$

Now suppose incomes rise so that we have, say:

$$\begin{aligned} P &= 30 - 2Q^2 \\ &= (20 - 2Q)^2 + 10 = g(Q) + 10 \end{aligned}$$

Then the graph moves up by 10. That is, these are parallel curves where the *vertical* distance is 10 (not the closest perpendicular distance which the eye sees and appears to show the graphs get closer together). You could try plotting these graphs to see this for yourself.

On the other hand a rightward shift of, say, 5 would be:

$$\begin{aligned} P &= g(Q - 5) = 20 - 2(Q - 5)^2 \\ &= 20 - 2Q^2 + 20Q - 50 \\ &= -2Q^2 + 20Q - 30 \end{aligned}$$

This is not the same as $g(Q)+10$.

In general, if $C > 0$, then $f(x) + C$ shifts vertically up by C, and $f(x) - C$ shifts vertically down by C.

However, if $d > 0$, $f(x + d)$ shifts to the left by d and $f(x - d)$ shifts to the right.

Thus although in the language of economists we normally speak of a demand curve shifting to the right (or left), and this book follows that convention, when adding a constant term to the right-hand side of a function as above, it is in fact mathematically correct to describe it as a movement upwards (or downwards).

Summary

We have now shown how we can establish market equilibrium mathematically and also considered what happens if market equilibrium changes as a result of shifts in the curves.

PROBLEMS AND APPLICATIONS

1 The inverse of the supply function is given by $P = 2 + 0.0032Q_s$. The demand function is $P = 20 - 0.004Q_D$.
   a. Draw a graph of these functions.
   b. Read off the market equilibrium quantity and price from the graph.
   c. Confirm your answer in b) with a calculation.

2 Producers in a perfectly competitive market provide their output along the supply function $Q_s = -5 + 2P$. Market demand is given by $Q_D = 10 - P$. Calculate the inverses of the two functions.

3 The inverse supply function $P = 30 + \frac{1}{8}Q_s$ shows the willingness of producers to sell their output for different prices. The government introduces a new tax on the product that the producers will have to pay to the tax authorities. For each unit of output sold producers have to pay €32.50.
   a. Calculate the shifted new supply function and show the new and old supply functions in a diagram.
   b. $P = 160 - 0.2Q_D$ represents market demand. Sketch the demand function in the graph from a) and read of the old and new equilibrium.
   c. Verify your answers to b) algebraically.

4 The table below shows the demand function and the supply function for a good in a perfectly competitive market.
   a. What are the quantity traded and the price in the market equilibrium?
   b. Are the supply and the demand linear functions?
   c. Plot the demand and the supply function from the data in the table.

d. Assume there is a change in demand, the product in question all of a sudden is very fashionable. How could you show this in a fourth column in the table?

Price [€/unit]	Quantity supplied	Quantity demanded
0.00	0.0	800.0
5.00	0.0	775.0
17.50	0.0	712.5
30.00	0.0	650.0
42.50	100.0	587.5
55.00	200.0	525.0
67.50	300.0	462.5
80.00	400.0	400.0
92.50	500.0	337.5
105.00	600.0	275.0
117.50	700.0	212.5

5 The supply function is $P_s = c + dQ$. What is the first derivative of this function with respect to the quantity $\left(\frac{dP_s}{dQ}\right)$? What is this telling you?

4 ELASTICITY AND ITS APPLICATIONS

In this chapter, we will provide an overview of the mathematics of elasticity and then follow this up with a review of demand elasticity taking a specific example from a UK business, *The Times* Newspaper, and calculation of both own-price and cross-price elasticities of demand using various elasticity measures to which you have already been introduced. In doing so we will develop a technique for deriving a demand function from a few observations on price and quantity. Then we extend the analysis of demand elasticity to cover the technique of partial differentiation. Finally, we develop the analysis of the elasticity of supply.

INTRODUCTION

The sensitivity of consumer demand to price changes is an important topic. We will often need to know, for example, not just that a lower price leads to an increased quantity demanded, but the extent of that increase. This sensitivity of demand to price changes we call own-price elasticity of demand. We will often be interested also in the sensitivity of demand to changes in the price of other goods. This we call cross-price elasticity of demand. How sensitive consumer demand is to changes in income is measured by income elasticity of demand. Suppliers will also change the amount of output offered for sale when there is a change in price. The sensitivity of supply to price changes is referred to as elasticity of supply.

THE MATHEMATICS OF ELASTICITY

Point Elasticity of Demand

The value for elasticity can vary at every point along a straight line demand curve. Point elasticity of demand allows us to be able to be more specific about the elasticity at different points. In the formula given below, the numerator (the top half of the fraction) describes the change in quantity in relation to the base quantity and the denominator the change in price in relation to the base price.

$$\textit{Price elasticity of demand} = \frac{\left(\dfrac{Q_2 - Q_1}{((Q_2 + Q_1)/2)}\right) \times 100}{\left(\dfrac{(P_2 - P_1)}{((P_2 + P_1)/2)}\right) \times 100}$$

If we cancel out the 100s in the above equation and rewrite it a little more elegantly we get:

$$\textit{Price elasticity of demand} = \frac{\Delta Q}{Q} / \frac{\Delta P}{P}$$

Where the $\Delta Q = Q_2 - Q_1$

Re-arranging the above we get:

$$\textit{Price elasticity of demand} = \frac{\Delta Q}{Q} \times \frac{P}{\Delta P}$$

There is no set order required to this equation so it can be re-written as:

$$\textit{Price elasticity of demand} = \frac{\Delta Q}{\Delta P} \times \frac{P}{Q}$$

Note that the expression $\Delta Q/\Delta P$ is the reciprocal of the slope of a linear demand curve. Figure 4.1 shows the graph of two straight line demand curves, D_1 and D_2, given by the equations:

$$P = 20 - 5Q_D \qquad \text{(D1)}$$

$$P = 20 - 4Q_D \qquad \text{(D2)}$$

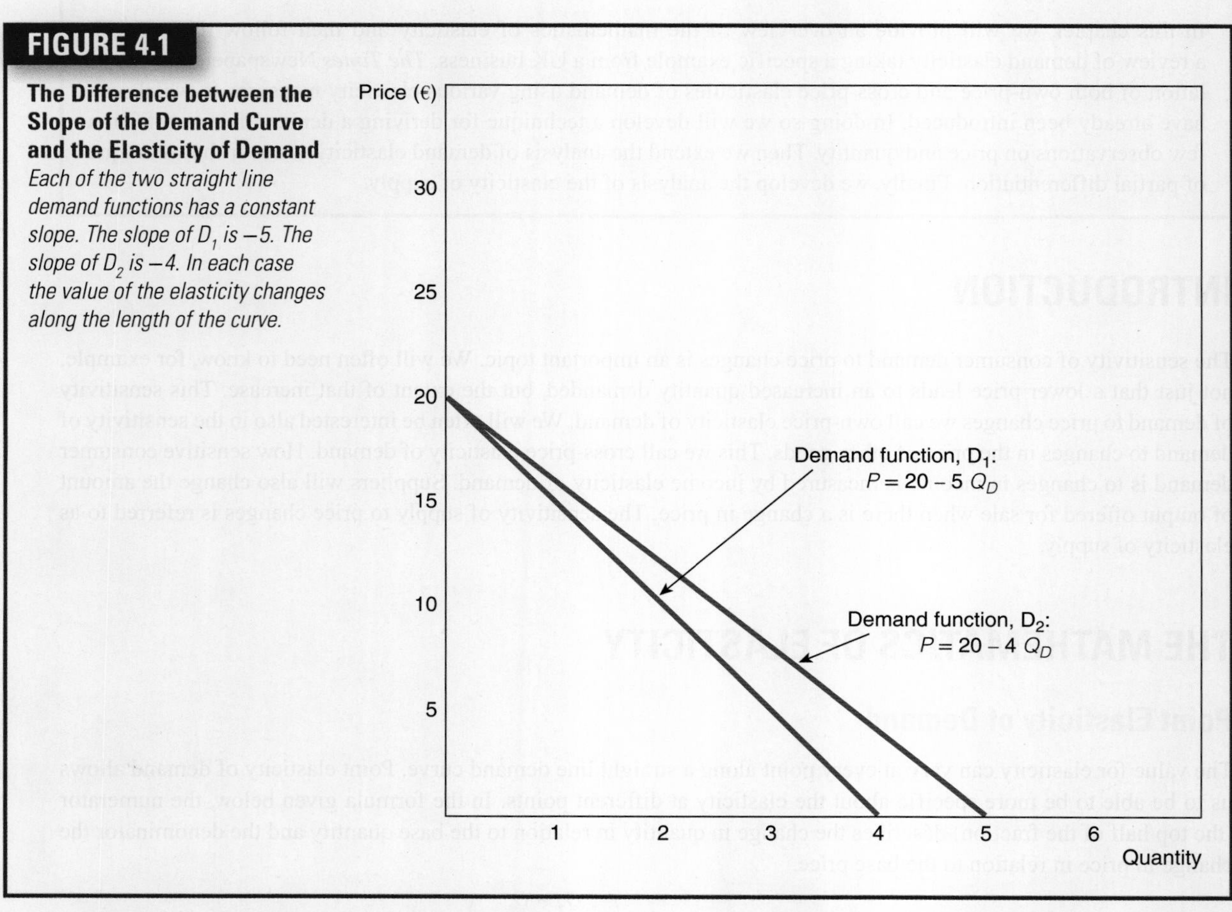

FIGURE 4.1

The Difference between the Slope of the Demand Curve and the Elasticity of Demand

Each of the two straight line demand functions has a constant slope. The slope of D_1 is –5. The slope of D_2 is –4. In each case the value of the elasticity changes along the length of the curve.

For demand curve D_1, the vertical intercept is 20 and the horizontal intercept is 4 and so the slope of the line D_1 is –5. For demand curve D_2, the vertical intercept is 20 and the horizontal intercept is 5, the slope of the line D_2 is –4. To verify this let us take demand curve D_1, if price were 10 then the quantity would be $10 = 20 - 5Q_D$. Rearranging this gives:

$$5Q_D = 20 - 10$$

Dividing both sides by 5 gives $Q = 2$.
Looking at demand curve D_2, if price were 10, then the quantity would be:

$$Q = 5 - 0.25(10)$$
$$Q = 5 - 2.5$$
$$Q = 2.5$$

Now let us assume that price falls from 10 to 5 in each case. The quantity demanded for D_1 would now be:

$$5 = 20 - 5Q$$
$$Q = 3$$

For D_2 the quantity would be:

$$Q = 5 - 0.25(5)$$
$$Q = 3.75$$

Representing this graphically for demand curve D_1, we get the following as shown in Figure 4.2.

FIGURE 4.2

Measuring the Elasticity of a Demand Curve
When the price changes from 10 to 5, quantity increases from 2 to 3. The elasticity of demand in this part of the demand curve is therefore given as $\frac{1}{-5} \times \frac{10}{2} = -1$.

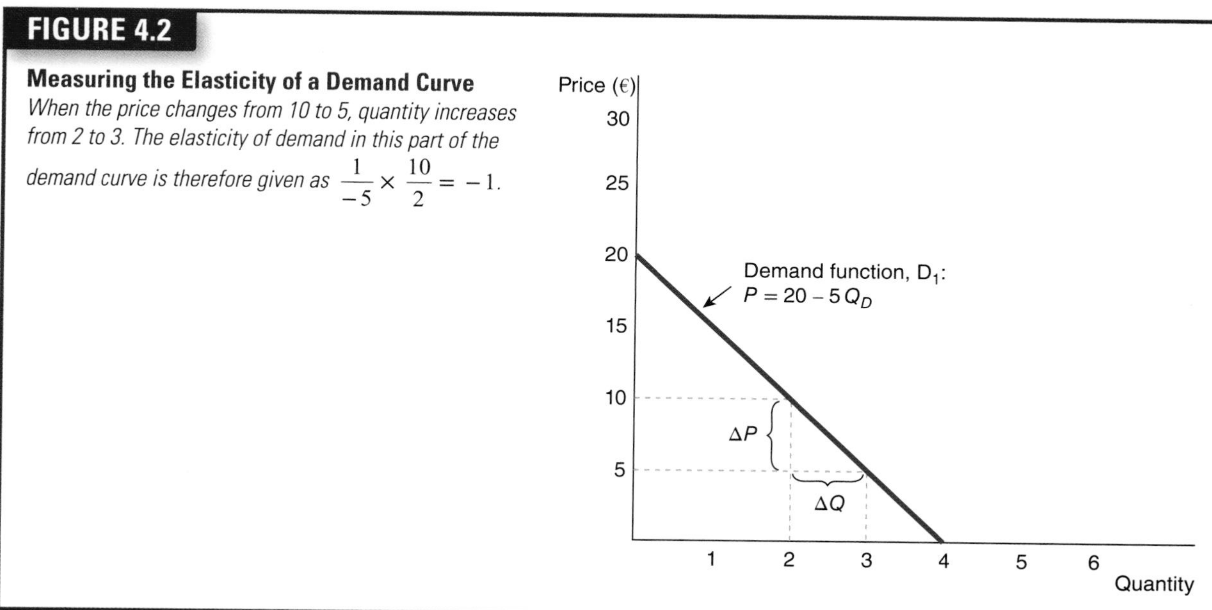

The slope of the line as drawn is:

$$\frac{\Delta P}{\Delta Q} = \frac{-5}{1}$$
$$= -5$$

The slope is the same at all points along a linear demand curve. The initial price, prior to a change, will give different ratios at different points on the demand curve. Again, using demand curve D_1, the ratio of P/Q at the initial price of 10 is 10/2 = 5. At a price of 5, the ratio of P/Q given by the demand curve D_1 would be 5/3 = 1.67.

Going back to our formula:

$$\text{Price elasticity of demand} = \frac{\Delta Q}{\Delta P} \times \frac{P}{Q}$$

The first part of the equation, ($\Delta Q/\Delta P$) is the reciprocal of the slope of the demand curve and the second part of the equation P/Q gives us a specific point on the demand curve relating to a particular price and quantity combination. Multiplying these two terms gives us the price elasticity of demand at a particular point and so is referred to as *point elasticity of demand.*

The price elasticity of demand when price changes from 10 to 5 in demand curve D_1 above, would be:

$$\text{Price elasticity of demand} = \frac{1}{-5} \times \frac{10}{2}$$
$$= -1$$

If we were looking at a fall in price from 15 to 10 we would get:

$$\text{Price elasticity of demand} = \frac{1}{-5} \times \frac{15}{1}$$
$$= -3$$

And if looking at a price fall from 5 to 2.5 then we would get:

$$\textit{Price elasticity of demand} = \frac{0.5}{-2.5} \times \frac{5}{3}$$
$$= -0.33$$

Calculus

The demand curve is often depicted as a linear curve but there is no reason why it should be linear, and it can be curvilinear. To measure elasticity accurately in this case economists use calculus. The rules of calculus applied to a demand curve give a far more accurate measurement of the price elasticity of demand at a particular point.

For a linear demand function, the approximation to the point elasticity at the initial price and quantity is given by:

$$\frac{(Q_2 - Q_1)}{(P_2 - P_1)} \times \frac{P_1}{Q_1}$$

which gives exactly the same result as the point elasticity which is defined in terms of calculus and is given by:

$$\frac{dQ}{dP} \times \frac{P}{Q}$$

Point elasticity defined in terms of calculus gives a precise answer; all the other formulae are approximations of some sort. The formula looks similar but it must be remembered that what we are talking about in this instance is an infinitesimally small change in quantity demanded following an infinitesimally small change in price. In the formula, dQ/dP is the derivative of a linear demand function – the rate of change of the demand function at a specific point. Given our basic linear equation of the form $Q = a - bP$, the power function rule (in this case, P is raised to the power 1) gives dQ/dP as the coefficient of P.

Take the following demand equation:

$$Q = 60 - 3P$$

We calculate dQ/dP as -3.

To find the price elasticity of demand when price = 15 first of all we need to find Q:

$$Q = 60 - 3P$$
$$Q = 60 - 3(15)$$
$$Q = 15$$

Substitute this into the formula to get:

$$\textit{Price elasticity of demand} = -3\left(\frac{15}{15}\right)$$
$$\textit{Price elasticity of demand} = -3$$

It is useful to remember that given an elasticity figure we can calculate the expected change in demand as a result of a change in price. For example, if the price elasticity of demand (*ped*) is given as –0.6 then an increase in price of 5 per cent will result in a fall in quantity demanded of 3 per cent. By using the inverse of the elasticity equation, for any given value of price elasticity of demand we can calculate how much of a price change is required to bring about a desired change in quantity demanded. Suppose that a government wanted to reduce the demand for motor vehicles as part of a policy to reduce congestion and pollution. What sort of price change might be required to bring about a 10 per cent fall in demand?

Assume that the price elasticity of demand for motor vehicles is –0.8. The inverse of the basic elasticity formula is:

$$\frac{1}{ped} = \frac{\%\Delta P}{\%\Delta Q}$$

Substituting our known values into the formula we get:

$$\frac{1}{-0.8} = \frac{\%\Delta P}{-10}$$
$$-1.25 = \frac{\%\Delta P}{-10}$$
$$\%\Delta P = 12.5$$

To bring about a reduction in demand of 10 per cent, the price of motor vehicles would have to rise by 12.5 per cent.

Other Elasticities

Income and cross elasticity of demand are all treated in exactly the same way as the analysis of price elasticity of demand above.

Point income elasticity is:

$$\textit{Income elasticity of demand} = \frac{\Delta Q}{\Delta Y} \times \frac{Y}{Q}$$

Using calculus:

$$\textit{Income elasticity of demand} = \frac{dQ}{dY} \times \frac{Y}{Q}$$

For cross elasticity the formula is:

$$\textit{Cross elasticity of demand} = \frac{\Delta Qa}{\Delta Pb} \times \frac{Pb}{Qa}$$

Where Qa is the quantity demanded of one good, a, and Pb is the price of a related good, b (either a substitute or a complement). For a substitute $\frac{dQa}{dPb} > 0$ and for a complement, $\frac{dQa}{dPb} < 0$.

$$\textit{Cross elasticity of demand} = \frac{dQa}{dPb} \times \frac{Pb}{Qa}$$

In Chapter 3 we saw that demand can be expressed as a multivariate function where demand is dependent on a range of variables which include the price of the good, the price of other goods, incomes and so on. It is possible to calculate the elasticities of all these other factors using the same principles as those outlined above. In each case it is usual to calculate the elasticity with respect to a change in one of the variables whilst holding the others constant.

For example, take the demand equation $Q_D = 1400 - 4P + 0.04Y$. This equation tells us that demand is dependent on the price and also the level of income (Y).

From this equation we can calculate the price elasticity of demand and the income elasticity of demand. In this example we will use calculus to find both elasticities assuming $P = 50$ and $Y = 8000$.

Given these values:

$$Q_D = 1400 - 4(50) + 0.04(8000)$$
$$Q_D = 1400 - 200 + 320$$
$$Q_D = 1520$$

With:

$$\frac{dQ}{dP} = -4$$
$$ped = -4\left(\frac{50}{1520}\right)$$
$$ped = -0.132$$

Given:

$$\frac{dQ}{dY} = 0.04$$

Income elasticity of demand (yed):

$$yed = \frac{dQ}{dY} \cdot \frac{Y}{Q}$$
$$yed = 0.04\left(\frac{8000}{1520}\right)$$
$$yed = 0.21$$

Now look at this demand equation:

$$Qa = 100 - 8Pa - 6Pb + 4Pc + 0.015Y$$

This equation gives the relationship between demand and the prices of other goods labelled *a*, *b* and *c* respectively. We can use this to find the respective cross elasticities.

Assume that the price of good *a* is 20, the price of good *b*, 40, the price of good *c*, 80 and $Y = 20\,000$.

Substituting these into our function gives:

$$Qa = 100 - 8Pa - 6Pb + 4Pc + 0.015Y$$
$$Qa = 100 - 8(20) - 6(40) + 4(80) + 0.015(20\,000)$$
$$Qa = 100 - 160 - 240 + 320 + 300$$
$$Qa = 320$$

The change in demand of good *a* with respect to changes in the price of good *b* is given by:

$$\frac{dQa}{dPb} = -6$$

Then the:

$$\begin{aligned} \text{cross elasticity of demand} &= -6\left(\frac{40}{320}\right) \\ &= -6(0.125) \\ &= -0.75 \end{aligned}$$

The relationship between goods *a* and *b* is that they are complements – a rise in the price of good *b* will lead to a fall in the quantity demanded of good *a*.

The change in demand of good *a* with respect to changes in the price of good *c* is given by:

$$\frac{dQa}{dPc} = 4$$

$$\begin{aligned} \text{Cross elasticity of demand} &= 4\left(\frac{80}{320}\right) \\ &= 4(0.25) \\ &= 1 \end{aligned}$$

In this case the relationship between the two goods is that they are substitutes – a rise in the price of good *c* would lead to a rise in the quantity demanded of good *a*.

Price Elasticity of Supply

Many of the principles outlined above apply also to the price elasticity of supply. The formula for the price elasticity of supply using the point method is:

$$\text{Price elasticity of supply} = \frac{\Delta Qs}{\Delta P} \times \frac{P}{Qs}$$

Using calculus:

$$\text{Price elasticity of supply} = \frac{dQs}{dP} \times \frac{P}{Qs}$$

However, we need to note a particular issue with price elasticity of supply which relates to the graphical representation of supply curves.

This is summarized in the following:

- A straight line supply curve intersecting the *y*-axis at a positive value has a price elasticity of supply > 1.
- A straight line supply curve passing through the origin has a price elasticity of supply = 1.
- A straight line supply curve intersecting the *x*-axis at a positive value has a price elasticity of supply < 1.

To see why any straight line supply curve passing through the origin has a price elasticity of supply of 1 we can use some basic knowledge of geometry and similar triangles.

Figure 4.3 shows a straight line supply curve S_1 passing through the origin. The slope of the supply curve is given by $\frac{\Delta P}{\Delta Q_s}$. We have highlighted a triangle, shaded green, with the ratio $\frac{\Delta P}{\Delta Q_s}$ relating to a change in price of 7.5 and a change in quantity of 1. The larger triangle formed by taking a price of 22.5 and a quantity of 3 shows the ratio of the price and quantity at this point (P/Q). The two triangles formed by these are both classed as similar triangles – they have different lengths to their three sides but the internal angles are all the same. The ratio of the sides must therefore be equal as shown by equation (1) below:

$$\frac{\Delta P}{\Delta Qs} = \frac{P}{Qs} \tag{1}$$

Given our definition of point elasticity of supply, if we substitute equation 1 into the formula and rearrange we get:

$$Price\ elasticity\ of\ supply = \frac{\Delta Q_S}{\Delta P} \times \frac{P}{Q_S}$$

Therefore:

$$Price\ elasticity\ of\ supply = 1$$

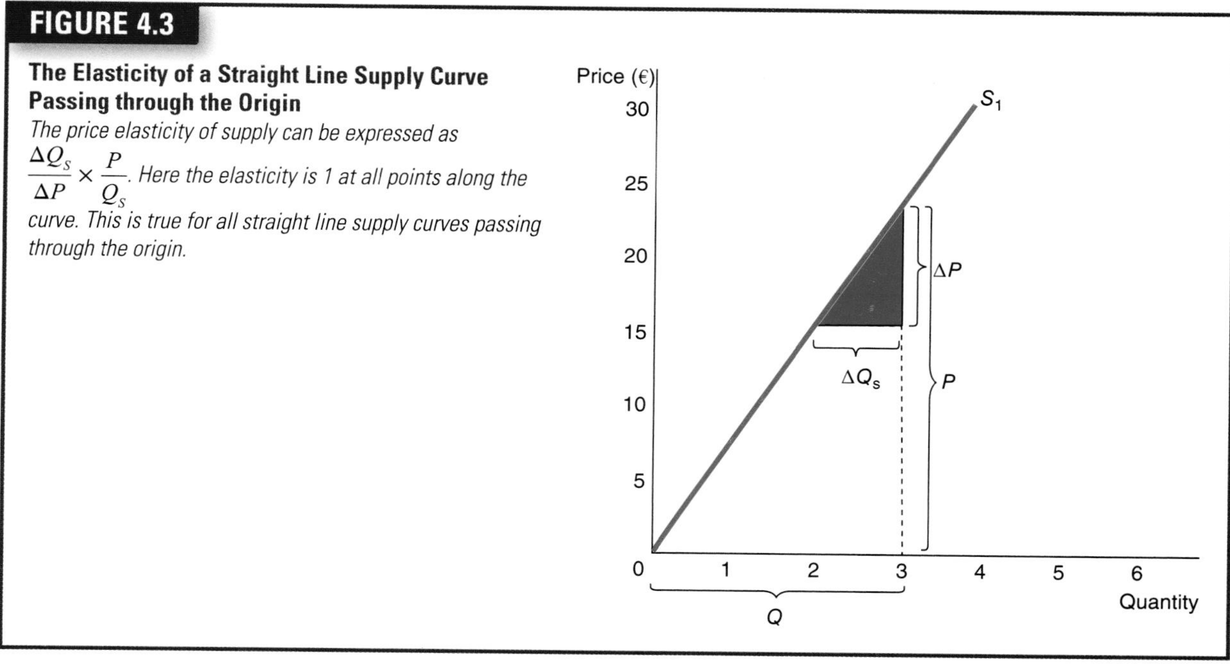

FIGURE 4.3

The Elasticity of a Straight Line Supply Curve Passing through the Origin

The price elasticity of supply can be expressed as $\frac{\Delta Q_S}{\Delta P} \times \frac{P}{Q_S}$*. Here the elasticity is 1 at all points along the curve. This is true for all straight line supply curves passing through the origin.*

Elasticity and Total Expenditure/Revenue

It is strictly correct to use the term 'total expenditure' in relation to the demand curve to accurately reflect the fact that demand is related to buyers and when buyers pay for products this represents expenditure. Many books use the term expenditure and revenue interchangeably, because what consumers spend is what firms receive as revenue. However, in this short section we are going to refer to revenue.

Total revenue is found by multiplying the quantity purchased by the average price paid. This is shown by the formula:

$$TR = P \times Q$$

Total revenue can change if either price or quantity, or both, change. This can be seen in Figure 4.4 where a rise in the price of a good from P_0 to P_1 has resulted in a fall in quantity demanded from Q_0 to Q_1.

We can represent the change in price as ΔP so that the new price is $(P + \Delta P)$ and the change in quantity as ΔQ so that the new quantity is $(Q + \Delta Q)$ so TR can be represented thus:

$$TR = (P + \Delta P)(Q + \Delta Q)$$

If we multiply out this expression as shown then we get:

$$TR = (P + \Delta P)(Q + \Delta Q)$$
$$TR = PQ + P\Delta Q + \Delta PQ + \Delta P\Delta Q$$

In Figure 4.4, this can be seen graphically.

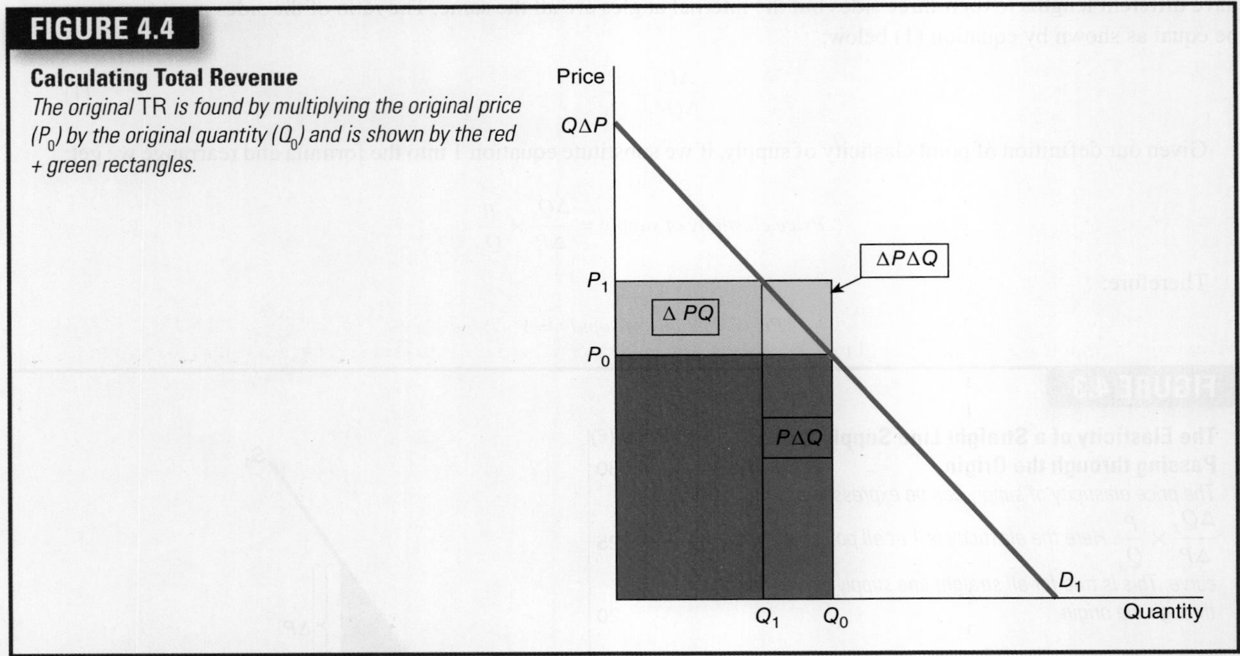

FIGURE 4.4

Calculating Total Revenue

The original TR is found by multiplying the original price (P_0) by the original quantity (Q_0) and is shown by the red + green rectangles.

As a result of the change in price there is an additional amount of revenue shown by the blue rectangle (ΔPQ). However, this is offset by the reduction in revenue caused by the fall in quantity demanded as a result of the change in price shown by the green rectangle ($P\Delta Q$). There is also an area indicated by the yellow rectangle which is equal to $\Delta P\Delta Q$. This leaves us with a formula for the change in *TR* as:

$$\Delta TR = Q\Delta P + P\Delta Q + \Delta P\Delta Q$$

Let us substitute some figures into our formula to see how this works in practice. Assume the original price of a product is 15 and the quantity demanded at this price is 750. When the price rises to 20 the quantity demanded falls to 500.

Using the equation:

$$TR = PQ + P\Delta Q + \Delta PQ + \Delta P\Delta Q$$

TR is now:

$$TR = 15(750) + 15(-250) + 5(750) + 5(-250)$$
$$TR = 10\,000$$

The change in *TR* is:

$$\Delta TR = Q\Delta P + P\Delta Q + \Delta P\Delta Q$$
$$\Delta TR = 750(5) + 15(-250) + 5(-250)$$
$$\Delta TR = 3750 - 3750 - 1250$$
$$\Delta TR = -1250$$

In this example the effect of the change in price has been negative on *TR*. We know from our analysis of price elasticity of demand that this means the percentage change in quantity demanded was greater than the percentage change in price – in other words, price elasticity of demand must be elastic at this point (>1). For the change in *TR* to be positive, therefore, the price elasticity of demand must be <1.

We can express the relationship between the change in *TR* and price elasticity of demand as an inequality as follows:

$$\textit{Price elasticity of demand} = \frac{\Delta Q}{\Delta P} \times \frac{P}{Q} > 1$$

When price increases, revenue decreases if price elasticity of demand meets this inequality. Equally, for a price increase to result in a rise in revenue *ped* must meet the inequality below:

$$\textit{Price elasticity of demand} = \frac{\Delta Q}{\Delta P} \times \frac{P}{Q} < 1$$

DEMAND ELASTICITY: THE UK NEWSPAPER INDUSTRY

Does a firm know about the position and elasticity of its demand curve, as we often assume, or is it the case that the firm knows only one spot on the demand curve, the current price and how much it is selling at that price? In practice there are ways of establishing information about other parts of the demand curve, at least to some extent, although it may well involve cost for a firm to do so.

One way of getting more information about demand is to experiment by changing price and seeing what happens to quantity demanded. The firm could lower price by, say, 33 per cent below its current level and observe the extent to which quantity demanded rises. It could, of course, then raise price above its current level and observe the extent to which the quantity demanded falls. It can try to establish the demand curve via a pattern of trial and error, therefore. This has two problems. First, it may be very expensive for the firm to do it. They may incur a period with a higher price and discover that demand has fallen considerably as a result. When they lower their price again, they may have lost part of their market to rivals and can't get it back. Markets may not be flexible.

In addition, it must be noted that we draw the demand curve with a *ceteris paribus* assumption. We assume that nothing else changes, other than the price of the product. Suppose that the firm raises its price for, say, six months and then observes that during that period demand is now 20 per cent less. It cannot hold constant all the other things that affect demand: incomes, the price of substitutes and so on. So the change in the quantity demanded may not simply be because of the change in price. It may be any of a host of other factors which have shifted a whole demand curve. So the firm will have to take this into account.

A variant on the above is to use a test market. It may be possible to select a small part of a market where a firm can vary price and observe the effect on demand. Table 4.1 gives an illustration of just this approach. Some years ago, the UK newspaper, *The Times*, considered lowering price from 45p per copy to 30p in order to increase market share. It experimented by offering its newspaper at the lower price for one month only in a small part of the UK, the area of North Kent. The table shows the effect on sales of *The Times* and the effects on its major competitors.

Assuming this sample period and area to be representative of the whole market and assuming that the *ceteris paribus* assumption holds, we can try to estimate the own-price elasticity of demand.

We can also estimate the cross-elasticity of demand for competitors' newspapers with respect to the price of *The Times*. For example, we can see the effect on *The Independent* whose price remained unchanged during that one month period.

TABLE 4.1 **Sales of The Times in response to a Price Cut.**

Sales in Kent County area (number of copies per day)

Title	Net Sale	Difference
The Times		
Base 31/07	11 565	
Week 4 28/08	13 266	+ 14.7%
The Independent		
Base 31/07	9133	
Week 4 28/08	8885	– 2.7%
The Guardian		
Base 31/07	9009	
Week 4 28/08	8474	– 5.9%
The Telegraph		
Base 31/07	44 196	
Week 4 28/08	44 116	– 0.2%
Total market		
Base 31/07	73 902	
Week 4 28/08	74 741	+ 1.1%

By using a short period this minimises the possibility of other factors changing. For example, no other newspaper altered its price during that time. However, the information obtained in such an experiment is still limited. We have to assume that the test market is typical of the whole.

We also need to make a further assumption about the shape of the demand curve between the two points we have established. The information regarding the demand for *The Times* is taken from table 4.1 and plotted in Figure 4.5.

FIGURE 4.5

Own-Price Demand Curve for *The Times*

Two points on a demand curve are sufficient to establish the whole curve only if it is known to be a linear relationship. If the curve is non-linear there are many possible demand curves that can pass through two points.

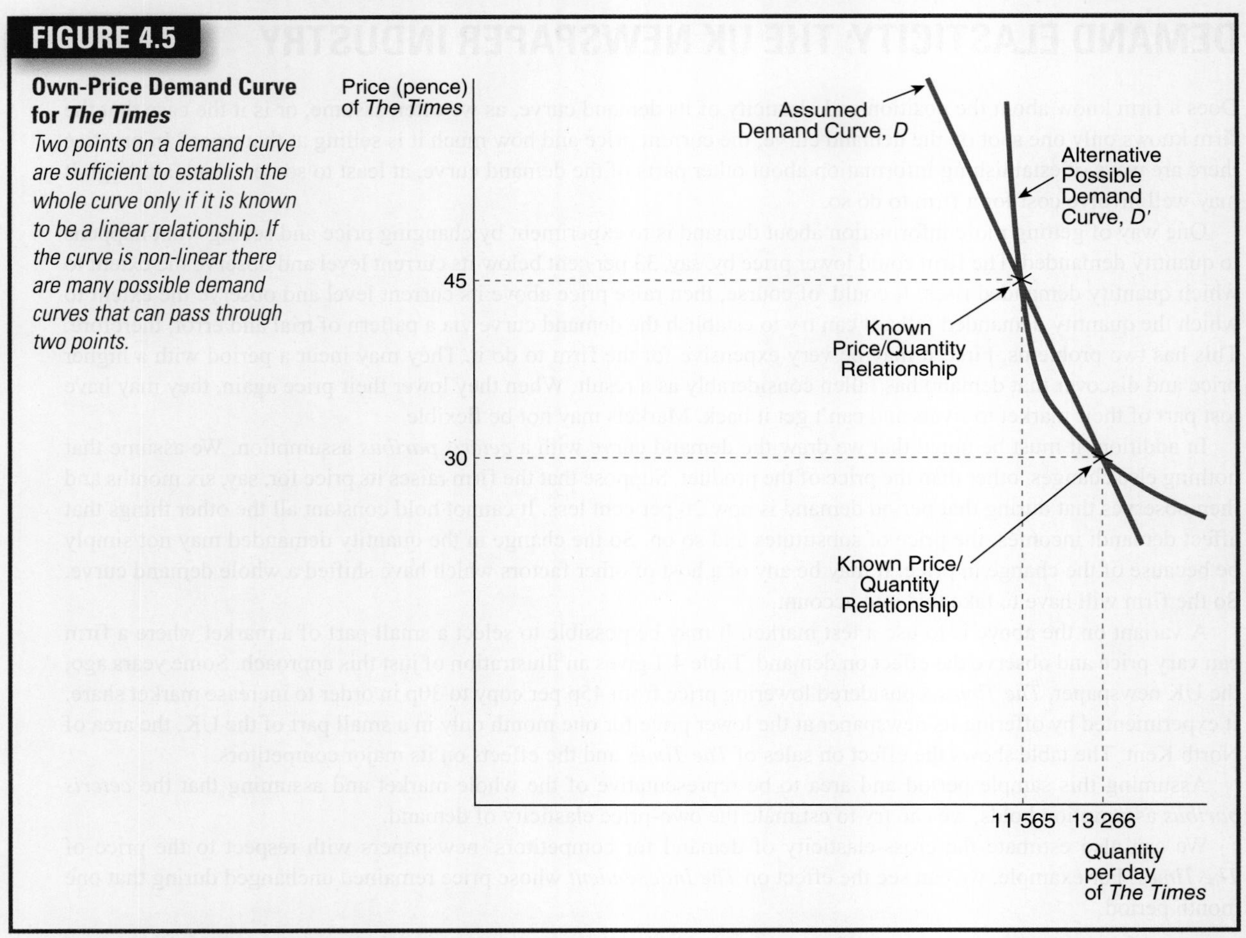

Figure 4.5 shows quantity demanded at a price of 45 pence and also at 30 pence. However, we do not know the rest of the curve. We will assume it is a linear relationship, *D*, but it might not be. An alternative is shown in Figure 4.5 also as *D*'. If the demand curve is a straight line, then two points is enough to define the curve but if it's not, then more points are needed. In general, if it's of order *n*, then we need *n* + 1 points. So for a quadratic function (of order 2), which has U-shaped graph, we need three points. Although there are other possible functions we will not be meeting them in the course of this book. With this in mind, however, we will proceed on the basis that we have a linear demand function.

We will make similar assumptions about the cross-price demand curve for *The Independent* with respect to the price of *The Times*. Figure 4.6 plots information from Table 4.1 regarding the demand for *The Independent* with respect to the price of *The Times*. It shows the quantity of *The Independent* demanded when the price for *The Times* is 45 pence and 30 pence, respectively. We will assume that this cross-price demand curve is also a linear relationship.

Given the information established, and the assumptions we have made, we will work out the own-price elasticity of demand and the cross-price elasticity of demand using a number of different measures of elasticity.

In each case we calculate the value of demand elasticity by four different measures:

i. Arc elasticity using percentage changes.
ii. Arc elasticity using the midpoint formula.
iii. Point elasticity.
iv. Point elasticity using calculus.

FIGURE 4.6

Cross-Price Demand Curve for *The Independent* with Respect to the Price of *The Times*

If we assume a linear cross-price demand curve we can establish the cross elasticity of demand for The Independent with respect to The Times.

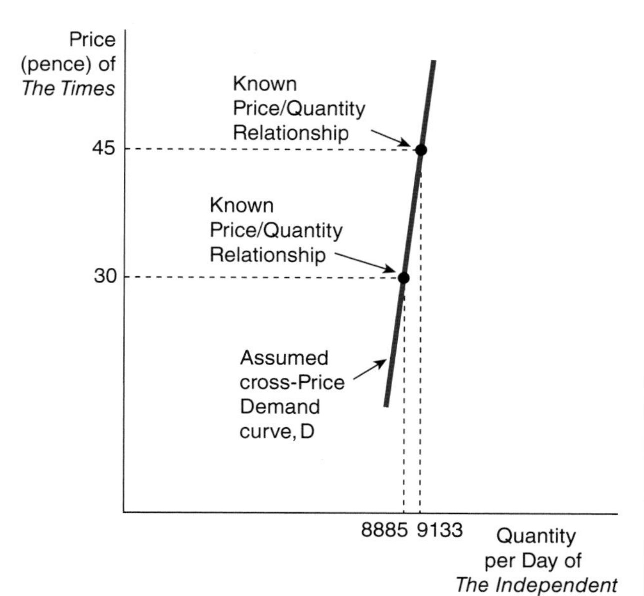

Own-price Demand Elasticity Using Percentages

One way to calculate elasticity is to use percentages changes. We cannot use absolute changes. If the price of a bag of sausages is cut from €2 to €1, consumers recognize this as a substantial price cut. The reduction in price of a BMW from €100 000 to €99 999 is regarded as trivial even though the price cut is the same (€1). We need to consider proportionate changes. One way to do that is to use percentages. The formula here is as follows:

$$\textit{Price elasticity of demand (ped)} = \frac{\%\Delta Q_d}{\%\Delta P}$$

Where:

$\%\Delta Q_d$ is percentage change in quantity demanded.

$\%\Delta P$ is percentage change in price.

Referring to the price cut of *The Times* from 45 pence to 30 pence the percentage price reduction is given as:

$$\%\Delta P = \frac{\Delta P_{dT}}{P_{dT}} \times 100 = \frac{-15}{45} \times 100 = -33.33\%$$

Where P_{dT} is the price of *The Times*.

The percentage change in quantity demanded resulting form that price cut is given as:

$$\%\Delta Q_d = \frac{\Delta Q_{dT}}{Q_{dT}} \times 100 = \frac{13\,266 - 11\,565}{11\,565} \times 100 = \frac{1701}{11\,565} \times 100 = 14.71\%$$

Where Q_{dT} is the quantity demanded of *The Times*.

Now we can calculate the elasticity of demand:

$$\textit{Price elasticity of demand} = \frac{14.71}{-33.33} = -0.44$$

We can interpret this number in the following way. For every 1 per cent fall in the price of *The Times* one would anticipate a 0.44 per cent increase in quantity sold. That means that own-price demand for *The Times*, on this measure, is inelastic.

The terminology used to summarise the degree of elasticity is given below using the absolute value, that is, we ignore the minus sign. If:

- ped > 1 then demand is price elastic, demand is relatively sensitive to price changes,
- ped = 1 then demand is unit elastic,
- ped < 1 then demand is price inelastic, demand is relatively insensitive to price changes.

A value of −0.44 suggests that the own-price elasticity of demand for *The Times* is inelastic. Later we shall consider how *The Times* newspaper used this information in making a national pricing decision.

Cross-price Elasticity of Demand for *The Independent* with Respect to the Price of *The Times* Using Percentages

$$\textit{The cross-price elasticity of demand} = \frac{\%\Delta Q_d \text{ of good } X}{\%\Delta P \text{ of good } Y}$$

In our case we have:

$$\frac{\%\Delta Q_{dI}}{\%\Delta P_T}$$

Where:
Q_{dI} is quantity demanded of *The Independent*
P_T is price of *The Times*

$$\%\Delta Q_{\text{dI}} = \frac{\Delta Q_{\text{dI}}}{Q_{\text{dI}}} \times 100 = \frac{8885 - 9133}{9133} \times 100 = \frac{-248}{9133} \times 100 = -2.72\%$$

We take the percentage change of price of *The Times* ($\%\Delta P_T$) from our calculations above. We have already worked that out to be −33.33%.

So the cross-price elasticity of demand $= \dfrac{-2.72}{-33.33} = 0.08$

We can interpret this number in the following way. For every 1% fall in the price of *The Times*, one would anticipate a 0.08% fall in the quantity of *The Independent* sold. Cross-price demand is positive. *The Times* and *The Independent* are substitute goods. However, the value shows cross-price demand to be very inelastic. They are not regarded by consumers as very close substitutes at all.

The Accuracy of the Arc Elasticity Measure Using Percentages

Using arc elasticity as a measure is unsatisfactory in a number of ways. The price elasticity of demand generally varies at different points along the curve. In particular, a straight line downward sloping demand curve becomes less elastic as price falls. This measure, however, is simply some average of all those different elasticities. More important still, the percentage change is not symmetric. The percentage change between any two points will depend upon the chosen starting value. Assume *The Times* now raises its price from 30 to 45 pence and demand falls from 13 266 to 11 566 copies sold. Plugging this information into the formula for arc elasticity means we get a different degree of elasticity even though we are on the same section of the demand curve:

$$\%\Delta P = \frac{\Delta P_{dT}}{P_{dT}} \times 100 = \frac{+15}{+30} \times 100 = +50\%$$

The percentage change in quantity demanded resulting from the price increase is given as:

$$\%\Delta Q_d = \frac{\Delta Q_{dT}}{Q_{dT}} \times 100 = \frac{13\,266 - 11\,565}{13\,266} \times 100 = \frac{1701}{13\,266} \times 100 = 12.82\%$$

The elasticity of demand for the price increase will be:

$$\textit{Price elasticity of demand} = \frac{-12.82}{50} = -0.26$$

We now have a quite different result. For a fall in price we calculated price elasticity as −0.44 whilst for a rise in price ped was −0.26. We obtained these different values even though we have been measuring elasticity over exactly the same arc of the demand curve. Demand is still shown to be inelastic but the degree of inelasticity appears significantly different for an increase compared with a decrease in the price.

We find a similar problem when we calculate the cross-price elasticity of *The Independent* with respect to *The Times* for an increase in the price of *The Times* from 30 to 45 pence.

$$\textit{The cross-price elasticity of demand} = \frac{\%\Delta Q_d \text{ of good } X}{\%\Delta P \text{ of good } Y}$$

In our case we have:

$$\frac{\%\Delta Q_{dI}}{\%\Delta P_T}$$

Where:
Q_{dI} is quantity demanded of *The Independent*.
P_T is price of *The Times*.

$$\%\Delta Q_{dI} = \frac{\Delta Q_{dI}}{Q_{dI}} \times 100 = \frac{9133 - 8885}{8885} \times 100 = \frac{248}{8885} \times 100 = 2.79\%$$

We take the percentage change of the price of *The Times*, $\%\Delta P_T$, from our calculations above. The increase in price from 30 to 45 pence represents a price change of 50 per cent.

So the cross-price elasticity of demand $= \frac{2.79}{50} = 0.06$.

Again we now have a different result even though we are measuring elasticity over exactly the same arc of the demand curve. Cross-price demand is still shown to be inelastic but the degree of inelasticity is a little different for an increase compared with a decrease in the price of *The Times*.

Own-price Demand Elasticity Using a Midpoint Formula

The midpoint formula for ped is given as follows:

$$\frac{(Q_{dT}2 - Q_{dT}1)}{(Q_{dT}2 + Q_{dT}1)/2} \div \frac{(P_T2 - P_T1)}{(P_T2 + P_T1)/2}$$

Where:
$Q_{dT}1$ = Original quantity of *The Times* demanded per week
$Q_{dT}2$ = New quantity of *The Times* demanded per week
P_T1 = Original price of *The Times*
P_T2 = New price of *The Times*

For this midpoint formula we don't divide the change in quantity by the starting quantity, and the change in price by the starting price. What we are doing is to divide the change in quantity by the average of the two quantities, and the change in price by the average of the two prices. By using an average we avoid having to specify the starting point and the ending point.

Let's find the elasticity of demand for *The Times* using this method. Substituting the values for price and quantity we have:

$$\begin{aligned} ped &= \frac{(13266 - 11565)}{(24831)/2} \div \frac{(30 - 45)}{(30 + 45)/2} \\ &= \frac{1701}{12415.5} \div \frac{-15}{37.5} \\ &= 0.137 \div (-0.4) \\ &= -0.34 \end{aligned}$$

The use of this midpoint elasticity formula is symmetric with respect to the two prices and quantities. It is also independent of the units of measurement so we have an unambiguous measure of elasticity of – 0.34. Not surprisingly, this value lies between the two values we calculated using the percentage change method.

Cross-price Elasticity Using a Midpoint Formula

Now we will use this method to find the cross elasticity of demand for *The Independent* with respect to the price of *The Times*, Xped. Substituting the values for price and quantity we have:

$$\frac{(Q_{dI}2 - Q_{dI}1)}{(Q_{dI}2 + Q_{dI}1)/2} \div \frac{(P_T2 - P_T1)}{(P_T2 + P_T1)/2}$$

Where:
$Q_{dI}1$ = Original quantity of *The Independent* demanded per week
$Q_{dI}2$ = New quantity of *The Independent* demanded per week
P_T1 = Original price of *The Times*
P_T2 = New price of *The Times*
Using our data as previously:

$$= \frac{(8885 - 9133)}{(18018)/2} \div \frac{(30 - 45)}{(30 + 45)/2}$$
$$= \frac{-248}{9009} \div \frac{-15}{37.5}$$
$$= -0.028 \div (-0.4)$$
$$= 0.07$$

As for own-price elasticity, the value of the cross-elasticity we obtain for this midpoint formula is between the two values we obtained using the percentage change method.

Own-price Elasticity Using a Point Elasticity Formula

Now we turn to point elasticity of demand and calculate its value, again using our example of *The Times* newspaper. Here we make use of a formula that we have examined earlier. However, as we shall see, it is not the most precise method of calculating point elasticity, which requires the use of calculus. The formula is:

$$ped = \frac{\Delta Q}{\Delta P} \times \frac{P}{Q}$$

Where:
Q is quantity demanded
ΔQ is change in quantity demanded
P is Price
ΔP is change in price.

Recall that this measure gives us elasticity at a particular point of the demand curve. So we will calculate point elasticity where $P_{dT} = 45$, the original price, and then where $P_{dT} = 30$, the new lower price.

First, elasticity of demand at the original price:

$$\frac{\Delta Q_{dT}}{\Delta P_T} \times \frac{P_T}{Q_{dT}} = \frac{1701}{-15} \times \frac{45}{11\,565} = -113.4 \times 0.0039$$
$$= -0.44$$

Now we calculate elasticity of demand at the lower price:

$$\frac{\Delta Q_{dT}}{\Delta P_T} \times \frac{P_T}{Q_{dT}} = \frac{1701}{-15} \times \frac{30}{13\,266} = -113.4 \times 0.0023$$
$$= -0.26$$

As we move down a negatively sloped demand curve with a constant slope, we expect demand to become less elastic. This is what we have found here. At a price of 45p demand elasticity is –0.44. At a price of 30p it is –0.26.

Notice that this gives us an unambiguous definition of elasticity, in contrast to the arc elasticity formula we used earlier.

Cross-elasticity of Demand Using Point Elasticity

First we find cross-price point elasticity at the original price of *The Times*, 45p:

$$\frac{\Delta Q_{dI}}{\Delta P_T} \times \frac{P_T}{Q_{dI}} = \frac{-248}{-15} \times \frac{45}{9133} = 16.53 \times 0.005$$
$$= 0.083$$

Now we calculate cross-price elasticity at the lower price:

$$\frac{\Delta Q_{dI}}{\Delta P_T} \times \frac{P_T}{Q_{dI}} = \frac{-248}{-15} \times \frac{30}{8885} = 16.53 \times 0.003$$
$$= 0.05$$

Notice that the cross-price demand curve is inelastic. Also notice that given the assumption of a straight line relationship, it is less elastic at the lower price, although in this particular case the difference is very small and we need to show the result to three decimal places to see the difference. At either point the cross-price demand curve is very inelastic. You can also see that the result varies little from what we found using a measure of arc elasticity.

Own-price Point Elasticity Using Calculus

Finally, we will use calculus to calculate our measures of elasticity. We have done this previously from a known demand function but here we do not have one. However, we will be able to work out a demand function from the two points on the curve that we have; first for *The Times*, then for *The Independent* with respect to *The Times*.

In Chapter 3 we took a demand function and from it we were able to find the combination of price and quantity at any point on the demand curve. Now we will engage in a little 'reverse engineering'. We know two points on the demand curve for *The Times*. We will use this information to establish the demand function. When we have done this we can differentiate it. Then we can proceed to find the elasticity of demand. Before we do that, let's explain the principle of establishing a function from two known points on the curve. We begin with the two points on the demand curve that we know. The equation for an inverse straight line downward sloping demand function is:

$$P = a - \mathrm{b}Q_D$$

Where a and b are constants.

We have two known points on the demand curve for *The Times*. We know price and quantity at both 45p and 30p so we have:

$$45 = a - 11\,565b \qquad (1)$$

and:

$$30 = a - 13\,266b \qquad (2)$$

Rearranging (1) we have:

$$a = 45 + 11\,565b \qquad (3)$$

Rearranging (2) we have:

$$a = 30 + 13\,266b \qquad (4)$$

We can now solve for a and b using (3) and (4) as simultaneous equations. As we have seen there are various ways to solve for two simultaneous equations. This time we will do it as follows. We will set the two equations equal to each other to find b and then solve for the remaining unknown, a.

$$\begin{aligned} 45 + 11\,565b &= 30 + 13\,266b \\ 13\,266b - 11\,565b &= 15 \\ 1701b &= 15 \\ b &= 15/1701 \\ &= 0.0088 \end{aligned}$$

Having found the value for b we can substitute into either of our simultaneous equations to find the value for a. If we use equation (3) we have:

$$\begin{aligned} a &= 45 + (11\,565 \times 0.0088) \\ &= 146.7 \end{aligned}$$

To confirm this result we can do the same procedure by using equation (4):

$$\begin{aligned} a &= 30 + (13\,266 \times 0.0088) \\ &= 146.7 \end{aligned}$$

So now our reverse engineering has established an equation to give us the demand for *The Times*.

$$\begin{aligned} P &= a - bQ_D \\ P &= 146.7 - 0.0088Q_D \end{aligned}$$

So:

$$\begin{aligned} P - 146.7 &= -0.0088Q_D \\ (P - 146.7)/-0.0088 &= Q_D \end{aligned}$$

If we now swap sides and multiply out we get:

$$Q_D = -(P/ - 0.0088) - (146.7/ - 0.0088)$$
$$Q_D = -P/0.0088 - (146.7/ - 0.0088)$$
$$Q_D = -113.6364P + 16\,670.4546$$

This is the equation for Q_D which we need to differentiate Q_D with respect to P.
This gives:

$$\frac{dQ_D}{dP} = -113.6364$$

First we find the elasticity at the original price of *The Times*:

$$\frac{dQ_{dT}}{dP_T} \times \frac{P_T}{Q_{dT}}$$

And $\frac{dQ_D}{dP} = -113.6364$.

So:

$$-113.6364 \times \frac{45}{11\,565}$$
$$= -0.44$$

Now we calculate elasticity at the lower price:

$$\frac{dQ_{dT}}{dP_T} \times \frac{P_T}{Q_{dT}}$$
$$= -113.6364 \times \frac{30}{13\,266}$$
$$= -0.26$$

This is an identical answer to that which we got using the previous point elasticity method. Any small difference we might have found would simply be explained by rounding errors. Differentiating will give an exact answer if we have exact numbers to input, but then so will looking at the difference between two points, assuming we have a straight line. Keep in mind, though, that the value of the elasticity is different at different points along a negatively sloped straight line demand curve. In other words, P/Q is changing along the length of the curve.

Cross-price Point Elasticity Using Calculus

Now, finally we calculate the cross elasticity of demand for *The Independent* with respect to the price of *The Times* using calculus.

For the own-price demand curve we produced a demand function from two known points and from that function we were able to find the combination of price and quantity at any point on the demand curve and use this information to establish demand elasticity. Now we use the same basic procedure to establish a cross-demand function in order to calculate cross-price elasticity. We begin with the two points on the cross-demand curve that we know. The equation for an inverse straight line upward sloping demand function is:

$$P = a + bQ_D$$

Where a and b are constants.

For a negative own-price demand curve we expect a to be positive and b to be negative. However, for a cross-demand curve where the goods in question are substitutes we expect b to be positive. As for a, it might be negative or positive or indeed zero.

We have two equations for the demand for *The Independent* with respect to the price of *The Times*. We know the quantity of *The Independent* demanded when *The Times*' price is 45p and when it is 30p so we have:

$$45 = a + 9133b \quad (5)$$

$$30 = a + 8885b \quad (6)$$

As before, we will solve for b. This time we will use the row operation method. Then we will use that value to find the value of a.

Subtracting (2) from (1) gives us

$$15 = 248b \tag{7}$$

Rearranging (7) we have:

$$\begin{aligned} b &= 15/248 \\ &= 0.06 \end{aligned} \tag{8}$$

Having found b we can now find a:

$$\begin{aligned} a + (9133 \times 0.06) &= 45 \\ a + 547.98 &= 45 \\ a &= -503 \end{aligned}$$

To confirm this result we can do the same procedure using equation (6):

$$\begin{aligned} a + (8885 \times 0.06) &= 30 \\ a + 533.1 &= 30 \\ a &= -503 \end{aligned}$$

So now our reverse engineering has established an equation to give us the demand for *The Independent* with respect to the price of *The Times*.

$$\begin{aligned} P &= a + bQ_D \\ P &= -503 + 0.06Q_D \\ P + 503 &= 0.06Q_D \\ Q_D &= (P + 503)/0.06 \\ Q_D &= (P/0.06) + (503/0.06) \\ Q_D &= (1/0.06)P + 8383 \\ Q_D &= 16.67P + 8383 \end{aligned}$$

This is the equation for Q_D which we need to differentiate Q_D with respect to P.
This gives:

$$\frac{dQ_D}{dP} = 16.67$$

First we find cross-price point elasticity at the original price of *The Times*:

$$\begin{aligned} &\frac{dQ_{dI}}{dP_T} \times \frac{P_T}{Q_{dI}} \\ &16.67 \times \frac{45}{9133} \\ &= 16.67 \times 0.005 \\ &= 0.083 \end{aligned}$$

Now we calculate cross-price elasticity at the lower price:

$$\begin{aligned} &\frac{dQ_{dI}}{dP_T} \times \frac{P_T}{Q_{dI}} \\ &16.67 \times \frac{30}{8885} \\ &= 16.67 \times 0.003 \\ &= 0.05 \end{aligned}$$

Again, this is the same answer to that which we got using the previous point elasticity method with any small difference attributable to rounding errors. Differentiating will give an exact answer if we have exact numbers to input, but then so will looking at the difference between two points, assuming, as we did, that we have a straight line.

The Times Price Change: A Surprising Decision?

It is clear that whatever means we use to calculate elasticity, the demand for *The Times* in the price range examined was inelastic. This leaves us to explain a problem. In the light of this information we would expect a firm to raise its price, not lower it. Raising price means increasing revenue whilst having to produce less. Profit maximisation requires the firm to be on the elastic part of the demand curve if it has the power to choose its price. But *The Times* went ahead with a price cut nationally! Was this an irrational business decision? The answer is no.

The data we used and the estimates we made are of the short-term effect. In the longer term, the results might well be different. In particular, *The Independent* was still producing newspapers. If a lower price of *The Times* had caused one or more of the other newspapers to drop out of the market the long-run elasticity would have been quite different. After some time it became clear that no other newspaper was about to cease production so *The Times* reversed its price cut and raised price towards the elastic part of the demand curve.

The Independent became an online-only newspaper in March 2016.

DEMAND ELASTICITY USING PARTIAL DIFFERENTIATION

If we have sufficient information about the demand for a product, we can isolate the effect of a change in any one of the variables using partial differentiation. Often the demand for a product depends on a number of factors: price, price of other goods, income and so on. Partial differentiation works in the following way. We differentiate with respect to just a single variable in the function, treating the other variables as constants. We can do this with each of the variables in turn. Let us illustrate with the following example. Let's assume that we know the demand for wine at a restaurant. For simplicity we will assume that there is only one house red wine, one house white wine and one fixed-price meal. Currently the owner sells a bottle of red wine for €10, a bottle of white wine for €10 and a meal for €16. Experience of running the restaurant has enabled the owner to determine a demand function for red wine as follows:

$$Q_R = 200 - 2P_R + 0.5P_W^2 - 0.25P_M$$

Where:

Q_R = quantity of red wine sold in bottles per week

P_R = price of red wine sold per bottle

P_W = price of white wine sold per bottle

P_M = price of a restaurant meal

With this information we can use partial differentiation to see the precise effect on sales of red wine when any of these variables changes. Let's remind ourselves first of the general relationships we might expect and then we will see how we can determine the size of these changes.

Figure 4.7 shows the general relationship between the price of red wine and quantity of red wine demanded. Recall that the demand curve is drawn on the assumption that all other factors affecting demand are held constant. In this case, by assumption, that means the price of white wine and the price of the restaurant meals are unchanged. Shortly we will focus on the effect of changes in the price of red wine on the quantity of red wine demanded. That is, we are considering movements along the demand curve of Figure 4.7.

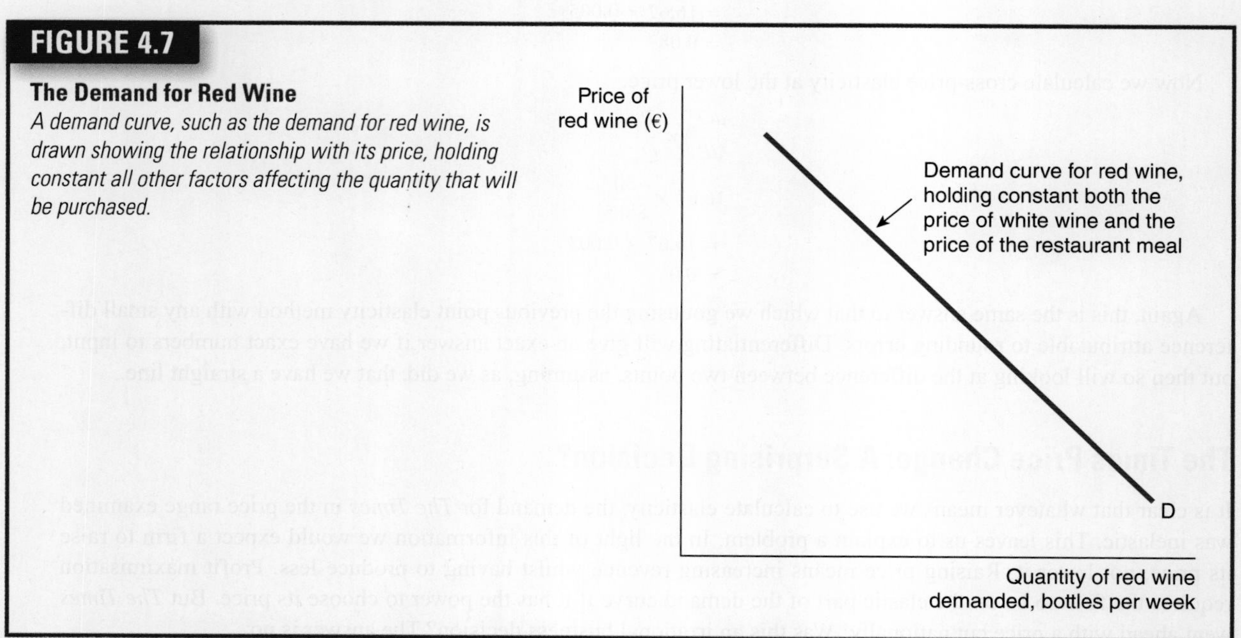

FIGURE 4.7

The Demand for Red Wine

A demand curve, such as the demand for red wine, is drawn showing the relationship with its price, holding constant all other factors affecting the quantity that will be purchased.

Panels (a) and (b) in Figure 4.8 show alternative ways of seeing the general effect of a change in the price of white wine on the demand for red wine. If the restaurateur increases the price of white wine, a substitute for red wine, the demand curve for red wine shifts to the right. More red wine is demanded at each price than before as shown in Panel (a) of Figure 4.8. Panel (b) shows that same basic information in a different form. We have plotted the cross-price

FIGURE 4.8

The Effect of a White Wine Increase on the Demand for Red Wine

When the price of white wine increases we can show its effect on the demand for red wine in either of two ways. We can see the effect as a shift in the demand for red wine, as shown in panel (a). Alternatively, we can see it as a movement along the cross-price demand curve for red wine with respect to the price of the substitute, white wine, as shown in panel (b).

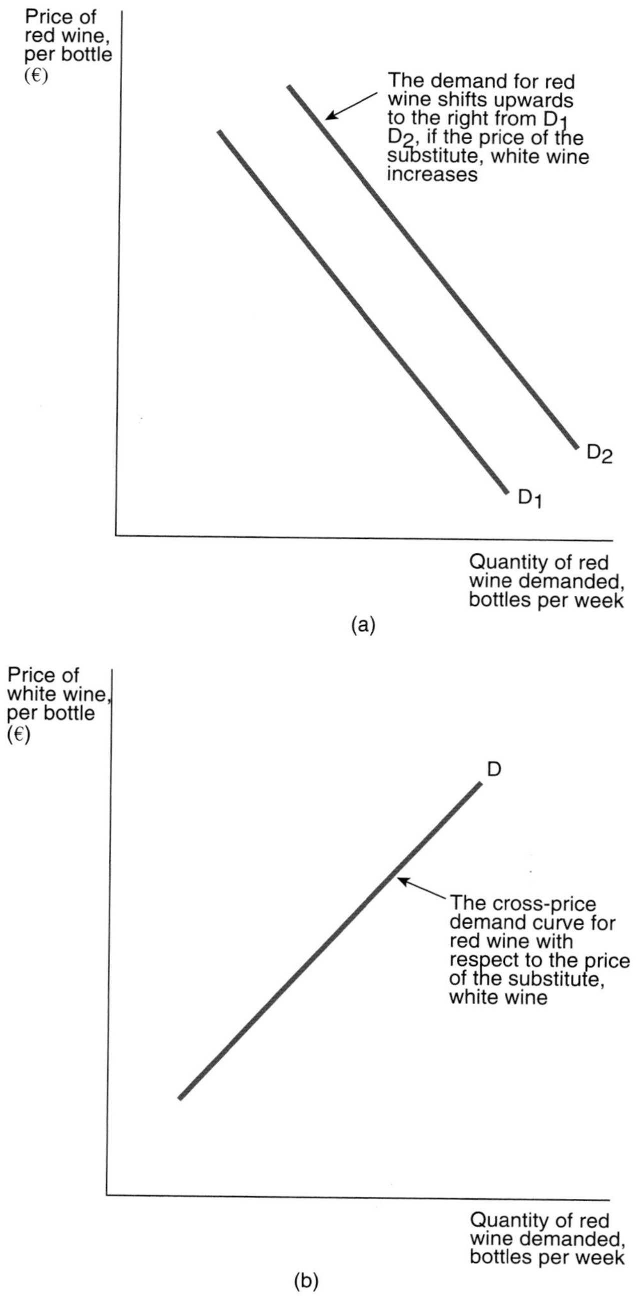

demand curve for red wine with respect to the price of white wine. The effect of an increase in the price of white wine on the quantity of red wine demanded is shown this time as a movement along the cross-price demand curve. Here we hold everything else constant, including the price of red wine. Partial differentiation will allow us to see these effects.

Panels (a) and (b) in Figure 4.9 show alternative ways of seeing the general effect of a change in the price of the restaurant meal on the demand for red wine.

FIGURE 4.9

The Effect of Restaurant Meal Increase on the Demand for Red Wine

When the price of restaurant meals increases we can show its effect on the demand for red wine in either of two ways. We can see the effect of the demand for red wine, as shown in panel (a). Alternatively we can see it as a movement along the cross-price demand curve for red wine with respect to the price of its complement, restaurant meals, as shown in panel (b).

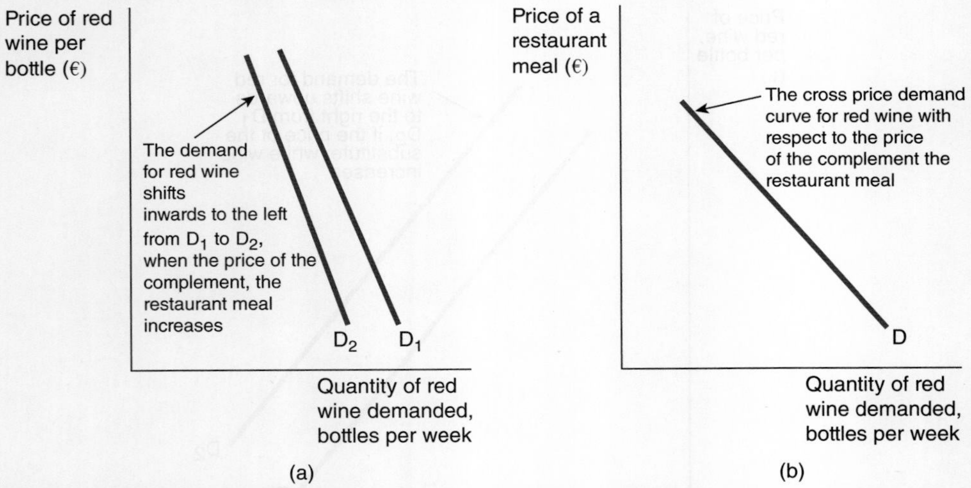

If the restaurateur increases the price of their meals the demand for red wine shifts to the left. Less red wine is demanded at each price than before, as shown in Panel (a) in Figure 4.9. Now consider Panel (b). It shows that same basic information in a different form. We have plotted the cross-price demand curve for red wine with respect to the price of restaurant meals. The effect of an increase in the price of the meal on the quantity of red wine demanded is shown as a movement along the cross-price demand curve. Again we hold constant everything else, including the price of red wine. Notice that the cross-price demand curve for red wine with respect to the price of white wine is positively sloped since these are substitute goods. However, the cross-price demand curve for red wine with respect to the price of the meal is negatively sloped as these are complementary goods.

Now we are ready to begin the process of partial differentiation. Our function is:

$$Q_R = 200 - 2P_R + 0.5P_W^2 - 0.25P_M$$

Currently red wine and white wine are each sold at €10 a bottle and the meal is €16. Substituting these values into the equation gives us:

$$Q_R = 200 - 2(10) + \frac{1}{2}(10)^2 - \frac{1}{4}(16)$$

So currently the number of bottles of red wine sold each week is:

$$Q_R = 200 - 20 + 50 - 4$$
$$= 226 \text{ bottles of house red per week.}$$

What happens if the restaurateur feels the need to change prices? We need to calculate the elasticities of demand. We begin with own-price elasticity of demand, the demand for red wine with respect to its own price. So we partially differentiate the demand function. This means following the standard rules for differentiating but keeping everything else constant except the price of red wine.

The partial derivative is given as:

$$\frac{\partial Q_R}{\partial P_R} = -2$$

The own-price elasticity of demand, as we have seen before in other contexts, is:

$$\frac{\partial Q_R}{\partial P_R} \times \frac{P_R}{Q_R}$$

Given the current price of red wine as €10 a bottle and the current quantity sold as 226 bottles per week we have:

$$-2 \times \frac{10}{226}$$
$$= -0.09$$

The negative sign is expected. The own-price demand curve is negatively sloped. So roughly speaking, a one per cent price cut on red wine would increase the quantity of red wine sold by 0.09 per cent, *ceteris paribus*.

Now we can see the effect on the demand for red wine is the restaurateur changes the price of something else. Look next at the price of white wine. Here we need the cross-price elasticity of demand for red wine with respect to the price of white wine. So we partially differentiate the appropriate bit of the demand function as follows. The appropriate partial derivative this time is:

$$\frac{\partial Q_R}{\partial P_W} = P_W$$

We know that $P_W = 10$ and cross-price elasticity is:

$$\frac{\partial Q_R}{\partial P_W} \times \frac{P_W}{Q_R}$$
$$= 10 \times \frac{10}{226}$$
$$= 0.44$$

The elasticity of demand for red wine with respect to the price of white wine is 0.44. The positive number indicates that they are substitutes. The degree of closeness of substitutes we found by partial differentiation. We held all other things constant and found that, roughly speaking, a one per cent increase in the price of white wine leads to a 0.44 per cent increase in the demand for red wine. So if the restaurateur feels that the price of white wine will have to go up, the effect on red wine sales is known.

Finally, we can see how sensitive is the demand for red wine with respect to the price of the restaurant meal. We partially differentiate our function, this time with respect to the meal.

$$\frac{\partial Q_R}{\partial P_M} = -0.25$$

Cross-price elasticity is given as:

$$\frac{\partial Q_R}{\partial P_M} \times \frac{P_M}{Q_R}$$
$$= -0.25 \times \frac{16}{226}$$
$$= -0.02$$

The elasticity of demand for red wine with respect to the price of the meal is –0.02. The negative number indicates that these are complements. The degree of closeness of complementarity we found by partial differentiation. We held all other things constant and found that, roughly speaking, a one per cent increase in the price of the meal leads to a 0.02 per cent fall in the demand for red wine.

The technique of partial differentiation has allowed us to isolate the effect on the dependent variable of changing any independent variable.

SUPPLY ELASTICITY

We have already shown you how to calculate elasticity of supply. We saw earlier that a straight-line supply curve passing through the origin has unit elasticity. We showed this with a little geometry. Here we use some algebra to help our understanding of this. Consider figure 4.10. All three supply curves shown, S_1, S_2 and S_3 have the same unit elasticity at any point.

FIGURE 4.10

Three Illustrative Supply Curves

All straight line supply curves passing through the origin have an elasticity of demand equal to 1 along their whole length.

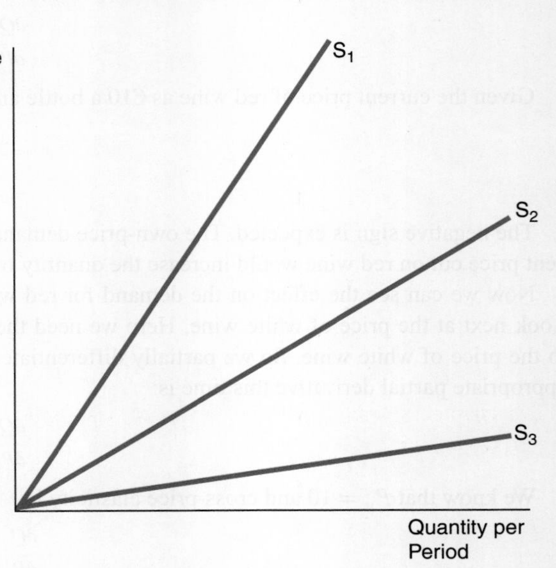

We will now demonstrate this.

$$Q_s = a + bP \qquad (1)$$

Where:
Q_s = quantity supplied
P = price
a and b are constants
Note that if the supply curve passes through the origin, then a must be equal to zero. So our supply curves can be represented as:

$$Q_s = bP \qquad (2)$$

We have already seen that one formula for demand elasticity is:

$$ped = \frac{dQ_d}{dP} \times \frac{P}{Q_d} \qquad (3)$$

Where:
ped is price elasticity of demand
Q_d is quantity demanded
P is price
In just the same way one formula for supply elasticity is:

$$pes = \frac{dQ_s}{dP} \times \frac{P}{Q_s} \qquad (4)$$

Where:
pes = price elasticity of supply
But the slope of the supply curve, b, is:

$$b = \frac{dQ_s}{dP} \qquad (5)$$

That is, b is the slope of the equation and the inverse of the slope of the curve. (Remember that when we plot the diagram we plot the inverse supply curve.)
Now substitute this term into equation (4) and we get:

$$pes = b \times \frac{P}{Q_s} \qquad (6)$$

Now we substitute equation (2) into equation (6) to obtain:

$$pes = b \times \frac{P}{bP}$$
$$= \frac{bP}{bP}$$
$$= 1$$

So any supply curve with a straight line passing through the origin is of the form:

$$Q_s = bP$$

and will have unit elasticity along its length.

Summary

In this chapter we have covered a great deal of ground so let us summarize the main things that we have considered with regard to elasticity:

- Elasticity measures all focus on proportionate, not absolute changes.
- Elasticity of demand and supply can be measured in a variety of ways. Some ways give more precise measurements than others.
- Cross elasticity measures the responsiveness of demand for one good to changes in the price of another.
- Income elasticity of demand measures the responsiveness of demand to income changes.
- Elasticity of supply measures the responsiveness of supply to price changes.

PROBLEMS AND APPLICATIONS

1 Look again at the table in Chapter 3 Problem 4 (reproduced below) and calculate the own-price elasticity of demand.

a. The price is increased from €30 to €42.5. How high is the price elasticity of demand using the regular and the midpoint methods?

b. Would you expect a larger or smaller value for the elasticity when you change the price from €92.50 to €105 per unit? Explain your thinking.

c. Confirm your result from b) with a calculation.

Price (€/unit)	Quantity supplied	Quantity demanded
0.00	0.0	800.0
5.00	0.0	775.0
17.50	0.0	712.5
30.00	0.0	650.0
42.50	100.0	587.5
55.00	200.0	525.0
67.50	300.0	462.5
80.00	400.0	400.0
92.50	500.0	337.5
105.00	600.0	275.0
117.50	700.0	212.5

2 A linear demand function has the general shape $P = a - bQ$.

a. Calculate the point price elasticity of demand as a formula of a and b.

b. Calculate the axis intersections of the demand function.

c. Show that the demand elasticity is falling as you move from the upper-left corner of a graph downwards along the demand function.

d. Prove that a linear demand function always has a point with a unit elasticity ($ped = -1$) and that this point is halfway between 0 and the respective axis intersections on the price and quantity axis.

3 The quantity of ice cream (Q_i) on any given day is influenced by the price of ice cream (P_i), the price of frozen yogurts (P_y), the outside temperature (t) and whether it is a weekday ($we = 0$) or weekend ($we = 1$). This is expressed with $Q_i = Q_i(P_i, P_y, t, we)$ with the specification $Q_i(P_i, P_y, t, we) = -75P_i^2 + 10P_i + 500 + 5t + 50P_y + 100we$.

a. Write out the demand function on a Saturday ($we = 1$) with 25 degrees Celsius outside.
b. Calculate the price elasticity of demand as a function.
c. Now again assume that you have a day on the weekend with a temperature of 25 degrees Celsius and the price of one unit of frozen yogurt is at $P_y = 1.5$ (€/unit). How high is the point own-price elasticity of demand and €1.0 per unit of ice cream?
d. Calculate the point cross-price elasticity of ice cream with respect to the price of frozen yogurt. Assume the data from problem c) still hold.

4 A journal article from 2008 provides estimates of price elasticities for various food items. (Thiele, Silke (2008). 'Elastizitäten der Nachfrage privater Haushalte nach Nahrungsmitteln – Schätzung eines AIDS auf Basis der Einkommens- und Verbrauchsstichprobe 2003.' *Agrarwirtschaft* 57(5):258–68.)

a. The price estimated elasticity of demand of all households for vegetables was estimated to be 0.55. Explain what this means.
b. How do you think this elasticity was calculated, using a midpoint method, point elasticity, or something else?
c. The price elasticity of demand for beef was measured for different consumer groups, i.e. distinguished by income or age. The price elasticity of demand for beef by poorer consumers was 0.89 whereas it was 0.39 for the richer consumers. Give a plausible explanation.
d. Estimates were also provided for cross-price elasticities of demand. The cross-price elasticity between fruits and milk products was −0.04, the value for fruits against potatoes/ rice / pasta + 0.04. Explain the term cross-price elasticity and the meaning of the signs of the values given.
e. The article mentioned provides estimates for income elasticities of demand. It states that the income elasticity of bread and breakfast cereals is around 0.3. Explain.

5 There is an intuitive interdependence between the total expenditure of consumers in a market and the price elasticity of demand. Remember that the quantity sold depends on the price along the demand function $Q_d = Q(P)$ or the inverse of the demand function $P_d = P(Q)$. Starting with the fact that total expenditure of consumers on a good is the product of price and quantity ($E(Q) = P \times Q(P)$), show how the ratio of the change in the expenditure (E(Q)) to a change in the market price relates to the elasticity *ped* in a formula.

5 BACKGROUND TO DEMAND: CONSUMER CHOICES

In this chapter, we will extend and develop the theory of marginal utility and relate this theory to the demand curve for an individual consumer. Next we extend our analysis from the individual to the whole market. Finally, we visit the mathematics of indifference theory. In so doing we will see that consumer choice is an illustration of the problem of constrained optimisation that we discussed in Chapter 2.

MARGINAL UTILITY

Why do people wish to consume goods and services? Clearly, it is because consumption gives them something they value, or as economists tend to say, it gives them utility. The more we consume the greater our utility up to some point at which additional units of consumption produce no increased satisfaction. However, although utility increases with consumption, it increases at a decreasing rate. Figure 5.1 illustrates this.

Since total utility rises more slowly as more is consumed, marginal utility, the change in total utility must be falling. At $Q = 10$ units of consumption an additional unit adds nothing to the individual's total welfare. Total utility (TU) does not change. Marginal utility (MU) is zero. In other words maximum utility occurs at the level of consumption at which marginal utility is zero. Beyond 10 units of consumption TU is declining. However, it is feasible that it will just stay constant. In this case another unit doesn't reduce TU but doesn't add to it either. MU would then be zero for consumption beyond 10 units.

Suppose we have a consumer with a total utility function of:

$$TU = 100Q - 5Q^2$$

Where:

TU = total utility and

Q = quantity of a good consumed.

This is sketched out in panel (a) of Figure 5.1. If we know the total utility function we can calculate not only total utility but marginal utility for any level of consumption.

Using the power rule of differentiation:

$$\frac{dTU}{dQ} = 100 - 10Q$$

So MU (marginal utility), the rate at which utility changes as the quantity of consumption increases, = $100 - 10Q$

Having established a function for both total utility and marginal utility, let's focus first on total utility. What is total utility at zero consumption?

$$\begin{aligned} TU &= 100Q - 5Q^2 \\ &= (100 \times 0) - (5 \times 0^2) \\ &= 0 - 0 \\ &= 0 \end{aligned}$$

That is, the total utility function begins at the origin.

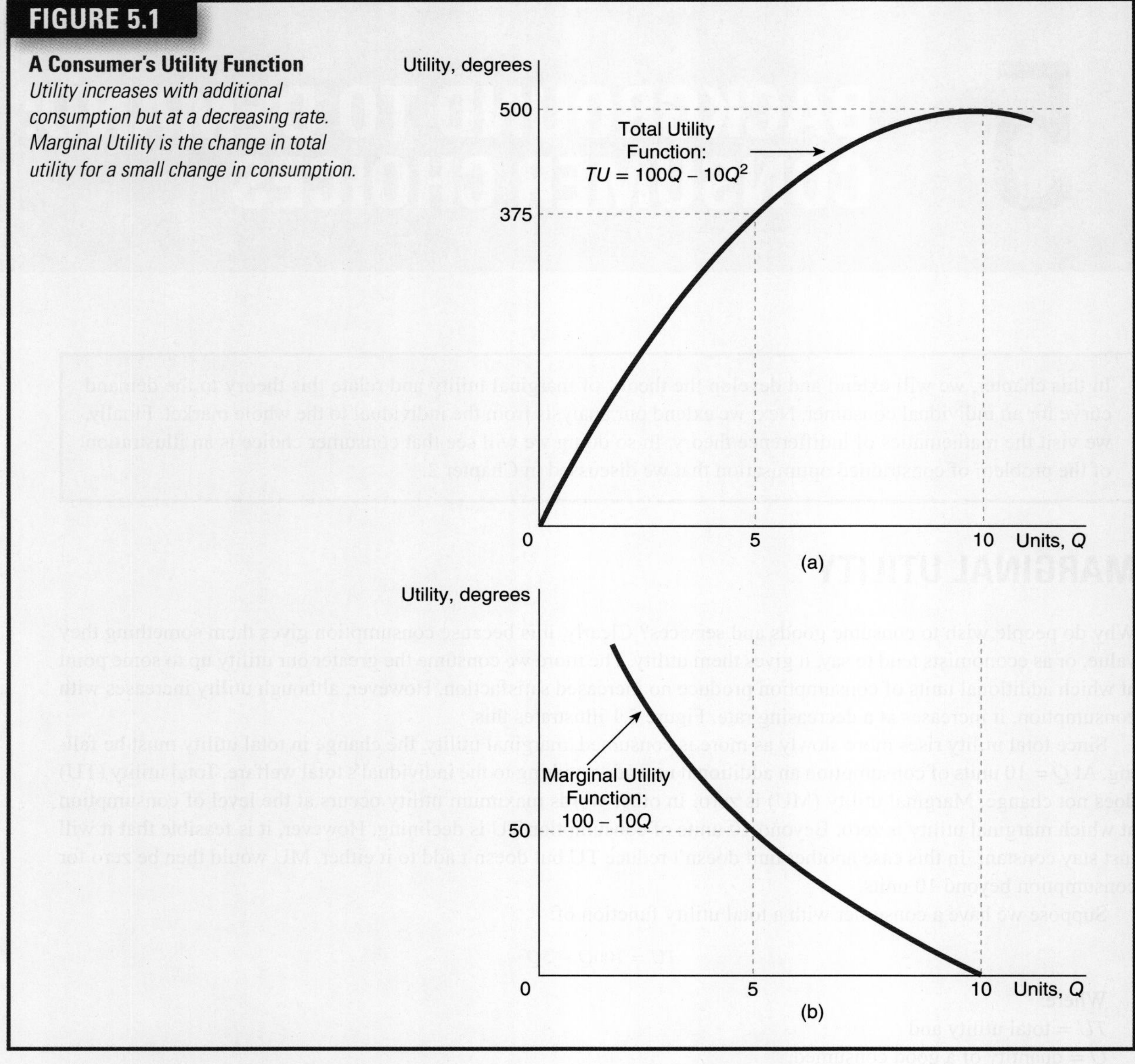

FIGURE 5.1

A Consumer's Utility Function
Utility increases with additional consumption but at a decreasing rate. Marginal Utility is the change in total utility for a small change in consumption.

At what point is the total utility maximized? We know that where total utility is at its maximum, marginal utility is zero. So at what point is marginal utility, MU, zero? To find this, we set the marginal utility function to zero:

$$\frac{dTU}{dQ} = 0$$

$$100 - 10Q = 0$$

$$10Q = 100$$

$Q = 10$ where $MU = 0$

Marginal utility is zero at 10 units of consumption as shown in Panel (b) of Figure 5.1 and this is where total utility is maximized as shown in Panel (a) of Figure 5.1.

What is total utility at this level of consumption?

$$TU = (100 \times 10) - (5 \times 10^2)$$
$$= 1000 - 500$$
$$= 500$$

Figure 5.1 also illustrates TU and MU at 5 units of consumption. We can use the functions to calculate utility at this level of consumption.

For TU:

$$\begin{aligned} TU &= 100Q - 5Q^2 \\ &= (100 \times 5) - (5 \times 5^2) \\ &= 500 - 125 \\ &= 375 \textit{ units of utility} \end{aligned}$$

For MU:

Set $\frac{dTU}{dQ}$, where $Q = 5$

$$MU = 100 - 10Q$$
$$MU = 100 - (10 \times 5)$$
$$MU = 100 - 50$$
$$MU = 50 \textit{ units of utility}$$

In the same way we can calculate *TU* and *MU* for any level of consumption.

The Equi-Marginal Principle

Assume that consumption of any good depends upon the utility derived and on the price of the good in question, the price of other goods and the level of the consumer's income. Further assume that consumers arrange consumption to maximize well-being. This means consuming goods such that the last euro spent on any good gives the same utility as the last euro spent on any other good. Formally, this means arranging expenditure such that, where MU is marginal utility, *P* is price and *A, B* ... *N* are the various goods the consumer purchases. Given these assumptions:

$$\frac{MU_A}{P_A} = \frac{MU_B}{P_B} = \frac{MU_N}{P_N}$$

This is often referred to as the equi-marginal principle. Notice that we are assuming that there is some way in which we can measure the degrees of utility a consumer enjoys. We are assuming that we can attach a value to the benefit of an extra unit of consumption. In other words, you know how much satisfaction you get when you consume more of a good, but can you in fact place a monetary value on it? Here we assume that this is possible.

Marginal Utility and the Individual Demand Curve

If the price of a good falls, our consumer will no longer be maximizing welfare with this present consumption pattern. They will rearrange their expenditure. If P_A falls, MU_A must fall to restore the consumption pattern to maximize utility. But what brings about a fall in MU? In Panel (b) of Figure 5.1, MU will fall when consumption increases. So as price falls, consumption increases.

This explains why the demand curve slopes downwards. The demand curve has a negative slope because although total utility increases with consumption, marginal utility declines as more is consumed. The individual's demand curve reflects declining marginal utility.

Figure 5.2 shows declining MU for a consumer of a particular product. This time we measure utility in terms of a monetary amount. At point X price is P_1 and quantity demanded is Q_1 because that's where MU = *P*. Similarly, at point Z the lower price P_2 causes the consumer to increase consumption, increasing total utility but reducing marginal utility. Here at P_2 with a consumption of Q_2 equilibrium is restored. Again quantity demanded is where MU = *P*. In general, a utility maximizing consumer's marginal utility is the same as the demand curve.

From the Individual Demand Curve to the Market Demand Curve

The individual demand curve shows what any individual consumer will demand at different prices but how do we establish a **market** demand curve, the amount demanded of a good by the whole market at different prices? Consumers are different. Each will have different preferences and react differently to price changes, although we would expect all to increase consumption as price falls, *ceteris paribus*. We can sum all these individual consumers' demands at each price to obtain the market demand curve. We sum the individual demand curves horizontally.

FIGURE 5.2

Marginal Utility and an Individual Demand Curve
When price falls, consumption increases. Although total utility increases, marginal utility declines. The decline in marginal utility explains the downward sloping nature of the demand curve.

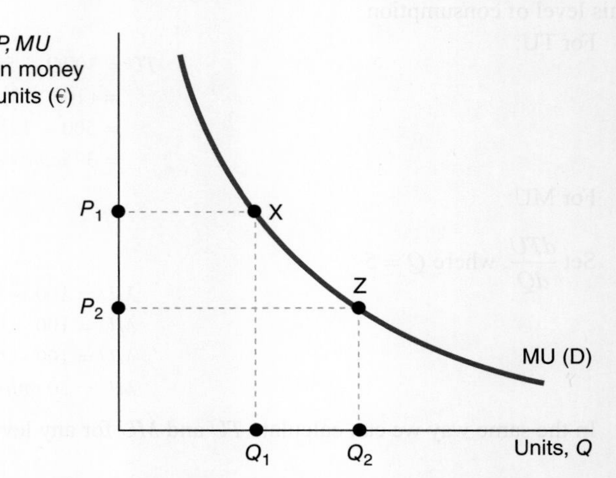

We can see how to do this by making a simplifying assumption that there are only two consumers of a good, consumers A and B, each with a known demand curve.

$$Q_{DA} = 10 - \frac{1}{2}P$$
$$Q_{DB} = 16 - P$$

In order to plot and see these demand curves in a standard way we need to produce them in their inverse form. For Consumer A:

$$Q_{DA} = 10 - \frac{1}{2}P$$
$$\frac{1}{2}P = 10 - Q_{DA}$$
$$P = 20 - 2Q_{DA}$$

For Consumer B:

$$Q_{DB} = 16 - P$$
$$P = 16 - Q_{DB}$$

Now we plot these individual inverse demand curves as shown in Figure 5.3.

FIGURE 5.3

Individual Demand Functions for Consumers A and B
In order to plot a demand curve it is necessary to produce an inverse demand curve, making price rather than quantity the subject of the function.

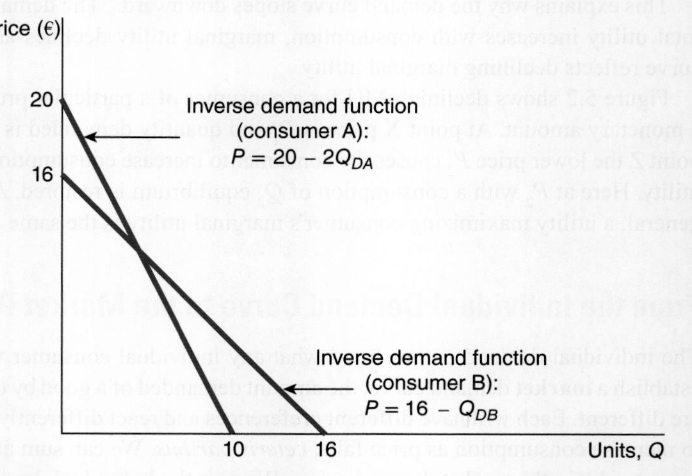

To sum the curves horizontally, we use each of three price ranges:

1. When $P > 20$ there is nothing to sum. Nobody is willing to buy.
2. When the price is more than 16 but less than 20, that is $16 < P < 20$ we have only one consumer buying so our horizontal summation is for just $Q_D = 10 - \frac{1}{2}P$
3. When the price is more than zero but less than 16, $0 < P < 16$, we have both consumers buying so our horizontal summation is:

$$Q_D = \left(10 - \frac{1}{2}P\right) + (16 - P)$$

$$Q_D = 26 - \frac{3}{2}P$$

Now we can find the inverse form of the horizontal summation so that we can plot it:

$$QD = 26 - \frac{3}{2}P$$

$$\frac{3}{2}P = 26 - Q_D$$

$$P = 17\frac{1}{3} - \frac{2}{3}Q_D$$

The two individual demand functions and the market demand function (the summed demand curve) is shown in Figure 5.4. You can see that at a price of zero quantity demanded would be 26. From the diagram Consumer A would buy 10 and Consumer B 16.

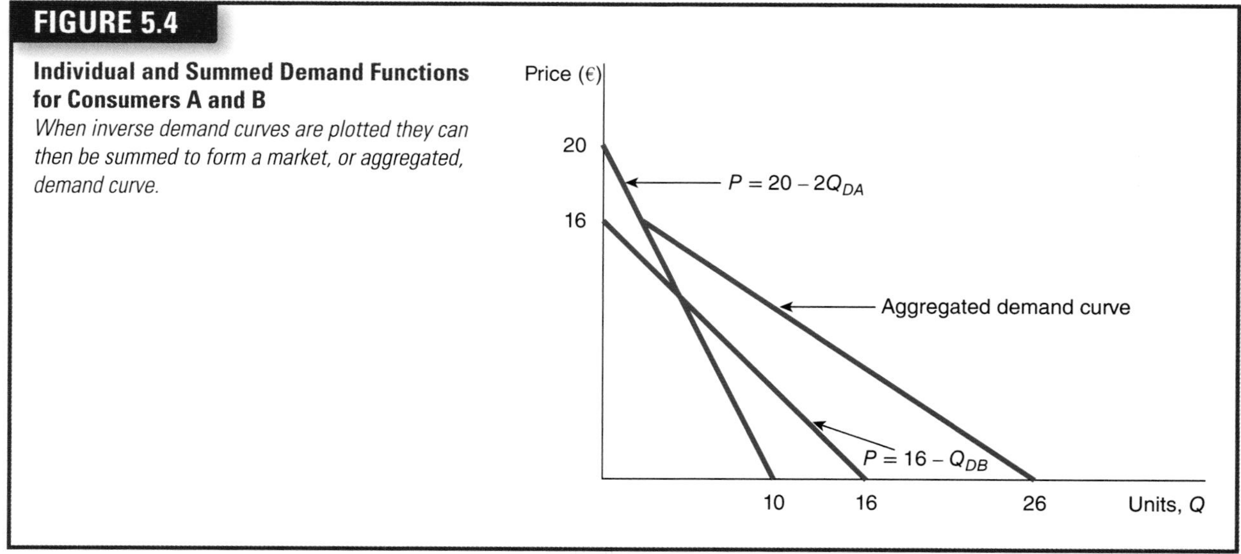

FIGURE 5.4

Individual and Summed Demand Functions for Consumers A and B
When inverse demand curves are plotted they can then be summed to form a market, or aggregated, demand curve.

Mathematically we can substitute $P = 0$ into the inverse demand equation:

$$0 = 17\frac{1}{3} - \frac{2}{3}Q_D$$

$$Q_D = 26$$

We can summarize this process in Table 5.1.

TABLE 5.1

Price Range	Relevant Demand Functions	Horizontal Sum of Demand Curves	Inverse Demand Function
>20	None	N/A	N/A
16–20	Consumer A	$Q_D = 10 - \frac{1}{2}P$	$P = 20 - 2Q_D$
0–16	Consumers A and B	$Q_D = \left(10 - \frac{1}{2}P\right) + 16 - P = 26 - \frac{3}{2}P$	$P = 17\frac{1}{3} - \frac{2}{3}Q_D$

We have seen how, in principle, we can sum individual demand curves to form a market demand curve. This tells us quantity demanded by the market at each price and we know how this quantity is divided up among consumers of the product.

In Chapter 10 we will return to the summation of individual demand curves when we look at a particular category of goods known as public goods.

EXTENDING THE MATHEMATICS OF INDIFFERENCE THEORY

We are going to explore the equilibrium condition for a consumer this time using indifference theory. Assume that a consumer is interested in only two goods, *X* and *Y*, and wants to enjoy the best possible combination of these two goods, given the limit placed by the budget constraint. Formally our consumer's decision rule can be stated thus:

$$Max\ Utility = U(XY)$$

Subject to $P_X X + P_Y Y \leq M$
Where:
X and *Y* are units of the two goods
P_X and P_Y are the price of *X* and *Y* respectively
M is the monthly budget

We assume that TU = *XY*, so that total utility in our consumer's case is determined by the product of *X* and *Y* (i.e. *X* and *Y* multiplied together), not the addition of *X* and *Y*. These are not substitute goods. Utility depends upon the consumption of *X* and *Y* taken together.

You can read ≤ as 'is equal to or less than' although in our case we will assume that our consumer plans to spend the entire limited budget available, that is:

$$P_X X + P_Y Y = M$$

The optimum choice for the consumer will be the point where the highest available indifference curve is tangential to the budget line, i.e.

$$\frac{MU_X}{MU_Y} = \frac{P_X}{P_Y}$$

Suppose that our consumer has a monthly budget constraint M = €1200; further, suppose that the price of a unit of *X* is €40 and the price of a unit of *Y* is €100. We can now establish the budget line if all income is spent on *X*:

$$Max\ X = \frac{M}{P_X} = \frac{1200}{40} = 30\ units$$

If all income is spent on *Y*:

$$Max\ Y = \frac{M}{P_Y} = \frac{1200}{100} = 12\ units$$

There are no power terms in the budget equation. It is the equation of a straight line (a linear equation). The budget line for this equation is given in Figure 5.5.

We also show values for one other point on the diagram. Suppose for example that our consumer were to divide expenditure equally between both items, i.e. €600 on each of *X* and *Y*.

$$Expenditure\ on\ X = P_X X = 40 \times 15 = €600$$
$$Expenditure\ on\ Y = P_Y Y = 100 \times 6 = €600$$

FIGURE 5.5

A Consumer's Budget Constraint

A budget constraint shows all of the combinations of goods available to the consumer, given the limitations imposed by income and prices. Any point on the budget line involves spending all of the consumer's income.

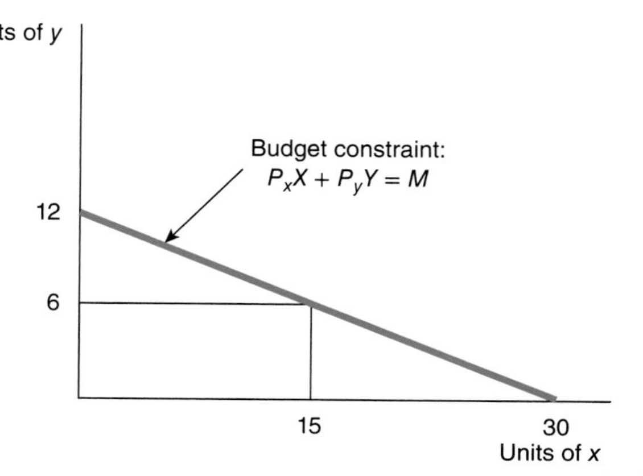

We show this combination as Point C on Figure 5.5. This point is, of course, one of just many on the line. So far we just know that the consumer's optimal combination will be found somewhere along this budget line.

Now we need to find MU_X and MU_Y for our particular consumer. We are assuming that the consumer has a utility function given as:

$$TU = XY$$

Now to find marginal utility of X and marginal utility of Y we need to partially differentiate the above expression. So partially differentiating TU with respect to X and holding Y constant the X term disappears and we are left with:

$$\frac{\partial TU}{\partial X} = Y$$

Similarly, we can find:

$$\frac{\partial TU}{\partial Y} = X$$

If this seems strange you can think of the total utility function as:

$$TU = X^1Y$$

This says we have an X term of X to the power of one.

Now it should be clear that when you differentiate the term X^1 the X term disappears entirely to leave Y. By similar reasoning:

$$\frac{\partial TU}{\partial Y} = X$$

So:

$$MU_X = Y \text{ and}$$

$$MU_Y = X$$

As shown in MT when the consumer is optimizing choices:

$$\frac{MU_X}{MU_Y} = \frac{P_X}{P_Y}$$

Since, by assumption, $MU_X = Y$ and $MU_Y = X$, we can write:

$$\frac{Y}{X} = \frac{P_X}{P_Y}$$

$$\frac{Y}{X} = \frac{40}{100}$$

$$X = \frac{100Y}{40}$$

$$X = 2.5Y$$

We can now solve for X and Y. We have two equations and two unknowns. The equations are:

$$\text{Budget line: } 40X + 100Y = 1200$$

And:

$$X = 2.5Y$$

Substituting $X = 2.5Y$ into the budget line gives:

$$100Y + 100Y = 1200$$
$$Y = 1200/200$$
$$Y = 6$$

If $X = 2.5Y$ and $Y = 6$:

$$X = 2.5 \times 6$$
$$X = 15$$

Our consumer's optimal combination is 6 units of good Y and 15 units of good X which turns out to be Point C in Figure 5.6.

FIGURE 5.6

A Consumer's Equilibrium Consumption

To maximize utility the consumer's optimal combination of the two goods is where the marginal rate of substitution is equal to the relative prices. In this case it will be a consumption bundle of 6 units of good Y and 15 units of good X. This is shown as point C.

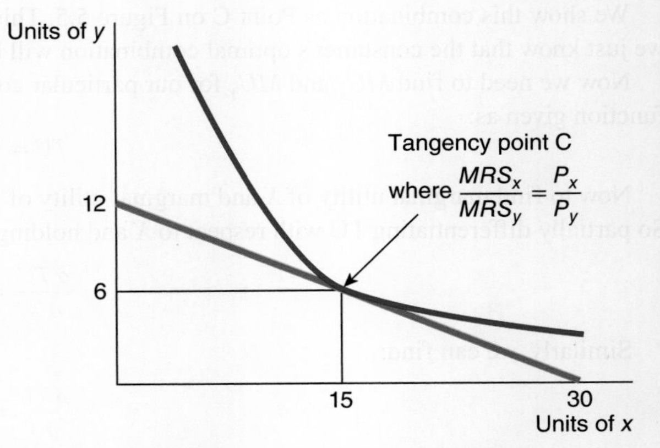

PROBLEMS AND APPLICATIONS

1 In the chapter the total utility function $TU = 100Q - 5Q^2$ was used. Would it matter for the decision-making of a household if we were to write $TU = 2468 + 100Q - 5Q^2$ instead?

2 Imagine a consumer travelling outside of their home country but in the European Union with a mobile telephone. For travelling abroad, they do not have a flat-rate for telephone minutes or online access. Telephone calls cost €0.20 per minute and each megabyte of data volume costs €0.50. Her overall budget for telecommunication on this trip is limited to €10.

a. Express this budget constraint in an equation and rearrange terms so that you can see the telephone minutes she can afford as a linear function of the data volume she has used.

b. How high is the opportunity cost of another megabyte of data volume in minutes of telephone calls?

c. Show the budget constraint in a graph, where you measure the data volume on the horizontal axis and telephone minutes on the vertical axis.

d. Show in an equation and in the graph the effect of a reduction in the budget from €10 to €8 for the trip.

e. Imagine a new regulation of the EU that leaves the price of telephone calls the same, but limits the price to €0.40 for a megabyte of data volume when traveling in the European Union. How does this change the constraint with a €8 budget?

f. Keep the budget at €10 and assume that the difference telephone company offers a tariff where telephone minutes cost €0.25 but data volume only €0.40/megabyte. Show this in the equation and your graph.

3 Jacob and Oliver are arguing about the value of sweet versus salty snacks. Oliver would prefer one bag of salt pretzels and three bars of chocolate per week (point $O_1 = (1, 3)$) over a combination of two bags of pretzels and two chocolate

bars (point $O_2 = (2, 2)$). Jacob, however, is indifferent between having two bags of pretzels with two chocolate bars ($O_2 = J_2 = (2, 2)$) and a combination of four chocolate bars with just one bag of pretzels ($J_1 = (1, 4)$) or even one chocolate bar if he gets 4 bags of pretzels with it ($J_3 = (4, 1)$). (Since we are discussing average weekly consumption pretzel bags and chocolates can be in fractions.)

a. Sketch the preferences of Jacob and of Oliver with indifference curves in Figure 5.7.
b. In your graph the two indifference curves will necessarily intersect at two bags of pretzels and two chocolates (2, 2). Is this a violation of the standard assumptions of the properties of indifference curves?
c. Assume both young men have a budget of €6 to spend on snacks per week in scenario 1 (denoted with superscript^1). A bag of pretzels costs P_1^1 = €2/bag and a chocolate bar is priced at P_2^1 = €1/bar. Could any of the two reach a household optimum at two bags of pretzels and two chocolates (2, 2)?
d. Show and explain Oliver's optimum consumption choice in scenario 2 (denoted with superscript ^{2}), when the price of a chocolate bar is still at $P_2^1 = P_2^2$ = €1/bar but the pretzels cost P_1^2 = €1.5/bag now and his budget for snacks is reduced to €4.5.
e. Assume a falling price for chocolates. Show that for Jacob the two snacks are substitutes. [You can do this in the abstract, not oriented at any of the prices or budgets given above.]

FIGURE 5.7

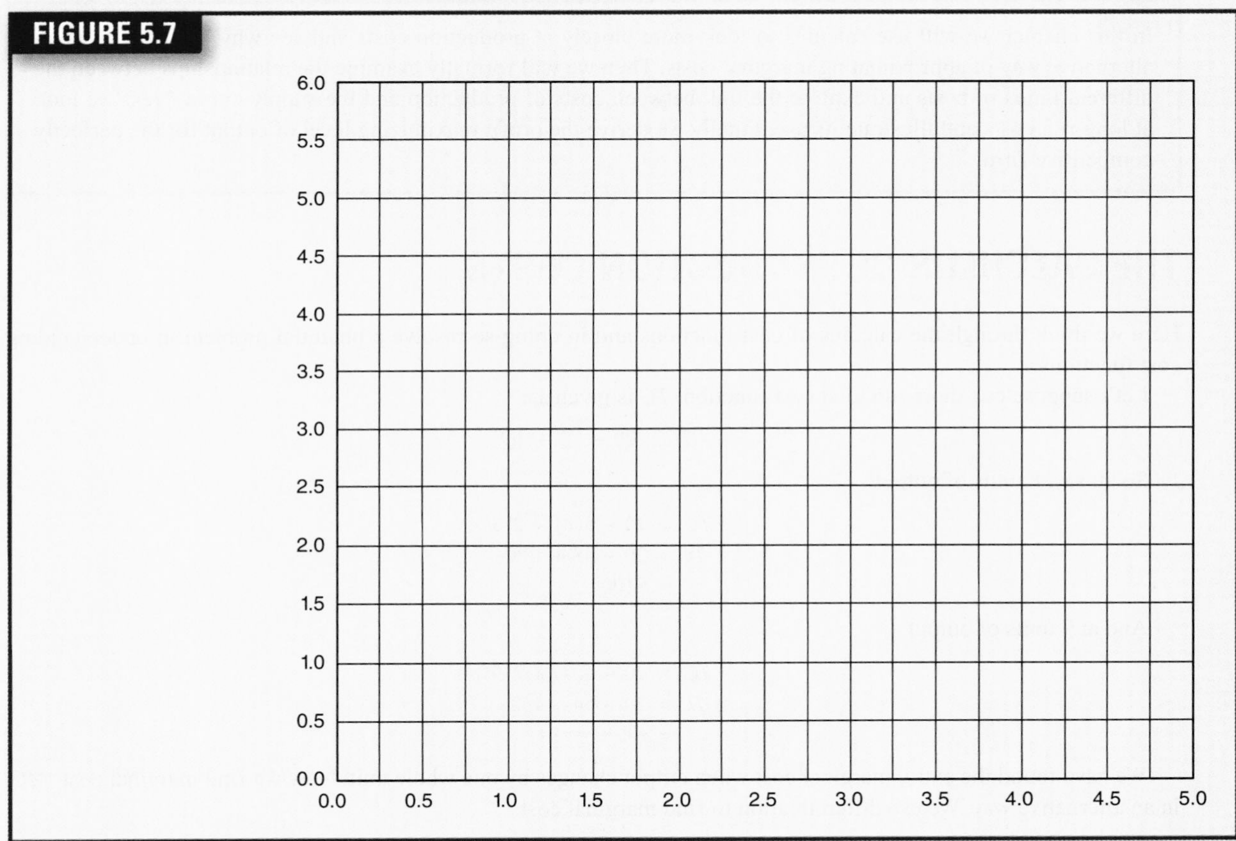

4 Assume that the utility of a household only depends on the consumption of goods X and Y. The utility function is given by $TU = U(Y, X) = X^{\frac{3}{4}}Y^{\frac{1}{4}}$. Calculate the marginal rate of substitution.

5 Assume the utility function is still $TU = U(Y, X) = X^{\frac{3}{4}}Y^{\frac{1}{4}}$. Plugging in some numbers will give you for example $U(0.05, 8000) = 8000^{\frac{3}{4}}\,0.05^{\frac{1}{4}} = 400$ and $U(0.4, 4000) = 8000^{\frac{3}{4}}\,0.05^{\frac{1}{4}} = 400$. So these points represent the same level of utility and therefore, they are on the same indifference curve. Since $U(0.1, 16000) = 16000^{\frac{3}{4}}\,0.1^{\frac{1}{4}} = 800$, the combination of 0.1 units of Y and 16000 units of X represents a higher utility of 800. Please show, using examples like the above, that the 'Four Properties of Indifference Curves' defined in Mankiw/Taylor hold for the utility function given. (You may also use some of the results from the previous problem.)

6 BACKGROUND TO SUPPLY: FIRMS IN COMPETITIVE MARKETS

In this chapter we will use calculus to look more closely at production costs and see why calculus gives an alternative way of approximating marginal costs. Then we will formally examine the relationships between the different kinds of costs and explore the link between costs of production and the supply curve. Next we look at long-run costs and illustrate its use. Finally we derive the profit maximizing level of output for the perfectly competitive firm.

THE CALCULUS OF PRODUCTION COSTS

Here we think through the calculus of cost functions and in doing so resolve a potential problem in understanding cost functions.

Let's suppose our short-run total cost function, TC is given as:

$$TC = 20 - 6Q + 2Q^2$$

So at, say, 8 units of output:

$$\begin{aligned} TC &= 20 - 6(8) + 2(8^2) \\ TC &= 20 - 48 + 128 \\ &= €100 \end{aligned}$$

And at 9 units of output:

$$\begin{aligned} TC &= 20 - 6(9) + 2(9^2) \\ TC &= 20 - 54 + 162 \\ &= €128 \end{aligned}$$

We have found the extra, marginal cost when output changes by one whole unit. Now we find marginal cost, MC, in an alternative way. We use differentiation to find marginal cost:[1]

$$\begin{aligned} \frac{dTC}{dQ} &= \frac{d(20 - 6Q + 2Q^2)}{dQ} \\ &= 4Q - 6 \end{aligned}$$

At $Q = 8$, $MC = -6 + (4 \times 8) = €26$.

You might expect that since MC is the additional cost of one unit, the cost of 9 units must be the cost at 8 units (€100) plus a further €26 for the 9th unit produced which = €126. This seems to contradict the calculation we made above where we substituted the output of 9 units into the TC function which gave us the answer: $Q = 9$, $TC = €128$!

Can you see the reason for this contradiction? Which is the right answer?

[1] Remember that by differentiating we are finding the rate of change of total cost, that is marginal cost, at a point on the curve. This is especially useful when the variable we are examining is infinitely divisible. In our example here the firm may only be able to produce whole units.

The answer obtained by using calculus is not as accurate but is easier to calculate. For the exact value we need to find TC at both $Q = 8$ and $Q = 9$ and then subtract to find the marginal cost. Note that calculus tells us the rate of change at a point, say MC at 8 units. Discrete changes, as for example the change from 8 to 9 units can only be approximate because MC is continuously changing over that range of output. However, we can use calculus to get an approximate change and this will become increasingly accurate for smaller and smaller percentage changes in Q. For example, suppose we change from $Q = 100$ to $Q = 101$.

Consider first the answer we get without using calculus.

$$TC = 20 - 6Q + 2Q^2$$

So at $Q = 100$ we have:

$$TC = 20 - 600 + 20\,000$$
$$= 19\,420$$

At $Q = 101$ we have:

$$TC = 20 - 606 + 20\,402$$
$$= 19\,816$$

This is a difference of 396. That is, $MC = 396$. This is the correct answer. It shows the additional cost associated with a one unit increase in output from 100 to 101.

Using calculus we established that:

$$MC = 4Q - 6$$

Then at 100 the formula gives:

$$MC = 400 - 6 = 394.$$

At 101 the formula gives:

$$MC = 404 - 6 = 398$$

It isn't surprising that we have a different answer at 100 from the answer we had at 101. The slope of the curve is continuously changing.

Using calculus, then, gets us very close to the correct value. However, if you try the same calculations for a change from $Q = 1000$ to $Q = 1001$ the change we are now discussing is proportionately much smaller. You would expect the answer to be closer to the exact value. By calculus we have $MC = 3994$ at 1000 and 3998 at 1001, versus the exact value of 3996. This is the same absolute error that we had for the lower output but it is a much smaller relative error.

The Relationship Between Different Kinds of Costs

There are a variety of kinds of production costs for firms in both the short and the long run. Here we formalize the relationships mathematically.

Short-run Costs

The main short-run costs are:

- TFC: Total Fixed Costs
- TVC: Total Variable Costs
- TC: Total Cost
- AFC: Average Fixed Costs
- AVC: Average Variable Costs
- ATC: Average Total Costs
- MC: Marginal Costs

It is in the nature of fixed costs that they don't change as output changes. So we can write:

$$TFC = a$$

Where a is a constant.

Variable costs, by nature, vary with output. There are many possibilities but we could write:

$$TVC = bQ + cQ^2 + dQ^3$$

Where b, c and d are constants.

Notice that there is no stand-alone constant term. All costs are variable.

Total costs are the sum of variable costs and fixed costs, so we could write:

$$TC = a + bQ + cQ^2 + dQ^3$$

Average fixed costs are fixed costs per unit of output, that is fixed costs divided by output, Q. We write:

$$AFC = \frac{a}{Q}$$

Average variable costs are variable costs per unit of output, that is variable costs divided by output, Q. We write:

$$AVC = \frac{bQ + cQ^2 + dQ^3}{Q}$$
$$= b + cQ + dQ^2$$

Average total costs are total costs per unit of output, that is total costs divided by output, Q. We write:

$$ATC = \frac{a + bQ + cQ^2 + dQ^3}{Q}$$
$$= \frac{a}{Q} + b + cQ + dQ^2$$

Alternatively, we can define average total cost as the sum of AFC and AVC:

$$AFC = \frac{a}{Q}$$
$$AVC = b + cQ + dQ^2$$
$$ATC = \frac{a}{Q} + b + cQ + dQ^2$$

Finally, consider marginal cost, MC. To find marginal cost we differentiate the total cost function with respect to output.

$$TC = a + bQ + cQ^2 + dQ^3$$
$$\frac{dTC}{dQ} = b + 2cQ + 3dQ^2$$

Notice that the slope of TVC is the same as the slope of TC. So we can differentiate the total variable cost function with respect to output and obtain the same answer:

$$TVC = bQ + cQ^2 + dQ^3$$
$$\frac{dTVC}{dQ} = b + 2cQ + 3dQ^2$$

Let's take an example. Suppose a firm has fixed costs of 64 euros and its variable costs per period are given as:

$$TVC = 5Q + 3Q^2 + 2Q^3$$

That is, $a = 64$, $b = 5$, $c = 3$ and $d = 2$. Let's further suppose that the firm wishes to know costs if it produces 4 units of output per period, that is, $Q = 4$.

Then:

$$TVC = 20 + 48 + 128 = 196$$
$$TC = 64 + 20 + 48 + 128 = 260$$
$$AFC = \frac{64}{4} = 16$$
$$AVC = \frac{20 + 48 + 128}{4} = 49$$
$$ATC = AFC + AVC = 16 + 49 = 65$$

Alternatively we can write:

$$ATC = \frac{TC}{Q} = \frac{260}{4} = 65$$

$$\begin{aligned} MC = \frac{dTC}{dQ} &= \frac{d(64 + 5Q + 3Q^2 + 2Q^3)}{dQ} \\ &= 5 + 6Q + 6Q^2 \\ &= 5 + 6 \times 4 + 6 \times 4^2 \\ &= 5 + 24 + 96 \\ &= 125 \end{aligned}$$

Long-run Costs

For the long run, the relationships are fewer. All costs are variable so there is no distinction between fixed and variable costs. In the short run costs associated with capital are fixed, because the volume of capital cannot be changed. In the long run all factors, including capital, are variable, so all costs are variable also. There is no constant term in the long-run total cost curve, *LTC*.

$$LTC = eQ + fQ^2 + gQ^3$$

Where *e, f* and *g* are constants.

Long-run average costs, *LATC*, are total costs per unit of output, that is long-run total costs divided by output, *Q*.

$$\begin{aligned} LATC &= \frac{eQ + fQ^2 + gQ^3}{Q} \\ &= e + fQ + gQ^2 \end{aligned}$$

Long-run marginal cost, *LMC*, is found by differentiating the LTC function with respect to output:

$$\begin{aligned} LTC &= eQ + fQ^2 + gQ^3 \\ \frac{dLTC}{dQ} &= e + 2fQ + 3gQ^2 \end{aligned}$$

To illustrate, suppose a firm has long-run costs of the form:

$$LTC = 6Q + 4Q^2 + 2Q^3$$

That is, $e = 6, f = 4$, and $g = 2$. Let's further suppose that the firm wishes to know costs if it produces 10 units of output per period in the long run, that is, $Q = 10$. Note that there is no fixed-cost term in the long run. All costs are variable.

$$LTC = 60 + 400 + 2000 = 2460.$$

$$LATC = \frac{2460}{10} = 246$$

$$\begin{aligned} LMC = \frac{dLTC}{dQ} &= \frac{d(6Q + 4Q^2 + 2Q^3)}{dQ} \\ &= 6 + 8Q + 6Q^2 \\ &= 6 + 8 \times 10 + 6 \times 10^2 \\ &= 6 + 80 + 600 = 686 \end{aligned}$$

THE RELATIONSHIP BETWEEN COSTS AND THE SUPPLY CURVE

Now we know what any individual producer under conditions of perfect competition, will supply at different prices. Each producer supplies an output to the market at which marginal cost equals price.

This establishes that the firm's short-run marginal cost curve, SRMC (above average variable cost), is the firm's supply curve.

How do we establish a **market** supply curve, the amount supplied of a good by the whole market at different prices? Suppliers may be different. Each may have different production costs, although we would expect all to face an upward sloping SRMC (individual supply function). We can sum all these individual suppliers' marginal cost curves at each price to obtain the market supply curve. We sum the individual supply curves. Let's take an example to see how this can be done.

For a perfectly competitive industry we would expect a large number of firms but to illustrate the derivation of the supply curve we will simplify and assume that there are only two firms, A and B, each with a known supply curve.

$$Q_A = P - 2$$
$$Q_B = 0.5P - 1.5$$

In order to plot and see these supply curves in a standard way we need to produce them in their inverse form. For Firm A:

$$Q_A = P - 2$$

So the inverse form is:

$$P = 2 + Q_A$$

For Firm B:

$$Q_B = 0.5P - 1.5$$

So the inverse form is:

$$0.5P = 1.5 + Q_B$$
$$P = \frac{1.5 + Q_B}{0.5}$$
$$P = 3 + 2Q_B$$

Now we plot these individual inverse supply curves (cost functions). They are shown in Figure 6.1 To see how they are plotted focus on Firm A first. Note that at a price of €2 we have:

$$P = 2 + Q_A$$

So when $P = 2$

$$2 = 2 + Q_A$$
$$Q_A = 0$$

This point is labelled R on Figure 6.1.

FIGURE 6.1

Firms' Individual Supply Functions

As with demand curves, we must find the inverse form of supply curves to plot them in the usual way. Points G and H show points on the supply function $P = 3 + 2Q_B$. Points R and T show points on the supply function $P = 2 + Q_A$.

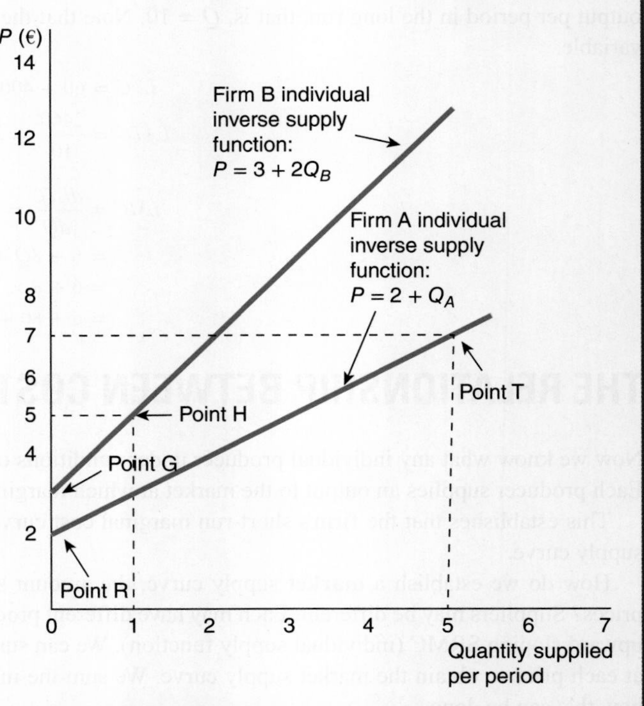

Now choose one other spot on this straight line supply function. Let's find Q_A when price is, say, 7.

$$7 = 2 + Q_A$$

So when $P = 7$:

$$Q_A = 5$$

This is labelled as point T on Figure 6.1. Remember that two points on a straight line is enough to define the whole curve.

Now focus on Firm B.

At a price of €3 we have:

$$P = 3 + 2Q_B$$

So when $P = 3$:

$$3 = 3 + 2Q_B$$
$$Q_B = 0$$

This is labelled point G on Figure 6.1.

Now choose one other spot on this straight line supply function. Let's find Q_B when price is, say, 5.

$$P = 3 + 2Q_B$$

So when $P = 5$:

$$5 = 3 + 2Q_B$$
$$2Q_B = 2$$
$$Q_B = 1$$

This is labelled point H on Figure 6.1.

We can now sum the curves horizontally to find the market supply (Q_M). We do it over each of three price ranges:

1. When P takes a value from 0 to 2 there is nothing to sum. No firm is willing to supply.
2. When the price is more than 2 but less than 3, we have only one supplier so our horizontal summation is for just Firm A.
3. When the price is more than 3, we have both suppliers selling, so our horizontal summation is:

$$Q_M = (P - 2) + (0.5P - 1.5)$$
$$Q_M = 1.5P - 3.5$$

Now we can find the inverse form of this horizontal summation so that we can plot it:

$$Q_M = 1.5P - 3.5$$
$$1.5P = Q_M + 3.5$$
$$P = \frac{Q_M + 3.5}{1.5}$$
$$P = \frac{2}{3}Q_M + 2.33$$

To plot this we have redrawn Figure 6.1 as Figure 6.2 and added this summed supply curve on the same diagram as the individual supply functions. You can see that at a price of less than €2 quantity supplied would be 0. Now let's consider one other point as an illustration of how we construct this summed inverse supply curve. What is the outcome when price is €5?

We can substitute $P = 5$ into the inverse supply function:

$$P = \frac{2}{3}Q_M + 2.33$$
$$5 = \frac{2}{3}Q_M + 2.33$$
$$\frac{2}{3}Q_M = 2.67$$
$$Q_M = 4$$

This is labelled as point J on Figure 6.2.

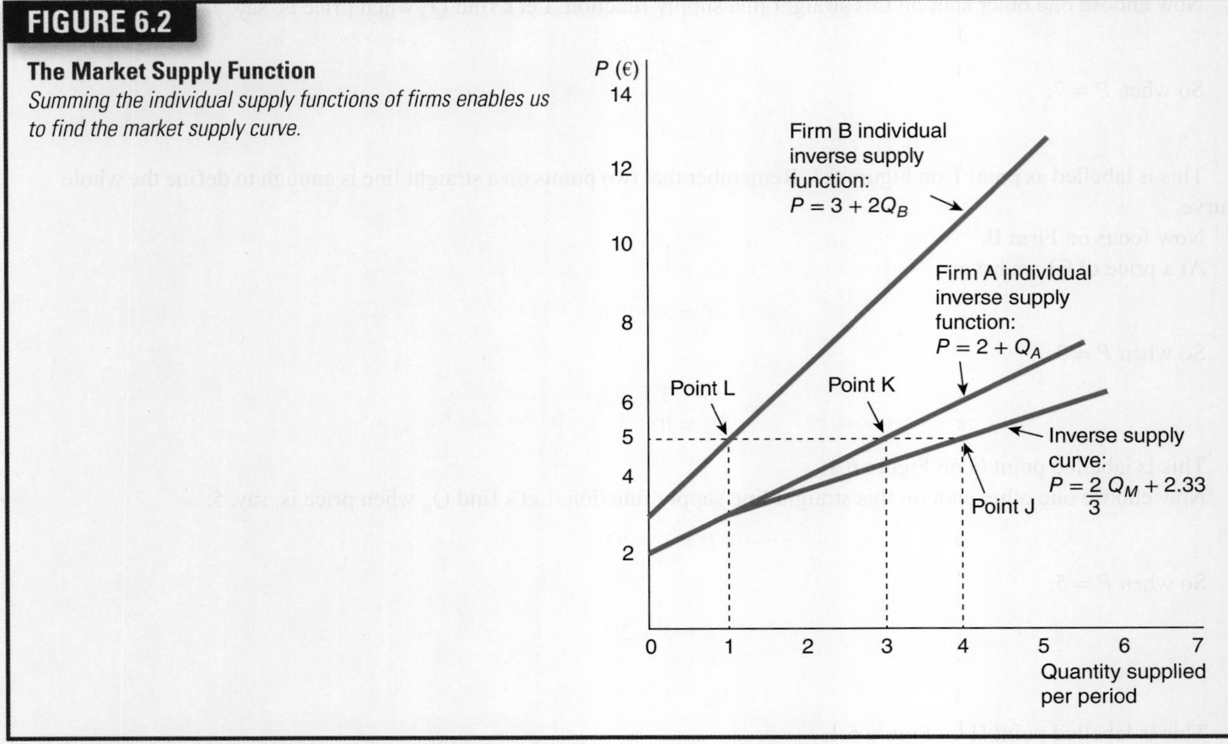

FIGURE 6.2

The Market Supply Function

Summing the individual supply functions of firms enables us to find the market supply curve.

Who is supplying these four units per period?

The supply from firm A at this price of €5 is:

$$P = 2 + Q_A$$
$$5 = 2 + Q_A$$
$$Q_A = 3$$

So firm A supplies three units per period to the market when price is €5 per unit. This point is labelled point K on Figure 6.2.

The supply from firm B at this price of €5 is found as follows:

$$P = 3 + 2Q_B$$
$$5 = 3 + 2Q_B$$
$$2Q_B = 2$$
$$Q_B = 1$$

So firm B supplies one unit per period to the market when price is €5 per unit. This point is labelled point L on Figure 6.2.

We can summarize what we have done in the form of a table, Table 6.1.

TABLE 6.1 **Summary of Supply Functions**

Price Range	Relevant Supply Functions	Horizontal Sum of Firms' Supply Curves	Inverse Supply Function
0–2	None	-	-
2–3	Firm A	$Q_M = P - 2$	$P = 2 + Q_M$
> 3	Firms A and B	$Q_M = (P - 2) + (0.5P - 1.5P)$ $= 1.5P - 3.5$	$P = \frac{2}{3} Q_M + 2.33$

We now know how we can sum individual supply curves to form a market supply curve. Given the individual supply functions we can establish quantity supplied by the market at each price and know how this quantity is divided up among suppliers of the product.

COSTS IN THE LONG RUN: EDUCATING STUDENTS

In this section we look at a real world problem. What is the best number of students for a university to educate so that the cost per student is minimized? We will see how this problem was handled for Universities in the US. Essentially what we are attempting is to find the level of output, where output means the number of students, which would be at the bottom of the average cost curve in Figure 6.3. This lowest point on the curve is often called minimum efficient scale, or MES.

Estimates were made by looking at the costs of many different universities. This suggested that for research universities, those who put great emphasis on research among the staff, the cost function was:

$$LATC = 80\,842 - 3997.24\,FTE + 61.83\,FTE^2$$

Where:

LATC = Long-Run Average Total Cost

FTE = Full-time Equivalent students (in 000s)

This tells us the average cost of educating any number of students. However, we need to find the number of students taught which represents MES. This is where the rate of change of AC is zero as shown by the tangent drawn to the bottom of ATC in Figure 6.4.

To find the rate of change of LATC we need to find the derivative of LATC with respect to FTEs and set this to zero to find the local minimum:

$$\frac{dLATC}{dFTE} = 0$$

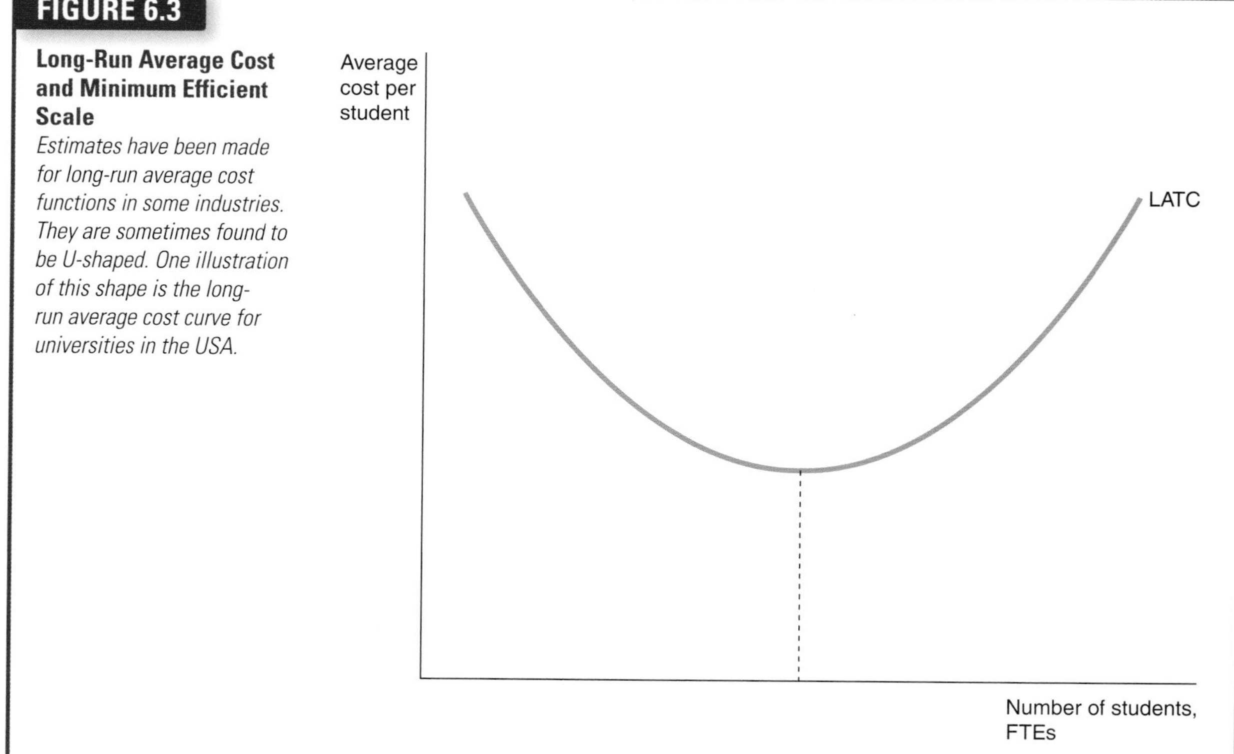

FIGURE 6.3

Long-Run Average Cost and Minimum Efficient Scale

Estimates have been made for long-run average cost functions in some industries. They are sometimes found to be U-shaped. One illustration of this shape is the long-run average cost curve for universities in the USA.

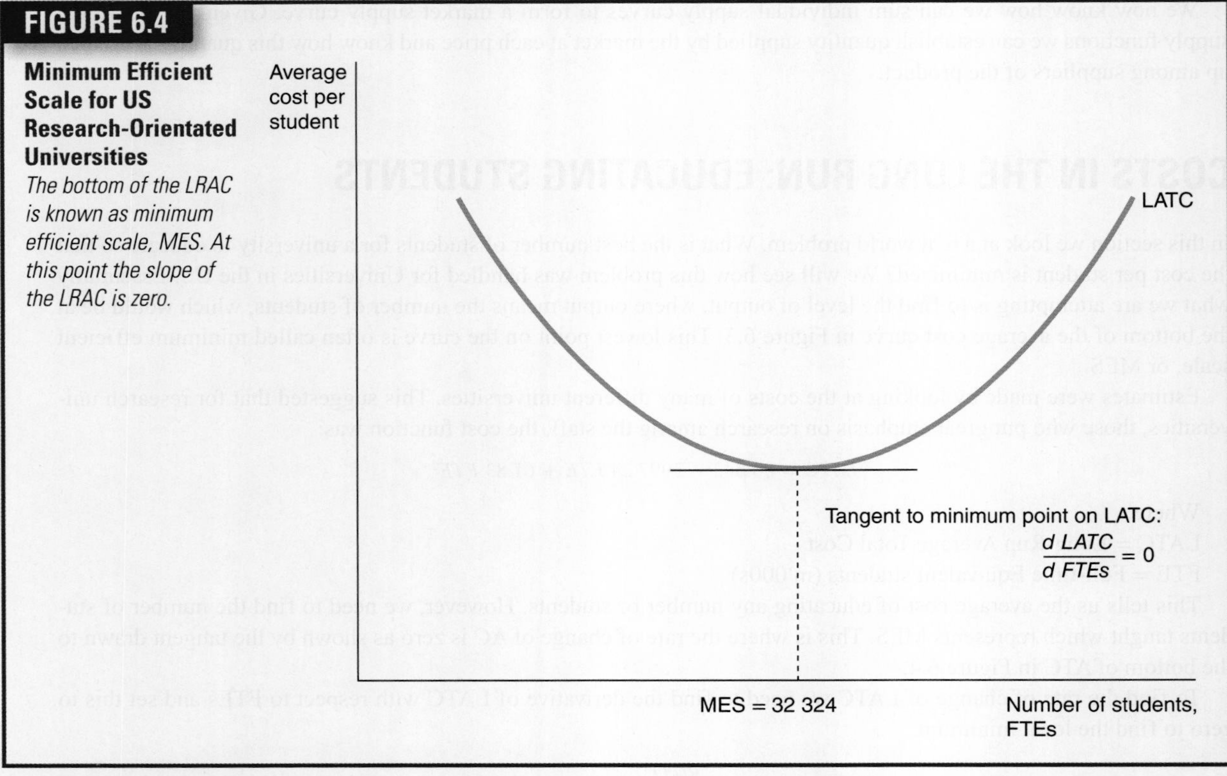

FIGURE 6.4

Minimum Efficient Scale for US Research-Orientated Universities

The bottom of the LRAC is known as minimum efficient scale, MES. At this point the slope of the LRAC is zero.

In this case:

$$123.66\,FTE - 3997.24 = 0$$
$$123.66\,FTE = 3997.24$$
$$FTE = 32.324$$

MES occurs at 32 324 full-time equivalent students at research-orientated universities.

For universities placing less emphasis on research, the cost function was estimated at:

$$LATC = 24\,189 - 1890.16\,FTE + 57.74\,FTE^2$$

Where:

LATC = Long-Run Average Total Cost

FTE = Full-time Equivalent students (in 000s)

Again we need to find the derivative of ATC with respect to FTEs, this time for the less research-orientated universities:

$$\frac{d\,LATC}{d\,FTE} = 0$$

$$115.48\,FTE - 1890.16 = 0$$
$$115.48\,FTE = 1890.16$$
$$FTE = 16.368$$

MES for these universities is 16 368 full-time equivalent students.[2] That is, MES is lower for less research-orientated universities in the USA than for those who place a great deal of emphasis on research. This result is summarized diagrammatically in Figure 6.5.

[2] Not all students are full time. Some are part time and are treated accordingly. So, for example, two students each studying half-time, are treated as the equivalent of one full time student.

FIGURE 6.5

Minimum Efficient Scale for US Universities with a Lower Research Orientation

MES for USA universities with less research orientation is also U-shaped. However, MES for these universities is at a lower level of output, that is, they need fewer students than universities that are research-orientated to minimize long-run average cost.

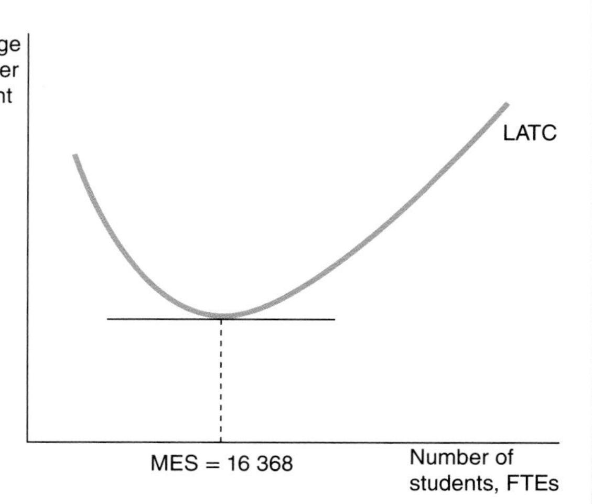

PROFIT MAXIMIZATION IN PERFECT COMPETITION

Now we show how to derive the level of output which maixmizes short-run profit for the perfectly competitive firm. We need to know both the revenue and the short-run cost functions.

Suppose the market price is €30 per unit, then total revenue:

$$TR = 30Q$$

Where Q = quantity per period.

We show this diagrammatically in Figure 6.6.

Notice that TR = 0 when $Q = 0$

Also note that if price per unit had been higher the total revenue function would still have risen from the origin. It would still be a straight line but it would have a steeper slope. For example, Figure 6.6 also shows the total revenue function when price per unit is €40 given by the function:

$$TR = 40Q$$

FIGURE 6.6

The Total Revenue Function for a Perfectly Competitive Firm

The total revenue function for a perfectly competitive firm is a straight line and it begins at the origin. Its slope is determined by the price of the output. A higher price means that the total revenue curve, TR, will be steeper, although it will still begin at the origin.

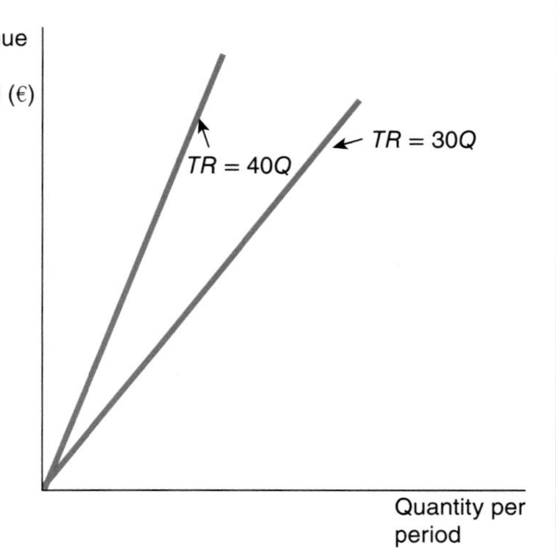

It can be seen that the slope of this function is much steeper than that for the function $TR = 30Q$. This is because the firm is receiving a higher amount of revenue for each unit sold. Now let's suppose that our short-run cost function, TC is given as:

$$TC = 20 - 6Q + 2Q^2$$

We have sketched this relationship in Figure 6.7. You can see that for this firm there is a range of output where revenue exceeds costs but the profit maximizing firm wishes to find the output at which revenue exceeds costs by the greatest amount. This must be where the tangent to the total cost curve, marginal cost, has the same slope as the total revenue curve, marginal revenue, shown by the output level Q_{MAX} in Figure 6.7.

FIGURE 6.7

Total Revenue and Total Cost Functions for a Perfectly Competitive Firm

The Revenue and cost functions for the firm enable us to calculate the profit maximizing level of output. This occurs where MR = MC. MR is the slope of the total revenue function, TR. MC is the slope of the total cost function, TC. These two functions have the same slope at the profit maximizing level of output, Q_{MAX}.

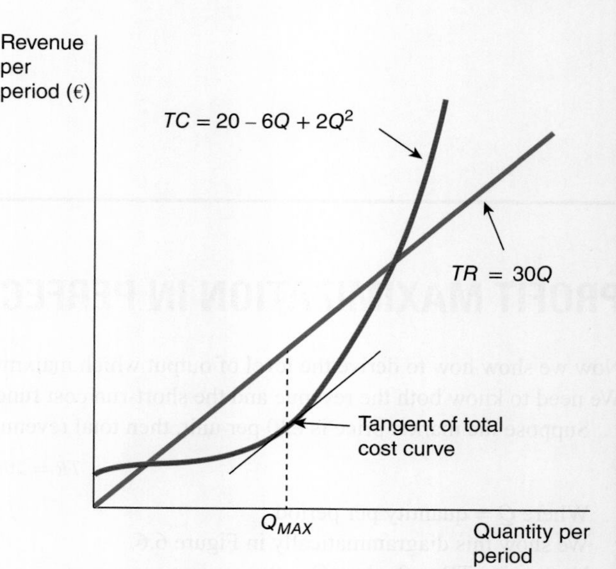

Alternatively, we can find profit in the following way:

Profit, (π), per period is Total Revenue minus Total Cost.

$$\pi = TR - TC$$

In our case:

$$\pi = 30Q - (20 - 6Q + 2Q^2)$$
$$= 36Q - 2Q^2 - 20$$

Now look at Figure 6.8. Here we show the profits curve which is $TR - TC$ for each level of output. It is where revenue exceeds costs by the greatest amount that profit is maximized. At that point the slope of the profit function is zero. The horizontal line indicates that as we increase output profit neither rises nor falls. There is no change in profit at that level of output. The slope of the line is therefore zero.

Now we differentiate profit with respect to output:

$$\frac{d\pi}{dQ} = 0$$
$$36 - 4Q = 0$$
$$4Q = 36$$
$$Q = 9$$

This is shown in Figure 6.8.

The profit maximizing level of output for the competitive firm, given a price of €30 and the cost function $TC = 20 - 6Q + 2Q^2$, is 9 units per period. We can now see how much profit, π, is made.

$$\pi = 36Q - 2Q^2 - 20$$
$$= 324 - 162 - 20$$
$$= 142$$

FIGURE 6.8

A Profits Curve for a Perfectly Competitive Firm

Given the cost and revenue functions we can calculate a profits function, where profit is TR – TC. The top of the profits function is where MC = MR. In this case profit maximization occurs at a level of output of nine units $Q_{MAX} = 9$.

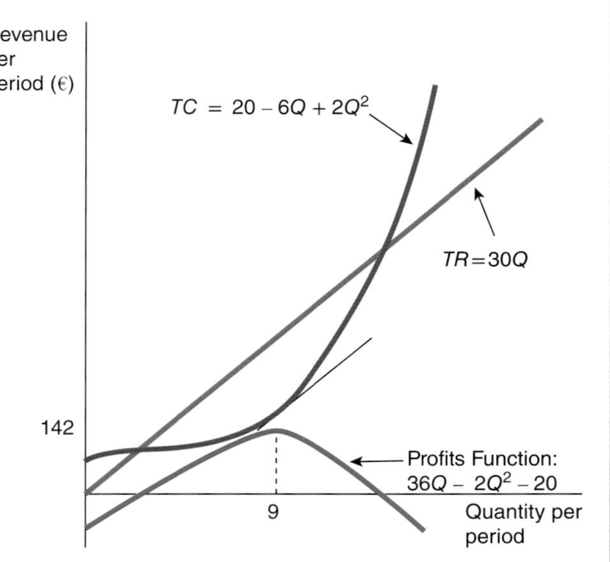

Maximum possible profit is €142 per period.

In Table 6.2. we show the profit to be made at each of the levels of Q, 8, 9 and 10. Notice that profit is only marginally less at 8 and at 10 units. It is particularly worth noting that at 8 units, costs are rising faster than revenue. However, it is still worth expanding to nine units because the 9th unit adds more to revenue than to costs. Profit maximization is always where marginal cost = marginal revenue.

We have only considered profit maximization in one market structure, that of perfect competition. Later we will return to the question of profit maximization under other market structures.

TABLE 6.2 **Profit at Various Possible Output Levels**

Quantity	Total Costs	Revenue	Profit
8	100	240	140
9	128	270	142
10	160	300	140

PROBLEMS AND APPLICATIONS

1 Assume a firm in a perfectly competitive market produces under the cost structure $TC(q) = q^3 + 4q^2 + 20q + 2400$. $TC(q)$ shows total cost as a function of the output quantity q. The table below shows cost levels, average and marginal cost respectively. Tabulated are values at increments of half an output unit.

a. How high are the fixed costs?
b. Calculate variable costs for the production of 3 output units ($q = 3$).
c. How high are the average total costs and average fixed costs at $q = 5$?
d. Determine average variable costs for 6 units of output.
e. What are the marginal costs at an output of 4 using calculus?
f. The column Δ Total cost shows the difference in total cost for half an output unit. Which number is missing in this column at 7 units of output?
g. Explain the difference between the columns 'Marginal cost' and 'Δ Total cost'.

Different Kinds of Cost Functions

Quantity	Total cost (€)	Fixed cost (€)	Variable cost (€)	Average total cost (€/unit)	Average fixed cost (€/unit)	Average variable cost (€/unit)	Marginal cost (€/unit)	Δ Total cost
0.0	2400.00	2400.00						
0.5	2411.13	2400.00	11.13	4822.25	4800.00	22.25	24.75	11.13
1.0	2425.00	2400.00	25.00	2425.00	2400.00	25.00	31.00	13.88
1.5	2442.38	2400.00	42.38	1628.25	1600.00	28.25	38.75	17.38
2.0	2464.00	2400.00	64.00	1232.00	1200.00	32.00	48.00	21.63
2.5	2490.63	2400.00	90.63	996.25	960.00	36.25	58.75	26.63
3.0	2523.00	2400.00		841.00	800.00	41.00	71.00	32.38
3.5	2561.88	2400.00	161.88	731.96	685.71	46.25	84.75	38.88
4.0	2608.00	2400.00	208.00	652.00	600.00	52.00		46.13
4.5	2662.13	2400.00	262.13	591.58	533.33	58.25	116.75	54.13
5.0	2725.00	2400.00	325.00			65.00	135.00	62.88
5.5	2797.38	2400.00	397.38	508.61	436.36	72.25	154.75	72.38
6.0	2880.00	2400.00	480.00	480.00	400.00		176.00	82.63
6.5	2973.63	2400.00	573.63	457.48	369.23	88.25	198.75	93.63
7.0	3079.00	2400.00	679.00	439.86	342.86	97.00	223.00	
7.5	3196.88	2400.00	796.88	426.25	320.00	106.25	248.75	117.88
8.0	3328.00	2400.00	928.00	416.00	300.00	116.00	276.00	131.13
8.5	3473.13	2400.00	1073.13	408.60	282.35	126.25	304.75	145.13
9.0	3633.00	2400.00	1233.00	403.67	266.67	137.00	335.00	159.88
9.5	3808.38	2400.00	1408.38	400.88	252.63	148.25	366.75	175.38
10.0	4000.00	2400.00	1600.00	400.00	240.00	160.00	400.00	191.63
10.5	4208.63	2400.00	1808.63	400.82	228.57	172.25	434.75	208.63
11.0	4435.00	2400.00	2035.00	403.18	218.18	185.00	471.00	226.38
11.5	4679.88	2400.00	2279.88	406.95	208.70	198.25	508.75	244.88
12.0	4944.00	2400.00	2544.00	412.00	200.00	212.00	548.00	264.13
12.5	5228.13	2400.00	2828.13	418.25	192.00	226.25	588.75	284.13
13.0	5533.00	2400.00	3133.00	425.62	184.62	241.00	631.00	304.88
13.5	5859.38	2400.00	3459.38	434.03	177.78	256.25	674.75	326.38
14.0	6208.00	2400.00	3808.00	443.43	171.43	272.00	720.00	348.63
14.5	6579.63	2400.00	4179.63	453.77	165.52	288.25	766.75	371.63
15.0	6975.00	2400.00	4575.00	465.00	160.00	305.00	815.00	395.38
15.5	7394.88	2400.00	4994.88	477.09	154.84	322.25	864.75	419.88
16.0	7840.00	2400.00	5440.00	490.00	150.00	340.00	916.00	445.13
16.5	8311.13	2400.00	5911.13	503.70	145.45	358.25	968.75	471.13
17.0	8809.00	2400.00	6409.00	518.18	141.18	377.00	1023.00	497.88
17.5	9334.38	2400.00	6934.38	533.39	137.14	396.25	1078.75	525.38
18.0		2400.00	7488.00	549.33	133.33	416.00	1136.00	553.63
18.5	10470.63	2400.00	8070.63	565.98	129.73	436.25	1194.75	582.63
19.0	11083.00	2400.00	8683.00	583.32	126.32	457.00	1255.00	612.38
19.5	11725.88	2400.00	9325.88	601.33	123.08	478.25	1316.75	642.88
20.0	12400.00	2400.00	10000.00	620.00	120.00	500.00	1380.00	674.13

2 A supplier is faced with average total cost $ATC(q) = 0.3q^2 + 0.5q + 0.9 + \frac{6.8}{q}$ of producing the quantity q.

a. How high are the fixed costs?
b. Write down the functions for total cost and for marginal cost.
c. Roughly sketch the function of average variable cost in one of the graphs below (You don't really need to calculate points along the function, just show the general idea).

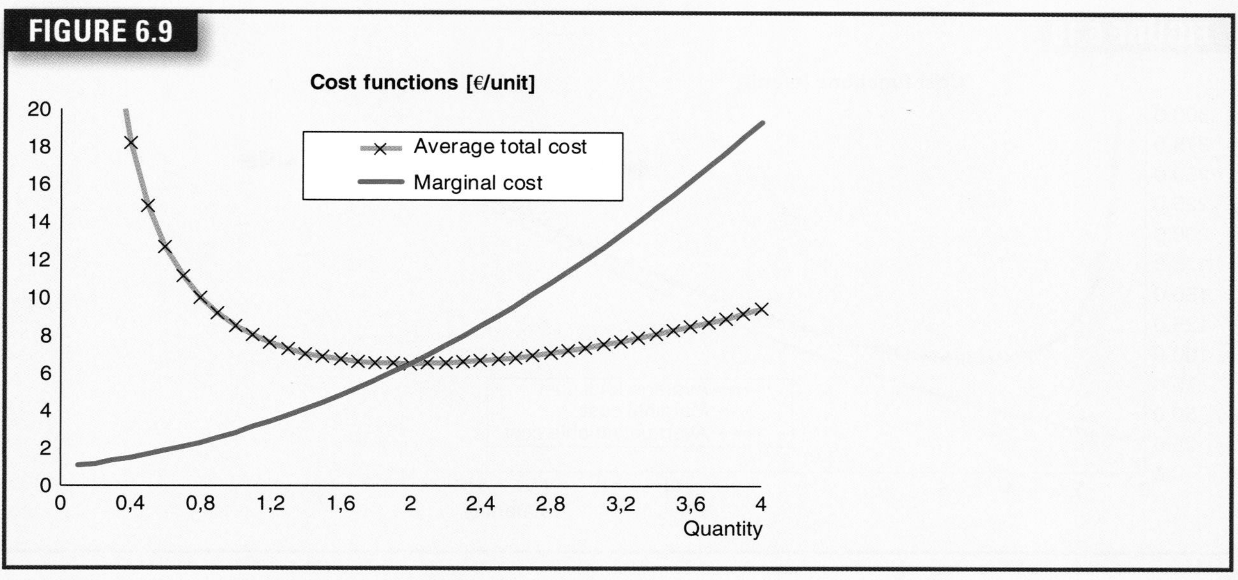

3 In the graph to the previous problem it appears that the marginal cost function (MC) intersects the average total cost function in the minimum of the ATC. Is that a coincidence? Use calculus based on $\text{ATC}(q) = \frac{TC(q)}{q}$ which is equivalent to $TC(q) = \text{ATC}(q) \times q$ and the product rule of differentiation to show that this is always the case.

4 The cost function is $TC(q) = 8q^3 - 4q^2 + 40q + 190$.

a. Write up the function of variable costs TVC(q) and the fixed cost (TFC).
b. Show the average total cost function ATC(q), average variable cost function AVC(q) and the average fixed cost (AFC(q)).
c. The text claims, that the slope of TVC is the same as the slope of TC. Calculate the first derivative of TC(q) and TVC(q), respectively, to show this for the function specified above.
d. Use calculus to finding the minimum of the AVC(q). (Recall i.e. from the discussion of a maximum in utility in Chapter 5 that a minimum or maximum of a function is found where the first derivative is equal to zero, here, where $\frac{dAVC(q)}{dq} = 0$.)
e. Since marginal costs are the same as the slope of TVC, should the MC(q) function also intersect the AVC(q) in its minimum? Show this for your solution from part d).

5 The cost of a firm in a perfectly competitive market to produce the output quantity q is given by $TC(q) = 0.25q^3 + 5q^2 + 25q + 187.5$. Marginal cost, average total cost, and average variable cost are depicted in the graph below.

a. For this firm the market price is a given constant P. Assume a price of P = €175 per unit of output sold and write the revenue function TR(q).
b. The profit for a firm in perfect competition is a function of quantity (q) only. Write out the profit function $\pi(q) = TR(q) - TC(q)$.
c. Show with the help of calculus that for a competitive firm $MR(q) = \frac{dTR(q)}{dq} = P$.
d. Use the first derivative of the profit function to show the general result from Mankiw/Taylor that firms maximize profits where $MR(q) = \frac{dTR(q)}{dq} = MC(q) = \frac{dTC(q)}{dq}$ (you need the conditions for a maximum of the function from Chapter 5).
e. Calculate the marginal cost function from the TC(q) above and explain its meaning.
f. Find the profit maximizing output quantity for the producer at the market price (P) of €200 per unit of output. (For the analytical solution you need the conditions for a maximum of the function from Chapter 4 and the solution to a quadratic function from Chapter 3.)
g. Check your solution for the profit maximizing quantity in the graph.
h. Which reaction of the producer would you expect in the short and in the long run, when the price falls to €75 per unit?

FIGURE 6.10

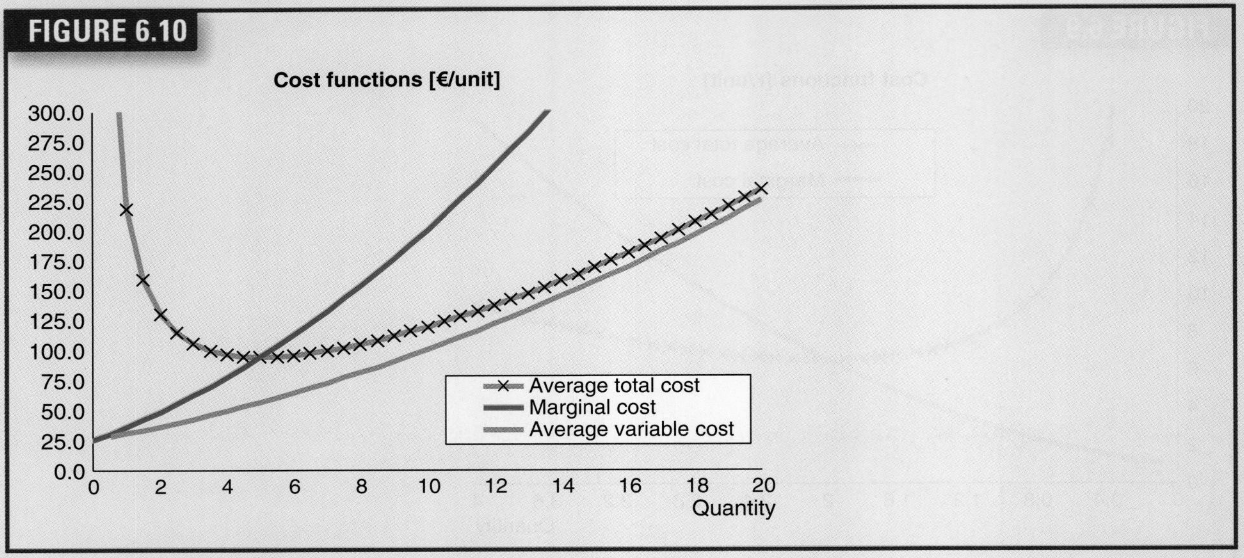

6 Please return to the function of total costs from problem 1 and the table there. Recall that from one row to the next the table shows an increase in output of 0.5 output units. So, if you try to find the results for the questions below from the table, sometimes you will not get a precise solution, but it will be good enough to provide the correct answers. Use calculus based on $TC(q) = q^3 + 4q^2 + 20q + 2400$ to solve the questions, and check your answers with the table.

a. Find the profit maximizing quantity at a price of €720 per unit and calculate the profit made.
b. At which quantity is the minimum of average total cost? Since the table shows steps of ½ units of q, how can you be sure to have found the exact minimum?
c. How long is the firm going to stay in the market at a price of €300 per unit?
d. If the market price were set at €631, what would happen to the profit of the firm if it would expand output from 13.0 to 13.5 units?
e. Assume the market has found a long-term equilibrium. In this equilibrium all firms in the market are identical (in technology and access to production factors). At this long-term stable price total market demand is running at 20 000 units. Explain how you find the long term equilibrium price and how many firms serve the market in that situation.

7 In 5 the cost function of a firm in a perfectly competitive market was given with the function $TC(q) = 0.25q^3 + 5q^2 + 25q + 187.5$. Use your knowledge that for a competitive firm the maximum of profit is where $P = MC(q)$ to solve the following problems.

a. Write out the inverse supply function.
b. At which quantity does this supply function start in the long term and in the short term? (A short glance at 6.9 should help you to find the solution quickly.)
c. Assume that all firms supplying the market have an identical cost structure to the total cost function given above. If there is a number of $n = 1000$ firms currently operating in the market, please specify the market supply function. When doing so, recall that the total quantity supplied to the market by n firms of the same size (Q_n) is for every given price (P) equal to the sum of the individual outputs (q_i=q) of all the firms or $Q_n = n \times q \Leftrightarrow q = \frac{Q_n}{n}$.

PART 3 MARKETS, EFFICIENCY AND WELFARE

7 CONSUMERS, PRODUCERS AND THE EFFICIENCY OF MARKETS

In looking at markets and efficiency, we will examine two ways of measuring consumer surplus. We will do this for both linear and non-linear supply and demand curves. This will include using integration, a technique to which you were introduced in Chapter 2. We will then focus on the measurement of producer surplus using similar techniques and use these concepts to explore what economists mean by the term 'value', and consider what is meant by 'value in exchange' and 'value in use'.

CONSUMER SURPLUS

Consumer surplus is the buyer's willingness to pay minus the amount actually paid. Figure 7.1 shows an inverse demand function $P = 20 - Q_D$ and an inverse supply function, $P = 8 + 2Q_S$ with an equilibrium price of €16 and equilibrium quantity bought and sold of 4 units. Total spending on the product by consumers is $4 \times 16 = €64$.

Consumer Surplus in a Competitive Market

All but the marginal consumer (the 4th buyer) is willing to pay a higher price than €16 to acquire the good. These consumers get consumer surplus equal to the difference they are willing to pay and the amount they actually pay. In Figure 7.1, this is indicated by the green shaded area.

How do we measure this area and place a value upon it? We can do so if we know the demand function and the equilibrium price. To begin with we will take the following demand and supply functions, $Q_D = 20 - P$ and $Q_s = \frac{1}{2}P - 4$. Their inverse forms are $P = 20 - Q_D$ and $P = 8 + 2Q_S$ respectively. The equilibrium price and quantity in equilibrium is given by setting $Q_D = Q_S$.

FIGURE 7.1

Consumer Surplus in a Competitive Market

Given the demand and supply functions, equilibrium is at P = 16 and Q = 4. The triangle representing consumer surplus is the area under the demand curve down to the equilibrium price. The area of this triangle is given as $A = \frac{hb}{2}$*, where h = height and b = base. Here,* $A = \frac{4 \times 4}{2} = 8$.

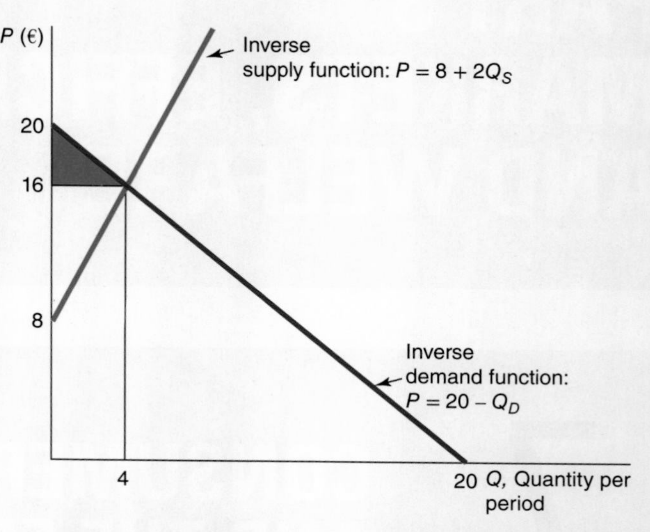

The equilibrium quantity is:

$$20 - Q_D = 8 + 2Q_S$$
$$3Q = 12$$
$$Q = 4$$

Now that we have established the equilibrium quantity we can find the equilibrium price by substituting $Q = 4$ into the equation of our demand curve:

$$P = 20 - Q_D$$
$$P = 20 - 4$$
$$P = 16$$

We can check that we have the correct value for P by substituting $P = 4$ into the equation of the supply curve:

$$P = 8 + 2Q_S$$
$$P = 8 + 8$$
$$P = 16$$

We have shown three points on Figure 7.1 that we have not discussed. (1) The point at which the demand curve cuts the vertical axis (the vertical intercept) is $P = 20$ at which point quantity demanded $Q_D = 0$. (2) The point at which the demand curve cuts the horizontal axis (the horizontal intercept) which is where price $P = 0$ and quantity demanded $Q_D = 20$ units. (3) The point at which the supply curve cuts the vertical axis which is the point at which the quantity supplied $Q_S = 0$, which occurs when $P = 8$.

These points can be found by the following method.

1. To find the price at which quantity demanded is zero we substitute into our demand equation a value of $Q = 0$:

$$P = 20 - Q_D$$

So if $Q_D = 0$, then $P = 20$

This is the choke price we introduced in Chapter 3.

2. To find the quantity demanded when the good has a zero price, we substitute into our demand equation a value of $P = 0$. A zero price is not uncommon. Many state produced goods and services, for example, are free at the point of use.

$$P = 20 - Q_D$$
$$0 = 20 - Q_D$$
$$Q_D = 20$$

3. To find the price at which $Q_S = 0$ we substitute into our supply equation a value of $Q = 0$:

$$P = 8 + 2Q_S$$
$$P = 8 + 0$$
$$P = 8$$

Calculating Consumer Surplus with Linear Demand and Supply Functions

Now we are ready to find consumer surplus in our example as shown by the shaded area in Figure 7.1. Given that the demand and supply curves are both linear functions, we can calculate consumer surplus using the formula for any triangle:

$$A = \frac{hb}{2}$$

Or alternatively expressed:

$$A = \frac{1}{2} b \times h$$

Where:
A = area
h = height
b = length of base

Using the first formulation we have:

$$A = \frac{4 \times 4}{2} = 8$$

Consumer surplus per period is €8. We have quantified the value that consumers place on the product in excess of what they have to pay for it. So given our demand and supply functions and the market price of €16, this value is €8.

PRODUCER SURPLUS

Producer surplus is the amount sellers are paid for a good over and above the (marginal) cost of production. The supply curve reflects the costs of supplying the market but most producers receive in excess of that. Given the demand and supply functions we have used, some producers are willing to offer more for sale at prices lower than the market price of €16. The marginal producer of the 4th unit is just prepared to offer this amount at the market price. Total producer surplus in a market, therefore, is the area above the supply curve but below the price. This is shown as the shaded area in Figure 7.2. We can use the same approach to calculating the producer surplus as we did in calculating consumer surplus when the demand and supply functions are linear by using the formula for calculating the area of a triangle. In this example, the triangle in question is the shaded area in Figure 7.2.

The total value of producer surplus is €16 per period.

The Effect of Shifts in Supply and Demand on Consumer and Producer Surplus

The market will remain in equilibrium unless something happens to shift the supply or demand curve (or both). Supply and demand can change if one of the factors other than price changes. Remember, a price change is shown as a movement along a demand (or supply) curve. A change in any other factor is shown as a shift of the whole curve. For example, a rise in labour costs shifts the supply curve for a good to the left and an increase in the price of a substitute would shift the demand curve for a good to the right. If something causes either the supply or demand curve to shift, then a new equilibrium price is formed and the amount of consumer and producer surplus will change. We will illustrate this by assuming that our demand function is unaltered but that there is a shift in supply.

FIGURE 7.2

Producer Surplus in a Competitive Market
Using the same supply and demand functions as before we can find producer surplus. This is the area above the supply curve up to the equilibrium price. Here, $A = \frac{4 \times 8}{2} = 16.$

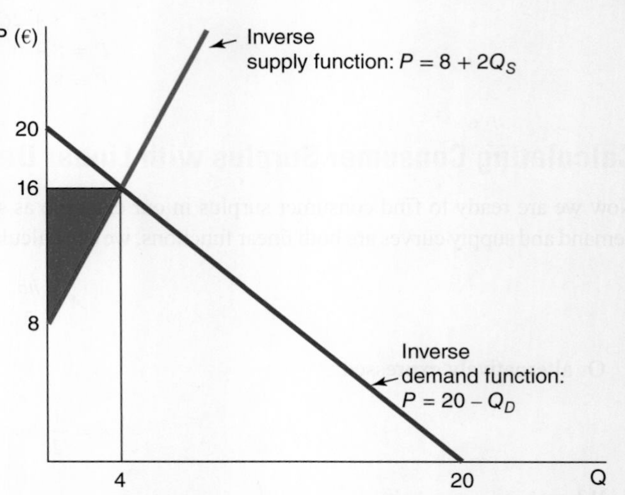

Suppose a fall in production costs means our supply function becomes:

$$P = 2 + 2Q_S$$

With an unchanged demand curve the new equilibrium quantity becomes:

$$20 - Q_D = 2 + 2Q_S$$
$$3Q = 18$$
$$Q = 6$$

Now that we have established the new equilibrium quantity we can find the new equilibrium price by substituting $Q = 6$ into the equation of our demand curve:

$$P = 20 - Q_D$$
$$P = 20 - 6$$
$$P = 14$$

We can check that we have the correct value for P by substituting $Q = 6$ into the equation of the new supply curve:

$$P = 2 + 2Q_S$$
$$P = 2 + 12$$
$$P = 14$$

We show all this diagrammatically in Figure 7.3.

The initial equilibrium price is given by the intersection of the demand and supply functions at $P = 16$ and $Q = 4$. As a result of a shift in the supply curve, the new equilibrium price is 14 and the equilibrium quantity now 6. The shift in the supply curve increases consumer surplus. The new consumer surplus is shown by the triangle ADE and the increase in consumer surplus is the area ECBD.

We calculated the original consumer surplus shown the by triangle ABC in Figure 7.3 as €8. As a result of the shift in the supply curve, the new equilibrium is shown by point D at a price of €14 and quantity of 6. The consumer surplus is now shown by the triangle ADE. Using the formula for a triangle:

$$A = \frac{6 \times 6}{2} = 18$$

Consumer surplus per period is €18. The effect of the shift in the supply curve is to lower equilibrium price. The lower price attracts new consumers into the market who previously would not have been prepared to pay above €14.

FIGURE 7.3

A Change in Consumer Surplus Resulting from a Change in Supply

The initial equilibrium price is given by the intersection of the demand and supply functions at P = 16 and Q = 4. As a result of a shift in the supply curve, the new equilibrium price is 14 and the equilibrium quantity now 6. The shift in the supply curve increases consumer surplus. The new consumer surplus is shown by the triangle ADE and the increase in consumer surplus is the area ECBD.

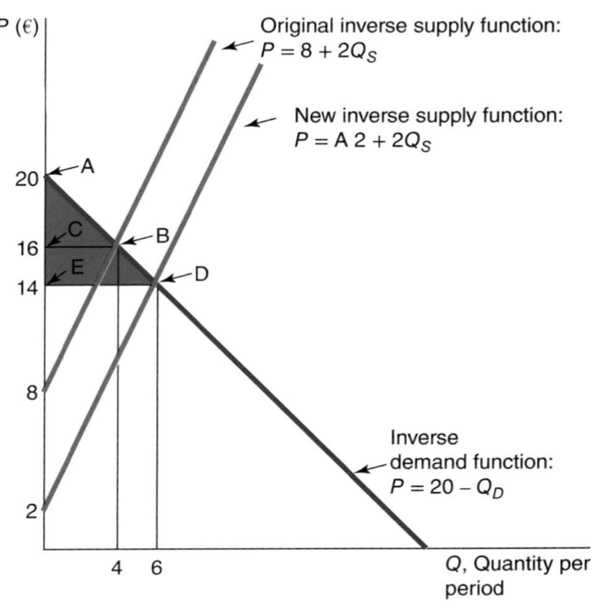

The total consumer surplus at the new price is shown by the triangle ADE in Figure 7.3 and the difference in consumer surplus by the area ECBD. The consumer surplus of existing consumers increases and consequently the total consumer surplus increases.

Note: the area ECBD is a trapezium and its area can be calculated by the formula:

$$A = \frac{a + b}{2}h$$

Where A = area, a and b are the two horizontal sides and h is the height.

The change in consumer surplus is given by the area of this trapezium which in this example is:

$$A = \left(\frac{(4 + 6)}{2}\right)2$$
$$= 10$$

The shift in supply changes producer surplus also. Recall that producer surplus is the amount a seller is paid for a good over and above the (marginal) cost of production. Figure 7.4 shows the original equilibrium at a price of €16 with the area of producer surplus shown by the triangle ABC, which we calculated as €16. As a result of the shift in the supply curve, the new equilibrium price is €14 and the equilibrium quantity, 6. The new area of producer surplus is given by the triangle DEF.

Calculating this area gives:

$$A = \frac{6 \times 14}{2} = 42$$

The total value of producer surplus increases from €16 per period to €42 per period.

The initial equilibrium price is given by the intersection of the demand and supply functions at $P = 16$ and $Q = 4$. The producer surplus is shown by the triangle GBC. As a result of a shift in the supply curve, the new equilibrium price is 14 and the equilibrium quantity now 6. The shift in the supply curve increases producer surplus. The new producer surplus is shown by the triangle DEF.

FIGURE 7.4

A Change in Producer Surplus Resulting from a Change in Supply

The initial equilibrium price is given by the intersection of the demand and supply functions at P = 16 and Q = 4. The producer surplus is shown by the triangle GBC. As a result of a shift in the supply curve, the new equilibrium price is 14 and the equilibrium quantity now 6. The shift in the supply curve increases producer surplus. The new producer surplus is shown by the triangle DEF.

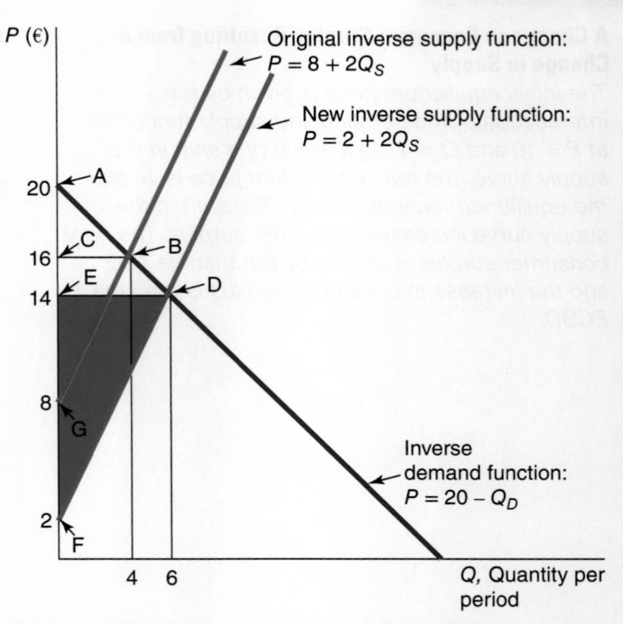

FINDING CONSUMER AND PRODUCER SURPLUS BY INTEGRATION

We have been able to make the calculations so far on the basis that the demand and supply functions were both linear functions. If the demand and supply functions are curvilinear, we need to calculate theses surpluses by an alternative method. We can use integration, a technique we introduced in Chapter 2. You may wish to re-read the section on integration there, if you are unsure of this technique. In the first instance, we are going to retain our linear curves in order to outline the concept of integration and its use.

Consider the diagram we have redrawn as Figure 7.5. We have labelled three areas: *A*, *B* and *C*. To find consumer surplus, we are interested in the market quantity from 0 to 4 and need to calculate area *A*. By integration we find the total area under the demand curve from 0 to 4. That is, we find area $A + B + C$. Once we have this, we can subtract area $B + C$. Area $B + C$ is the expenditure on the good given by $P_e \times Q_e$. (16×4 in this example). This will leave us with consumer surplus, area *A*.

Since this is the first time we have met integration since Chapter 2, we will go through the procedure step-by-step with this first example.

The integral of a function $f(x)$ with respect to some variable, *x*, is written as:

$$\int f(x)dx$$

Here the variable is the output quantity, *Q*, and we are interested in the range of output from zero to 4 units.

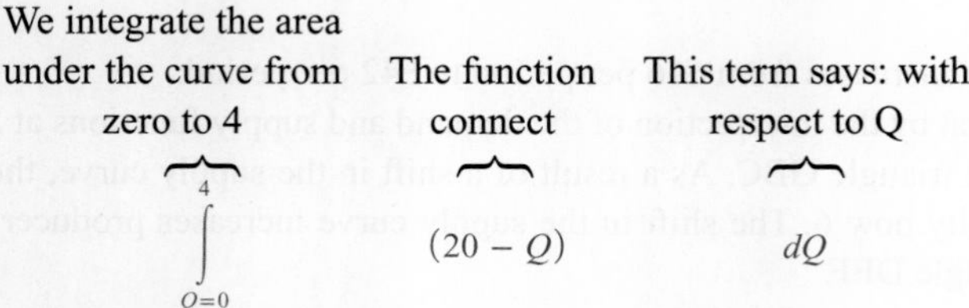

FIGURE 7.5

Finding consumer surplus and producer surplus by integration

To find consumer surplus by integration, we find the total area under the demand curve from 0 to 4. This is area A + B + C. This equals 72. Now we subtract area B + C which represents the expenditure on the good. This area is 16 x 4 = 64. Then consumer surplus = 72 – 64 = 8. To find producer surplus we need to find the area shown as area C. We can use integration to find area C. This is found to be 48. Now we subtract area C from the area of revenue, area B + C. Since this area = 64, the producer surplus is 64 – 48 = 16.

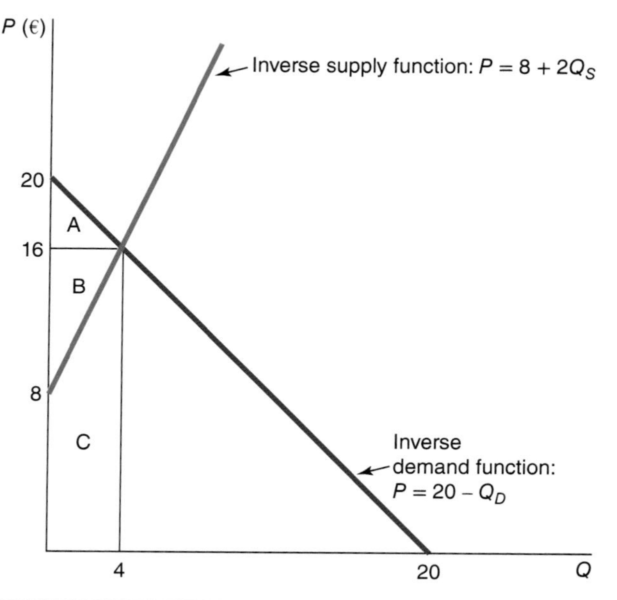

Now we integrate each term in turn.

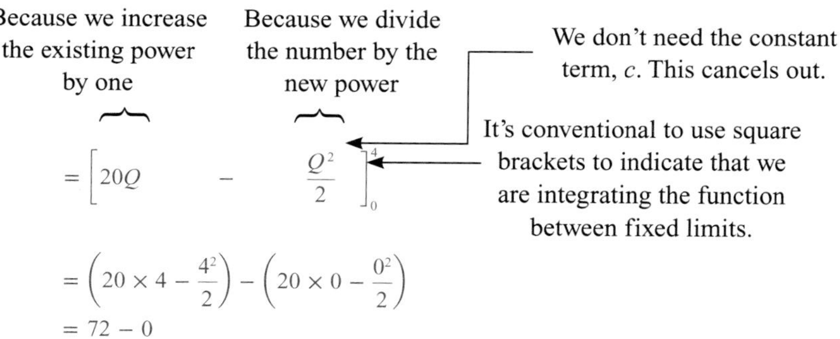

Because we increase the existing power by one
Because we divide the number by the new power
We don't need the constant term, c. This cancels out.
It's conventional to use square brackets to indicate that we are integrating the function between fixed limits.

$$= \left[20Q - \frac{Q^2}{2}\right]_0^4$$

$$= \left(20 \times 4 - \frac{4^2}{2}\right) - \left(20 \times 0 - \frac{0^2}{2}\right)$$

$$= 72 - 0$$

So area $A + B + C$ is 72.

$$\text{Area } B + C = P_e \times Q_e = 16 \times 4 = 64$$

Consumer surplus, Area $A = 72 - 64 = 8$.

This, of course, is the same as we found earlier by measuring the area of the triangle.

We can now find the producer surplus. First we are going to use integration to calculate the area under the supply curve given by C in Figure 7.5. When we have found this area we can subtract the total area of revenue (areas B and C given by $P_e \times Q_e$) to find the producer surplus, area B, in Figure 7.5.

Our inverse supply function is given as $P = 8 + 2Q_S$.

$$\int_0^4 (8 + 2Q)dQ$$

$$= 8Q + Q^2$$

$$= [8Q + Q^2]_0^4$$

$$= (8 \times 4 + 4^2) - (8 \times 0 + 0^2)$$

$$= 48 - 0$$

The area C, the area under the supply curve from 0 to 4, in Figure 7.5 is 48. To find producer surplus, area B we subtract area C from the total revenue (area $B + C$):

$$\begin{aligned} \text{Area } B + C &= P_e \times Q_e \\ &= 16 \times 4 \\ &= 64 \\ 64 - 48 &= 16 \end{aligned}$$

Area B, the producer surplus, is 16. This confirms what we found when we calculated the area of the triangle earlier. Integration is the inverse of differentiation, so you can check the result by differentiating again.

Integration with Non-linear Curves

Having outlined the basic concept and use of integration, we will now look at using the technique with non-linear curves. Integration is the only technique possible when using non-linear curves.

We will now find consumer surplus for a non-linear inverse demand curve given as:

$$P = 10 - \sqrt{Q_x^d}$$

Figure 7.6 sketches the curve for some values of P and Q.

To illustrate how to find consumer surplus, we need to choose a price and quantity on the curve. We will find consumer surplus when $Q = 16$. We can now find P by substitution:

$$\begin{aligned} P &= 10 - \sqrt{Q_x^d} \\ P &= 10 - \sqrt{16} \\ P &= 6 \end{aligned}$$

We have plotted these points on our demand curve in Figure 7.6. We now need to find Area A.

By integration we can find Areas A and B and then subtract Area B.

$$Area\ A = \int_0^{16} (10 - \sqrt{Q_x^d})\, dQ_x^d - P_e \times Q_e$$

Where P_e and Q_e are the equilibrium price and quantity respectively.

$$Area\ A = \left[10Q_x^d - \frac{2}{3} Q_x^{d^{\frac{3}{2}}} \right]_0^{16} - (6 \times 16)$$

FIGURE 7.6

Integration With a Non-Linear Demand Function

Consumer surplus with non linear functions can only be found by integration. If we have an inverse demand function given my $P = 10 - \sqrt{Q_x^d}$, and $Q = 16$, then $P = 6$. Consumer surplus is area A. By integration we find this area to be 21.33.

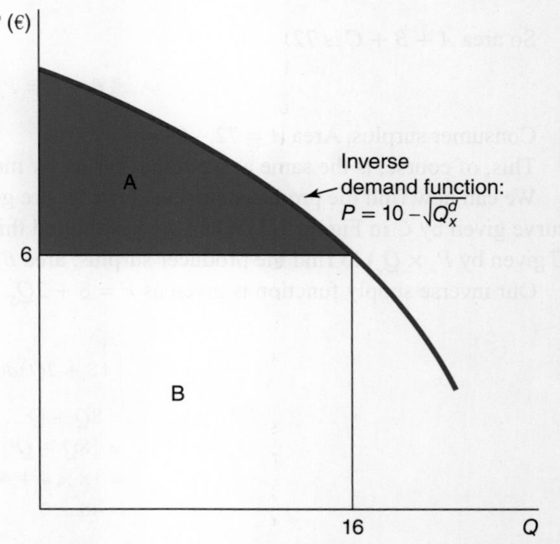

The second term in the square bracket may require explanation.

A standard rule for integration is that x^n gives $\frac{x^{n+1}}{n+1}$

The square root of Q can be expressed as $Q^{\frac{1}{2}}$ so integrating $Q^{\frac{1}{2}}$ gives $\frac{Q^{\frac{3}{2}}}{3/2}$

$$= \frac{2Q_x^{d\frac{3}{2}}}{3}$$

Substituting $Q = 16$ into our expression gives

$$\left(10 \times 16 - \frac{2}{3}16^{\frac{3}{2}}\right) - 96 = (160 - 42.67) - 96 = 117.33 - 96$$
$$= 21.33$$

The consumer surplus is 21.33.[1]

Understanding 'Value'

Having explored the terms consumer and producer surplus we can now comment briefly on the meaning that we give to the term 'value'. We distinguish 'Value in use' and 'Value in exchange'. Value in exchange is the total expenditure on the product by consumers, or alternately expressed, the total received by producers. For example, in terms of Figure 7.6 it would be area B. In contrast value in use is the total benefit to consumers of the product. Thus it includes not only what they spend but also their consumer surplus. In terms of figure 7.6 it is area $A + B$.

So what would happen to value if price were to rise? It would clearly reduce value in use. Whether it would reduce value in exchange depends on the price elasticity of demand. If demand is price inelastic a price rise increases value in exchange. If demand is price elastic value in exchange is reduced.

Summary

You have now explored some ideas about the efficiency of markets and analyzed techniques of measuring consumer and producer surplus. This has enabled you to gain an insight into the meaning of 'value'.

[1] NB to find the expression $16^{\frac{3}{2}}$ use a calculator. Find 16^3 then take the square root. The result this gives is 64.

PROBLEMS AND APPLICATIONS

1 Assume all the conditions for a perfectly competitive market are met. The inverse of the market demand function is $P_D = 1000 - 0.25Q_D$ and for the market supply the inverse is $P_S = 100 + 0.2Q_S$.
   a. Calculate the linear supply and demand functions.
   b. Read off the intersections on the horizontal and vertical axis for the demand and the supply function from your solution to the question above.
   c. Calculate the producer surplus with a price of €400 per unit.
   d. Calculate the consumer surplus with a price of €750 per unit.
   e. By how much does the consumer surplus change if the price falls from €750 per unit to €600 per unit?
   f. Find the equilibrium in an undisturbed market either graphically or through calculation.
   g. Calculate total welfare from the two components consumer surplus and producer surplus.

2 In a perfectly competitive market the demand function is $P_D(Q) = 1200 - 1.25Q$, whereas the supply function is $P_S(Q) = 200 + 0.75Q$.
   a. Calculate the price elasticity of demand at a price of $P_D = 1000$. (You can use the point elasticity or if you feel more comfortable with the midpoint-method, assume a price increase from $P^0{}_D = 1000$ to $P^1{}_D = 1025$).
   b. Please draw the linear supply function into the graph in Figure 7.7.
   c. Determine the market equilibrium, either by calculation or in the graph. Note the equilibrium price and quantity.

d. In the market equilibrium, calculate the social surplus from its components, the producer and the consumer surplus. Explain and show the respective areas in your graph.

e. An *ad valorem* (or specific) tax of 200 per unit of output is levied to be paid by the producers. Explain the three steps of your comparative static analysis.

FIGURE 7.7

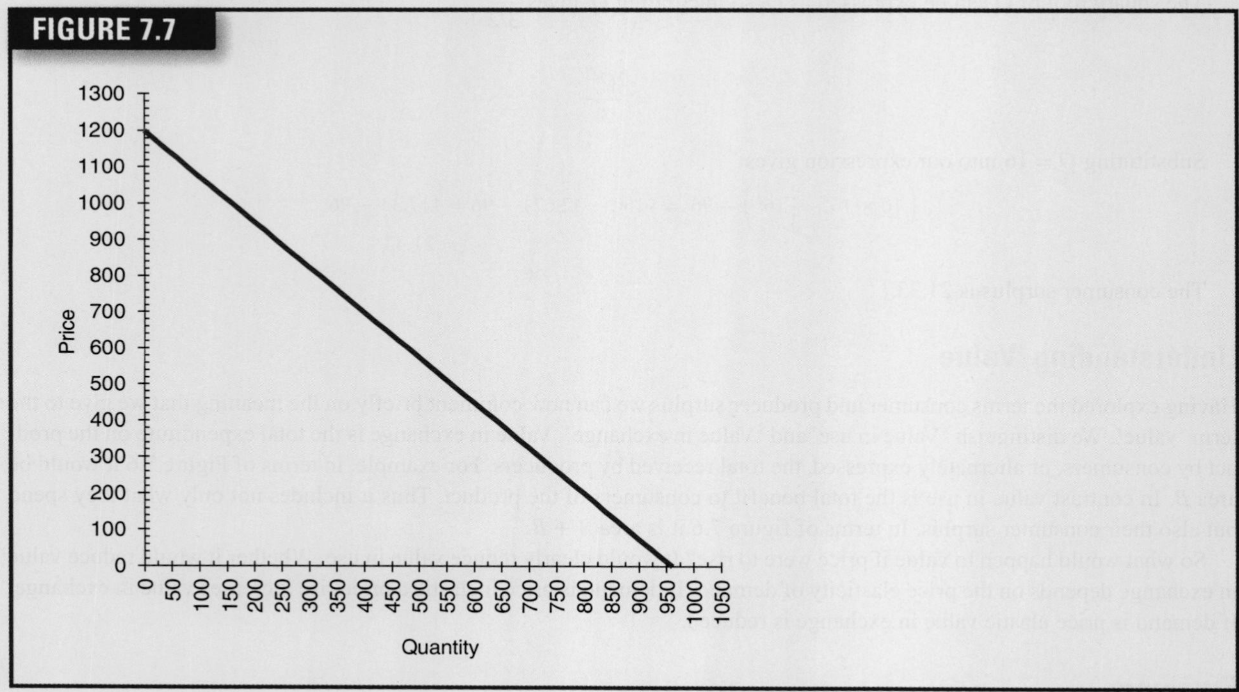

3 In the last chapter you have worked with cost functions and the maximization of profit to find out that the function of marginal cost is the supply function of an individual supplier for all prices above the minimum of average total cost. Adding horizontally all the marginal cost functions for the firms in the market results in the market supply function; this essentially tells us how much it costs to provide one more marginal unit of output to the market, if all firms join in the effort to produce this marginal unit. The inverse of the market supply function is: $P = \frac{3}{10\,000}Q^2 + \frac{8}{100}Q + 20$ for all prices higher than €20 per unit.

a. Find the producer surplus at a price of €800 using integration.

b. Assume there are 100 identical firms in the market. What is the individual supply function of the producer and what does the function of total cost for each of these producers look like?

8 SUPPLY, DEMAND AND GOVERNMENT POLICIES

In this chapter we look at the algebra of market disequilibrium, develop the analysis of a per unit tax and its effect on the supply curve and use some basic mathematics to examine the tax incidence in relation to elasticity of demand and supply. This will enable us to see the effects of placing taxes upon consumers rather than producers. Finally we look at the supply curve in the presence of *ad valorem* taxes.

PRICE CONTROLS, MARKET DISEQUILIBRIUM AND EXCESS DEMAND

The result of effective price controls by government is the disturbance of market equilibrium. We consider two examples. In the first the government sets a price ceiling below the market equilibrium level and creates excess demand. In the second example a price floor is set which the government maintains by purchasing excess supply.

An Effective Price Ceiling

First, assume that the government sets a price ceiling below the market equilibrium. If we know the demand and supply functions, we can calculate the extent of excess demand. Given the following general demand and supply functions:

$$P_D = a - bQ$$

and:

$$P_S = c + dQ$$

Excess demand is found by subtracting one from the other:

$$(a - bQ) - (c + dQ)$$

In the specific example which follows, given the supply and demand functions:

$$P_D = 20 - Q$$
$$P_S = 8 + 2Q$$

and assuming no government intervention, equilibrium will be:

$$20 - Q = 8 + 2Q$$
$$3Q = 12$$
$$Q = 4 \text{ and } P = 16$$

If the government price ceiling is below €16, we have excess demand. Suppose the price ceiling is set at €12, the quantity supplied will be:

$$P_S = 8 + 2Q_S$$
$$12 = 8 + 2Q_S$$
$$2Q_S = 4$$
$$Q_S = 2$$

Quantity demanded will be:

$$P_D = 20 - Q_D$$
$$12 = 20 - Q_D$$
$$Q_D = 8$$

Excess demand, therefore = 8 – 2 = 6.
We show this diagrammatically in Figure 8.1.

FIGURE 8.1

An Effective Price Ceiling

The initial equilibrium price is given by the intersection of the demand and supply functions at P = 16 and Q = 4. If the government imposes an effective price ceiling of €12, this reduces Q_S to 2 and increases Q_D to 8, creating an excess demand of 6.

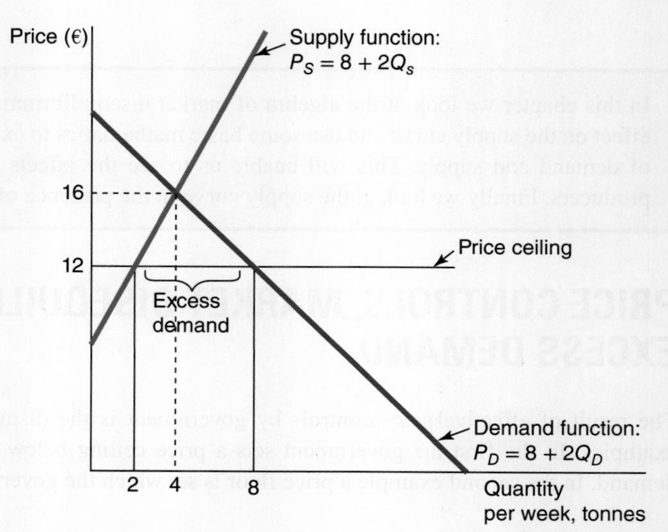

A Price Floor

If the government sets a price floor above equilibrium one way to maintain this price is for the government to purchase the excess supply. Suppose the price floor is set at €18. We first establish the excess supply. Quantity supplied at the price floor will be:

$$P_S = 8 + 2Q_S$$
$$18 = 8 + 2Q_S$$
$$2Q_S = 10$$
$$Q_S = 5$$

Quantity demanded at the price floor will be:

$$P_D = 20 - Q_D$$
$$18 = 20 - Q_D$$
$$Q_D = 2$$

Excess supply at the price floor, therefore, = 5 – 2 = 3.
The direct expenditure cost to the government of maintaining the price floor is:

$$P \times Q$$
$$18 \times 3 = €54 \textit{ per period.}$$

We show this diagrammatically in Figure 8.2.

FIGURE 8.2

A Price Floor

The initial equilibrium price is given by the intersection of the demand and supply functions at P = 16 and Q = 4. If the government imposes an effective price ceiling of €18, then Q_S increases to 5. Q_D falls to 2, creating an excess supply of 3. The government can maintain this price floor by purchasing the excess supply. The direct expenditure cost is therefore 3 × 18 = €54 per period.

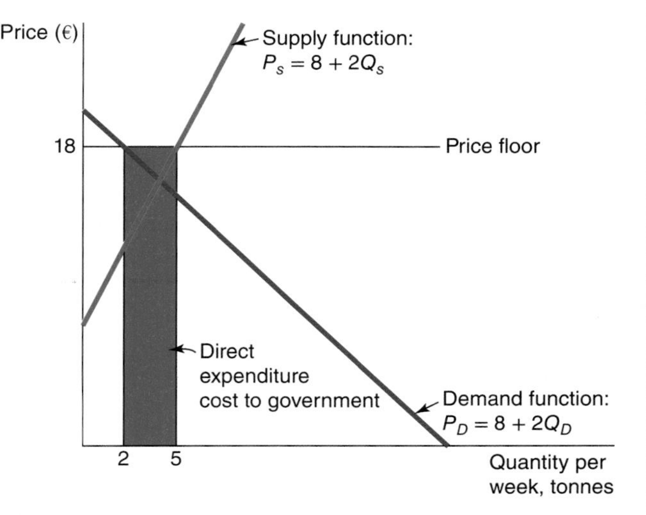

PER UNIT TAX AND SHIFTS IN THE SUPPLY CURVE

In Chapter 3, we outlined the algebra of a shift in the demand curve. Now we show an example of a shift in the supply curve. In this instance the circumstance that leads to a supply curve shift is the imposition of a tax. We review this briefly before extending the analysis later in this chapter to consider other indirect taxes, in particular an *ad valorem* tax (that is, a tax based on the value of the good). First consider the per unit tax.

A per unit tax is a specific tax on each unit of output sold set at a level that is independent of the price being charged in the market. Its imposition shifts the supply curve. Given a supply function:

$$P_S = c + dQ$$

With the addition of the tax, the supply function is now:

$$P_S = c + dQ + t$$

Where t is the tax per unit levied.

We can see an example of its effects on the market by using the supply and demand equations we used earlier and assuming a tax of €3 per unit, so $t = 3$.

Originally, with no tax and with no price ceiling or floor:

$$P_S = 8 + 2Q_S$$
$$P_D = 20 - Q_D$$

Market equilibrium was:

$$Q = 4 \text{ and } P = 16$$

The tax has altered the supply function but not the demand function so:

$$P_S = 8 + 2Q_S + 3$$
$$P_D = 20 - Q_D$$

The new equilibrium is:

$$20 - Q_D = 8 + 2Q_S + 3$$
$$20 - Q = 11 + 2Q$$
$$3Q = 9$$
$$Q = 3$$

The effect of the tax is to reduce equilibrium output from 4 to 3. We can now feed the new equilibrium output Q = 3 into one of the equations to establish the new market price. Let's take the demand function.

$$P_D = 20 - Q_D$$
$$= 20 - 3$$
$$= 17$$

The tax created a new supply curve but left the demand curve unaffected. The equilibrium price is higher and the equilibrium quantity is lower. However the new equilibrium price has not risen by the full extent of the tax. This can be seen diagrammatically in Figure 8.3.

In the next section we explore why the price rise is generally less than the size of the tax imposed.

FIGURE 8.3

Imposition of a Per Unit Tax on Suppliers

As a result of a tax of €3 the supply curve shifts upwards. The new equilibrium price is 17 and the equilibrium quantity is now 3. The shift in the supply curve increases the price but by less than the tax.

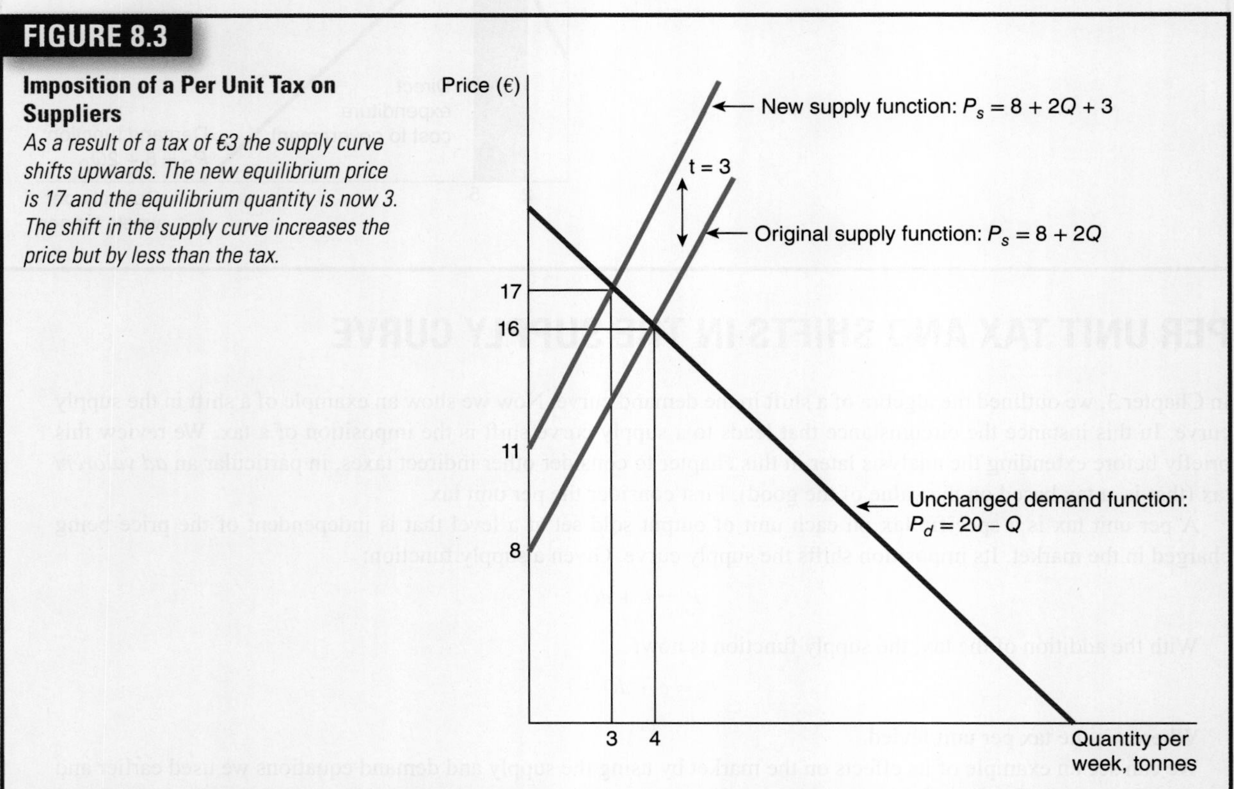

Tax Incidence and Elasticity of Demand and Supply

We have considered the effect of a tax on producers. The producers will attempt to pass the tax onto consumers in the form of a higher price such that the incidence of the tax is borne partly by consumers and partly by producers. We will now show how this can be calculated when the demand and supply elasticities are known. The formulae we use will tell us that the percentage of the tax borne by each of the two groups are as follows:

Percentage of tax borne by consumers:

$$\frac{E_S}{(E_D + E_S)} \times 100$$

Where: E_D is the elasticity of demand

E_S is the elasticity of supply

Percentage of tax borne by producers:

$$\frac{E_D}{(E_D + E_S)} \times 100$$

We will use these formulae to demonstrate the effect of demand and supply elasticities on the incidence of tax.

Assume two different markets, A and B, and that the elasticity of demand in market A is $\frac{1}{2}$ and in market B is 2. The elasticity of supply is the same in each market at 1. Note we are using absolute values for demand elasticity. We can ignore the minus sign for the purpose of these calculations.

The percentage of tax borne by consumers in Market A is:

$$\frac{1}{\frac{1}{2}+1} \times 100$$
$$= \frac{1}{1.5} \times 100$$
$$= 66.66$$

The percentage of tax borne by producers in Market A is:

$$\frac{\frac{1}{2}}{\frac{1}{2}+1} \times 100$$
$$= \frac{0.5}{1.5} \times 100$$
$$= 33.33$$

In Market A, therefore, 66 per cent, that is two-thirds of the tax is borne by consumers and 33 per cent, that is one-third by producers.

In market B, the percentage of tax borne by consumers is:

$$\frac{1}{2+1} \times 100 = 33.33$$

The percentage of tax borne by producers is:

$$\frac{2}{2+1} \times 100 = 66.66$$

In Market B, therefore, 33 per cent, that is one-third of the tax is borne by consumers and 66 per cent, that is two-thirds, by producers.

This result conforms to what we would have expected. For any given supply elasticity, the proportion of a tax borne by the consumer is less when demand is more price elastic. It also makes intuitive sense. When demand is price elastic consumers are more willing to accept price rises.

Now let us see what happens if the elasticity of demand in two markets, M and N, is the same but the elasticity of supply is different in each market.

Suppose now in markets M and N, demand elasticity = 1. In Market M supply elasticity = 1 and in market N, supply elasticity is 4.

In Market M, the percentage of tax borne by consumers is:

$$\frac{1}{1+1} \times 100 = 50$$

and the percentage of tax borne by producers is:

$$\frac{1}{1+1} \times 100 = 50$$

In Market M, 50 per cent, or one half, of the tax is borne by consumers and 50 per cent, by producers.

In Market N, the percentage of tax borne by consumers is:

$$\frac{4}{1+4} \times 100 = 80$$

And the percentage of tax borne by producers will be:

$$\frac{1}{1+4} \times 100 = 20$$

This analysis tells us that with a given constant demand elasticity, the more elastic the supply, the more the burden of the tax falls on the consumer. This also makes intuitive sense. When supply is elastic suppliers are less able and willing to absorb the increased costs.

SHOULD CONSUMERS OR PRODUCERS BE TAXED?

The incidence of the tax does not depend on the point at which the revenue is collected. One sometimes hears comments to the effect that it is producers who should pay the tax, not the consumer. In fact wherever the tax is placed initially it makes no difference as to who finally bears the burden of the tax. If the tax is placed on the suppliers it is in their interest to pass as much as possible of it onto the consumer. The extent that they are able to do this depends on consumer willingness to pay it. That is, it depends on how price elastic consumer demand is. In most cases producers will be obliged to bear part of the tax themselves. If, on the other hand, the tax is placed on the consumer, consumer resistance to the tax and the resulting fall in quantity demanded means that it pays suppliers to accept some of the burden. The final outcome is the same in either case; it makes no difference where the tax is initially placed. The incidence in the end is determined by the price elasticity of demand and price elasticity of supply. We can show this algebraically. Let's consider the effect of a government attempt to put the tax onto the consumer instead of the supplier.

We can think of this as a creating a reduction in consumer willingness to pay. At each price that the supplier receives, the consumer willingness to purchase is reduced because the consumer also has to pay the tax in addition to what is paid to the supplier. Diagrammatically we show the price as the price to the supplier, not the final market price. Because the consumer is being asked to pay the tax we shift the demand curve inwards as shown in Figure 8.4. Less is demanded at every price given that the consumer has to pay the tax on top of what is being paid to the producer.

$P_D = 20 - Q_D$ becomes:

$$P_D = 20 - Q_D - t$$
$$P_D = 20 - Q_D - 3$$
$$P_D = 17 - Q_D$$

The supply function is unchanged:

$$P_S = 8 + 2Q_S$$

We find equilibrium at:

$$8 + 2Q_S = 17 - Q_D$$
$$3Q = 9$$

The equilibrium outcome is Q = 3 and P = 17. (This is the final price that the consumer has to pay to include the tax imposed by the government.)

We have an identical result in terms of market equilibrium price and quantity.

This result is easier to see mathematically than diagrammatically. We show the outcome in Figure 8.4, this time showing the effect of the tax as creating a new demand function but leaving the supply curve unaffected. The diagram shows the new level of output being the same as when we shifted the supply function. However, the tax appears to have lowered the market price!

The reason is that the new equilibrium price of 14 is the price net of the tax. When we add the tax of 3 we get a price of €17, which was the outcome in Figure 8.3 where we showed the tax as an addition to suppliers' costs.

The Supply Curve and *Ad valorem* Taxes

So far we have considered only a per unit tax. Now we consider another kind, the *ad valorem* tax, which is the Latin for 'according to value'. The per unit or specific tax we have been considering in our analysis was a fixed amount. The *ad valorem* tax is a fixed proportion or percentage of the supply price and therefore varies in amount according to price. We denoted the per unit tax by t. We will denote the *ad valorem* tax rate by t' and refer to it as a percentage.

To be clear on the difference let's take an example.

If t' = 20% and the supply price is €10 the seller pays to the government:

$$t' \times P_S = 0.2 \times 10 = €2.$$

FIGURE 8.4

Imposition of a Per Unit Tax on Consumers

A tax can be seen as causing a reduction in consumer willingness to pay. In this case the €3 tax shifts the demand curve left. The equilibrium output is now 3 units as it was when we showed the tax as a shift in the supply curve. The equilibrium price is now seen to be 14 but this is the price net of the tax. The price including the tax is 14 + 3 = 17.

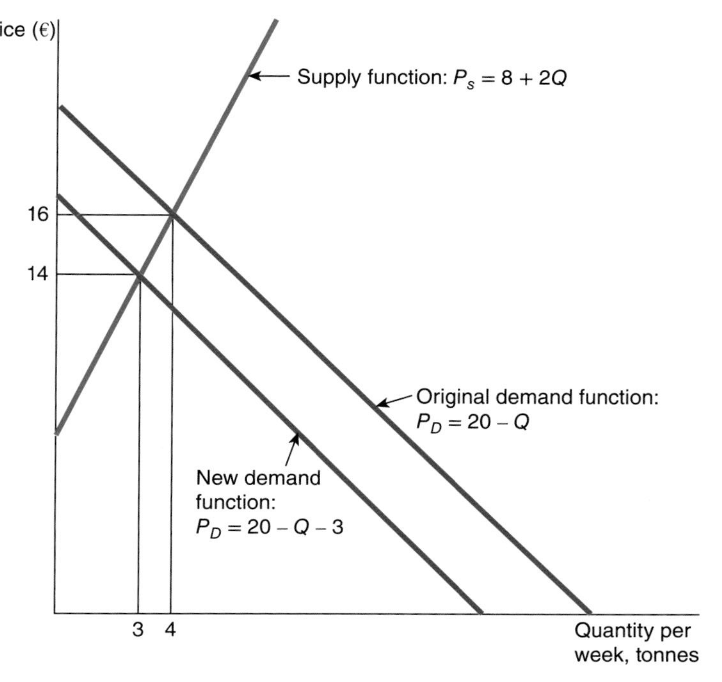

If t′ = 20% and the supply price is €50 the seller pays to the government:

$$t' \times P_S = 0.2 \times 50 = €10.$$

In our example the tax rate has remained constant (at 20%) but the amount of tax the supplier pays has not.

It's important to consider an *ad valorem* tax because many taxes of this kind are imposed by governments. Perhaps the best known example is Value Added Tax (VAT).

Now let's see how this kind of tax affects the supply function. Without the tax:

$$P_S = c + dQ$$

With a tax at a rate of t' we need to add it to the equation as a fixed proportion of the supply price:

$$P_S = c + dQ + t'(c + dQ)$$

Rearranging this by taking the common factor $c + dQ$ in front of the brackets gives us:

$$P_S = (c + dQ)(1 + t')$$

Illustrating the effect on a market we use the supply and demand functions we used earlier. Originally the supply function was:

$$P_S = 8 + 2Q_S$$

Now with the *ad valorem* tax it becomes:

$$P_S = (8 + 2Q_S)(1 + t')$$

Assuming a tax rate of $t' = 50\%$ we have:

$$P_S = (8 + 2Q_S)(1 + 0.5)$$
$$P_S = (8 + 2Q_S)(1.5)$$
$$= 12 + 3Q_S$$

The original equilibrium without any tax or any other government intervention had Q = 4 and P = 16. We can now find the new equilibrium, using the new supply function, thus:

$$12 + 3Q = 20 - Q$$
$$4Q = 8$$
$$Q = 2$$

We can find the price by substituting Q = 2 into either of the equations. For example:

$$P_D = 20 - Q_D$$
$$= 20 - 2$$
$$P_D = 18$$

How much of this price is tax? The government collects a tax of 50% (or 0.5) of the supply price of €18. This is collected on all units exchanged, namely 2.

$$\textit{Government revenue} = (0.5 \times 18) \times 2$$
$$= €18 \textit{ per period}$$

So given the supply and demand functions the 50 per cent tax creates a new equilibrium price of €18 and a new equilibrium quantity of 2 units per period. At this new equilibrium the government collects a tax of €18 per period.

We can summarize diagrammatically the effects of these taxes on willingness to supply. We do this in Figure 8.5.

The per unit tax increases suppliers' costs and shifts the supply curve parallel upwards by a constant amount as shown in panel (a) of Figure 8.5. The *ad valorem* tax also increases suppliers' costs and therefore also shifts the supply curve upwards but the shift is not parallel. This is shown in panel (b) of Figure 8.5. The higher the price the greater the absolute value of the tax. Therefore the higher the price the greater the reduction in willingness to supply will be.

FIGURE 8.5

The Effect of Government Taxation

A per unit tax shifts the supply curve parallel upwards. This is illustrated in panel (a). An ad valorem tax also shifts the supply curve upwards. However the size of the tax is related to the value of the product. The higher the price the greater the absolute value of the tax. Therefore the higher the price the greater the reduction in willingness to supply will be. Thus the shift in the supply curve is not parallel for an ad valorem tax.

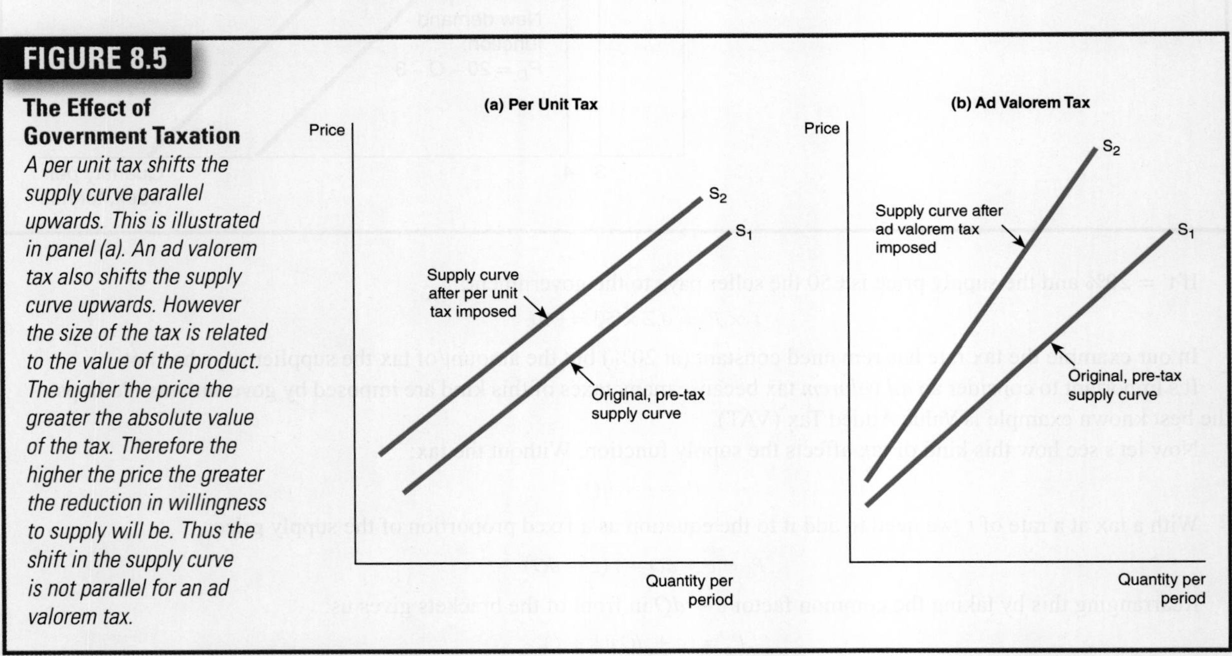

PROBLEMS AND APPLICATIONS

1 Consider again the perfectly competitive market from Chapter 7 Problem 1 with the inverse demand function $P_D = 1000 - 0.25Q_D$ and the inverse supply $P_S = 100 + 0.2Q_S$.

a. Recall the market equilibrium price and quantity as well as the total surplus from problem 1 in chapter 7.
b. Rearrange terms in both functions to show the demand and the supply function.
c. How large is the total (social) surplus in this market?
d. Will a price ceiling at €700/unit be effective?
e. If a price ceiling of €300/unit is imposed, how large are the quantity demanded and the quantity supplied and the resultant excess demand or supply?
f. Imagine the government sets a price floor at €700/unit. How much will consumers purchase and how much would producers like to supply to the market? Is there excess demand or supply?

g. Producers can only sell the quantity consumers are willing to purchase. Calculate the social surplus with the price floor at €700/unit in place.

h. Assume the government purchases any excess demand on the market that is caused by the policy intervention. How much would the government need to spend at a price ceiling of €700/unit?

2 The market for rental apartments is a competitive market with many landlords and many tenants. The long-term inverse supply function is $P_S = 2 + 0.0032X_S$ with P_S the rent in € per month and square meter and X_S is the floor space in thousands of square meters. The market demand function is $P_D = 20 - 0.004X_D$. Both functions are shown in the Figure 8.6.

a. Please label the functions appropriately and confirm the equilibrium price and the equilibrium quantity through a calculation.

b. Calculate the elasticity of supply around the equilibrium. Would you consider that elasticity value appropriate for the supply of rental apartments? (Without an actual empirical estimate you cannot really tell; so you should argue your case.)

c. Calculate the consumer surplus in the market equilibrium.

d. Spooked by recent steep increases in rents in larger cities, politicians want to place restrictions on further increases in rents. For simplicity sake, assume that this means rents cannot go higher than a certain level, a price ceiling is introduced. Show a price ceiling in the market and explain the market outcome under this policy.

e. Assume the government imposes a price ceiling of €8 per month and square meter. How much floor space are landlords willing to supply and how large is the demand at this price?

f. Discuss the welfare effects (in terms of consumer and producer surpluses) of a price ceiling of €8 per month per square meter. Compare the total surplus under the rent control policy with the situation before its introduction.

FIGURE 8.6

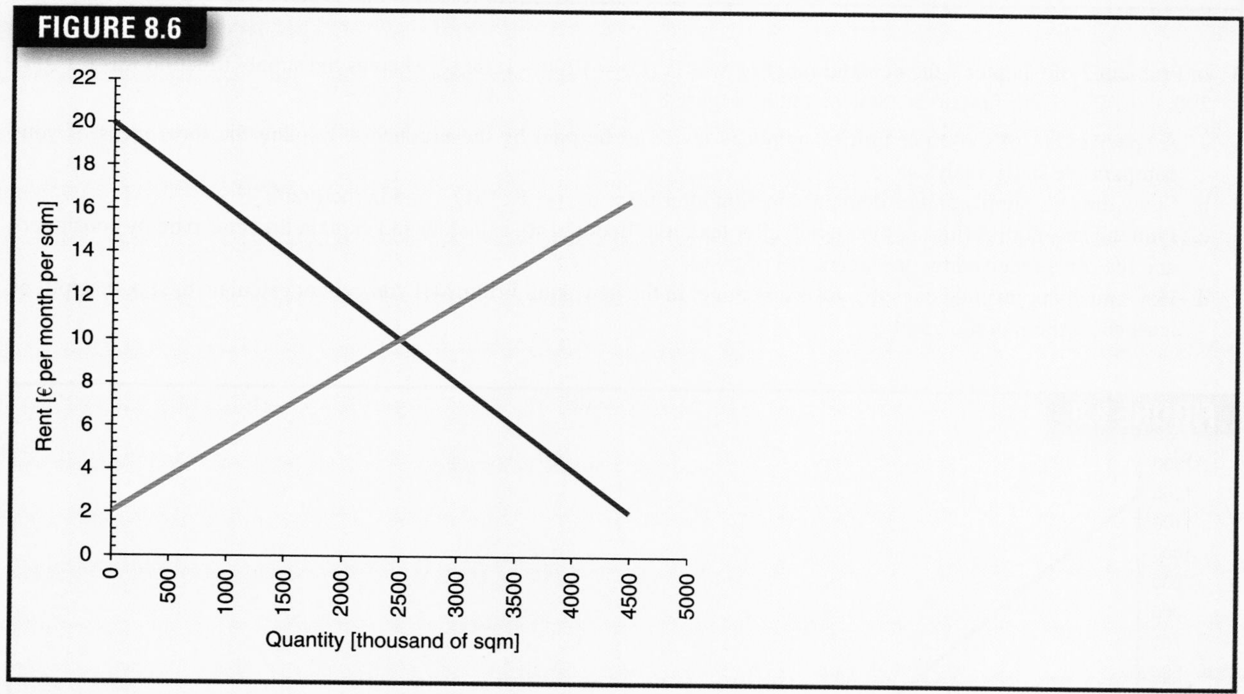

3 Total cost of a competitive firm in Chapter 6 Problem 5 was $TC(q) = 0.25q^3 + 5q^2 + 25q + 187.5$. A graph of marginal cost, average total cost, and average variable cost is reproduced as Figure 8.7:

a. Read off the profit maximizing quantity for the firm at the market price (P) of €200 per unit of output from the graph below.

b. The government is imposing a tax of €24.25 per output that each producer has to pay. How is this going to change the cost function and the function of marginal cost of the producer? Write out the functions as $TC^{Tax}(q)$ and $MC^{Tax}(q)$ respectively.

c. Sketch the marginal cost function including the tax and the average total cost function $ATC^{Tax}(q)$ into the graph.

d. If the market price were to stay at €200 per unit after the imposition of the tax, what would happen to the output quantity of an individual producer?
e. Is it plausible that the market price for consumers or producers remains the same as before taxation?

FIGURE 8.7

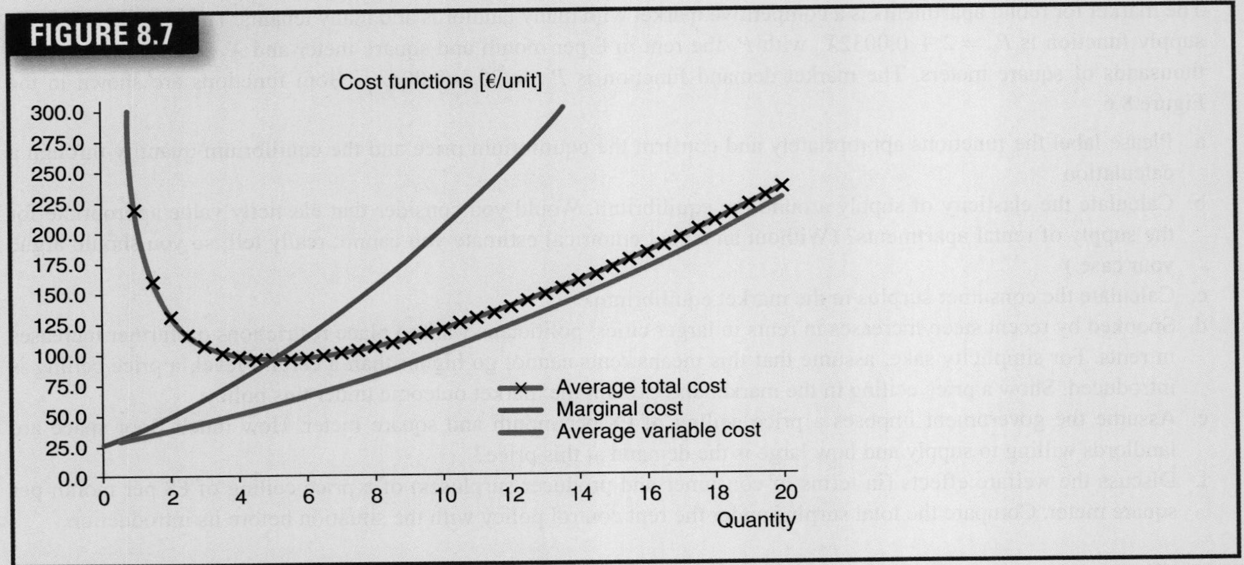

4 In Problem 2 of Chapter 7 the demand function was $P_D(Q) = 1200 - 1.25Q_D$, whereas the supply function was $P_S(Q) = 200 + 0.75Q_S$. Both functions are depicted in Figure 8.8.

a. A specific tax of €200 per unit of output is levied to be paid by the producers. Explain the three steps of your comparative static analysis.
b. Show the new supply and/or demand function after taxes as, i.e. $P_S^{Tax}(Q_S)$ and in the graph.
c. Find the new equilibrium in the market after taxation. In doing so, calculate and explain the price paid by consumers and the price received by producers, net of taxes.
d. How much tax revenue does the government get in the new equilibrium? (If you cannot calculate the tax receipts, at least show them in the graph.)

FIGURE 8.8

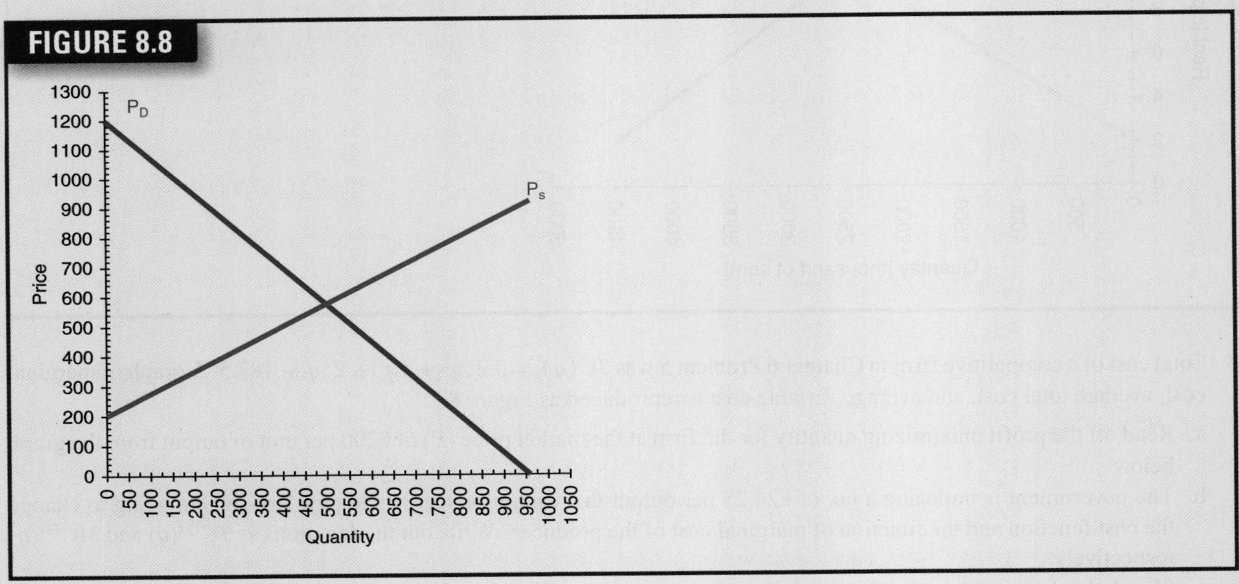

5 In a competitive market the demand function is $P_D(Q) = 1100 - 2Q_D$ and the inverse supply function $P_S(Q) = 102.5 + 0.5Q_S + 0.001(Q_S)^2$.

a. Calculate the price and quantity in the market equilibrium.
b. Use integral calculus to find the producer surplus at the market equilibrium.
c. Compute the total surplus in the market.
d. Impose a tax of €157.5 per unit paid by the producers and find the equilibrium quantity and the price after taxes for consumers and producers.
e. How much in taxes does the government receive?

6 Continue your analysis with the demand function $P_D(Q) = 1200 - 1.25Q_D$ and the inverse supply function $P_S(Q) = 200 + 0.75Q_S$. Now assume an *ad valorem* tax of 40 % is to be paid by producers in the market.

a. Calculate the new inverse supply function including the tax (recall that $P_S^{\text{Tax}} = P_S \times (1 + t'))$.
b. Show the supply function after taxes in the graph.
c. Find the new market equilibrium with the tax and note the price paid by consumers and the price net of taxes received by producers.
d. How much in taxes does the government receive?

PART 4 THE ECONOMICS OF THE PUBLIC SECTOR

9 THE TAX SYSTEM

In this chapter we extend our analysis of the effects of taxation on competitive markets. We will develop the link between elasticity and deadweight losses, extend the concept of elasticity and government revenue, and then show that the link between government revenue and elasticity extends to policy with regard to subsidies as well as to taxation.

INTRODUCTION: TWO IMPORTANT THINGS TO REMEMBER

In following this chapter you will need to remember two things, first about the nature of the demand curve and second, about the nature of the supply curve. We will begin the chapter with a short refresher about the nature of demand and supply curves, and elasticity.

First, recall what we have said about the demand curve. If it is a straight line downward sloping demand curve, the value of price elasticity varies along its length because the term $\frac{P}{Q}$ in the elasticity formula changes even for a straight line. As we move down a straight line demand curve, P decreases and Q increases, so $\frac{P}{Q}$ is changing. The demand curve is elastic at the top end, becomes less elastic as we move down along its length and inelastic at the lower end. Remember, it is *not* true that a flat curve, in itself, indicates elastic demand and a steep one indicates inelastic demand. What we can correctly say is that demand may be *relatively* elastic. For example, Figure 9.1 shows two downward sloping straight line demand curves. Both curves have elastic and inelastic sections, but demand is more elastic at point A on demand curve D_1 than it is at that point on D_2.

Let's illustrate. We have two demand functions on the same diagram in Figure 9.1. The shallower curve is a visual representation of an inverse demand function:

$$P = 20 - \frac{1}{3}Q_{D1}$$

The steeper curve is a visual representation of an inverse demand function:

$$P = 60 - 3Q_{D2}$$

FIGURE 9.1

Two Demand Functions with Different Elasticities

Each of the two demand curves has a constant slope. Elasticity of demand varies along each curve. The lower the price the more inelastic demand becomes. At any given price the steeper curve will have a more inelastic demand. For example, quantity demanded at a price of €15 is the same for either demand function, namely 15 units per period. However, the price elasticity of demand for the steeper demand curve at P = 15 is –3. The price elasticity of demand for the shallower demand curve at P = 15 is –1/3. At point A demand is relatively more elastic on demand curve D_1 than on D_2.

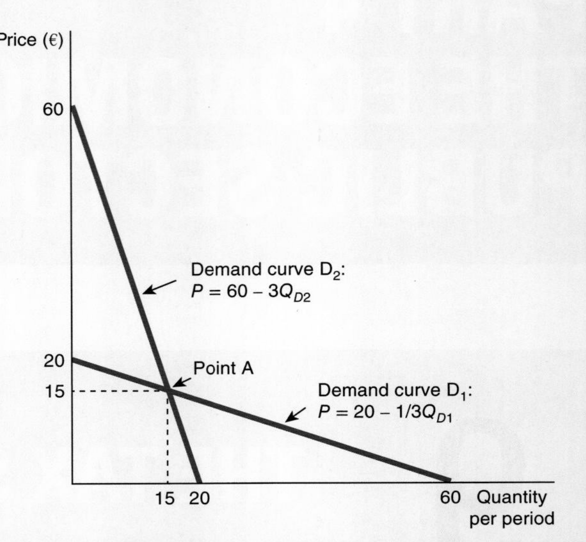

Quantity demanded at a price of €15 is the same for either demand function, namely 15 units per period. This is shown in Figure 9.1 as point A. We now calculate the point elasticity of demand at that price for each demand function. Begin with the shallower demand curve.

$P = 20 - \frac{1}{3}Q_{D1}$ is the inverse demand curve. To find the demand curve we use the following procedure:

$$P = 20 - \frac{1}{3}Q_{D1}$$
$$\frac{1}{3}Q_{D1} = 20 - P$$
$$Q_{D1} = 60 - 3P$$

If we are to find the price elasticity of demand (ped) at 15, we need to find Q.

$$Q_{D1} = 60 - 3P$$
$$Q_{D1} = 60 - 45$$
$$Q_D = 15$$

Now we can differentiate the expression:

$$Q_{D1} = 60 - 3P$$
$$\frac{dQ_{D1}}{dP} = -3$$
$$\text{ped} = \frac{dQ}{dP} \times \frac{P}{Q}$$
$$= -3 \times \frac{15}{15}$$
$$= -3$$

So the price elasticity of demand for this function at $P = 15$ is −3. Demand at this point on the curve is elastic. Now consider the steeper demand curve.

$$P = 60 - 3Q_{D2}$$

This is the inverse demand curve so we again need to find the demand curve.

$$P = 60 - 3Q_{D2}$$
$$3Q_{D2} = 60 - P$$
$$Q_{D2} = 20 - \frac{P}{3}$$

To find the ped at 15:

$$Q_{D2} = 20 - \frac{P}{3}$$
$$Q_{D2} = 20 - 5$$
$$Q_{D2} = 15$$

Now we can differentiate the expression:

$$Q_{D2} = 20 - \frac{P}{3}$$
$$\frac{dQ_{D2}}{dP} = -\frac{1}{3}$$
$$\text{ped} = \frac{dQ}{dP} \times \frac{P}{Q}$$
$$= -\frac{1}{3} \times \frac{15}{15}$$
$$= -\frac{1}{3}$$

The price elasticity of demand for this function at $P = 15$ is $-1/3$. Demand at this point on the steeper curve is inelastic.

At point A demand is relatively more elastic on demand curve D_1 than on D_2. At this point on demand curve D_1 demand is price elastic and at this point on D_2 it is price inelastic. Nevertheless, towards the bottom of D_1 demand becomes price inelastic and towards the top of D_2 demand is price elastic.

Now let's recall something important about supply elasticity that we explained in Chapter 4. Any straight line supply curve passing through the origin has an elasticity value equal to unity along its whole length. If a straight line supply curve cuts the vertical axis, supply is elastic along its whole length. If a straight line supply curve cuts the vertical axis, supply is inelastic along its whole length. Figure 9.2 shows three supply functions, S_1, S_2 and S_3.

FIGURE 9.2

Three Supply Functions with Different Elasticities

Any straight line supply curve passing through the origin has an elasticity value equal to unity along its whole length. If a straight line supply curve cuts the vertical axis, supply is elastic along its whole length. If a straight line supply curve cuts the vertical axis, supply is inelastic along its whole length.

The inverse supply function S_1 is of the form: $P = a + bQ_{S1}$. Since a is positive, supply is elastic. The inverse supply function S_2 is of the form: $P = cQ_{S2}$. Supply is unit elastic. The inverse supply function S_3 is of the form: $P = -d + eQ_{S3}$. Since d is negative, supply is inelastic.

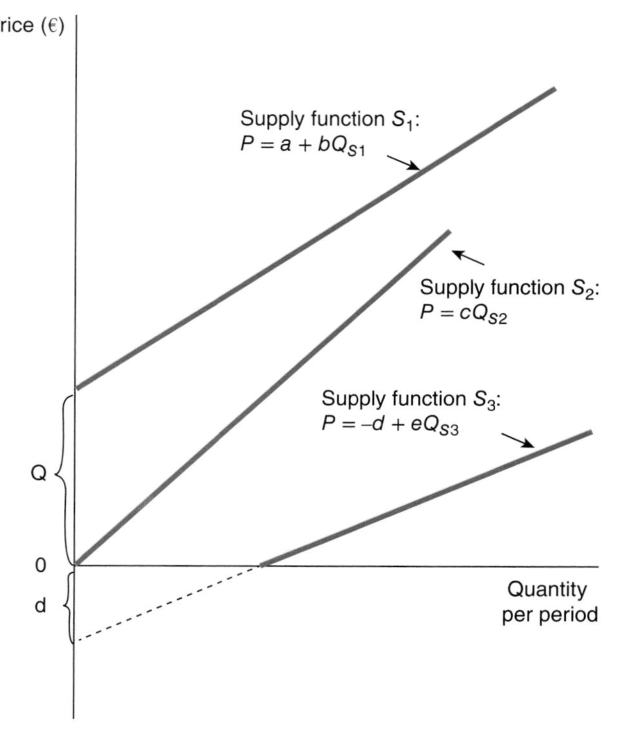

The inverse supply function S_1 is of the form:

$$P = a + bQ_{S1}$$

Where:
Q_{S1} = quantity supplied
P = price
a and b are constants, where a is the vertical intercept and b is the slope of the supply curve. Since a is positive, supply is elastic.

Now consider the inverse supply function S_2. This supply function is of the form:

$$P = cQ_{S2}$$

Where c is a constant determining the slope of the curve.

The supply curve passes through the origin so a must be equal to zero. Supply is unit elastic.

Finally look at the inverse supply function S_3. This supply curve is of the form:

$$P = -d + eQ_{S3}$$

Where d and e are constants. Supply is inelastic.

This refresher about demand and supply elasticities is important because it will help you to understand the rest of this chapter.

THE LINK BETWEEN ELASTICITY AND DEADWEIGHT LOSSES

We begin to examine this link by calculating the deadweight loss of a tax when we have a given demand curve and an elastic supply curve. To illustrate, suppose our supply and demand functions with no government intervention of any kind are as follows:

$$P = 80 + 2Q_S$$

So we have an elastic supply curve. The demand curve is:

$$P = 200 - Q_D$$

We can find market equilibrium as follows:
In equilibrium:

$$\begin{aligned} 80 + 2Q_S &= 200 - Q_D \\ 3Q &= 120 \\ Q &= 40 \end{aligned}$$

We can find P by substituting $Q = 40$ into either the supply or demand function. If we use the supply function we have:

$$\begin{aligned} P &= 80 + 2Q_S \\ &= 80 + 80 \\ &= 160 \end{aligned}$$

If we use the demand function we have:

$$\begin{aligned} P &= 200 - Q_D \\ &= 200 - 40 \\ &= 160 \end{aligned}$$

So the equilibrium quantity in a free market is 40 units and the equilibrium price is €160. This is shown in Figure 9.3.

In Chapter 8 we explained that a per unit tax is a specific tax on each unit of output sold, set at a level that is independent of the price being charged in the market. Its imposition shifts the supply curve. Diagrammatically it shifts the supply curve upward by the extent of the tax. Since the tax is a specific tax, the shift is parallel as shown in Figure 9.3.

FIGURE 9.3

Deadweight Loss with an Elastic Supply
The original equilibrium with no tax is $P = 160$ and $Q = 40$. The equilibrium quantity in this market with a tax of €30 per unit is $P = 170$ and $Q = 30$. The effect of the tax is to reduce equilibrium output from 40 to 30 and to raise the equilibrium price from €160 to €170. The tax shifts the supply curve upwards but leaves the demand curve unaffected. The value of the deadweight loss as a result of the imposition of the tax is $\frac{30 \times 10}{2} = €150$.

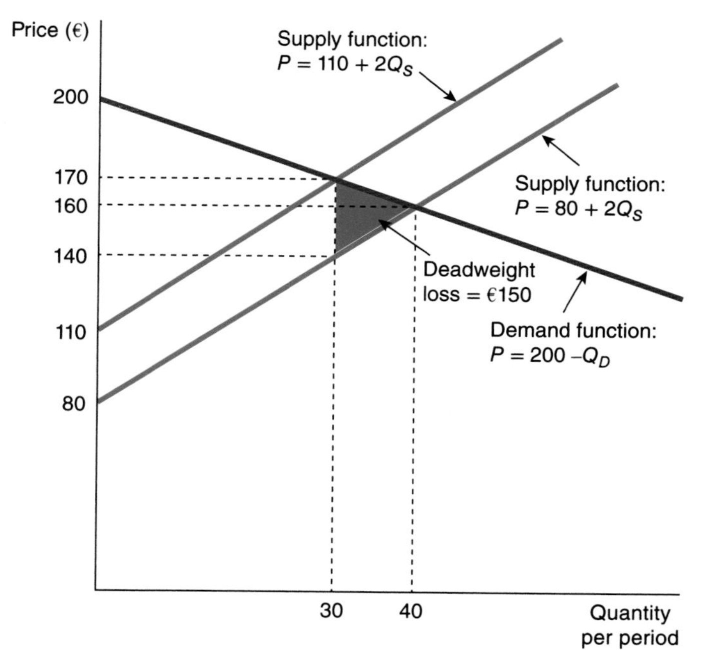

Our supply function $P = c + dQ$, becomes:

$$P = c + dQ + t$$

Where t is the tax per unit levied.

We will assume a per unit tax of €30. The tax has altered the supply function but not the demand function so in our case the supply function becomes:

$$P = 80 + 2Q_S + 30$$

After simplifying by collecting the like terms, this becomes:

$$P = 110 + 2Q_S$$

The new equilibrium will now be:

$$\begin{aligned} 110 + 2Q_S &= 200 - Q_D \\ 3Q &= 90 \\ Q &= 30 \end{aligned}$$

Again we can find P by substituting into either of our equations a value for Q where $Q = 30$. Given the supply function:

$$\begin{aligned} P &= 110 + 2Q_S \\ &= 110 + 60 \\ &= 170 \end{aligned}$$

If we use the demand function we should get the same result (always useful as a check):

$$\begin{aligned} P &= 200 - Q_D P_D = 200 - 30 \\ &= 170 \end{aligned}$$

The equilibrium quantity in this market with a tax of €30 per unit is 30 units and the equilibrium price is €170. This is also shown in Figure 9.3.

The effect of the tax is to reduce equilibrium output from 40 to 30 and to raise the equilibrium price from €160 to €170. The tax shifts the supply curve upwards but leaves the demand curve unaffected. The equilibrium price is higher and the equilibrium quantity is lower than would be the case without the tax.

Measuring The Deadweight Loss

Now we are ready to find the deadweight loss, the shaded area in Figure 9.3. This is the reduction in welfare as a result of the tax of €30.

As we have assumed straight line supply and demand functions this area can be calculated by the formula for any triangle:

$$A = \frac{hb}{2}$$

Or alternatively expressed:

$$A = \frac{1}{2}bh$$

Where:
A = area
h = height
b = length of base

Using the first formulation we calculate as follows. The base of the triangle is 30, the size of the tax. The height of the triangle is 10, the reduction in output as a result of the tax. So we have:

$$A = \frac{30 \times 10}{2} = 150$$

The value of the deadweight loss as a result of the imposition of the tax is €150.

Now we see what happens to the deadweight loss if we have a less elastic supply curve but the same demand function and the same level of tax. Our new supply function is:

$$P = -40 + 5Q_S$$

The demand function remains the same, namely:

$$P = 200 - Q$$

The equilibrium will now be:

$$\begin{aligned} -40 + 5Q_S &= 200 - Q_D \\ 6Q &= 240 \\ Q &= 40 \end{aligned}$$

We then find P by substituting Q = 40 into either the supply or demand function. If we use the supply function we have:

$$\begin{aligned} P &= -40 + 5Q_S \\ &= -40 + 200 \\ &= 160 \end{aligned}$$

If we use the demand function we have:

$$\begin{aligned} P &= 200 - Q_D \\ &= 200 - 40 \\ &= 160 \end{aligned}$$

Given these supply and demand functions, the equilibrium quantity in a free market is 40 units and the equilibrium price is €160. This is shown in Figure 9.4.

Again we assume a per unit tax of €30. Now the supply function becomes:

$$P = -40 + 5Q_S + 30$$

which when simplified becomes:

$$P = -10 + 5Q_S$$

The new equilibrium will be:

$$\begin{aligned} -10 + 5Q_S &= 200 - Q_D \\ 6Q &= 210 \\ Q &= 35 \end{aligned}$$

FIGURE 9.4

Deadweight Loss with an Inelastic Supply

With a steeper supply curve but the same demand curve as before, the original equilibrium with no tax is P = 160 and Q = 40. The equilibrium quantity in this market with a tax of €30 per unit is P = 165 and Q = 35. The effect of the tax is to reduce equilibrium output from 40 to 35 and to raise the equilibrium price from €160 to €165. The value of the deadweight loss as a result of the imposition of the tax is now $\frac{30 \times 5}{2} = €75$.

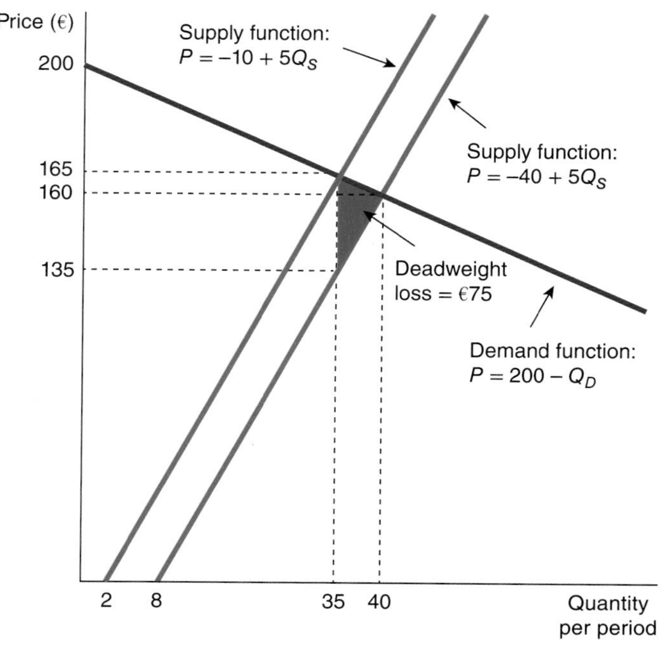

Again we can find P by substituting into either of our equations a value for Q where Q = 35. If we use the supply function this gives the equilibrium price as:

$$\begin{aligned} P &= -10 + 5Q_S \\ &= -10 + 175 \\ &= 165 \end{aligned}$$

If we use the demand function as our check, we get:

$$\begin{aligned} P &= 200 - Q_D \\ &= 200 - 35 \\ &= 165 \end{aligned}$$

The equilibrium quantity in this market with a more inelastic supply but the same size of tax of €30 per unit is now 35 and the equilibrium price is €165. This is also shown in Figure 9.4.

Measuring The New Deadweight Loss

The new deadweight loss, the shaded area in Figure 9.4, is the reduction in welfare as a result of the tax of €30 on the market with the more inelastic supply curve.

The base of the triangle is again 30, the size of the tax. The height of the triangle is now 5, the reduction in output as a result of the tax. So we have:

$$A = \frac{30 \times 5}{2} = 75$$

The deadweight loss is now €75. The same demand and the same size of tax but with a more inelastic supply means that we have a smaller deadweight loss.

Deadweight Losses and Demand Elasticity

Now we see what happens to the deadweight loss if we have a relatively more price elastic demand curve but the same supply function and the same level of tax.

We calculated the deadweight loss of a €30 per unit tax when the supply function was $P_S = 80 + 2Q_S$ and the demand function was $P_D = 200 - Q_D$, and found calculated the deadweight loss of €150.

Now we have a relatively price elastic demand function of $P_D = 180 - ½Q_D$ but our supply curve remains the same. The market equilibrium will be:

$$80 + 2Q_S = 180 - \frac{1}{2}Q_D$$

$$2\frac{1}{2}Q = 100$$

$$Q = 40$$

We then find P by substituting $Q = 40$ into either the supply or demand function. If we use the supply function we have:

$$P = 80 + 2Q_S$$
$$= 80 + 80$$
$$= 160$$

If we use the demand function we get:

$$P = 180 - \frac{1}{2}Q_D$$
$$= 180 - 20$$
$$= 160$$

The equilibrium quantity in a free market is 40 units and the equilibrium price is €160. This is shown in Figure 9.5.

FIGURE 9.5

Deadweight Loss with a Relatively Elastic Demand

Here we have a relatively more price elastic demand curve of $P_D = 180 - \frac{1}{2}Q_D$, but the same supply function and the same level of tax. The equilibrium quantity in a free market is 40 units and the equilibrium price is €160. Assuming a per unit tax of €30, the new equilibrium with a more elastic demand is $Q = 28$ and $P = 166$. The deadweight loss is now €180. The same supply function but with a more elastic demand means that a given tax causes a larger deadweight loss.

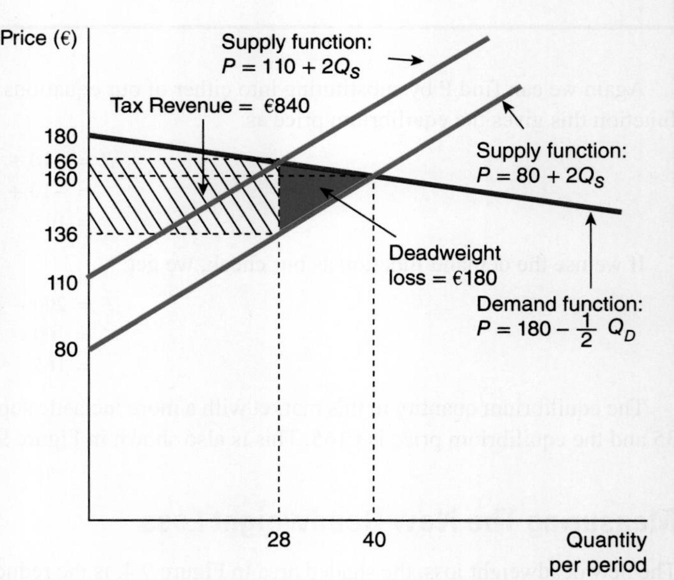

Assuming a per unit tax of €30, the supply function becomes:

$$P = -80 + 2Q_S + 30$$

which when simplified becomes:

$$P = 110 + 2Q_S$$

This shift in supply creates a new equilibrium:

$$110 + 2Q_S = 180 - \frac{1}{2}Q_D$$

$$2\frac{1}{2}Q = 70$$

$$Q = 28$$

Substituting $Q = 28$ into the supply function gives the equilibrium price:

$$\begin{aligned} P &= 110 + 2Q_S \\ &= 110 + 56 \\ &= 166 \end{aligned}$$

If we use the demand function we get:

$$\begin{aligned} P &= 180 - \frac{1}{2}Q_D \\ &= 180 - 14 \\ &= 166 \end{aligned}$$

The equilibrium quantity in this market with a more elastic demand but the same size of tax of €30 per unit is now 28 and the equilibrium price is €166. This is shown in Figure 9.5.

As before, we calculate the deadweight loss, the shaded area in Figure 9.5. The base of the triangle remains at 30, the size of the tax and the height of the triangle is now 12, the reduction in output as a result of the tax. This gives:

$$A = \frac{30 \times 12}{2} = 180$$

The deadweight loss is now €180. The same supply function but with a more elastic demand means that a given tax causes a larger deadweight loss.

The Relationship between Elasticity and Tax Revenue

We now turn to the question of the relationship between elasticity and tax revenue. In general, we can note that:

- A small tax creates a small deadweight loss but raises relatively little tax revenue.
- A medium size tax creates a larger deadweight loss but raises rather more tax revenue.
- A large tax creates a still larger deadweight loss but may well raise less tax revenue.

We now illustrate this with the supply and demand functions that we have been using. We will consider three different sizes of tax in the market that has been shown in Figure 9.5. We begin with a 'medium' size tax which we will assume to be €30. As a result of the tax we have a level of output of 28 units per period and a tax of €30 is paid on each of those units.

Hence the tax revenue is: $28 \times 30 =$ €840 per period. We have already calculated the deadweight loss at €180.

Now suppose the tax is much smaller at just €5 but the initial supply and demand functions remain the same. The original, pre-tax equilibrium we found as $Q = 40$ and $P = 160$. Now we calculate the new equilibrium output.

$$P = 180 - \frac{1}{2}Q_D$$

Supply with the €5 per unit tax becomes:

$$\begin{aligned} P &= 80 + 2Q_S + 5 \\ &= 85 + 2Q_S \end{aligned}$$

Market equilibrium can be calculated as:

$$\begin{aligned} 85 + 2Q_S &= 180 - \frac{1}{2}Q_D \\ 2\frac{1}{2}Q &= 95 \\ Q &= 38 \end{aligned}$$

The market price is found by substituting $Q = 38$ into either the supply or demand function. If we use the supply function we have:

$$\begin{aligned} P &= 85 + 2Q_S \\ &= 85 + 76 \\ &= 161 \end{aligned}$$

If we use the demand function we get:

$$\begin{aligned} P &= 180 - \frac{1}{2}Q_D \\ &= 180 - 19 \\ &= 161 \end{aligned}$$

We show this in Figure 9.6.

FIGURE 9.6

The Effect of a Small Tax of €5 per Unit

With the small tax of €5 there is a small shift of the supply curve and a small increase in price. In this case price rises by just €1. The deadweight loss is small at just €5. However, the total tax revenue is small, in this case just €190.

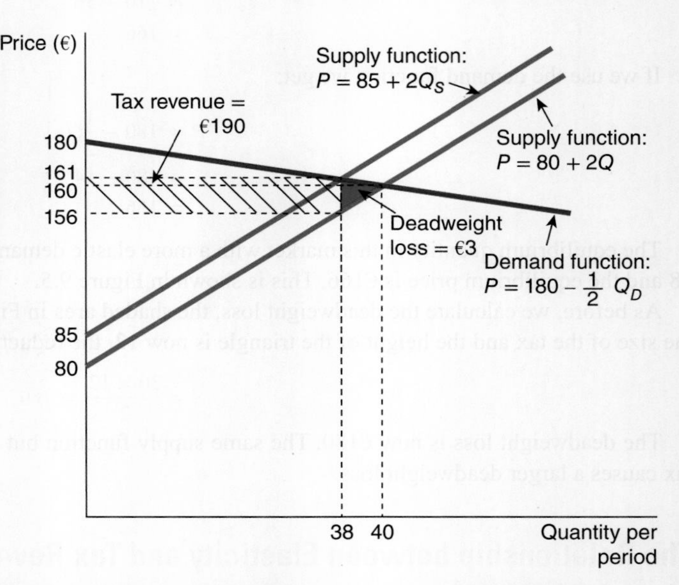

To calculate the deadweight loss, the base of the triangle is 5, the size of the tax, and the height of the triangle is now 2, the reduction in output as a result of the tax. So we have:

$$A = \frac{5 \times 2}{2} = 5$$

The deadweight loss is now just €5.

The tax revenue is the number of units now produced multiplied by the tax per unit:

$$38 \times 5 = €190$$

With the small tax we have a small deadweight loss and a small volume of tax revenue.

Finally, what is the effect of a large tax? We will use a sum of €80 per unit.

The original, pre-tax equilibrium we found as $Q = 40$ and $P = 160$. Now we calculate the new equilibrium output.

The supply function with a per unit tax of €80 becomes:

$$\begin{aligned} P &= 80 + 2Q_S + 80 \\ &= 160 + 2Q_S \end{aligned}$$

The equilibrium quantity is:

$$\begin{aligned} 160 + 2Q_S &= 180 - \frac{1}{2}Q_D \\ 2\frac{1}{2}Q &= 20 \\ Q &= 8 \end{aligned}$$

The equilibrium price using the supply function gives:

$$\begin{aligned} P &= 160 + 2Q_S \\ &= 160 + 16 \\ &= 176 \end{aligned}$$

To check using the demand function we get:

$$\begin{aligned} P &= 180 - \frac{1}{2}Q_D \\ &= 180 - 4 \\ &= 176 \end{aligned}$$

This is shown in Figure 9.7.

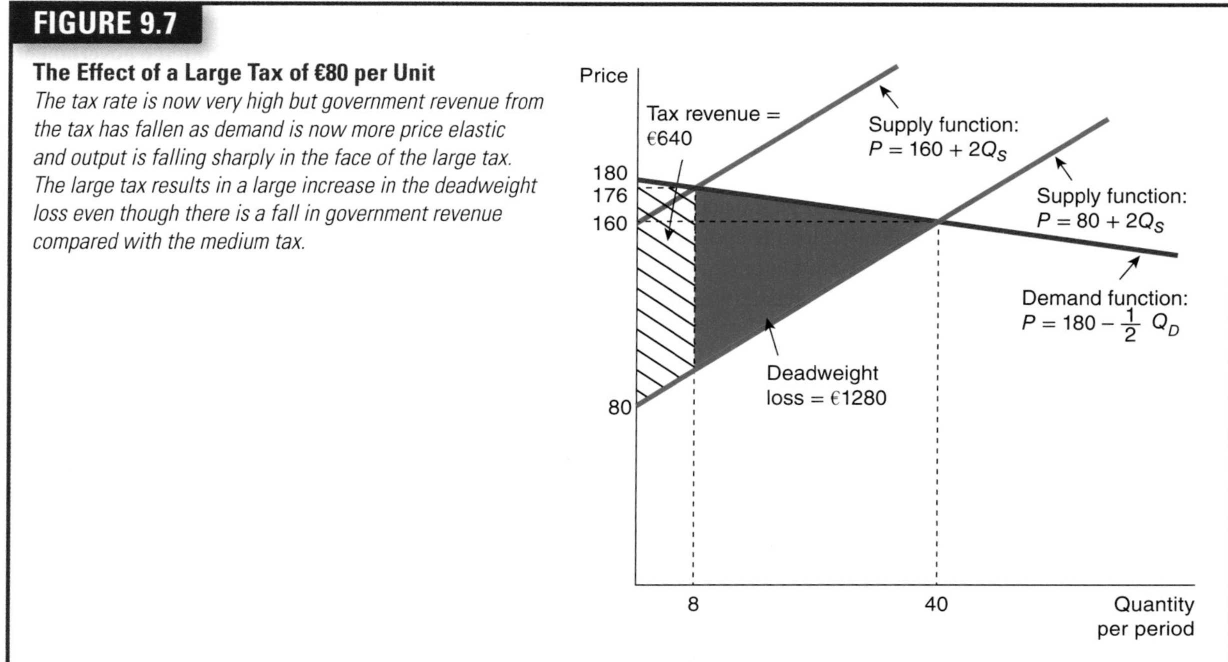

FIGURE 9.7

The Effect of a Large Tax of €80 per Unit

The tax rate is now very high but government revenue from the tax has fallen as demand is now more price elastic and output is falling sharply in the face of the large tax. The large tax results in a large increase in the deadweight loss even though there is a fall in government revenue compared with the medium tax.

The deadweight loss is given by the base of the triangle, which is now 80 (the size of the tax), and the height of the triangle which is now 32 (the reduction in output as a result of the tax). So we have:

$$A = \frac{80 \times 32}{2} = 1280$$

The deadweight loss is now very large at €1280.

The tax revenue is the number of units now produced multiplied by the tax per unit:

$$8 \times 80 = €640$$

Even though the tax rate is now very high government revenues have fallen as demand is now more price elastic and output is falling sharply in the face of the large tax level. The large tax has produced a significant increase in the deadweight loss but caused a fall in government revenue compared with the medium tax. We summarize these results in Table 9.1.

TABLE 9.1 **Deadweight Losses and Government Revenue in Response to Different Tax Rates**

Size of tax Per unit (€)	Deadweight Loss	Tax revenue
Small (5)	5	190
Medium (30)	180	840
Large (80)	1280	640

THE COSTS OF AGRICULTURAL SUPPORT

We have now seen how elasticity considerations affect consumers, producers and also government revenue when we look at tax policy at the micro level. However, elasticity considerations are also important with regard to government *expenditure* at the micro level. As an illustration of this idea we consider government expenditure on support for agriculture. Almost all governments offer some kind of agricultural protection rather than leaving farmers entirely to the open market. It isn't our intention to argue the case for or against this policy but to consider the costs of two possible policies towards agricultural protection. One of the forms of support is a *deficiency payment scheme*. This usually takes the form of getting the farmer to sell their crop on the open market but guaranteeing to pay a price to the farmer above the price that the market would set. The cost to government is, therefore, the difference between the price guarantee and the open market price multiplied by the amount of output produced by the agricultural industry as a whole. The individual farmer makes the supply decision on the basis that they will receive this additional payment from the government.

Another common form of support is *support price buying*. In this scheme the government acts as a consumer of agricultural output. It purchases the output itself in sufficient quantities to drive up the price to that which they feel the farmer should enjoy. Of course, under this scheme the produce cannot then be resold for this would simply depress the price again.

In the analysis that follows we ignore administrative costs. Which of these schemes is more costly to the government? The answer is that it depends upon the price elasticity of demand for the product in question.

We will use a little geometry to demonstrate this but you will need to remember the terminology we used to summarize the relationship between elasticity and revenue. We take the absolute value of the elasticity, that is, we ignore the sign. Then if:

- ped > 1, that is, demand is price elastic, demand is relatively sensitive to price changes, an increase in price will reduce revenue to the industry.
- ped = 1, that is, demand is unit elastic, an increase in price will leave revenue to the industry unchanged.
- ped < 1, that is, demand is price inelastic, demand is relatively insensitive to price changes, an increase in price will increase revenue to the industry.

Now we consider the first scheme, the deficiency payments scheme.

The Deficiency Payments Scheme

A diagrammatic representation of the effect of government policy is shown in Figure 9.8.

FIGURE 9.8

A Deficiency Payments Scheme

With no government intervention market equilibrium is $P = P_e$ and $Q = Q_e$. The government guarantees a price of P^X. Then farmers supply Q^X to the market. With this level of output they can receive a price of P'. The cost to the government of the deficiency payment is P^XABP'.

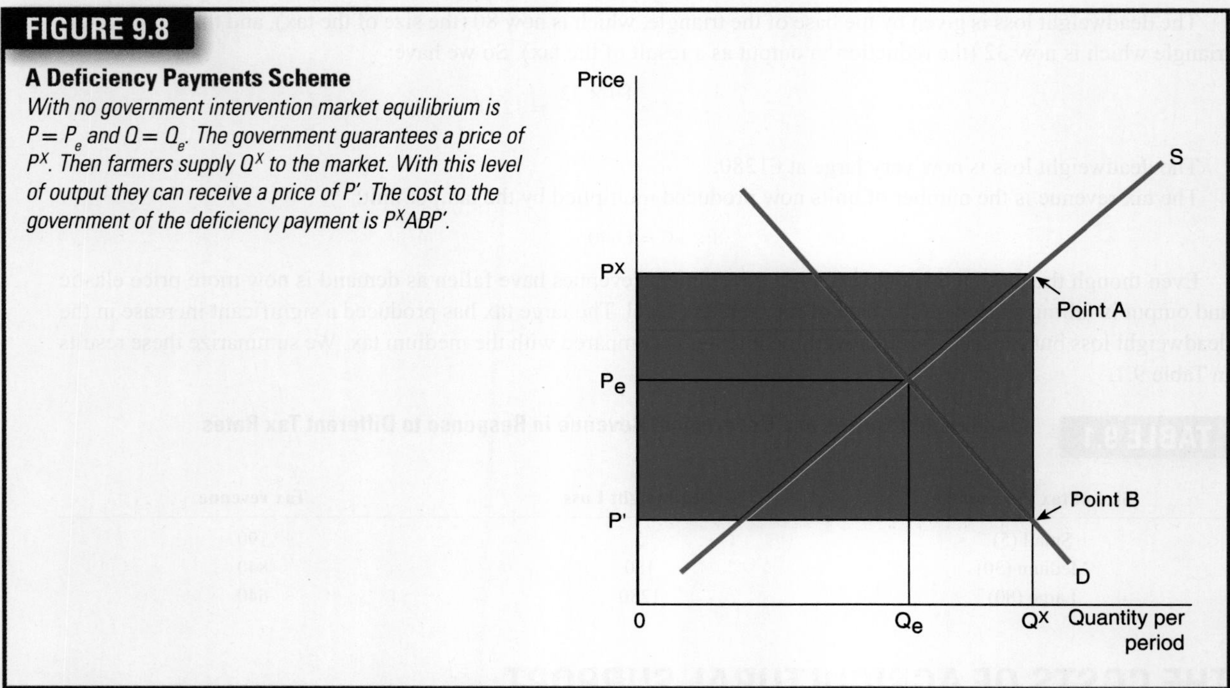

With no government intervention the market price would be at P_e and the quantity demanded on the market would be at Q_e. The government decides to guarantee farmers a price above P_e, which we will call P^X. At this price farmers supply Q^X to the market. With this level of output they can only secure a price of P', the price that consumers pay under this scheme. The government makes up the difference by paying farmers a deficiency payment of the difference between this price and the guaranteed price, P^X. It pays this on all units of output, Q^X. So the cost to government is the shaded area, P^XABP'. Now we consider the alternative scheme, the support price buying scheme. This is represented by Figure 9.9.

FIGURE 9.9

A Support Price Buying Scheme

Under a support price buying scheme the government purchases the commodity itself in sufficient quantities to achieve the desired price to the farmer. This shifts the demand curve. It becomes perfectly elastic from point C. At this price consumers are only willing to purchase Q but farmers will produce Q^X. The government must purchase the difference between Q^X and Q and pay the price P^X. Then the cost to the government is CAQ^XQ.

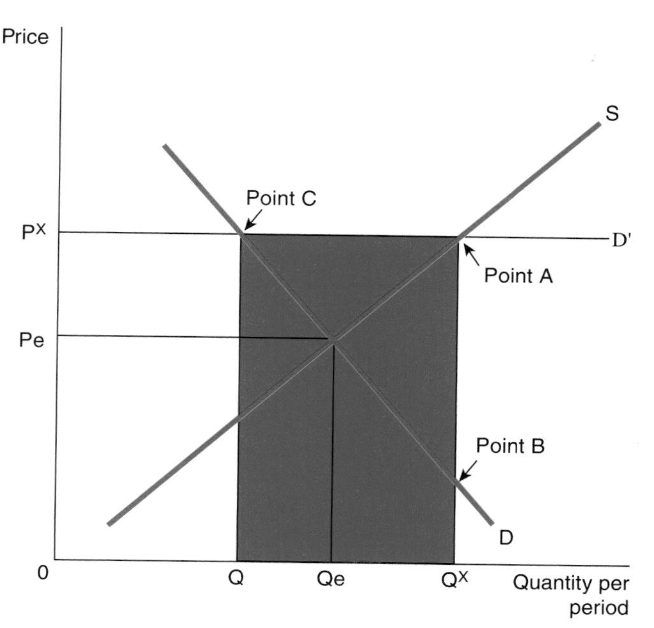

Under this scheme the government also sees to it that farmers receive a price of P^X, but this is achieved in a different way. The government purchases the commodity itself in sufficient quantities to achieve the desired price to the farmer. Its actions shifts the demand curve. It has to purchase whatever farmers wish to produce at this price. The demand curve with government purchasing becomes perfectly elastic from point C. At this price consumers are only willing to purchase Q but farmers will produce Q^X. Government therefore purchases the difference between Q^X and Q and pays the price P^X. So the cost to the government is CAQ^XQ.

Comparing the Costs of the Two Schemes

Now we can compare the cost of the support price buying scheme with the cost of the deficiency payments scheme. Figure 9.10 shows the market again so that we can compare the costs directly. To make things clearer we have eliminated the price and quantity that would be equilibrium if there were no government involvement at all.

As we have seen, the deficiency payments scheme costs:

$$P^XABP'$$

The support price buying scheme costs:

$$CAQ^XQ$$

Which is the larger area? First note that the area CABE is common to both so we are comparing two areas EBQ^XQ (part of the cost of the support price buying scheme) and P^XCEP' (part of the cost of the deficiency payment scheme). In principle there are three possibilities.

Possibility one:

$$P^XABP' = CAQ^XQ$$

Possibility two:

$$P^XABP' > CAQ^XQ$$

Possibility three:

$$P^XABP' < CAQ^XQ$$

First consider possibility one.

We begin by noting that CABE is common to both areas, i.e.:

$$P^XABP' = P^XCEP' + CABE$$

FIGURE 9.10

A Comparison of Costs of Two Support Schemes

The net cost to the government of the support price buying scheme over and above the deficiency payments scheme is $EBQ^XQ - P^XCEP'$. If EBQ^XQ is the greater area, as it must be if demand is elastic, then the cost of the support price buying scheme must be larger than the cost of the deficiency payments scheme.

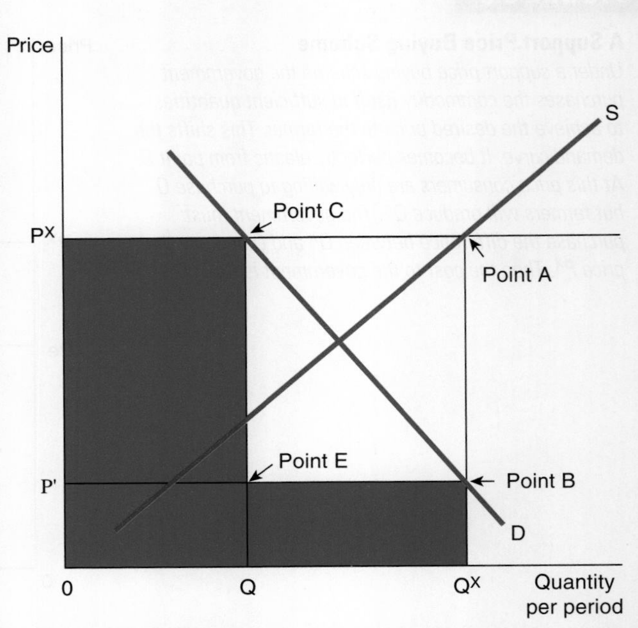

And:

$$CAQ^XQ = CABE + EBQ^XQ$$

Subtracting CABE from both sides gives us:

$$P^XCEP' + CABE = CABE + EBQ^XQ$$

Now add OP′EQ to both sides (adding the same value to both sides does not change the equation) and we get:

$$OP^X CQ = OP'BQ^X$$

These are the two shaded areas in Figure 9.10. Observe that each of these two areas represents total revenue from market sales at different prices, one when price is P' and one when price is P^X. If revenue is the same at two points on the demand curve, it follows that demand elasticity is unitary over that range. If demand is unit elastic, then, the subsidy cost of each of the two schemes will be the same.

Now consider possibility two, namely:

$$P^XABP' > CAQ^XQ$$

Then following the same reasoning as above:

$$OP^XCQ > OP'BQ^X$$

If revenue is greater at the higher price P^X, then it follows that demand is price inelastic over that range. As we have seen, where demand is price inelastic, a price rise decreases quantity demanded but increases revenue because the proportionate increase in price is greater than the proportionate decrease in quantity demanded.

We have shown that the net cost to the government of the support price buying scheme over and above the deficiency payments scheme is $EBQxQ - PxCEP'$. If $EBQxQ$ is the smaller area, and it is if demand is price inelastic, then the cost of the support price buying scheme must be less than the cost of the deficiency payments scheme.

Finally consider possibility three, namely:

$$P^XABP' < CAQ^XQ$$

Then following the same reasoning as above:

$$OP^XCQ < OP'BQ^X$$

This means that revenue is higher at the lower price, P'. That must mean that demand is price elastic. Remember that where demand is price elastic a price rise decreases quantity demanded but also decreases revenue because the proportionate increase in price is smaller than the proportionate decrease in quantity demanded.

We have shown that the net cost to the government of the support price buying scheme over and above the deficiency payments scheme is $EBQxQ - PxCEP'$. If $EBQxQ$ is the greater area, and it is if demand is price elastic, then the cost of the support price buying scheme must be larger than the cost of the deficiency payments scheme.

Summary

We have seen how the price elasticity of demand for a product becomes an important consideration for government with respect to taxation policy. Moreover, demand elasticity is also an important consideration with respect to subsidy policy.

PROBLEMS AND APPLICATIONS

1 Return to the demand and supply function from Chapter 8 Problem 1 $P_D = 1000 - 0.25Q_D$ and the inverse supply $P_S = 100 + 0.2Q_S$.

a. Calculate the consumer surplus, the producer surplus and the total surplus after the imposition of the tax of €90 per unit of output sold.

b. Show and explain the so-called deadweight loss of taxation. Do not forget the government tax receipts when you compare the total surplus before and after taxation.

c. Assume now that consumers have to pay the tax of €90 per unit to the authorities. Calculate the equilibrium after taxes and compare the prices paid by consumers and received by producers with your previous results.

d. With consumers having the obligation to pay the tax, go over your calculations for the tax burden, tax revenues and the welfare loss of taxation. Has anything changed?

2 In Problem 4 of Chapter 8, the inverse demand function was given by $P_D(Q) = 1200 - 1.25Q_D$ and $P_S(Q) = 200 + 0.75Q_S$ represented the inverse of the supply function. Again, assume a tax of €200 per unit is introduced.

a. Measure the tax burden of producers and consumers by comparing their respective prices before and after taxes. Which part of the tax burden is passed on to consumers and which remains with producers?

b. Is the equilibrium after taxes in the elastic or in the inelastic part of the demand function?

c. Assume an inelastic response of consumers to price changes (even if this was not the correct answer before). Use the elasticity reasoning to explain whether the tax revenue would increase or decrease, if the government were to raise the tax rate even higher than €200.

3 Again, use the inverse supply function $P_S(Q) = 200 + 0.75Q_S$. But instead of the function $P_D(Q) = 1200 - 1.25Q_D$, now suppose, that the inverse demand function is $P'_D(Q) = 800 - 0.45Q_D$.

a. If you draw this demand function in the same graph as before you will notice that it passes through the same intersection with the supply function as did the original demand function $P_D(Q)$. Show through a calculation which of the two demand functions is more elastic around the equilibrium (the easiest way to do this comparison is with the point elasticity method).

b. Calculate the new price paid by consumers after taxation along $P'_D(Q)$ as well as the price net of taxes received by producers when a tax of €200 per unit is introduced.

c. Calculate the percentage shares borne by producers and consumers in the tax burden with the new demand function and compare them with the distribution of the tax burden based on the original demand function. Explain the observed changes using the elasticities calculated above.

d. Calculate the tax revenues generated under the new demand function $P'_D(Q)$. Again, looking at the elasticities was this change in tax revenue to be expected?

e. Up to now you have discussed a per unit tax. Now, return to the tax regime of Problem 5 in Chapter 8 where producers have to pay an ad valorem tax of 40 per cent. Find the new equilibrium with taxes.

f. Which tax regime generates higher tax returns with the new demand function, the tax of €200 per unit or the tax of 40 per cent of value?

4 Reconsider the situation from Problem 2 in Chapter 8, with an inverse supply function $P_S = 2 + 0.0032X_S$ and an inverse demand function $P_D = 20 - 0.004X_D$. If the original intention of politicians was to provide everybody who would like to rent an apartment at €8 per square metre with the floor space demanded, then a price ceiling alone will not be sufficient. Formulate two policy alternatives that will achieve the goal and show how much government money will have to be spent on each one.

PART 5 INEFFICIENT MARKET ALLOCATIONS

10 PUBLIC GOODS, COMMON RESOURCES AND MERIT GOODS

In Chapter 10, we use some basic mathematics to show how we can arrive at the optimal level of public good provision. In doing so we will use what we learned in chapter five about summing individual demand curves to produce a market demand curve.

We shall also explore the mathematics of non-renewable resources. The tragedy of the commons involves the overuse of a resource that is renewable. How quickly would we expect non-renewable resources to be consumed?

THE OPTIMAL PROVISION OF PUBLIC GOODS

We begin our analysis by showing why we cannot sum horizontally individual demand curves to get a market demand curve if the good in question is a public good. To do this we return to our two consumers in Chapter 5. There we did sum the two demand curves horizontally because the good in question was a private good. Our two consumers had the following demand functions:

$$Q_{DA} = 10 - \frac{1}{2}P$$

$$Q_{DB} = 16 - P$$

Our summed market demand function for $0 < P < 16$ was:

$$Q_D = 26 - \frac{3}{2}P$$

Suppose now the market price is €6:

$$\begin{aligned} Q_D &= 26 - \frac{3}{2} \times 6 \\ &= 26 - 9 \\ &= 17 \end{aligned}$$

This is the total quantity demanded per period of time for the private good at a price of €6. Who consumes these units? First look at consumer A's consumption.

$$\begin{aligned} Q_{DA} &= 10 - \frac{1}{2}P \\ &= 10 - \frac{1}{2} \times 6 \\ &= 7 \end{aligned}$$

Now look at consumer B's consumption.

$$\begin{aligned} Q_{DB} &= 16 - P \\ &= 16 - 6 \\ &= 10 \end{aligned}$$

Consumer A consumes 7 of the 17 units supplied by the market at a price of €6, and consumer B consumes the other 10 units. Our two consumers consume different amounts of the good. This situation is depicted diagrammatically in Figure 10.1.

There we show the two consumers' inverse demand functions. For Consumer A the inverse demand function is found as follows:

$$\begin{aligned} Q_{DA} &= 10 - \frac{1}{2}P \\ \frac{1}{2}P &= 10 - Q_{DA} \\ P &= 20 - 2Q_{DA} \end{aligned}$$

For Consumer B the inverse demand function is found as follows:

$$\begin{aligned} Q_{DB} &= 16 - P \\ P &= 16 - Q_{DB} \end{aligned}$$

The diagram shows the consumption of each consumer and the total consumption at the price of €6.

FIGURE 10.1

Consumption of a Private Good

To find the market demand curve of a private good we sum horizontally the individual demand functions. If we assume just two individual consumers, A and B, the red line shows the market demand curve as the horizontal summation of their demand curves.

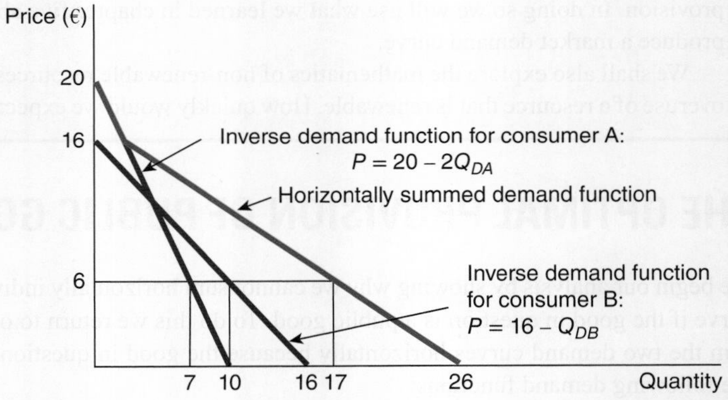

However, if it is a public good this is impossible. By definition access to public goods is the same for all consumers. An apple is not a public good. If one person eats it, others cannot do so. However, national defence is a public good. If the service of protection from foreign invasion is provided, all citizens can consume this service without reducing the amount of national defence available to others. This means that for a public good we must sum the individual demand curves vertically. Let's illustrate the process. Suppose we have a tiny community of just two people. Assume also there is a public good and our two consumers have preferences given by the above demand equations.

Notice we are using the same functions as in Chapter 5 but whereas the demand functions related to private goods this time the demand curves represent demand for a public good.

We can now sum these **inverse** demand curves to give the summed demand curve for the public good. Following the same procedure we used in Chapter 5 we can summarize the position in Table 10.1.

TABLE 10.1 **Summing Demand Curves for a Public Good**

Quantity Range	Relevant Demand Function	Vertical Summation of demand curves
0–10	Consumers A and B	$P = (20 - 2Q_{DA}) + (16 - Q_{DB}) = 36 - 3Q_D$
10–16	Consumer A	$P = 20 - 2Q_{DA}$
>16	None	–

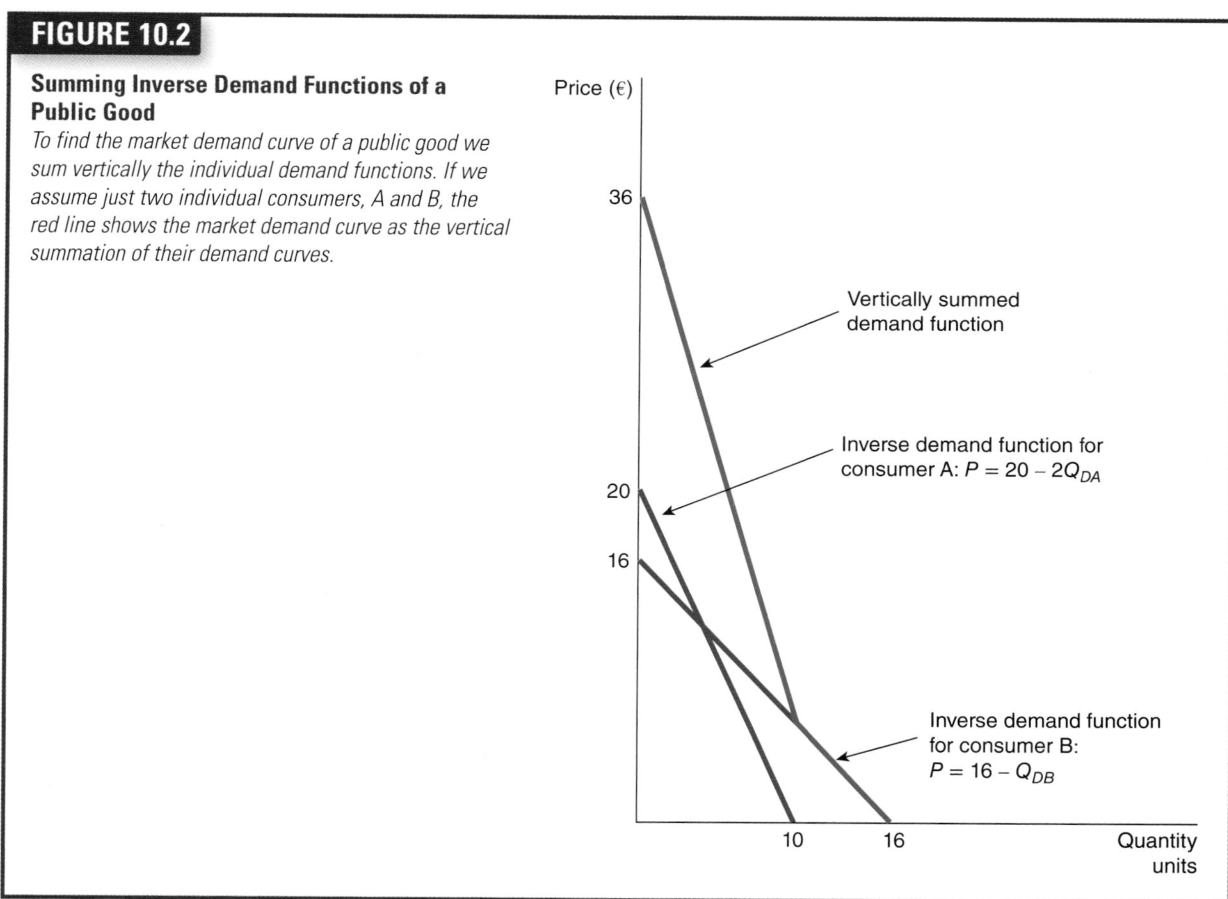

FIGURE 10.2

Summing Inverse Demand Functions of a Public Good

To find the market demand curve of a public good we sum vertically the individual demand functions. If we assume just two individual consumers, A and B, the red line shows the market demand curve as the vertical summation of their demand curves.

Adding the Costs of Production

Having found the demand curve for the public good we now need to consider the cost of its provision in order to establish the optimum level of output. Recall that the socially optimal provision of any good is the level of output at which $D = MC$. Assume now that MC is constant at €12. As we show in Table 10.1, over the output range from 0–10 the aggregate inverse demand function is $P = 36 - 3Q_D$. Then:

$$36 - 3Q_D = 12$$
$$3Q_D = 24$$
$$Q_D = 8$$

Optimal provision for this public good is 8 units per period of time. Although the consumers have different demand functions they both consume 8 units of output. Each may consume the same level of output because it is a public good. We show this diagrammatically in Figure 10.3.

Conclusion

To get a market demand curve we sum the individual demand curves. We sum horizontally for a private good and vertically for a public good.

FIGURE 10.3

Optimal Consumption of a Public Good

To find the optimal provision of a public good we find the level of output where marginal cost, MC, is equal to the marginal benefit to society, shown in the vertically summed demand function. In this instance, with MC = 12, optimal provision of the public good is 8 units.

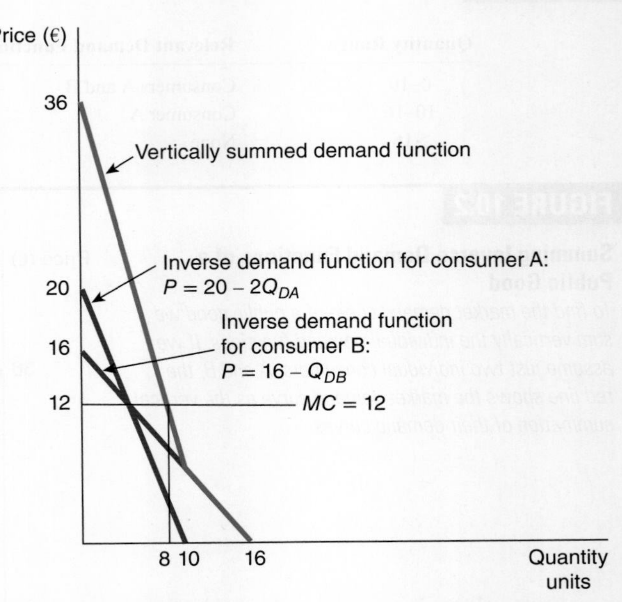

THE DEPLETION OF NON-RENEWABLE RESOURCES

Where resources are renewable, in order to maintain the sustainability of resource use, policies and regulation may be put in place to ensure that society doesn't use a resource faster than it can be replaced. However there is particular concern about non-renewable resources. How fast are these resources used up and what happens when they are all gone? Even where the resources are privately owned, society seems able to find ways of solving the problem. Forty years ago there was a prediction that almost all the main non-renewable resources would be used up within 40 years. Now the forecast is that most non-renewable resources will be used up in…. about 40 years!

We will not be discussing all aspects of this matter but we can explore a few concepts here about the rate at which resources are extracted and used. It may surprise you but we can expect the rate of resource extraction to be dependent upon the rate of interest. In order to explore this idea you need to understand a concept about the time value of money. We shall discuss this concept fully in Chapter 25 but there is a basic idea that you need to know now.

A sum of money received in the future is worth less than the same sum of money received now. The earlier you receive it the more it is worth because it can be invested at some interest rate. Armed with this insight we can see how much less money is worth to us in future.

Suppose the current rate of interest is r per cent. We know now how much less the money is worth in a year's time. To find its present value a sum received in a year's time is 'discounted' by $\frac{1}{1+r}$ where r is the rate of interest. So for a sum of P in a year's time its value now is only $P\left(\frac{1}{1+r}\right)$.

For example, if you receive €100 in one year's time and assume an interest rate of 10 per cent:

$$P\left(\frac{1}{1+r}\right) \text{ gives } 100\left(\frac{1}{1+0.1}\right) = €90.91$$

We say that this is the 'present value' of the €100 received in one year's time.

Restating this it means that if we had €90.91 now and we could invest it at a 10 per cent rate of interest we could turn it into €100 in a year. So we are indifferent between €90.91 now or €100 in a year's time.

In Chapter 25 we will see how to calculate the present value of a sum of money for any period into the future and we will see how to use this knowledge to understand business investment. For now we can use this idea to examine private decision-making about scarce resource extraction.

Resource Extraction

We begin with two assumptions. First, extracting the resource is costless (an assumption we will drop shortly). Second, we will consider only the possibility that the resource can be extracted now or in one period's time. After reading Chapter 25 you will see that this argument can be extended for any future time period. Consider our resource owner having two options: deciding whether to extract the resource now in period 0, or wait until next period, period 1.

If they choose option one, extract now, what do they have in a year's time?

$$P_0(1 + r)$$

If they wait a year to extract then they will have:

$$P_1$$

If there is no other reason to prefer current to future extraction they are indifferent between periods to extract when:

$$P_1 = P_0(1 + r)$$

Rearranging we get:

$$\frac{P_1}{1 + r} = P_0$$

$\frac{1}{1 + r}$ = the 'discount factor', the rate at which a sum next period is converted into its present value.

Rearranging again gives:

$$\frac{P_1}{(1 + r)} - P_0 = 0$$

We multiply both sides of the equation by $(1 + r)$. This gives us:

$$P_1 - P_0(1 + r) = 0$$

Now we divide both sides of the equation by P_0:

$$\frac{P_1}{P_0} - 1 = r$$

We reduce the left-hand side to a common denominator (that is $P_{0,}$ so we multiply the numerators P_1 by 1 and 1 by P_0) and we get:

$$\frac{P_1 - P_0}{P_0} = r$$

Suppose the price of a unit of the resource in period 0 is €100 and the interest rate is 5 per cent, then we have:

$$\frac{P_1 - 100}{100} = 5$$

This will hold if the resource owner is to be indifferent between the two periods of time. We therefore expect that, all other things being equal, resource prices will have to rise annually by the rate of interest. There is good reason to think that the rate of interest is the equilibrium rate of price increase for the resource. Suppose, for example, that resource owners expect resource prices to rise faster in the next period than implied by the interest rate. In that case little or no extraction would take place and scarcity will drive up P_0 until this expectation holds no longer.

The Presence of Extraction Costs

Now let's introduce extraction costs into the argument and assume that there are always extraction costs of C to extract a unit of the resource.

Now we have:

$$\frac{P_1 - C}{(1 + r)} = P_0 - C$$

Where C is the cost of extracting a unit.

As before we multiply both sides of the equation by $(1 + r)$:

$$P_1 - C - (P_0 - C)(1 + r) = 0$$
$$P_1 - C - P_0 - P_0 r + C + Cr = 0$$

We divide both sides by P_0:

$$\frac{P_1}{P_0} - \frac{C}{P_0} - 1 - r + \frac{C}{P_0} + \frac{Cr}{P_0} = 0$$

$$\frac{P_1}{P_0} - 1 - r + \frac{C_r}{P_0} = 0$$

$$\frac{P_1}{P_0} - 1 = r - \frac{C_r}{P_0}$$

We rearrange by reducing the left-hand side to a common denominator P_0 and taking the common factor r in front of the brackets on the right-hand side:

$$\frac{P_1 - P_0}{P_0} = r\left(1 - \frac{C}{P_0}\right)$$

So price will rise more slowly than r under these assumptions. To illustrate let's assume that:

$$P_0 = 100$$
$$r = 5\ per\ cent$$
$$C = 60$$
$$\frac{P_1 - 100}{100} = 0.05\left(1 - \frac{60}{100}\right)$$
$$= 0.02$$
$$P_1 - 100 = 2$$
$$P_1 = 102$$

Under these circumstances price will rise from period one to period two by 2 per cent when $r = 5$ per cent. Notice two things. First, $C < P_0$ always or no extraction would take place. Notice also that when $r = 5$ per cent we show this not as 5 but as 0.05. 5 per cent means 5/100 = 0.05.

Summary

Over time we would expect resource prices to rise. *Ceteris paribus* we would expect the rise to be related to the rate of interest. Where there are extraction costs we would expect prices to rise by less than the rate of interest.

PROBLEMS AND APPLICATIONS

1 In this chapter you have learned that the individual demand function is an expression of the maximum price a consumer is willing to pay for another (marginal) unit of a good. Public goods are characterized by non-excludability, so everybody can use the same quantity without rivalry in consumption. In order to find the marginal social benefit of the public good you can therefore add up all consumers' willingness to pay. A very small society consists of the consumers A, B and C. Their demand functions for the public good are: $Q_A = 100 - 5P_A$, $Q_B = 100 - 3\frac{1}{3}P_B$ and $Q_C = 50 - 2P_C$.

a. Invert the three demand functions to show the willingness to pay of the three consumers.
b. Find the function that represents the marginal social benefit of the public good.
c. The marginal cost of providing the public good are: $MC = 20 + 1.5Q_S$. Find the optimum quantity of the public good.

2 You have an amount of €3000 saved and have invested it in an asset that gives you a yield of 4 per cent annually. You get compound interest.

a. How much money will you have after four years?
b. How much money will you have after five years (including compound interest)?

3 Currently the price of a depletable raw material is at P_0 = €80/tonne. The interest rate is 3 per cent.

a. How high is the price of the raw material likely to be next year?
b. If the market price in a year is $P_n = 97.85$ how high was the price a year earlier P_{n-1}?
c. How high is the growth rate of the price of the raw material if there are extraction costs of C/tonne in each period?
d. The marginal cost to extract another tonne of material is €40/tonne and the starting price is P_0 = €80/tonne. Find the growth rate of the price of the resource.

11 MARKET FAILURE AND EXTERNALITIES

In this chapter we extend our knowledge of the deadweight loss of externalities and the use of optimal taxes to correct such market failures. Then we consider an approach to market failure in relation to the Coase theorem. We will use some basic mathematics to find an optimal volume of pollution with the Coase theorem.

EXTERNALITIES, DEADWEIGHT LOSSES AND OPTIMAL TAXES

Externalities create a problem for an efficient market that would otherwise maximize welfare. We will think through this problem of externalities in the context of pollution and in doing so examine the size of deadweight loss and the scope for government taxation policy to deal with the problem.

The analysis makes a number of key assumptions. We assume the market to be competitive and that there is adequate knowledge concerning the size of the externalities. We also assume that when governments intervene in the market there are no administrative and legal costs.

Externalities and Market Failure

As an illustration of the problem of externalities let us assume that some firms in the chemical industry are located by the side of a river. In the production of chemicals they create a by-product that they dispose of in the cheapest way possible. They put it into the river. This kills off fish stocks downstream in the fisheries industry. The dead fish stocks represent a cost to society; the cost is external to the chemical firm but internal to society. We will now use this scenario to analyze the effects of the externality and the effects of government attempts to internalise it by taxation.

Using supply and demand analysis we first establish the market price and output with no government intervention. We will assume that our inverse demand function is given by:

$$P = 30 - Q_D$$

The inverse supply function is the marginal private cost function MPC. Recall that the supply curve is the sum of the marginal cost curves of the firms in the industry. We showed this in Chapter 6.

$$P = 4 + Q_S$$

Then we can establish the equilibrium with no government intervention. The profit maximizing chemical firms can ignore the external cost so equilibrium quantity is found as:

$$30 - Q_D = 4 + Q_S$$

Rearranging to bring all the Q terms on one side we have:

$$2Q = 26$$
$$Q = 13$$

Having solved for Q we can now find the value of P by substituting $Q = 13$ into either the demand or supply equation. Take the demand equation:

$$P = 30 - Q_D$$
$$P = 30 - 13$$
$$P = 17$$

Had we used the marginal private cost function, the supply function, we would have obtained the same result:

$$P = 4 + Q_S$$
$$P = 4 + 13$$
$$P = 17$$

The equilibrium quantity without government intervention is 13 tonnes of the chemical in question and the equilibrium price is €17 per tonne. We have shown this result diagrammatically in Figure 11.1.

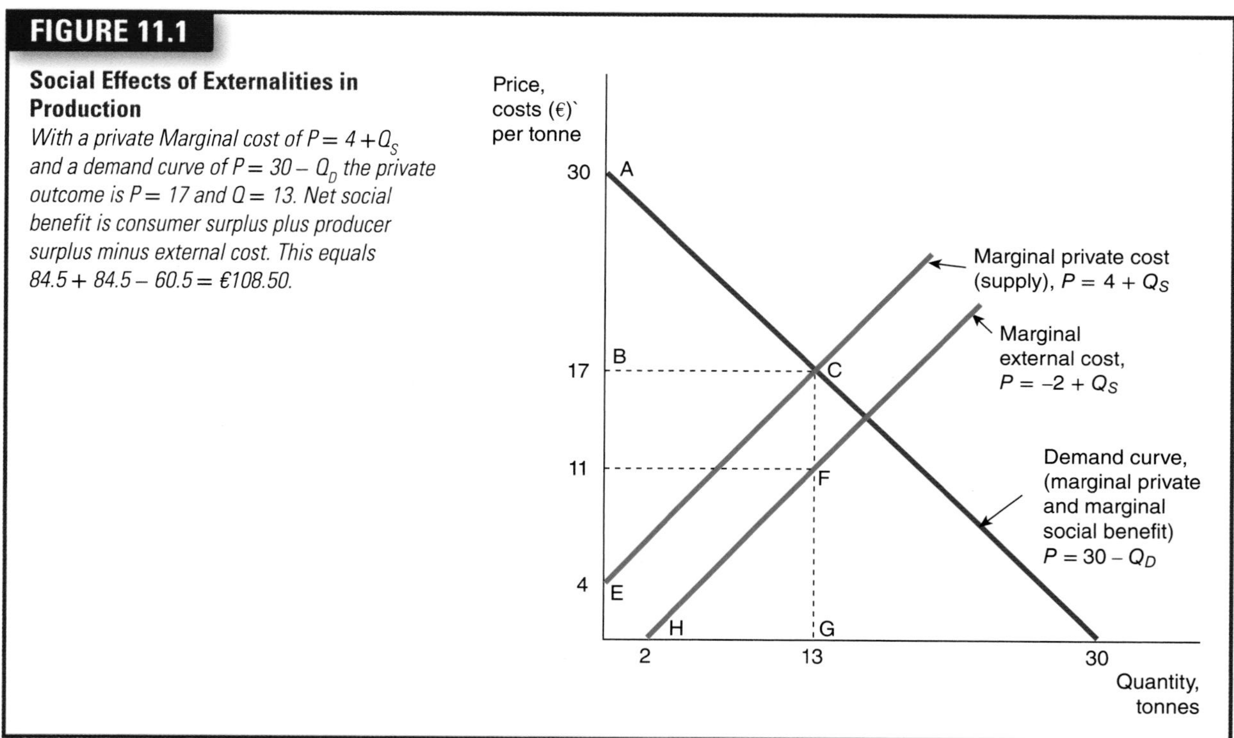

FIGURE 11.1

Social Effects of Externalities in Production

With a private Marginal cost of $P = 4 + Q_S$ and a demand curve of $P = 30 - Q_D$ the private outcome is $P = 17$ and $Q = 13$. Net social benefit is consumer surplus plus producer surplus minus external cost. This equals $84.5 + 84.5 - 60.5 =$ €108.50.

Net Social Benefit at the Private Optimum

Next we want to find the benefit to society from the production of this commodity at this private optimum output level. Net social benefit is:

$$\textit{Consumer surplus} + \textit{Producer surplus} - \textit{External cost}$$

Let's first calculate consumer surplus. Looking at Figure 11.1 we can see that this is the area ABC. We take the private optimum output and multiply that by the difference between the choke price (the lowest price at which demand is zero) and the equilibrium price. Finally we divide by two. Output is 13 and the equilibrium price is €17. The choke price is found as follows:

$$P = 30 - Q_D$$

So when $Q_D = 0$, $P =$ €30.

The difference between the choke price and the equilibrium price is 30 – 17 = €13.

In this example, both the output level and the distance between the choke price and the equilibrium price are 13. Using the formula for the area of a triangle we can calculate the consumer surplus:

$$A = \frac{13 \times 13}{2}$$
$$= \frac{169}{2}$$
$$= 84.5$$

Consumer surplus per period is €84.5.

Now let's calculate producer surplus. Referring to Figure 11.1 we can see that this is the area BCE. We take the private optimum output and multiply by the difference between the price at which $Q_S = 0$ and the equilibrium price. Then we divide the result by 2. Output is 13. The equilibrium price is €7. The price at which $Q_S = 0$ is found as follows:

$$P = 4 + Q_S$$

So when $Q_S = 0$, $P =$ €4.

The difference between this price and the equilibrium price is 17 – 4 = €13.

The producer surplus will be:

$$A = \frac{13 \times 13}{2}$$
$$= \frac{169}{2}$$
$$= 84.5$$

Producer surplus per period is €84.5. In this particular case it just so happens that consumer and producer surplus are the same.

Now we need to find the external cost of producing this private optimum level of output. This can be seen from the diagram as area FGH. This is because we can use the marginal external cost curve. The total external cost is the sum of all the marginal external costs from 0 to the private equilibrium output of 13.

The marginal external cost function is given as $-2 + Q$, so the curve cuts the horizontal axis at +2. The height of our triangle FGH is the segment GH, which is equal to 13 – 2. Therefore h = 11.

The base of the triangle is FG. This is the marginal external cost at 13 units. Therefore it is equal to $-2 + Q = -2 + 13 = 11$.

We have:

$$A = \frac{11 \times 11}{2}$$
$$= \frac{121}{2}$$
$$= 60.5$$

Total External Cost per period is €60.5.

Now we can find the benefit to society from the production of this commodity at this private optimum output level. Net social benefit is:

Consumer surplus + Producer surplus – External cost:

84.5 + 84.5 – 60.5

= €108.50

Net social benefit if the government does not intervene in the market is €108.50 per period.

How would this compare with net social benefit if the government intervenes by imposing an optimum tax on the chemical producer? To calculate this we must first find the socially optimal tax and the new equilibrium output resulting from it.

The Social Optimum Output and Price

We now need to find the socially optimal level of output. We know that *marginal private cost (MPC) + marginal external cost (MEC) = marginal social cost (MSC)*. Marginal cost borne by the firm is MPC. Marginal external cost is marginal cost external to the firm but internal to society. All of the marginal costs to society are either MPC or MEC. Hence we have a definition:

$$MSC = MPC + MEC$$

Since we know that MPC equals the inverse supply function, that is $4 + Q$, and $MEC = -2 + Q$, we add these together:

$$\begin{aligned}&(4 + Q) + (-2 + Q)\\&= 4 + Q - 2 + Q\\&= 2Q_S + 2\end{aligned}$$

The Marginal social cost of the chemical output is $2 + 2Q_S$.

This is shown in Figure 11.2. We have reproduced Figure 11.1 but have now added MSC.

The MSC curve's position can be found in either of two ways. The first way is to use the MPC function. So, for example:

If $Q = 0$, then MSC $= (2 \times 0) + 2 = 2$

And if, say, $Q = 13$, then MSC $= (2 \times 13) + 2 = 28$

It is a straight line function so any two points define its position on the diagram.

Alternatively we could find the same answer by adding the MPC and MEC separately:

$$\begin{aligned}&\text{If } Q = 0, \text{ then } MSC = MPC + MEC = 4 + 0 + (-2 + 0) = 2\\&\text{If } Q = 13, \text{ then } MSC = MPC + MEC = 4 + 13 + (-2 + 13) = 28\end{aligned}$$

The social optimum output is where marginal social cost is equal to marginal social benefit, MSC = MSB, but in our case we have, by assumption, no externalities in consumption so the social optimum output is also where marginal social cost equals marginal private benefit, MSC = MPB. MPB is the demand curve.

$$\begin{aligned}MSC &= 2 + 2Q_S\\MPB &= MSB = 30 - Q_D\\2 + 2Q_S &= 30 - Q_D\\3Q &= 28\\Q &= 9.33\end{aligned}$$

FIGURE 11.2

Internalising Externalities via an Optimal Tax

$MSC = MPC + MEC = 2Q_S + 2$. $MSB = 30 - Q_D$ so the socially optimal price and output is $P = 20.66$ and $Q = 9.33$. At this price and output consumer surplus is now 43.57, producer surplus is 43.52. The external cost is 26.86. Tax revenue is 68.39. Social benefit = 43.57 + 43.52 – 26.86 + 68.39 = €128.62. The original pre-tax social benefit was €108.5. The tax has improved social welfare by 128.62 – 108.5 = €20.12.

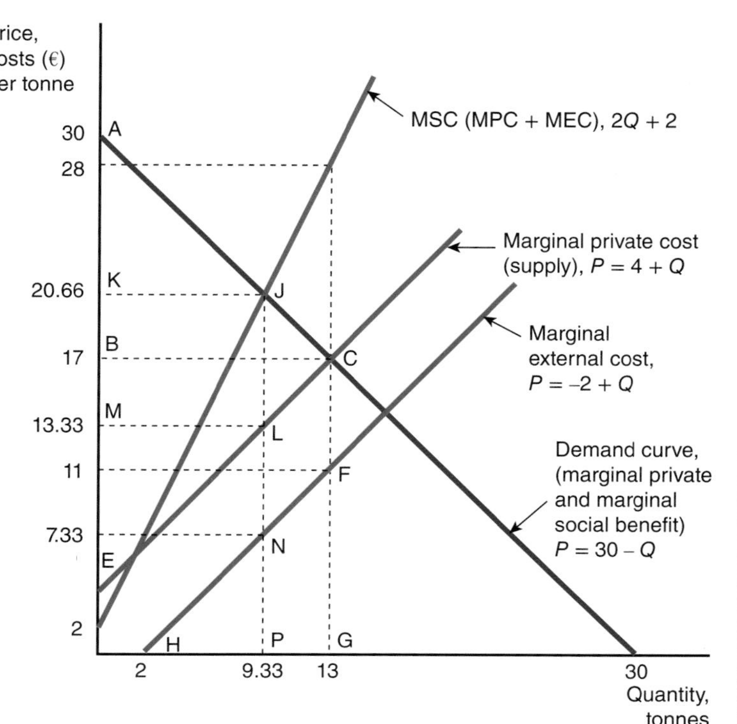

The socially optimum output is 9.33.

Now we can find the socially optimal price. If we use the demand curve we have:

$$P = 30 - Q_D$$
$$= 30 - 9.33$$
$$= €20.66$$

If we use the *MSC* function we have:

$$P = 2 + 2Q_S$$
$$= 2 + 18.66$$
$$= 20.66$$

The socially optimal price is €20.66. This socially optimum output and price we show in Figure 11.2. To achieve this, the government must impose a tax equal to the external cost so the tax will be:

$$-2 + Q$$

Now that the externality has been internalized, the chemical firm's marginal private costs are equal to the marginal social cost so the socially optimal output and price are achieved. Now we can find the extent to which the tax will raise welfare.

To do this we need to find the net social benefit at this price and output and compare it with the privately optimal price and output. So we must go through the same steps as before. We work out the new consumer surplus, then the new producer surplus. Then we can calculate the external cost of producing this output. After that we will need to calculate government revenue from the tax. This will then enable us to find the new social benefit.

Net Social Benefit at the Social Optimum

We begin with the new level of consumer surplus. This is smaller than before. It is now area AJK in Figure 11.2 which is:

$$A = \frac{9.33 \times (30 - 20.66)}{2}$$
$$= \frac{87.14}{2}$$
$$= €43.57$$

Consumer surplus per period is now €43.57.

Now let's calculate the new producer surplus. Referring to Figure 11.2 we can see that this is the area *MLE* (less than the price, because suppliers have to pay the tax). At an output level of 9.33 *MPC* equals €13.33. We know this because the *MPC* function is P= 4 + Q_S, so where Q_S is 9.33, *MPC* equals €13.33. The base of our triangle is *ME*, which 13.33 – 4. We can now find the area of the triangle MLE:

$$A = \frac{9.33 \times (13.33 - 4)}{2}$$
$$= \frac{87.05}{2}$$
$$= €43.52$$

Producer surplus per period is €43.52.

Next we find the new external cost. We expect this to be lower because the tax has reduced output. *MEC* at 9.33, the new level of output, is the area *NPH*, the sum of all the marginal costs from 2 to 9.33. We can use the formula for the area of a triangle whose base is 9.33 – 2 = 7.33. To determine the height, we consider:

$$MEC = -2 + Q_S$$

Q_S = 9.33 so *MEC* = –2 + 9.33 = €7.33

This is shown in Figure 11.2.

External cost, the area of the triangle NPH, is:

$$A = \frac{7.33 \times 7.\ 33}{2}$$
$$= \frac{53.73}{2}$$
$$= €26.86$$

The external cost at this level of output is €26.86.

Next we work out the tax revenue received as a result of the equilibrium level of production. Refer to Figure 11.2. The price is €20.66. The producer receives the supply price of:

$$P = 4 + Q_S$$

$P = 4 + 9.33 =$ €13.33 per unit so the tax per unit is €7.33.

The supply price of €13.33 is shown in Figure 11.2. So a tax of €7.33 on a level of output of 9.33 gives:

$$7.33 \times 9.33 = €68.39$$

The tax raises €68.39.

Now we can find the benefit to society from the production of this commodity at this socially optimal output level. Net social benefit is:

$$\textit{Consumer surplus} + \textit{Producer surplus} - \textit{External cost} + \textit{tax revenue}:$$
$$43.57 + 43.52 - 26.86 + 68.39$$
$$= €128.62$$

The original, pre-tax net social benefit was €108.50.

Now we can calculate the deadweight loss of the externality. It is the difference between net social benefit at the private optimum and net social benefit at the social optimum.

$$128.62 - 108.5 = €20.12$$

Table 11.1 summarizes these results.

TABLE 11.1 **Summary of costs and benefits of Production Externalities and Government Intervention (€)**

Benefit/Cost	No Tax	Socially Optimal Tax
Consumer Surplus	84.50	43.57
Producer Surplus	84.50	43.52
External Cost	60.50	26.86
Government Revenue	Zero	68.39
Net Social Benefit	108.50	128.62
Deadweight Loss	20.12	Zero

The private optimum is inefficient. Society misses out on potential benefits represented by the deadweight loss. This is the reduction in welfare for society if government fails to correct the externality. However, if the government imposes the optimal size of tax, all of the deadweight loss of the externality is removed.

Notice that in this example there are positive net benefits even at the private optimum. Banning all output reduces social welfare.

Our figures are only illustrative but this demonstrates the potential for misallocation of resources where there are externalities present and gives us a way of measuring their size when we can estimate the cost and benefit functions.

THE COASE THEOREM

Now we develop the Coase theorem. We will use the same basic problem as before but the Coase solution to the problem is very different from that of finding an optimal tax. Indeed, the government has no role to play. The market finds the socially optimal solution.

For this to be possible it requires that there are clearly established property rights. In this example, the river must be owned by either the fisheries or the chemical industry. It doesn't matter who the owner is. Bargaining between the firms will bring about the same optimal solution.

Let's set this up diagrammatically and then we will use a little maths to demonstrate the solution. Consider Figure 11.3. Here we show the effects of control of pollution measured along the horizontal axis, from zero control, where the chemical industry is free to dump whatever it wishes into the river, to 100 per cent control where there would be no dumping of chemical effluent at all. The vertical axis measures the cost of the control. The more control there is, the greater the cost to the chemical industry. The marginal cost of control rises because the chemical industry finds it ever more expensive to deal with its waste as the problem of waste disposal increases. However, the extent to which the chemical industry is harmed by control is the extent to which the fisheries industry benefits. The effect of the controls is symmetrical. Thus the marginal cost of control to the chemical industry represents the marginal benefit to the fisheries industry of that control, as shown in Figure 11.3.

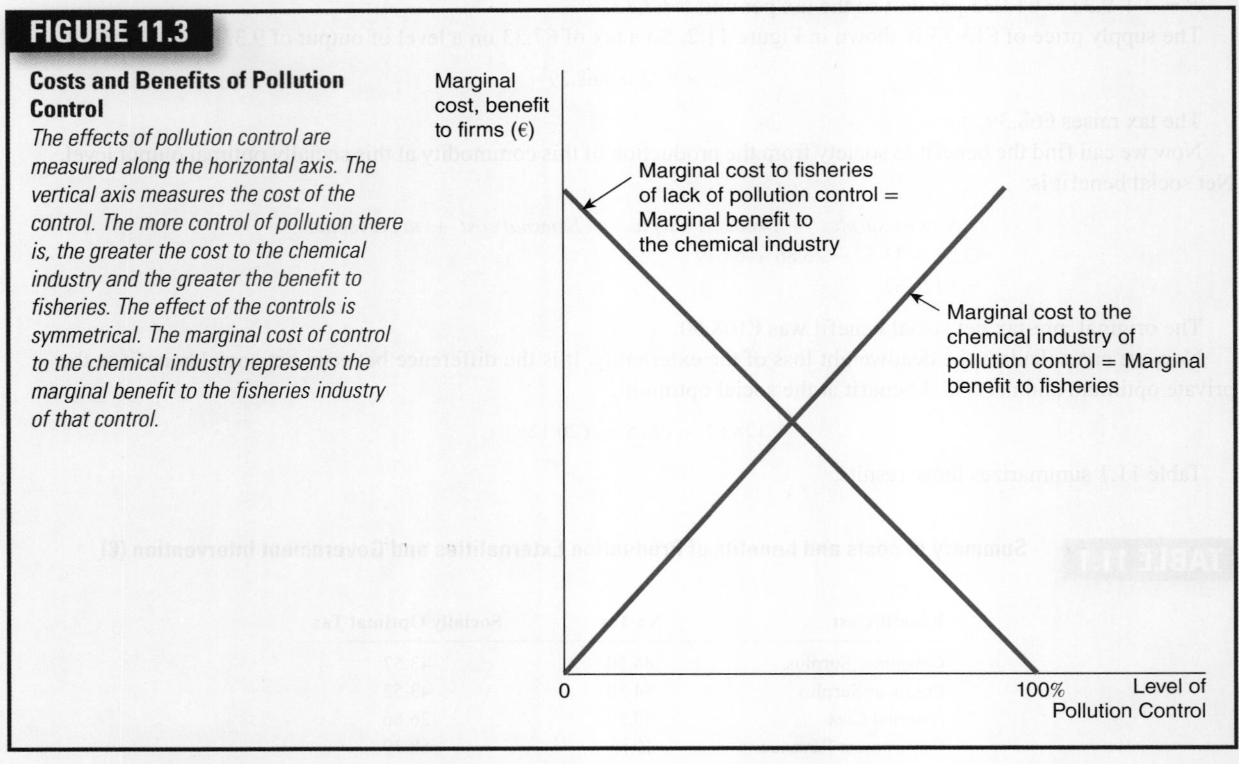

FIGURE 11.3

Costs and Benefits of Pollution Control

The effects of pollution control are measured along the horizontal axis. The vertical axis measures the cost of the control. The more control of pollution there is, the greater the cost to the chemical industry and the greater the benefit to fisheries. The effect of the controls is symmetrical. The marginal cost of control to the chemical industry represents the marginal benefit to the fisheries industry of that control.

Now consider the fisheries industry. It clearly benefits from 100 per cent control but as that control lessens, the damage to the fisheries industry rises. As the control lessens, the marginal cost of reducing control rises. We have shown this relationship in Figure 11.3, but remember the symmetrical nature of the relationship with the chemical industry. The increase in marginal cost to the fisheries industry of the reduction in pollution control is the marginal benefit to the chemical industry.

On first thought, therefore, it seems that if the fisheries industry owns the river it will insist on one hundred per cent control of dumping. Anything less will impose costs on itself. Similarly it might appear that if the chemical industry had the property rights to the river it would operate no control at all. Any degree of control imposes costs upon itself. However, the Coase theorem suggests that this is not the case.

Refer to Figure 11.4 where highlights the optimal degree of control. Let's suppose first that the river is owned by the chemical industry and there is no pollution control. Would there ever be some level of control introduced, at, say control level CL_1? The marginal cost to the chemical industry would be MC_1 but the marginal benefit to fisheries would be much higher at MC_2. It will therefore benefit the fisheries industry to pay the chemical industry to operate this level of control over the dumping of waste. A payment of somewhere between MC_1 and MC_2 would benefit both parties. The potential for a mutually beneficial trade would exist at any level of pollution control up to CL_{opt}, the optimal level of control.

We can now consider what would happen if the river were owned by the fisheries. Would control be at 100 per cent? Consider the level of pollution control represented by CL_2. The marginal cost to fisheries of this reduction in control is MC_3, but the benefit to the chemical industry is MC_4. The chemical industry could now successfully encourage the fisheries industry to agree to this reduction in control and to allow some dumping. This would, in principle, be true of any level of control greater than CL_{opt}. Negotiation between the two parties will bring about an optimal level of control regardless of the ownership of the resource.

FIGURE 11.4

The Optimal Level of Pollution Control

The marginal cost of control to the chemical industry represents the marginal benefit to the fisheries industry of that control. Negotiation between the two parties will bring about an optimal level of control, CL_{opt}, regardless of the ownership of the resource.

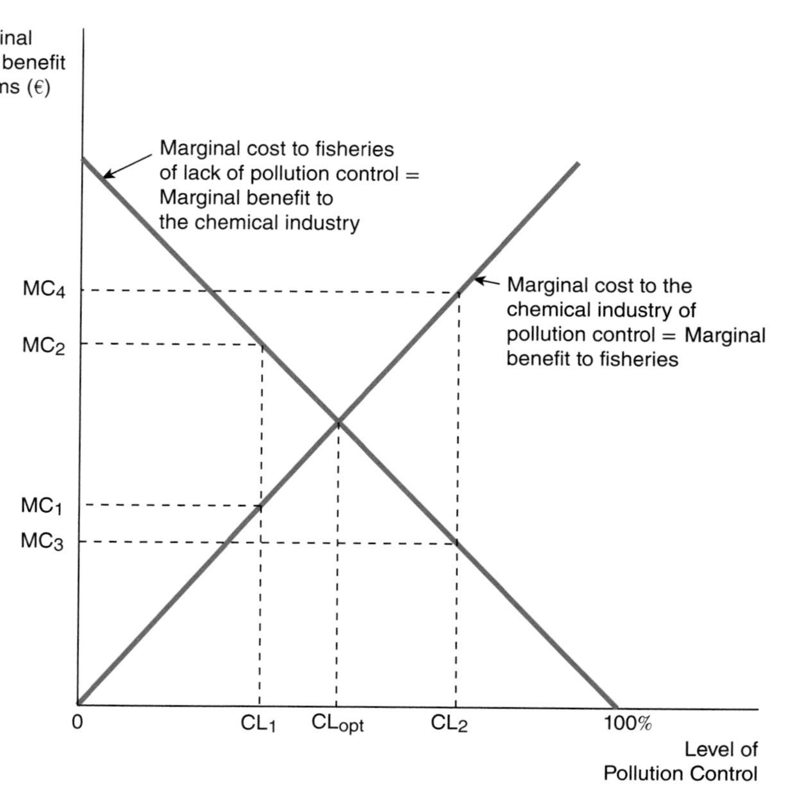

Determining the Optimum Level of Control

If we assume the cost functions we have been considering previously we can work out the optimum level of control. We can also analyze the effects of changes in technology on the optimal pollution levels.

Suppose the marginal cost functions are as follows.

The marginal cost of pollution to the chemical industry (Marginal Benefit to fisheries):

$$MC_c = 2Q$$

Where:

MC_c is marginal cost to the chemical industry

Q is the quantity of control of pollution

The marginal cost of pollution to fisheries (Marginal Benefit to the chemical industry):

$$MC_f = 100 - Q$$

Where:

MC_f is marginal cost to the fisheries

Q is the quantity of control of pollution

Trade will establish equilibrium where:

$$2Q = 100 - Q$$
$$3Q = 100$$
$$Q = 33.33$$

We would expect trade to establish a level of control of pollution of 33.33 per cent regardless of ownership of the river.

Now suppose technology changes. Let's assume that technological developments enable the chemical industry to find less expensive alternative means to dispose of chemical waste. The marginal cost of pollution control changes to, let's say:

$$MC_c = Q$$

A new optimal volume of control is established. The chemical industry is less willing to encourage the fisheries industry to allow pollution, so more pollution control is established. Our two cost functions are now:

$$MC_c = Q$$
$$MC_f = 100 - Q$$
$$100 - Q = Q$$
$$2Q = 100$$
$$Q = 50$$

The optimal volume of pollution control has risen from 33.33 per cent to 50 per cent as a result of technological change. Again the new optimum is reached without government intervention. This is shown in Figure 11.5.

A private solution of this sort requires a number of key conditions, foremost of which is the establishment of clear property rights to enable voluntary exchanges to take place. Whilst some common property rights such as beaches and rivers could be privatized, it is difficult to see how with current technology such rights could be established in, for example, air or the North Sea.

FIGURE 11.5

Optimal Volumes of Pollution and Technological Change

When marginal cost of pollution to the chemical industry (marginal benefit to fisheries) = MC_c = 2Q and marginal cost of pollution to fisheries (marginal benefit to the chemical industry) = MC_f = 100 – Q, trade establishes an equilibrium level of control at 33.33 per cent regardless of ownership of the river. If the marginal cost of pollution control changes to MC_c = Q, a new optimal volume of control is established at Q = 50 per cent.

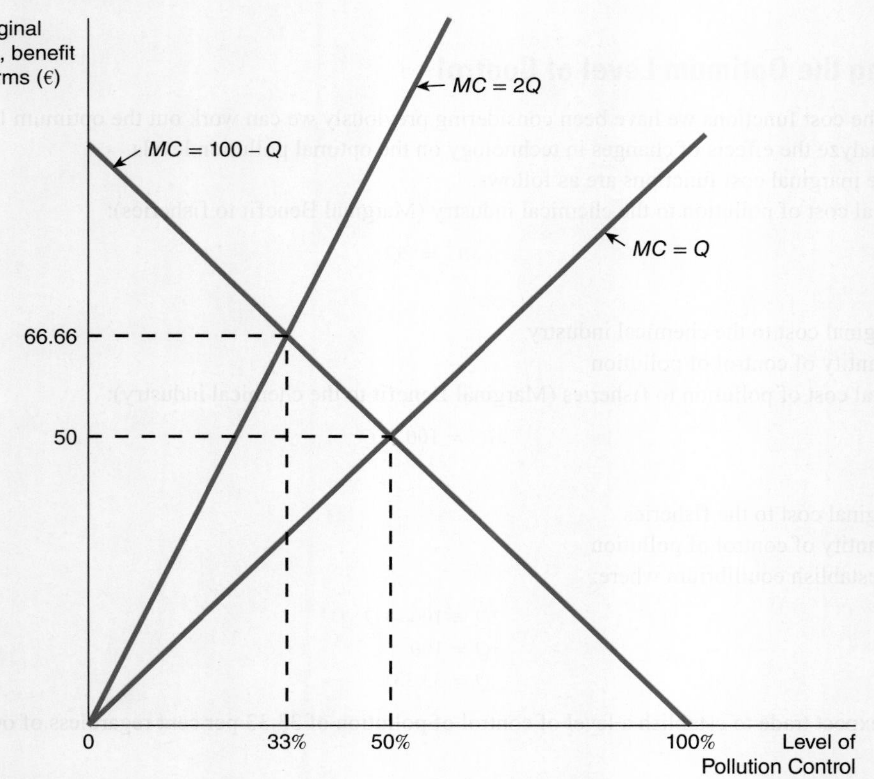

PROBLEMS AND APPLICATIONS

1 The (inverse) demand function for a good is $P_D = 2500 - 2.4Q_D$ which also shows the private and social marginal benefits (MSB). The inverse supply function $P_S = 50 + 2.5Q_S$ represents the private marginal cost of the output of a competitive industry. The production of the output is causing negative external effects with constant marginal cost of €490 per unit of output.

a. Find the market equilibrium price and quantity when producers do not take external cost into account when making production decisions.
b. Calculate the consumer and the producer surplus.
c. How high are the total external costs the society has to bear in the market without government intervention?
d. Determine the net social benefit, taking external effects into account.
e. Establish the function for marginal social cost.
f. How large is the socially optimal amount of output and how high are private and external marginal costs at this quantity?
g. Even at the socially desirable level of output some external effect remains. How high are the total external costs?
h. Calculate the net social benefit at the optimal output.
i. What is the magnitude of the welfare loss caused by the unregulated external effect (deadweight loss)?
j. How high is the optimal tax that brings the market to the socially desirable level of output?
k. Compare the total external cost with the tax revenue.

2 Again, use the demand function $MSB = P_D = 2500 - 2.4Q_D$ assuming there are no externalities associated with the consumption of the good. The private marginal cost is given by $P_S = 50 + 2.5Q_S$. Assume now that marginal external costs are not constant but the 'damage done' rises with the level of output. Marginal external costs are therefore an upward sloping function $MEC = 472.5 + 0.75Q_S$.

a. How large are the total external costs at the private market equilibrium and the net social benefit?
b. Find the function for marginal social cost.
c. Establishing the socially optimal level of output.
d. How high are the consumer surplus, total private and total external costs at the optimum quantity?
e. Compare the net social benefit of the market output and the optimal output.
f. The government internalizes the external cost through an optimal tax. What is the optimal tax rate, if a tax per unit is imposed?
g. How much revenue does the tax generate? Is this more or less than the total external cost of the optimal output?

3 Consider a product with negative external effects from consumption. Even though private demand (MPB) is still $P_D = 2500 - 2.4Q_D$, now you have external cost from the consumption of each unit of output of €490. If there are no externalities from the production of the good private marginal cost and marginal social cost are both equal to $P_S = 50 + 2.5Q_S$.

a. Will the industry's output be larger or smaller than the socially desirable level?
b. Confirm your answer above with a calculation of the optimal consumption quantity of the product.
c. How large are the consumer and producer surplus as well as the total external cost without government intervention?
d. If the optimal tax is set to internalize the external cost into the decision-making process of private agents, does it matter whether the tax has to be paid by producers or consumers?

4 For ease of calculation we have used linear functions so far in the examples of this chapter. In Chapters 2 and 3 you became familiar with different types of nonlinear functions, like logarithmic, exponential and quadratic functions or polynomials of higher degree. Think about which functions could depict the following circumstances appropriately.

a. For each unit of output a fixed amount of waste Z (tonnes/ unit of output) is generated. Each additional ton of waste causes the same external cost as all other tonnes. Write out a function depicting external marginal cost as a function of output.
b. The long-term damage to human health of a certain dangerous by-product of the output is accumulating over time. The more of the by-product is already emitted into the environment, the higher is the damage done by each additional unit of the dangerous by-product. Use a function to describe the marginal external cost.
c. Residues of fertilizers from farming land are washed into a lake. Crop output on the farm land is linear in the input of the fertilizer as is the washout. However, if the annual amount of fertilizer in the lake goes beyond a certain level K,

the water is going to tip over into the anaerobic state and all the fish will die. Until then nothing much happens. Which functional form could you use to describe the marginal external cost of farming output?

d. Assume that education (measured in years of schooling or studying) has positive external effects. However, increasing the time spent in school from five years to six years has a larger external benefit than an increase from 19 years to 20 years. Use an appropriate function to describe marginal external benefits of education.

5 An industry annually emits 200 units of hazardous materials into the environment. The external cost of these emissions (E) can be described by an increasing function; specifically, the marginal cost of tolerating another unit of emissions is close to zero when there are no emissions and they increase to €100 if 200 units of emissions have to be tolerated, i.e. $MC_{tolerating}(E) = 0.5E$. The marginal cost of tolerating another (marginal) unit of pollution can be seen as equivalent to the marginal benefit the society gains from avoiding this marginal unit of emissions. In our example we define X as the number of units of the hazardous material that were not emitted (avoided), so that $X = 200 - E \Leftrightarrow E = 200 - X$. The function of marginal benefits of emission avoidance then is $MBA(X) = MC_{tolerating}(200 - X) = 100 - 0.5X$.

For the X-industry emission avoidance comes at a rising cost; the more units of hazardous materials were already avoided (i.e. through filtering or cutting production) the more expensive it gets to avoid another unit. This increasing marginal cost of avoidance (reducing emissions) is given by:

$$MCA = 10 + 0.25X$$

a. Show the marginal benefits (MBA) and the marginal cost of avoidance (MCA) in a graph.
b. Calculate the optimum level of emission avoidance (reduction or control). Confirm your calculation from the graph.
c. Show and calculate the net benefit the society forgoes if no emission reductions take place and the population has to tolerate the full amount of $E = 200$ units of emissions.
d. How large are the excess costs over benefits if the industry has to stop production and reduce $X = 200$ units of emissions?
e. If the property rights are set up in a way that allows the X-industry to emit the hazardous materials, how is the Coase-solution reached and who is paying which amount to whom to make sure an optimal solution is achieved?
f. Reverse the property rights situation; now the population has a right to zero emissions. How is the Coase-solution achieved under ideal circumstances?

12 INFORMATION AND BEHAVIOURAL ECONOMICS

Consumer theory is often presented as though the consumer knows the availability and price of all products. In this chapter we extend consumer theory by an explicit recognition that information is imperfect and that finding the products you want will often involve the costs of searching.

INTRODUCTION

Many economists have questioned whether economic agents behave in a rational way. These agents might be consumers, or firms or governments. Economists have also pointed out that such agents often work with imperfect information. For example, consumers do not know all the goods available for purchase and firms do not know all possible opportunities for making investments and selling products. In this chapter we focus on consumers only. Furthermore, we do not assume irrationality, only that they make choices with limited information.

We look at one basic model of consumer decision-making. Other models make more realistic assumptions but these are beyond the scope of this book.

SEARCH COSTS

The standard economic model assumes that the consumer has perfect information. The consumer knows all the goods and services that are of interest, where they can be found and at what price. It is also further assumed that the consumer accurately gauges how much utility a good will bring. As you will know from your own experience, life is often not so straightforward. You are not sure where to get the products you want, you don't know how much they will cost, they may be at different prices in different locations and you may be disappointed after you have bought the good and used it – in other words it fails to yield as much utility as expected.

In this section we explore the idea that consumers lack perfect information in one specific sense; they do not know where the good is at its lowest price. We will assume a uniform good, identical wherever it is purchased. The only variable is the price paid. We will further assume that consumers know some things about the price being charged in different places. They know the lowest price for which it can be bought but not where that is. Here is the problem: a consumer can go into a shop and discover the price being charged. They can decide it might be worth trying another place, which may or may not lead to finding a lower price. In exploring these different options there are costs involved in the search. It may not involve travel costs at all. It may well be possible to search and buy online. Even so, searches use up scarce time. Is any additional search worth it to the consumer?

The Costs and Benefits of Searching

Suppose every search costs the consumer €4 in time and in other costs. How many searches will the consumer make? It depends upon the expected benefit in terms of a lower price. Can we work out that expected benefit? The expected benefit of a search will tend to decline with every additional search. As more information is gained, the chances of finding a still lower price get smaller. The marginal cost of searching may well be constant over a range of search activity, although eventually the cost will rise, mainly because the opportunity cost of search time will increase. Here we will assume that the marginal cost of searching is constant. The assumption is that a rational consumer will continue searching until the marginal cost of the search is equal to the marginal benefit.

By assumption, the benefit obtained from searching is not in terms of finding a better good but of finding a lower price. We can get a good idea of the benefit of another search with a formula. It isn't precise, for reasons we shall explore shortly, but it is generally a good approximation.

$$\textit{Expected price} = \textit{Lowest Price} + \frac{\textit{Price range}}{\textit{Number of searches} + 1}$$

Let's use an example to illustrate. A consumer is looking to buy a particular smart phone. They know that one-fifth of the customer outlets will be charging €140, one-fifth charging €120, one-fifth €100, one-fifth €80 and one-fifth €60. You know this but you do not know which places are charging which price. The expected price from one random visit we can calculate as follows.

The lowest price is €60. The price range is €80, the difference between the highest price, €140 and the lowest price, €60. Therefore, using the formula above, we have:

$$\textit{Expected price} = 60 + \frac{80}{1 + 1}$$

$$\textit{Expected price} = \text{€}100$$

This is an approximation. The example we have given is uniformly distributed, so the approximation is close. Had the vast majority of shops been charging €140 and just one or two charging lower prices, then the expected price from a single visit would be different and the above formula would not be valid.

Alternatively we could have calculated it as:

$$(\tfrac{1}{5} \times 140) + (\tfrac{1}{5} \times 120) + (\tfrac{1}{5} \times 100) + (\tfrac{1}{5} \times 80) + (\tfrac{1}{5} \times 60)$$
$$= 28 + 24 + 20 + 16 + 12$$

The expected price from one search = €100.

What of the expected price of a second search? Using the formula we have:

$$\textit{Expected price of second search} = 60 + \frac{80}{3}$$
$$= \text{€}86.66$$

The expected price of a third search will be:

$$\textit{Expected price of third search} = 60 + \frac{80}{4}$$
$$= \text{€}80$$

The expected price of a fourth search will be:

$$\textit{Expected price of fourth search} = 60 + \frac{80}{5}$$
$$= \text{€}76$$

The expected price of a fifth search will be:

$$\textit{Expected price of fifth search} = 60 + \frac{80}{6}$$
$$= \text{€}73.33$$

For each further search the expected price will be less than the previous price but the rate of decline will be slower.[1]

Now we can calculate the marginal benefit of an additional search. It will be the difference in the price of n searches minus the difference in the price of $n+1$ searches. These numbers are presented Table 12.1.

[1] The formula is also approximate for all searches after the first one. As additional searches are undertaken information about the price at some shops is discovered, so the expected price is changing slightly. When all visits have been undertaken except one, the expected price of the last search is not some weighted average of possibilities. The price is certain and known.

TABLE 12.1 **The Marginal Costs and Benefits of Searching**

Number of searches	Expected Price (€)	Marginal Benefit of Search (€)	Marginal Cost of Search (€)
1	100	-	4
2	86.66	13.33	4
3	80	6.67	4
4	76	4	4
5	73.33	2.67	4

This can be represented diagrammatically as in Figure 12.1.

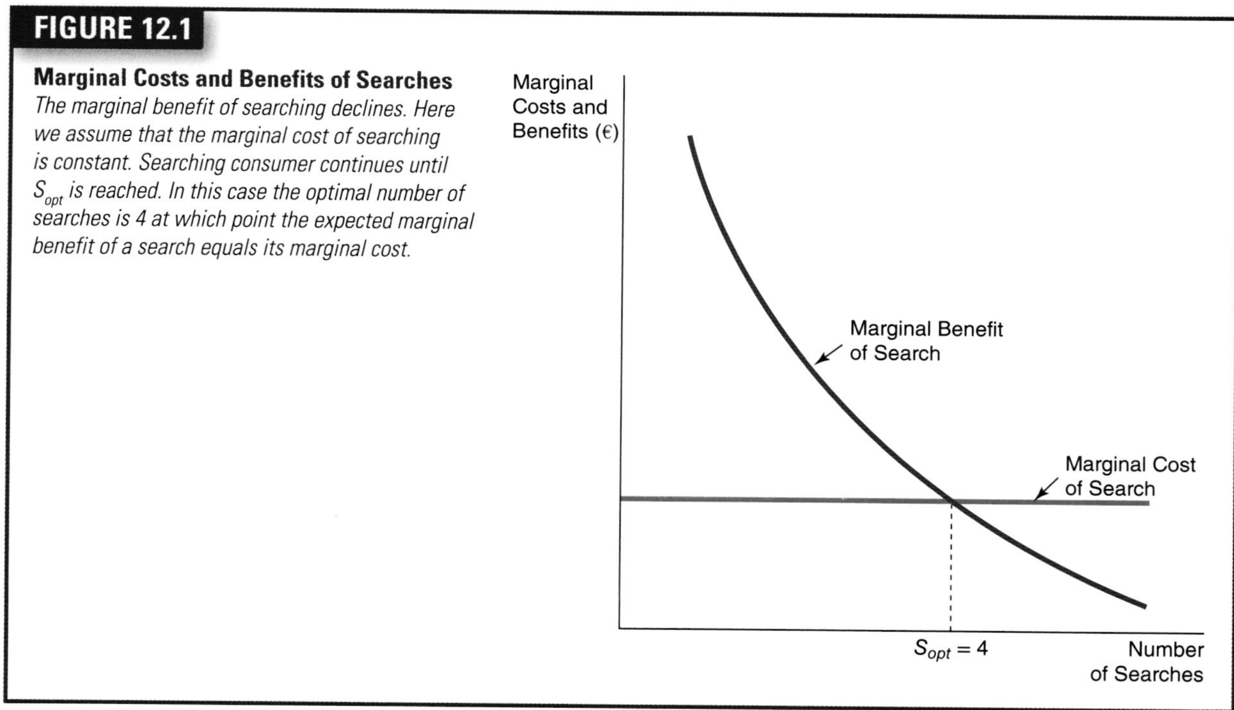

FIGURE 12.1

Marginal Costs and Benefits of Searches

The marginal benefit of searching declines. Here we assume that the marginal cost of searching is constant. Searching consumer continues until S_{opt} is reached. In this case the optimal number of searches is 4 at which point the expected marginal benefit of a search equals its marginal cost.

As the marginal benefit of searching declines and the marginal cost of searching is constant, the consumer continues searching until S_{opt} is reached. The number of searches will vary between consumers depending upon the nature of the good and upon the value placed on the costs of searching. Some will place a different value on the costs of search and this will lead to a different level of S_{opt} but the principle should now be clear.

Search Costs and Consumer Behaviour

We can now extend our understanding of consumer behaviour in the light of this analysis of search costs. Several things follow from our analysis:

1. In our example we assumed that the good for which the consumer is searching was identical in every outlet. The only issue was the price. In principle we can extend this idea to a good where its detailed nature varies between outlets. In the case of a smartphone, it might be, for example, that the aftercare service will vary. The difficulty of applying our formula is that we have to assign money values to these variations in product quality.
2. The higher the price of a product, the greater the benefit of a search will be, so S_{opt} will tend to be larger. More searches will tend to be worthwhile. Most people tend not to invest time searching for a lower price of a carton of yoghurt between supermarkets.
3. Similarly, *ceteris paribus*, a wider range of prices causes S_{opt} to be larger. The potential benefit of an additional search will be greater if prices are not all clustered close to the mean.

4. An analysis of search costs helps to explain why the law of one price is sometimes not observed in practice. The law of one price suggests that competition forces firms to supply the same good at the same price. There are several reasons why this may not be so in practice. One reason is as follows. You will observe that in many towns that attract tourists, prices can vary for essentially the same goods. Some places are known as 'tourist traps'. Tourists can be thought of as those with high search costs. You only have a limited time in the town so you feel unable to spend time hunting for a cafe with lower prices. Locals have low search costs because they will make many purchases over a period so the search costs are spread over many products. Thus there are two markets here, a tourist market and a locals' market. This is an equilibrium position with high-priced sellers selling to fewer people and low-priced sellers happy to sell at lower prices because they sell greater volumes.

Limits to the Formula

We said that our formula was only an approximation. Now we consider the two reasons why this is so.

First, the formula is only precise where we have continuous data rather than the discrete data of our example.[2] Ideally we should have data that conforms to a normal distribution such as the ones shown in Figure 12.2. In this case the mean is 100, as in our example. The normal distribution can take a variety of shapes but has to be symmetrical about the mean. We show two normal distribution curves in Figure 12.2 to illustrate this point.

FIGURE 12.2

Examples of Normal Distributions

A normal distribution is symmetrical about the mean. However, there are many such normal distributions, of which the diagram illustrates two.

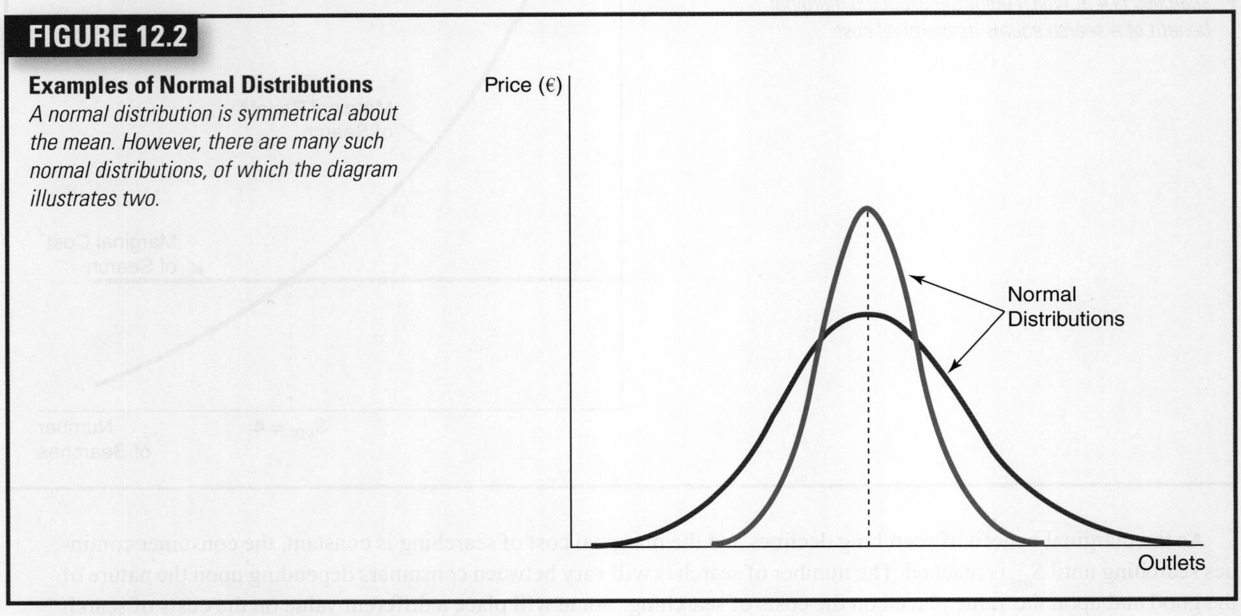

However, if we plot the data from our example, which we have done in Figure 12.3, you can see that, because we have used discrete rather than continuous data, it is only an approximation to the normal curve. In general, we can say that as the number of data sets increases, the value obtained by the formula becomes ever more accurate. Nevertheless, the formula represents a good approximation even with discrete data, so long as it approximates to the normal curve.

Second, the formula requires that the distribution is indeed normal. Often such data might be skewed, as for example in Figure 12.4. This would be the case if, in our smart phone example, more of the outlets were known to have a price below the mean average price.

Finally one might note that technological change can lower search costs. For some goods, for example, one can gather a lot of price information quickly with an internet search. Search costs are low. However, substantial differences in price are still observed for many goods so our formula still has much predictive power.

[2] Discrete data can only take certain values. For example, rolling a dice will give a value of 1, 2, 3, 4, 5 or 6. It cannot take a value of, say, 5.5. Here you cannot half values. Continuous data can take any value, for example time. You could run a marathon in two hours or in two hours and half a second.

FIGURE 12.3

Assumed Price Dispersal for a Mobile Phone

Discrete data may approximate a normal distribution. Such an example is given in the diagram.

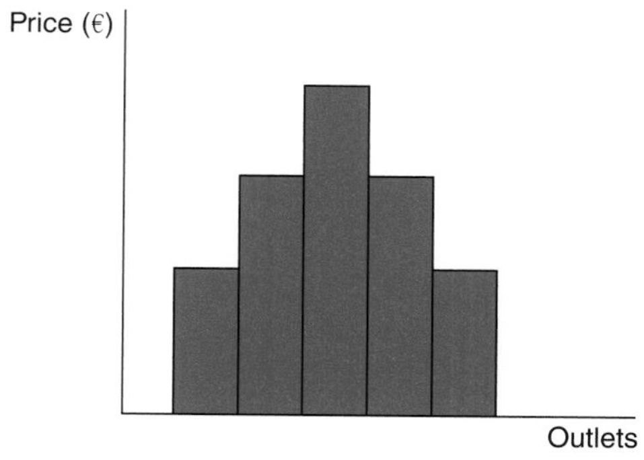

Price (€)

Outlets

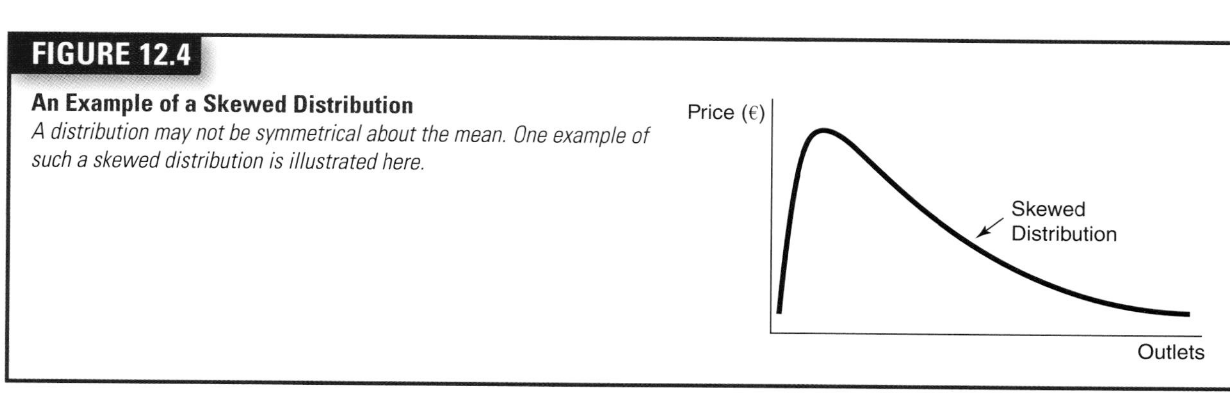

FIGURE 12.4

An Example of a Skewed Distribution

A distribution may not be symmetrical about the mean. One example of such a skewed distribution is illustrated here.

PROBLEMS AND APPLICATIONS

1 You are shopping for strawberries at the beginning of the season when prices can vary widely between €2 per kilogram and €6 per kilogram.

   a. Which price would you expect for your first search?
   b. How large is the benefit you expect from your second search?
   c. Assume that finding the price in the next store or fruit stall along the road costs you €0.20. If you're planning to buy a whole kilogram of strawberries, is it worth your while to conduct a second and third search?
   d. What is the optimal number of searches to conduct?

2 In the above example marginal search costs remain constant, no matter the number of searches conducted. This is not always the case.

   a. Explain a scenario in which marginal search costs increase with the number of searches already done and describe this in the function.
   b. Think about a different scenario in which search costs decline as you do more searches. Again, spell out your thinking in the functional form.

3 How does the existence of online shopping and price comparison websites alter search cost?

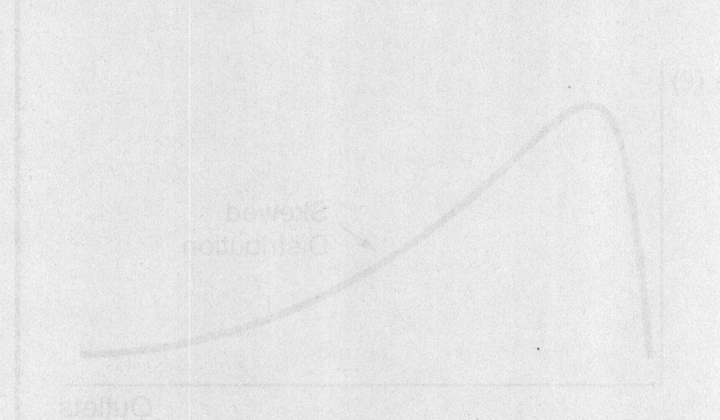

PART 6 FIRM BEHAVIOUR AND MARKET STRUCTURES

13 FIRM'S PRODUCTION DECISIONS

In this chapter we begin by explaining the concept of a production function. Then we look at one form of relationship between output and inputs in the long run, that seen in the Cobb–Douglas production function. Next we illustrate this function from oil production. Then we use a Cobb–Douglas function to consider short-run production and finally, we examine another kind of production function, the Leontief production function.

PRODUCTION FUNCTIONS

A production function expresses the relationship between the quantities of factors such as labour, land, capital and raw materials, and the volume of output these factors produce. The production function might relate to resources used to produce output within a firm, or within an industry, or even for a whole economy. However, since our interest is in developing an understanding of firm behaviour we will focus on production within a firm.

The production function might have the form of:

$$Q = f(K, L)$$

Where:
Q = units of output per day
K = units of capital, perhaps in machine hours per day
L = units of labour, perhaps in person hours per day
Now we consider one particular form, the Cobb–Douglas production function.

The Cobb–Douglas Production Function

The Cobb–Douglas production function is of particular interest because it has been found to be a form that is often present in industrial production. In principle it can be used to examine the relationship between the output of a firm and any number of inputs, but most commonly it focuses on the relationship between output and just two inputs, that of capital and labour. It is multiplicative (rather than additive) to reflect the fact that production requires both labour *and* capital. A firm with lots of capital and no labour will produce nothing. Similarly, a firm with labour but no capital will often produce nothing. The function stresses the importance of the interaction between workers and capital. Suppose, for example, production happens when a worker and machine interact. The number of such interactions, and hence production, that occurs will depend on the product of machine and worker numbers, according to some power law.

Other laws are possible, depending on the nature of the production, but we expect Q to increase with increasing capital and labour.

The Cobb–Douglas production function can be represented as:

$$Q = A \times K^a \times L^b$$

Where:

A = constant

a, b = power terms with positive values

To illustrate such a relationship let's suppose that:

$$A = 100$$
$$K = 64$$
$$L = 100$$
$$a = \frac{1}{3}$$
$$b = \frac{1}{2}$$

Let's work out what the level of output, Q, these inputs can generate for the firm.

$$\begin{aligned} Q &= 100 \times (64)^{\frac{1}{3}} \times (100)^{\frac{1}{2}} \\ &= 100 \times 4 \times 10 \\ &= 4000 \end{aligned}$$

Then 64 units of capital + 100 units of labour will yield the firm 4000 units of output per day.

Now let's explore what happens to output if we change the volume of inputs. Suppose we double each of the inputs. How much more output will the firm get? Will it double? Will it more than double? Will it less than double? Now we will have:

$$Q = 100 \times (2K)^{\frac{1}{3}} \times (2L)^{\frac{1}{2}}$$

To help the calculation we can take each of our two variables and break them down to give:

$$(2K)^{\frac{1}{3}} = 2^{\frac{1}{3}} \times K^{\frac{1}{3}}$$
$$(2L)^{\frac{1}{2}} = 2^{\frac{1}{2}} \times L^{\frac{1}{2}}$$

So we can now substitute into the production function and write:

$$\begin{aligned} Q &= 100 \times (2^{\frac{1}{3}} \times K^{\frac{1}{3}})(2^{\frac{1}{2}} \times L^{\frac{1}{2}}) \\ &= 2^{\frac{1}{3}} \times 2^{\frac{1}{2}} \times (100 \times K^{\frac{1}{3}} \times L^{\frac{1}{2}}) \end{aligned}$$

The terms in the brackets give the original level of Q. So the new level of Q is the original level of Q multiplied by $2^{\frac{1}{3}} \times 2^{\frac{1}{2}} = 2^{\frac{5}{6}}$.

$$2^{\frac{5}{6}} = 1.78$$

The original output Q was 4000 units. Now with the twice the volumes of K and L, Q will be:

$$4000 \times 1.78 = 7120$$

When inputs double from K = 64 and L = 100, output increases 1.78 times, that is less than double. Doubling the inputs less than doubled the outputs. If this is the case we have 'decreasing returns to scale'. Had our function been such that doubling the inputs doubles the output, we would have constant returns to scale. If doubling inputs more than doubles output, then there are increasing returns to scale. Alternatively expressed, whether we get decreasing, constant or increasing returns to scale depends on the n, which in the above example was 5/6. In summary:

If $n < 1$, we have decreasing returns to scale.
If $n = 1$, we have constant returns to scale.
If $n > 1$, we have increasing returns to scale.

In our particular case n is < 1 at 5/6.

Let's see what happens if the firm expands but to a smaller extent. Let's see the effect on output if we increase the volume of inputs by 50 per cent, rather than by 100 per cent. This gives:

$$Q = 100 \times (1.5K)^{\frac{1}{3}} \times (1.5L)^{\frac{1}{2}}$$

Or we can write:

$$\begin{aligned} Q &= 100 \times \left(\left(\frac{3}{2}\right)^{\frac{1}{3}} \times K^{\frac{1}{3}}\right)\left(\left(\frac{3}{2}\right)^{\frac{1}{2}} \times L^{\frac{1}{2}}\right) \\ &= \left(\frac{3}{2}\right)^{\frac{1}{3}} \times \left(\frac{3}{2}\right)^{\frac{1}{2}} \times \left(100 \times K^{\frac{1}{3}} \times L^{\frac{1}{2}}\right) \\ &= \left(\frac{3}{2}\right)^{\frac{5}{6}} \times \left(100 \times K^{\frac{1}{3}} \times L^{\frac{1}{2}}\right) \end{aligned}$$

The terms in the brackets represent the original level of Q. The new level of Q is the original level of Q multiplied by the new factor $\left(\frac{3}{2}\right)^{\frac{5}{6}}$.

$$\left(\frac{3}{2}\right)^{\frac{5}{6}} = 1.402$$

Had the firm increased its inputs by 50 per cent, output would only have increased by 40.2 per cent. The increase in the output, Q, will be:

$$4000 \times 1.402 = 5608$$

Again we have found decreasing returns to scale. Notice that we do not always get whole numbers. To make life easier we are assuming that K and L can be infinitely divisible.

The returns to scale would be different for different industries because they use different production processes. But even for different firms in the same industry, there might be different relationships between the firm's inputs and outputs. The nature of the production process leads to a difference in the nature of the production function. Here we can see that n will vary at different levels of production even within the same firm.

Are there any other combinations of labour and capital that could yield the same level of output, 4000 units per period? There are many combinations. The firm can substitute capital for labour or labour for capital. Given this particular production function we can find some of these alternative combinations.

$$\begin{aligned} Q &= A \times K^a \times L^b \\ Q &= 4000 \\ A &= 100 \\ a &= \frac{1}{3} \\ b &= \frac{1}{2} \end{aligned}$$

We are solving for K and L:

$$\begin{aligned} 4000 &= 100 \times K^{\frac{1}{3}} \times L^{\frac{1}{2}} \\ K^{\frac{1}{3}} \times L^{\frac{1}{2}} &= 40 \end{aligned}$$

Let's assume that the volume of capital is not 64 but double that, i.e. 128. What would the required volume of labour be, so that we get the same level of output, 4000 units per period?

$$
\begin{aligned}
L^{\frac{1}{2}} &= \frac{40}{K^{\frac{1}{3}}} \\
&= \frac{40}{(128)^{\frac{1}{3}}} \\
&= \frac{40}{\sqrt[3]{128}} \\
&= \frac{40}{5.04} \\
&= 7.94 \\
L &= (7.94)^2 \\
&= 63.04
\end{aligned}
$$

So if we wanted to achieve the same level of output of 4000 units with double the volume of capital, the necessary amount of labour would fall to 63.04 units per period.

Let's see what would happen if we now increased the volume of labour by 50 per cent, i.e. it would now be 150 units. What would the required volume of capital be, so that the output is again 4000 units per period?

$$
\begin{aligned}
4000 &= 100 \times K^{\frac{1}{3}} \times L^{\frac{1}{2}} \\
K^{\frac{1}{3}} \times L^{\frac{1}{2}} &= 40 \\
K^{\frac{1}{3}} &= \frac{40}{L^{\frac{1}{2}}} \\
K^{\frac{1}{3}} &= \frac{40}{(150)^{\frac{1}{2}}} \\
&= \frac{40}{\sqrt{150}} \\
&= \frac{40}{12.25} \\
&= 3.27 \\
K &= (3.27)^3 \\
&= 34.97
\end{aligned}
$$

To yield 4000 units of output per period with 150 units of labour, we would need 34.97 units of capital.

Plotting Isoquants

Three combinations of K and L that will produce 4000 units of output per day have been calculated and plotted as a curve in Figure 13.1. This curve is called an 'isoquant' and depicts all combinations of capital and labour which can be used to produce a given level of output. Two other isoquants have also been drawn, one connecting combinations of capital and labour which can be used to produce 5608 units and one for 7120 units.

Production Decisions in the Oil Industry

One example of the application of a Cobb–Douglas production function is the oil industry. What happens if the industry wishes to get more oil flowing through its pipelines? How much more horsepower and how much bigger pipes are required to achieve a given increase in capacity? An estimate of the production function for oil has been made to answer these questions.[1]

[1] L Cockenboo (1955). *Crude Oil Pipelines and Competition in the Oil Industry*. Cambridge, MA: Harvard University Press.

FIGURE 13.1

Production Isoquants for a Cobb–Douglas Production Function

There are various combinations of K and L that can produce 4000 unit per day. All these combinations are represented by the isoquant labelled Q = 4000. There is a whole series of isoquants for different possible levels of output. Here we show one for Q = 5608 units and one for Q = 7120 units.

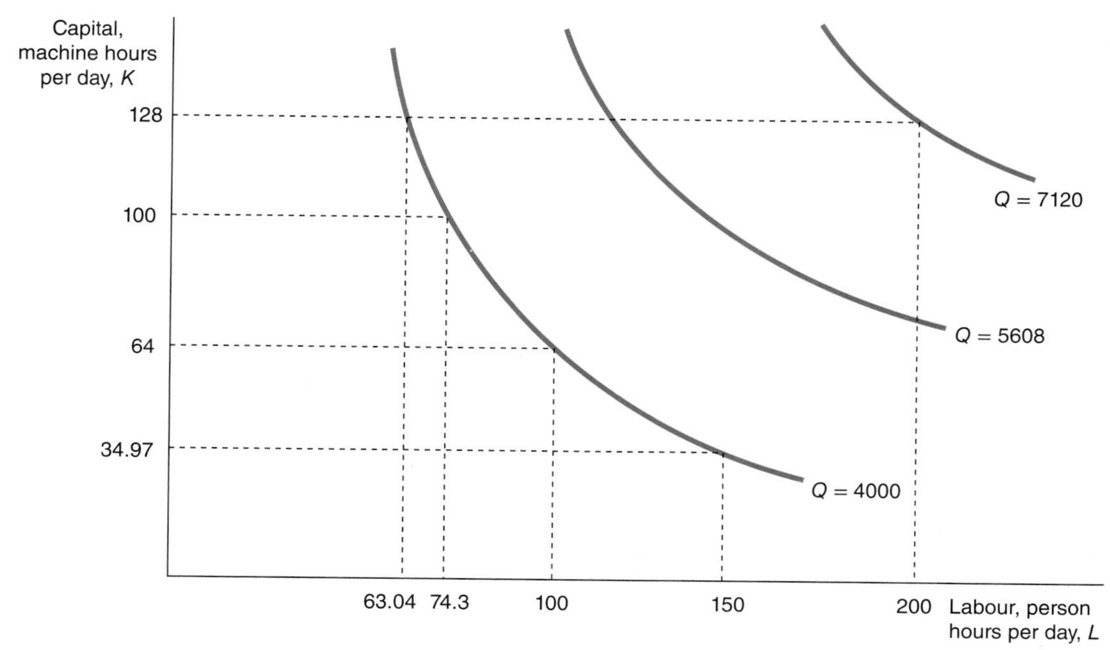

The production function is:

$$Q = A \times H^{0.37} \times K^{1.73}$$

Where:

Q = the volume of oil throughput

A = a constant (which depends on the nature of the terrain and the type of oil)

H = hydraulic horsepower

K = size of the pipe through which the oil will flow

In this case do we get increasing, decreasing or constant returns to scale? The exponents of H and K, when summed, are greater than one:

Exponent of $H = 0.37$

Exponent of $K = 1.73$

Summing the exponents we have $0.37 + 1.73 = 2.1$.

Unlike our earlier example the oil pipeline case exhibits increasing returns to scale. That is to say, in general, the larger the pipeline and the greater the horsepower from the pumping station the more cost-effective it is.

Short-Run Production

Moving along any particular isoquant, adjusting the volume of K and L, is a long-run decision. However, we can use the isoquants to examine the effect of short-run decisions. In the short run the firm can adjust the volume of labour but not capital. Figure 13.2 shows a situation in which a firm takes a long-run decision to operate with K_1 capital. In the short run it cannot vary this level of capital but it can vary the volume of labour, choosing between L_1, L_2, L_3 and L_4. This will determine on which of the isoquants it operates. For example, a decision to increase labour input from L_1 to L_2 increases output from $Q = X_1$ to $Q = X_2$.

FIGURE 13.2

Increasing Labour Inputs with a Fixed Volume of Capital

In the short run the firm can adjust the volume of labour but not capital. If a firm is currently operating with K_1 capital, it can vary output by varying the volume of labour, choosing between L_1, L_2, L_3 and L_4. This will determine on which of the isoquants it operates. For example, a decision to increase labour input from L_1 to L_2 increases output from $Q = X_1$ to $Q = X_2$.

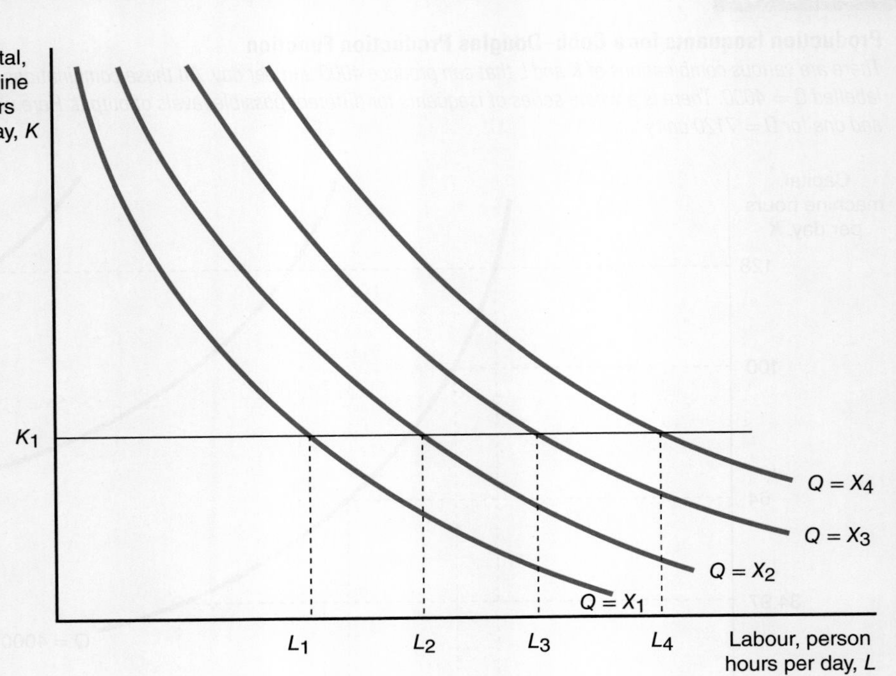

The level of output that is possible by varying labour with a fixed volume of capital determines a short-run production function. The additional output generated by a small increase in labour input is the marginal product of labour, MP_L. We will now show how to calculate MP_L for any level of labour input. We will make the assumption that labour is infinitely divisible so that we can use calculus.

The short-run production function might be:

$$Q = 200L^{\frac{1}{2}} - 7.07L$$

The marginal product of labour MP_L is given as:

$$\frac{dQ}{dL} = 100L^{-\frac{1}{2}} - 7.07$$

We will calculate MP_L at various levels of labour usage to see what happens to MP_L as labour usage increases. First, we find MP_L at one unit of labour:

$$\begin{aligned} MP_L &= 100 \times 1^{-\frac{1}{2}} - 7.07 \\ &= 100 \times \frac{1}{\sqrt{1}} - 7.07 \\ &= 100 - 7.07 \\ MP_L &= 92.93 \end{aligned}$$

One extra unit of labour increases output by 92.93 units.

At 20 units of labour we have:

$$\begin{aligned} MP_L &= 100 \times 20^{-\frac{1}{2}} - 7.07 \\ &= 100 \times \frac{1}{\sqrt{20}} - 7.07 \\ &= 100 \times \frac{1}{4.47} - 7.07 \\ &= 22.37 - 7.07 \\ MP_L &= 15.30 \end{aligned}$$

At this larger level of labour usage an extra unit of labour adds less to output. This is illustrative of what is known as 'the law of diminishing returns'.

At 200 units of labour we have:

$$\begin{aligned} MP_L &= 100 \times 200^{-\frac{1}{2}} - 7.07 \\ &= 100 \times \frac{1}{\sqrt{200}} - 7.07 \\ &= 100 \times \frac{1}{14.14} - 7.07 \\ &= 7.07 - 7.07 \\ MP_L &= 0 \end{aligned}$$

Adding an extra unit of labour when the firm is already employing 200 units of labour adds nothing to the total volume of output. The marginal product of labour is zero.

At a larger volume of labour usage we might then expect marginal product to be negative. At 250 units of labour we have:

$$\begin{aligned} MP_L &= 100 \times 250^{-\frac{1}{2}} - 7.07 \\ &= 100 \times \frac{1}{\sqrt{250}} - 7.07 \\ &= 100 \times \frac{1}{15.81} - 7.07 \\ &= 6.33 - 7.07 \\ MP_L &= -0.74 \end{aligned}$$

MP_L is negative.

Employees have very little capital with which to work. Now they begin to get in each other's way. The extra unit of labour reduces output. No profit maximising firm would employ labour to the point where MP_L is negative.

We have sketched this relationship in Figure 13.3. This is just one of a series of short-run curves. With a greater volume of capital the function will take the same shape, but be above the one sketched in Figure 13.3 and MP_L would become zero at a greater level of labour input.

FIGURE 13.3

A Marginal Product of Labour Curve

A short-run production function shows the maximum possible level of out that can be produced with varying levels of labour input, holding the volume of capital constant. Marginal product declines with additional inputs of labour. Eventually marginal product = 0.

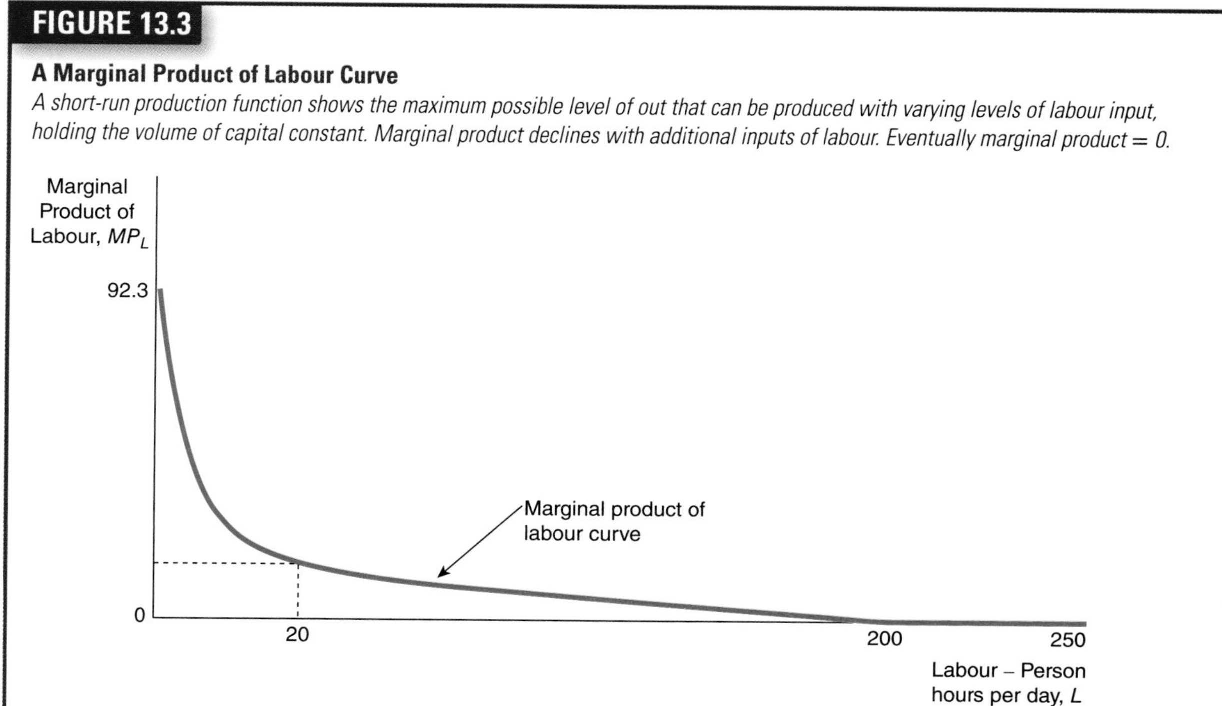

THE LEONTIEF PRODUCTION FUNCTION

In this section we consider a different type of long-run production process. Imagine a process where capital and labour must be used in fixed proportions. The firm needs one person to operate one machine. A second machine without a second person to operate it can produce no output. Similarly, a second person without a second machine cannot produce any output. This kind of process is called the Leontief production function. If usage of one input is increased without an increase in the other input, output cannot increase. Then, assuming again a two-input process, with just capital and labour required, we have:

$$Q = min\ (aK, bL)$$

This states that Q will be equal to aK or bL, whichever is the smaller. To illustrate, suppose a firm requires a fixed proportion of 2 machines and 5 units of labour to obtain output. That is, $a = 2$ and $b = 5$. Furthermore, assume the firm currently has 4 machines and 7 units of labour. That is $K = 4$ and $L = 7$. Then:

$$\begin{aligned} Q &= min\ (2 \times 4, 5 \times 5) \\ &= min\ (8, 25) \\ &= 8 \end{aligned}$$

The firm can produce only 8 units of output per period.

This kind of production process can also be represented by a set of isoquants. Let us take our earlier example of a firm needing a fixed ratio of one person and one machine and assume that this combination of K and L can produce 20 units of output per day. Figure 13.4 shows a combination on the isoquant $Q = 20$. If the firm hires an extra unit of labour without increasing capital it has $1K$ and $2L$. It can produce no extra output. It remains on the same isoquant. Given that it has $1K$, it will remain on the same isoquant however much extra labour it hires.

FIGURE 13.4

Isoquants for a Leontief Production Function

A Leontief production function is one in which capital and labour must be used in fixed proportions. If usage of one input is increased without an increase in the other input, output cannot increase.

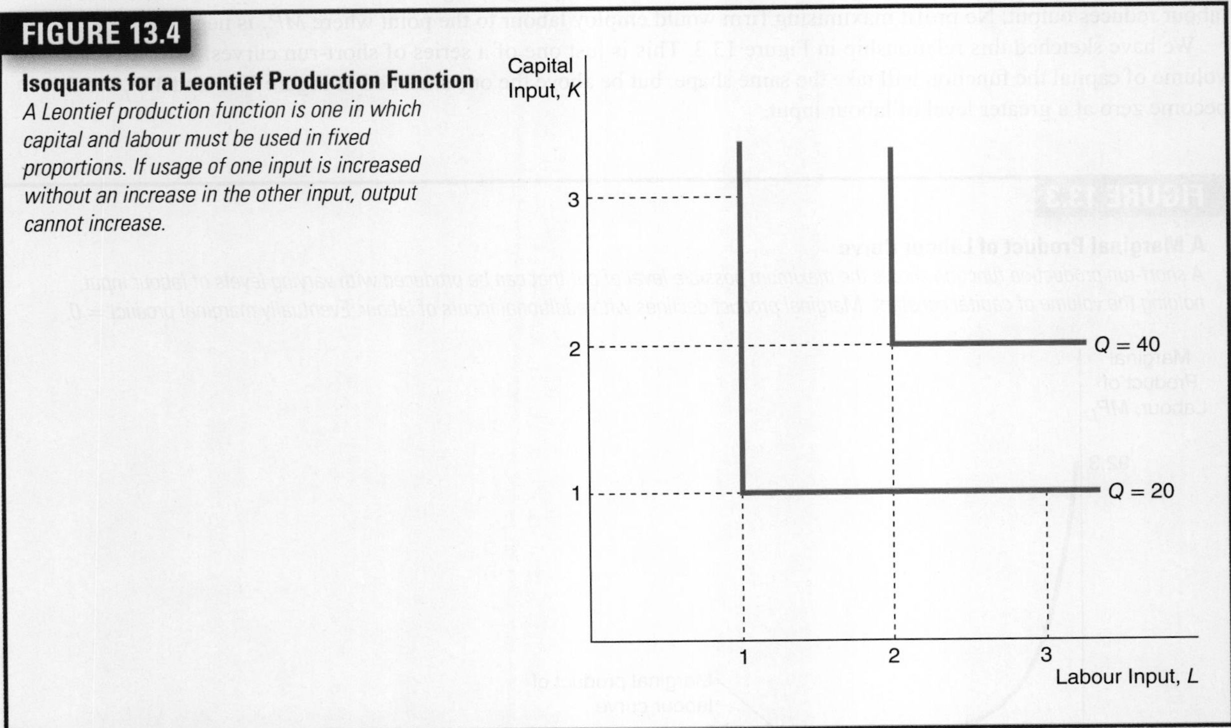

If the firm invests in more capital without hiring more labour, total output does not rise at all. 2K plus one L or 3K plus one L gives Q = 20 units of output per day. However, 2K plus 2L produces Q = 40 units of output per day. In general, all Leontief production functions will have isoquants of this shape. K and L are perfect complements.

PROBLEMS AND APPLICATIONS

1 Consider the production function $Q = f(L, K) = 25 \times L^{\frac{3}{4}} \times K^{\frac{1}{2}} = 25\sqrt[4]{L^3}\sqrt{K}$, where output is Q, labour input (L) and the input of capital (K).

a. How much output is generated with $L = 4$ and $K = 50$?
b. How much labour (L) input is required to produce 1000 units of output with $L = 25$?
c. Find the function that returns the value of K for any level of Q and L.
d. Sketch the isoquant that represents an output of $Q = 750$ units in the diagram below. (You can use your result from the previous stage to calculate 4 points, this will be enough to sketch the graph.)
e. What happens to output if you increase both factor inputs by 100 per cent?
f. Does the function exhibit decreasing or increasing returns to scale?
g. Show the function for the marginal product of labour.
h. Derive the marginal rate of technical substitution for the production function given above.
i. Assume that total costs are 250, an hour of labour is paid the wage rate $w = 20$ and a unit of capital has costs of 5. What is the optimal combination of capital and labour to produce the maximum output?

FIGURE 13.5

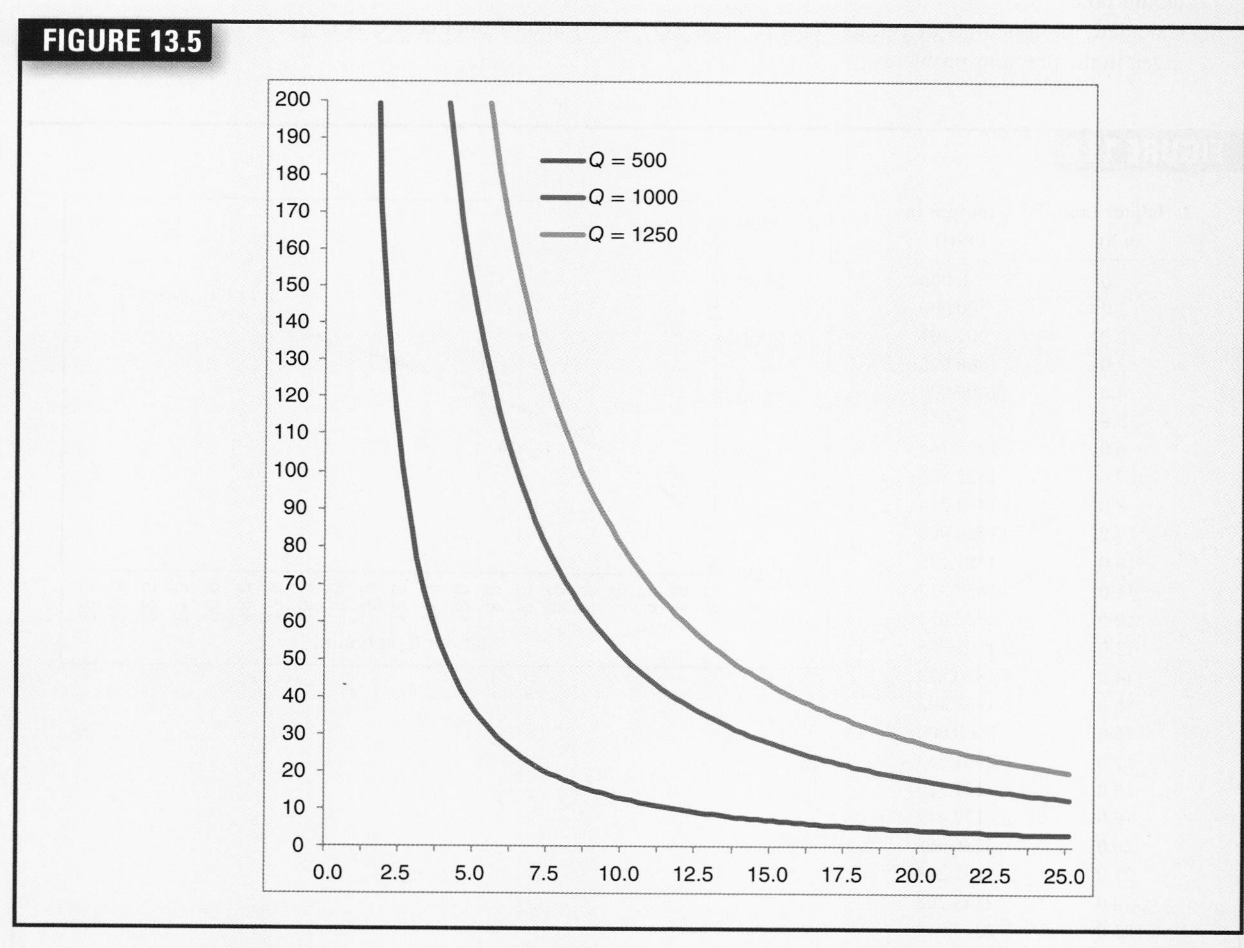

2 The output (Q) of a firm is a function of the labour input (L) and the input of capital (K); the production function is: $Q = f(L, K) = 100 \times L^{\frac{1}{2}} \times K^{\frac{1}{2}} = 100\sqrt{L \times K}$. Assuming a fixed input of capital of $K = 25$ units this simplifies to $Q = 500 \times L^{\frac{1}{2}} = 500\sqrt{L}$. This function is shown as a graph and in a table below.

a. What is the marginal product of labour measuring?
b. Calculate the marginal product of labour at 4 hours of labour input from the table or the function. (The calculation based on the table will only give you an approximate measure, but that is okay here.)
c. Write out the function for the marginal product of labour at a fixed input of $K = 25$ units.
d. Derive the function for the marginal product of labour for a function of the general type $Q = AL^uK^v$ and for the production function $Q = 100 \times L^{\frac{1}{2}} \times K^{\frac{1}{2}}$ given above.
e. Does the function specified in this problem exhibit a diminishing or increasing marginal product of labour?
f. What happens to the marginal product of labour if you increase the capital input in production from 25 to 100 units?
g. Go back to the setup with $K = 25$ and assume capital inputs cost $I =$ €10 per unit. How large are the fixed cost of the production?
h. Show the formula for average fixed cost.
i. What are the variable costs and total costs of producing 1000 units of output, if you have to pay $w =$ €30 per labour hour?
j. Calculate the functions of variable cost ($C_v = C_v(Q) = \ldots$) and of total cost $C = C(Q) = \ldots$ at the factor prices given in the previous problems.

FIGURE 13.6

L (labour input in h)	X (output in units)
0	0.000
1.0	500.000
2.0	707.107
3.0	866.025
4.0	1000.000
5.0	1118.034
6.0	1224.745
7.0	1322.876
8.0	1414.214
9.0	1500.000
10.0	1581.139
11.0	1658.312
12.0	1732.051
13.0	1802.776
14.0	1870.829
15.0	1936.492
16.0	2000.000
17.0	2061.553
18.0	2121.320
19.0	2179.449
20.0	2236.068
21.0	2291.288
22.0	2345.208
23.0	2397.916
24.0	2449.490
25.0	2500.000
26.0	2549.510
27.0	2598.076

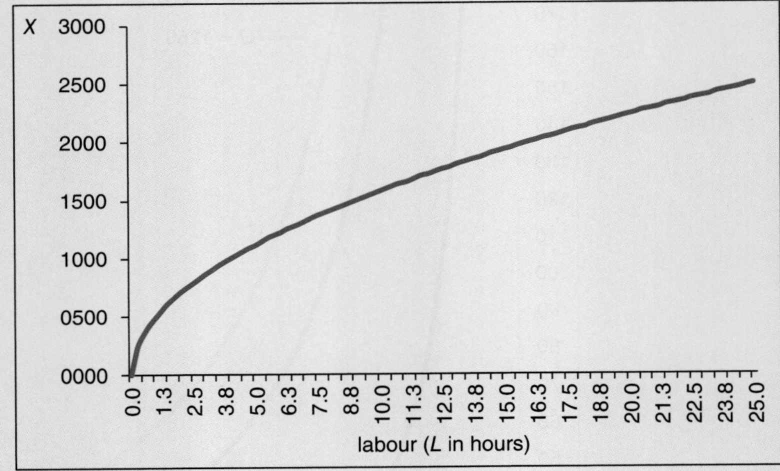

14 MARKET STRUCTURES I: MONOPOLY

In this chapter we focus on the mathematics of monopoly pricing. We look at the following: the relationship between average and marginal revenue for the monopolist, the principles of short-run output, price and profit determination in monopoly, the relationship between marginal revenue and elasticity of demand, the level of output and price with perfectly competitive firms, the nature of demand elasticity and its relationship to monopoly pricing, and finally the price and output decisions of a firm that has the power to engage in price discrimination.

THE RELATIONSHIP BETWEEN AVERAGE REVENUE (AR) AND MARGINAL REVENUE (MR)

We begin with the relationship between average revenue, demand, and marginal revenue. In perfect competition a firm can always choose to sell an additional unit of output without needing to lower its price. As a result marginal revenue is the same as the price. Its demand curve is perfectly elastic. However, when a firm has a measure of monopoly power, it faces a negatively sloped demand curve. If it wishes to sell more units per period it must lower price on all the other units it has been selling. (The exception to this rule is where it can price discriminate – something we will look at later in this chapter.) This means that the extra revenue generated by another unit of sales is less than the price. Marginal revenue is less than average revenue. This is shown in Figure 14.1, which also shows that with a straight line downward sloping demand function the slope of the MR curve is twice that of the demand curve, the AR curve. Alternatively expressed, the distance OA is equal to the distance AB. We now show why this is the case.

The linear demand curve takes the form:

$$P = a - bQ$$

Average revenue (AR) = total revenue (TR) divided by output $AR = \frac{TR}{Q}$ which can be rearranged to give:

$$TR = AR \times Q.$$

We also know that price is equal to average revenue ($P = AR$).
Consequently, $TR = P \times Q$.
Substituting for P gives:

$$TR = Q(a - bQ)$$

Multiplying through gives:

$$TR = aQ - bQ^2$$

Differentiating the total revenue gives MR:

$$\frac{dTR}{dQ} = a - 2bQ$$

Hence the slope of $AR = -b$ and the slope of $MR = -2b$.

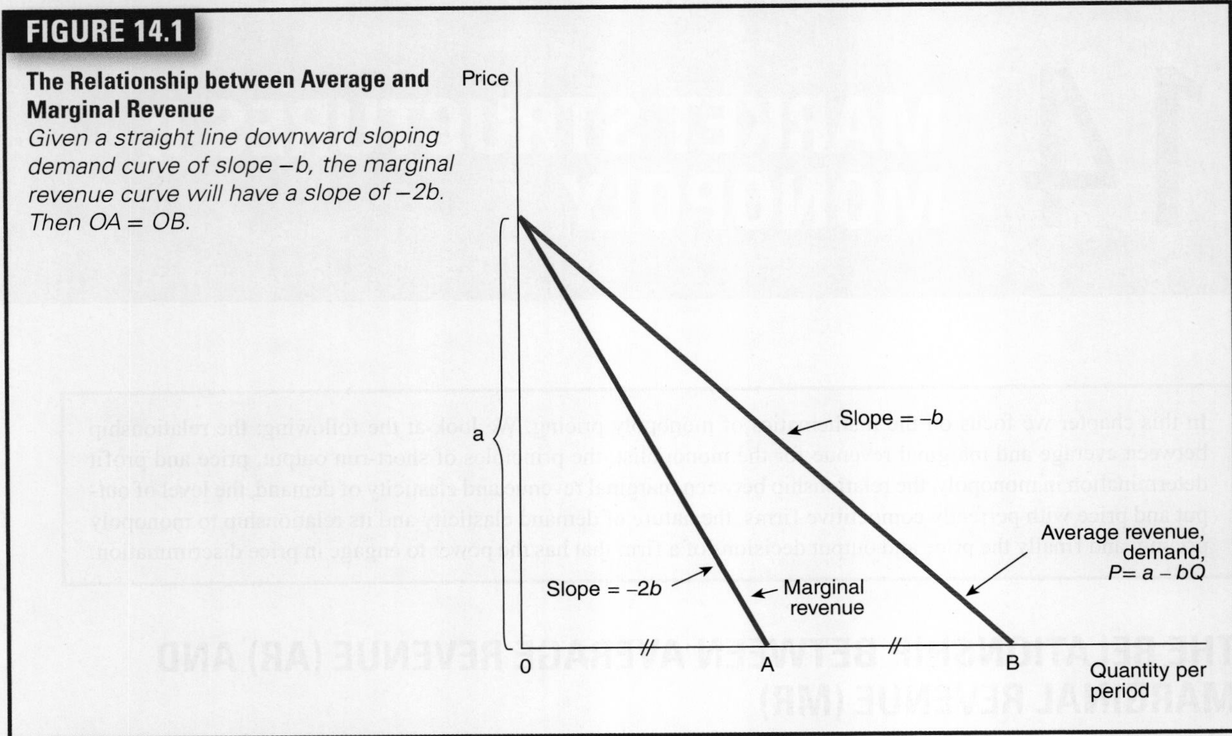

FIGURE 14.1

The Relationship between Average and Marginal Revenue

Given a straight line downward sloping demand curve of slope −b, the marginal revenue curve will have a slope of −2b. Then OA = OB.

THE MONOPOLIST'S OUTPUT, PRICE AND PROFIT

A monopolist maximizes profit by setting marginal cost, MC, equal to marginal revenue, MR. It is always worth adding another unit to the level of output if the addition to revenue, MR, is greater than the addition to cost, MC. This can be expressed in an alternative way. The monopolist maximizes profit by selecting an output where the difference between total revenue and total cost is greatest. We will now take an example of a monopolist with known revenue and cost conditions and show mathematically as well as diagrammatically how this firm behaves in the short run.

Let us suppose that a firm has a known demand schedule given by:

$$P = 288 - 3Q_D$$

Where:
P = price in euros
Q_D = output per period
It has a short-run total cost schedule given by:

$$STC = 40 + 0.6Q^2$$

Where:
STC = Short-Run Total Cost

We can now calculate the output and price that will maximize profit. Recall that, whereas the perfectly competitive firm has to accept the price given by supply and demand, the monopolist has more control over price. The monopolist can choose output and let the demand curve determine the price, or set price and let the demand the demand curve determine output.

Finding the Profit Maximizing Output and Price

Marginal revenue is found by differentiating the total revenue function with respect to output. Total revenue, TR is given by multiplying average revenue (price) by output:

$$TR = P \times Q \text{ and } P = 288 - 3Q_D$$

This gives:

$$TR = (288 - 3Q_D) \times Q$$
$$= 288Q_d - 3Q^2$$

$$MR = \frac{dTR}{dQ}$$
$$= 288 - 6Q$$

Marginal revenue is 288 – 6*Q*. If output were 10 units, for example, MR would be 288 – 6(10) = €228. The STC function tells us what it costs to produce a given level of output. The marginal cost is found by differentiating STC with respect to output.

$$MC = \frac{dSTC}{dQ}$$

Since $STC = 40 + 0.6Q^2$.

$$MC = 1.2Q$$

If output were 10 units, then MC would be 1.2(10) = €12. The production of the 10th unit would cost €12 and would generate €228 in additional revenue. It is worth producing this 10th unit because it adds €216 to profit. The monopolist expands output up to a point where MC = MR. Given we now know the functions for both MC and MR, we can set these equal to each other to find the profit maximizing output.

Profit maximization occurs where MR = MC:

$$288 - 6Q = 1.2Q$$
$$7.2Q = 288$$
$$Q = 40$$

The level of output which maximizes this monopolist's profit is 40 units of output per period.

Figure 14.2 shows relationships of this kind. The slope of STC, namely MC, is equal to the slope of TR, namely MR. At this point profit is maximized.

The Monopolist's Profit Maximizing Output *Profits are maximized where total costs exceed total revenue by the greatest amount. At this output level the slope of the STC curve = the slope of the TR curve.*

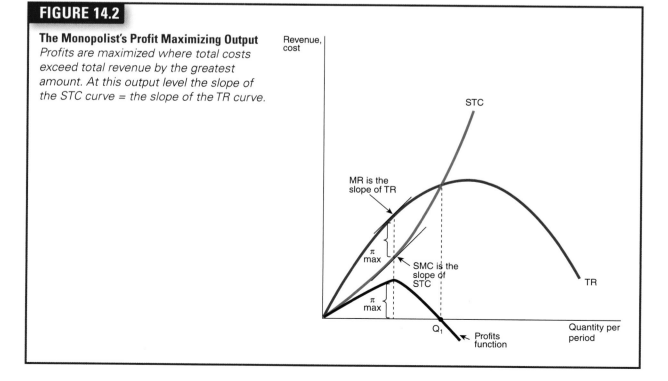

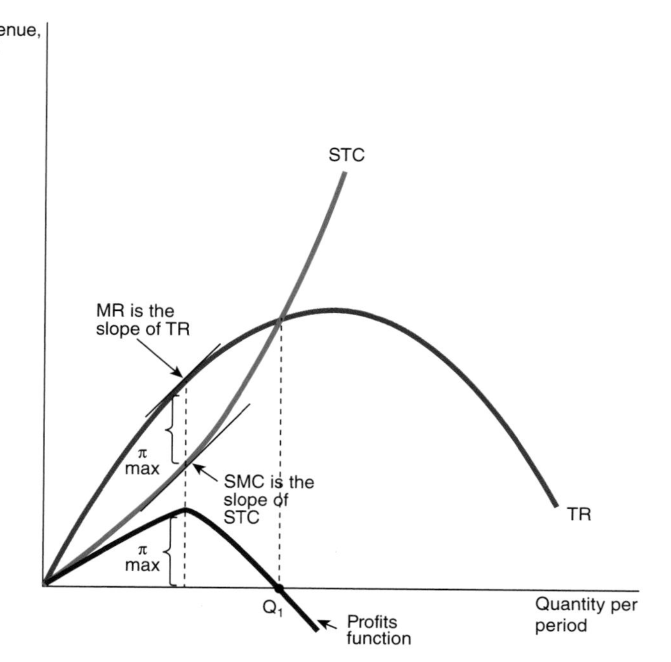

Now that we know the quantity of output, we can work out the price to be charged. This is the highest price possible subject to the constraint imposed by the demand curve.

$$P = 288 - 3Q_D$$
$$Q = 40$$
$$P = 288 - 3(40)$$
$$P = 288 - 120$$
$$P = 168$$

The price/output decision is to make 40 units per week at a price of €168 per unit.

Finding the Monopolist's Profit

The short-run profit per period is given by $\pi = \text{TR} - \text{STC}$ where π = profit per period.

We substitute our total revenue and total cost functions into the profit equation:

$$\begin{aligned}\pi &= (288Q - 3Q^2) - (40 + 0.6Q^2)\\ &= 288Q - 3Q^2 - 40 - 0.6Q^2\\ &= 288Q - 3.6Q^2 - 40\end{aligned}$$

We know that profit maximization is when $Q = 40$, so substituting $Q = 40$ into the above gives:

$$\begin{aligned}\pi &= (288 \times 40) - (3.6 \times 40^2) - 40\\ &= 11\,520 - 5760 - 40\\ &= 5720\end{aligned}$$

Short-run profit is €5720 per period.

Profit per unit is found by taking the profit and dividing by the output:

$$\frac{\pi}{Q} = \frac{5720}{40}$$
$$= €143 \text{ per unit}$$

Figure 14.2 shows this maximum profit level in two ways. First it is the distance between STC and TR, labelled max π. However, we have also shown a profits function. This is the level of profit at every possible level of output. So for example at output level Q_1, revenue equals costs so profits are zero. The monopolist can make a profit at any output level up to Q_1 but it is maximized at max π, the top of the profits curve.

An alternative way of finding total short-run profit at the chosen level of output of 40, and a useful way to check our maths, is to find profit per unit of output, then multiply the result by the level of output. Here we find the difference between average revenue and short-run average cost, which is then multiplied by output, in our case, 40.

Another way of calculating profit per unit is the difference between average revenue and average total cost (AR – ATC). We know that AR = 288 – 3Q and for a firm with an output level of 40 we have:

$$\begin{aligned}\text{AR} &= 288 - (3 \times 40)\\ &= 288 - 120\\ &= €168\end{aligned}$$

Now we find ATC, which is STC/Q.

$$\begin{aligned}\text{ATC} &= \frac{40 + 0.6Q^2}{Q}\\ &= \frac{40 + (0.6 \times 1600)}{40}\\ &= 25\end{aligned}$$

AR – ATC, therefore, is 168 – 25 = €143. This is the same value we found by using the formula $\frac{\pi}{Q}$ for calculating profit per unit. Multiplying this result by 40 gives, 143 × 40 = €5720.

This confirms our monopolist's profit level as €5720 per period.

The Relationship between Marginal Revenue and Elasticity

Another useful relationship for the monopolist is that between marginal revenue, MR, and price elasticity of demand. The relationship can be summarized in the formula:

$$MR = P\left(1 + \frac{1}{E}\right)$$

Where E = price elasticity of demand.

For a negatively sloped demand curve we would normally expect E to be negative.

Let's first see where the formula comes from. For small changes in price and quantity the change in revenue, marginal revenue, can be expressed as:

$$\Delta R = P\Delta Q + Q\Delta P$$

Where:

ΔR = change in revenue

P = price

Q = quantity

Now divide both sides of this equation by ΔQ. Then:

$$\frac{\Delta R}{\Delta Q} = P + Q\left(\frac{\Delta P}{\Delta Q}\right)$$

But $\frac{\Delta R}{\Delta Q}$ is in fact marginal revenue, MR. So:

$$MR = P + Q\left(\frac{\Delta P}{\Delta Q}\right)$$

Now we factor out P. Note that taking an expression, multiplying by P and then dividing it by P doesn't change the expression:

$$MR = P + \frac{P\left(Q\frac{\Delta P}{\Delta Q}\right)}{P}$$

$$= P\left(1 + \frac{Q}{P} \times \frac{\Delta P}{\Delta Q}\right)$$

From Chapter 4 we know that:

$$E = \frac{\Delta Q}{\Delta P} \times \frac{P}{Q}$$

Where:

E = price elasticity of demand

So the term $\frac{Q}{P} \times \frac{\Delta P}{\Delta Q}$ is equal to $\frac{1}{E}$

Substituting into the MR equation gives:

$$MR = P\left(1 + \frac{1}{E}\right)$$

Now let's illustrate its use. Suppose A company is currently charging €4 for its chocolate bar. It knows demand elasticity at that point on its demand curve; we will assume it is −2.

How much extra revenue is generated by selling an additional bar?

Focus first on the term in the bracket. Substituting −2 for E gives:

$$\left(1 + \frac{1}{-2}\right)$$

$$= 1 - \frac{1}{2}$$

$$= \frac{1}{2}$$

Now multiply this by price:

$$4 \times \frac{1}{2} = €2$$

The sale of an extra bar of chocolate for this firm yields an extra €2 of revenue. If MC < 2 it is profitable to expand output.

Comparison with Perfect Competition

In a previous chapter we looked at the price/output decisions of perfectly competitive firms. How do such decisions compare with that of the monopolist? Let us assume that costs are the same for both structures. Let us also assume that we have the same industry demand curve, in this case we are assuming $AR = 288 - 3Q$. Bear in mind that the demand curve for a monopolist is always the same as the industry demand curve whereas for a perfectly competitive firm, the individual firm's demand is perfectly elastic.

Under these circumstances the marginal cost curve to the monopolist is the same as the supply curve to the perfectly competitive industry. Remember from our study of perfect competition that the supply curve is the sum of the marginal cost curves of the firms (above average variable cost).

Using our illustrative monopolist we can now compare the output and price that would obtain if this were a perfectly competitive structure. In equilibrium under perfect competition, supply is equal to demand. The monopoly equivalent is where $SMC = D$. If the monopolist produced where $SMC = D$ we would have the following output. Given that our SMC function is $SMC = 1.2Q$ and the demand function is $P = 288 - 3Q_D$, setting SMC equal to demand gives:

$$1.2Q = 288 - 3Q$$
$$4.2Q = 288$$
$$Q = \frac{288}{4.2}$$
$$Q = 68.57$$

The output under perfect competition given these functions is 68.57 units (assuming that units of output are divisible). This is larger than the monopolist's output which we calculated at 40 units. The price under perfect competition is given by:

$$\text{AR} = 288 - 3Q$$
$$Q = 68.57$$
$$\text{AR} = 288 - (3 \times 68.57)$$
$$= 288 - 205.71$$
$$= €82.29$$

The perfectly competitive price is €82.29. This is lower than the monopolist's price which we calculated at €168. We summarize the results of our comparison in Table 14.1.

TABLE 14.1 **A Comparison of Monopoly and Perfect Competition for an Illustrative Monopolist**

Market Structure	Output per period	Price (€)
Monopoly	40	168
Perfect Competition	82.3	68.59

We expect the monopolist to have a lower output and set a higher price compared to a firm operating in perfect competition. The extent of the difference in output and price will depend upon the cost and demand functions.

The Deadweight Loss of Monopoly Power

Given the assumptions of the model of perfect competition, the market allocates scarce resources efficiently. Hence, there is optimal use of scarce resources, total surplus is maximized with no deadweight loss. In contrast, monopoly equilibrium results in a deadweight loss.

We can calculate the size of this deadweight loss of monopoly power and represent the area of deadweight loss in Figure 14.3. In perfect competition *SMC* is the short-run supply curve so output would be where $S = D = 82.33$ units per period. Given the monopolists demand curve, the price would correspond with point *C* where the *SMC* curve cuts the demand curve. The monopolist, however, restricts output to where $MC = MR$ and charges the maximum possible price at this output level. The monopolist's output is 40 units per period and point *B* on the demand curve gives the monopoly price of €168 per unit. Given that the *SMC* function is a linear function, the resulting *SMC* curve in Figure 14.3 is a straight line. We know that the *MC* function is $MC = 1.2Q$, and given the profit maximizing level of output where $MC = MR$ is $Q = 40$, this gives *MC* and *MR* both equal to €48 which is represented as point *E* in Figure 14.3. Diagrammatically the area we are calculating can be seen as area *BCE* in Figure 14.3.

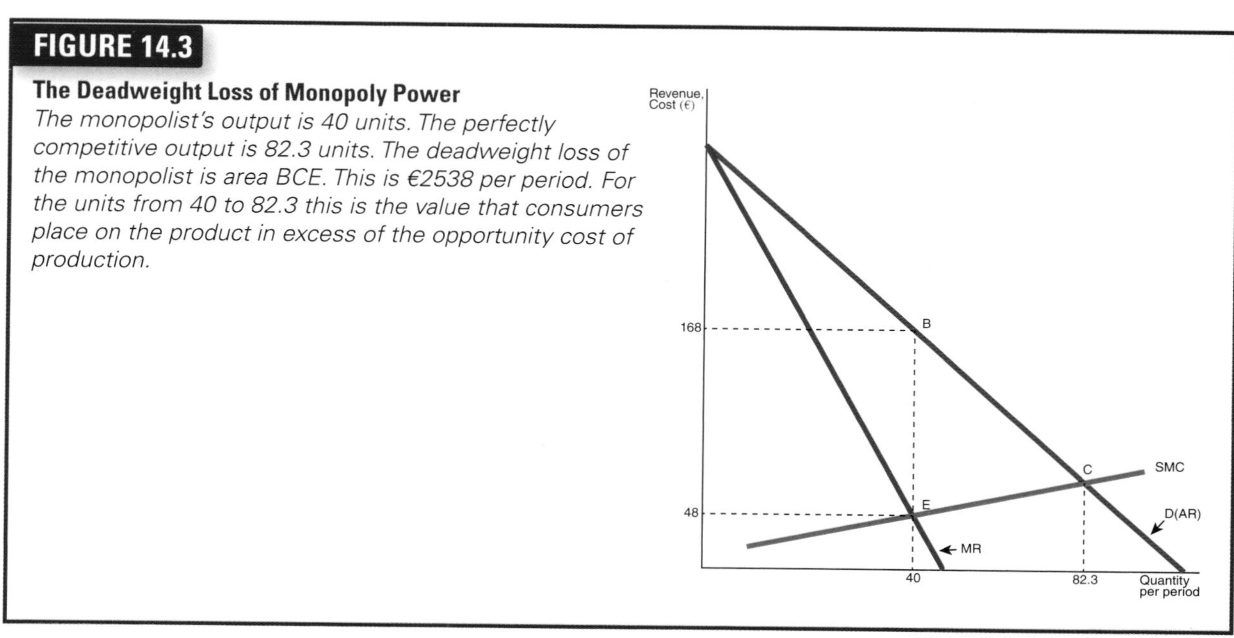

FIGURE 14.3

The Deadweight Loss of Monopoly Power

The monopolist's output is 40 units. The perfectly competitive output is 82.3 units. The deadweight loss of the monopolist is area BCE. This is €2538 per period. For the units from 40 to 82.3 this is the value that consumers place on the product in excess of the opportunity cost of production.

We can use the formula for the area of a triangle to calculate the size of the deadweight loss.

The height of this triangle is the same as the difference between the output of the perfectly competitive industry (82.3 units) and that of the monopolist (40 units) which equals 42.3. The base of the triangle, BE = 120, is the difference between the price charged by the monopolist (€168), minus the marginal revenue at 40 units (€48).

$$A = \frac{hb}{2}$$

Where A = area

h = height

b = length of base

Plugging in our values we have:

$$A = \frac{42.3 \times 120}{2}$$
$$= \frac{5076}{2} = 2538$$

The deadweight loss per period is €2538. For the units from 40 to 82.3 we have quantified the value that consumers place on the product in excess of the opportunity cost of production.

Elasticity of Demand and its Relationship to Monopoly Pricing

The monopolist will always choose an output that is on the elastic section of the demand curve. If demand is price elastic, marginal revenue must be positive. Marginal cost will also be positive so $MC = MR$, the profit maximizing output, must be where demand is price elastic. Alternatively, one could think about it in the following way. Suppose output is currently where demand is price inelastic and marginal revenue is negative. Then the monopolist, by raising price, can raise revenue while needing to produce a smaller level of output.

Now consider the output which the perfectly competitive industry will produce. Output will be larger, so given a straight line demand function, demand will be less price elastic. We cannot say *a priori* (from what we know) whether demand will be price elastic or inelastic at this point. It depends upon the nature of the demand and cost conditions. Let's check to see what we have in the case of our illustrative monopolist.

First, what is demand elasticity at the profit maximizing output, $MC = MR$, which we found to be at 40 units of output with a profit maximizing price of €168?

Price elasticity of demand is given by the formula:

$$ped = \frac{dQ_d}{dP} \times \frac{P}{Q_d}$$

Where:
ped is price elasticity of demand
Q_d is quantity demanded
P is price
In our example, $P = €168$, and Q_D is 40.
The inverse demand equation is $P = 288 - 3Q$ and rearranging to express the function in terms of quantity we get:

$$P = 288 - 3Q_D$$
$$3Q_D + P = 288$$
$$3Q_D = 288 - P$$
$$Q_D = 96 - \frac{1}{3}P$$

Differentiating Q with respect to P gives us:

$$\frac{dQ}{dP} = -\frac{1}{3}$$

So *ped* is:

$$-\frac{1}{3} \times \frac{168}{40} = -1.40$$

Demand elasticity is –1.40. It is as we anticipated, price elastic.

We will now see how price elastic demand is at the socially optimal, perfectly competitive output. We can be sure it will be less elastic, but by how much?

This time we still have $\frac{dQ}{dP} = -\frac{1}{3}$ but we have a price, P, of €68.59 and an output, Q, of 82.3.

The *ped* will be:

$$ped = -\frac{1}{3} \times \frac{82.83}{68.59}$$

$$ped = -0.40$$

Demand is less price elastic at –0.40. Indeed, we have moved down the demand curve into the inelastic section.

PRICE DISCRIMINATION

Price discrimination occurs where a firm with monopoly power can charge different prices for the same good in different markets. In the case of perfect price discrimination, all consumer surplus is transferred to the producer. However, another form of price discrimination, which is more common, is what is called third degree price discrimination.

This is where a firm with monopoly power can sell the same product into two different markets and charge a different price in each market. This requires several conditions.

1. The firm must have some monopoly power.
2. The two markets must have different price elasticities of demand (we shall see why shortly).
3. There must be barriers to arbitrage. Arbitrage is the process of buying a product in a market where price is low, and re-selling it in a market where price is high. The firm must be able to keep its two markets separate. If consumers being charged a higher price are able to buy in the lower priced market they will do so.

We show such a price discriminating monopolist in Figure 14.4.

FIGURE 14.4

Third Degree Price Discrimination

If a monopolist has two markets with different elasticities of demand, price discrimination is possible. The monopolist charges a price of P_A in market A, producing a quantity Q_A. An output of Q_B and a price of P_B is chosen for market B. The higher price is in market A, where demand is relatively price inelastic.

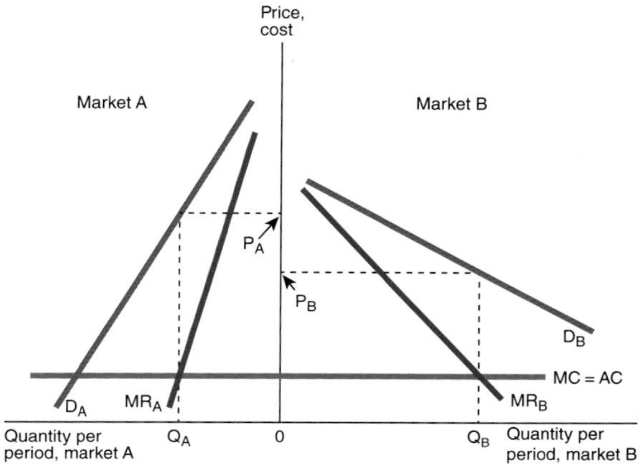

The representation of third degree price discrimination in this way is sometimes referred to as a 'tent diagram'. In market A we show increases in output by moving from zero to the left and in market B increases in output are shown by moving from zero to the right. Average and therefore marginal costs are assumed to be constant. There is just one output that is to be distributed between the two markets. The demand curves (the average revenue curves), reflect different relative elasticities, with market A demand being relatively price inelastic and market B being relatively price elastic. Also shown are the associated marginal revenue curves. Remember that MR has twice the slope of AR in each case.

Maximizing profit in market A requires an output where MC = MR which gives an output level to be sold in that market of Q_A with an associated price of P_A. Similarly we have an output of Q_B and a price of P_B for market B. Profit maximizing thus gives a different price in the two markets, the higher price being in market A, where demand is relatively price inelastic.

Notice that MR is the same in each market even though price is different. If this were not so it would pay the monopolist to transfer units of output between the markets. We can now see why elasticity of demand in the two markets must be different if successful price discrimination is to be possible.

We require that:

$$MR_A = P_A\left(1 + \frac{1}{E_A}\right) = MR_B = P_B\left(1 + \frac{1}{E_B}\right)$$

Where:

A denotes market A

B denotes market B

Then, if $E_A = E_B$, $P_A = P_B$, price will be the same in both markets; there can be no price discrimination.

Price discrimination makes it possible for the firm to charge different prices in different markets, allowing maximum profit to be made.

The Mathematics of Third Degree Price Discrimination

We will now explore some of these key ideas taking a mathematical example to illustrate. Suppose that a firm has two markets that are separable. In market A the demand function is given as:

$$P_A = 400 - 3Q_A$$

In market B the demand function is:

$$P_B = 200 - Q_B$$

The total cost function is given as:

$$TC = 50 + 3Q$$

Before we consider the price and output decision we will check to see that price elasticity of demand is different in the two markets. Given that these are downward sloping linear functions, demand elasticity in each market varies along the length of the curve. There is an elastic section and an inelastic section in both cases. However, at any given price, demand elasticity in market A will be different from market B. Let us pick an arbitrary price to illustrate. What is price elasticity of demand at P = 100 in each of the two markets? Consider market A first.

First, we need to find the demand function in terms of quantity demanded from the inverse demand function given above.

$$P_A = 400 - 3Q_A$$
$$3Q_A = 400 - P_A$$
$$Q_A = 133\frac{1}{3} - \frac{1}{3}P_A$$

Differentiating Q with respect to P:

$$\frac{dQ_A}{dP_A} = -\frac{1}{3}$$

Our illustrative price is €100 and at this price our inverse demand function gives the quantity demanded as:

$$P_A = 400 - 3Q_A$$
$$100 = 400 - 3Q_A$$
$$3Q_A = 300$$
$$Q_A = 100$$

At a price of €100, price elasticity will be:

$$\frac{dQ_A}{dP_A} \times \frac{P_A}{Q_A}$$
$$= -\frac{1}{3} \times \frac{100}{100}$$
$$= -0.33$$

Now let us compare this with market B.

First we need to find the demand curve from the inverse demand curve for market B.

$$P_B = 200 - Q_B$$
$$Q_B = 200 - P_B$$

Differentiating Q with respect to P:

$$\frac{dQ_B}{dP_B} = -1$$

Now we find Q_B from the inverse demand curve:

$$P_B = 200 - Q_B$$
$$100 = 200 - Q_B$$
$$Q_B = 100$$

At a price of €100, the price elasticity for market B is:

$$\frac{dQ_B}{dP_B} \times \frac{P_B}{Q_B}$$
$$= -1 \times \frac{100}{100}$$
$$= -1$$

At a price of €100, price elasticity of demand is −0.33 in market A, and −1 in market B. The price elasticity of demand is different in the two markets with demand in market A less elastic than in market B.

Finding the Price in Each of the Two Markets

Profit maximization requires the firm to set $MC = MR$ and it needs to do this in each of the two markets. Given that $TC = 50Q$, differentiating TC with respect to Q gives us marginal cost = $MC = 50$.

The marginal revenue function in market A, can be derived from the demand function for market A:

$$P_A = 400 - 3Q_A$$

Total revenue is $P \times Q$:

$$TR_A = (400 - 3Q_A)Q_A$$

Where: TR_A = total revenue in market A, so:

$$= 400Q_A - 3Q_A^2$$

$$MR_A = \frac{dTR_A}{dQ_A}$$
$$= 400 - 6Q_A$$

Setting MR_A equal to MC gives:

$$400 - 6Q_A = 50$$
$$6Q_A = 350$$
$$Q_A = 58.33$$

The firm should choose an output level of 58.33 units per period for market A. At this output, the maximum price it can charge is given by the demand function:

$$P_A = 400 - 3Q_A$$
$$= 400 - (3 \times 58.33)$$
$$= 400 - 175$$
$$= €225$$

The profit maximizing price for market A is €225.

Now we find the corresponding output and price for market B that maximizes profit. The marginal revenue function in market B (MR_B), is derived from the demand function for market B.

$$P_B = 200 - Q_B$$

Total revenue is $P \times Q$:

$$TR_B = (200 - Q_B)Q_B$$

Where TR_B = total revenue in market B, so:

$$= 200Q_B - Q_B^2$$

$$MR_B = \frac{dTR_B}{dQ_B}$$
$$= 200 - 2Q_B$$

Setting MR_B equal to MC we have:

$$\begin{aligned} 200 - 2Q_B &= 50 \\ 2Q_B &= 150 \\ Q_B &= 75 \end{aligned}$$

The firm should choose an output level of 75 units per period for market B. At this output level, but the maximum price it can charge is given by the demand function for market B:

$$\begin{aligned} P_B &= 200 - Q \\ &= 200 - 75 \\ &= €125 \end{aligned}$$

The profit maximizing price for market B is €125.

We have now shown that this price discriminator will charge different prices in different markets and charge the higher price in the market with the less price elastic demand. This is shown in Figure 14.5.

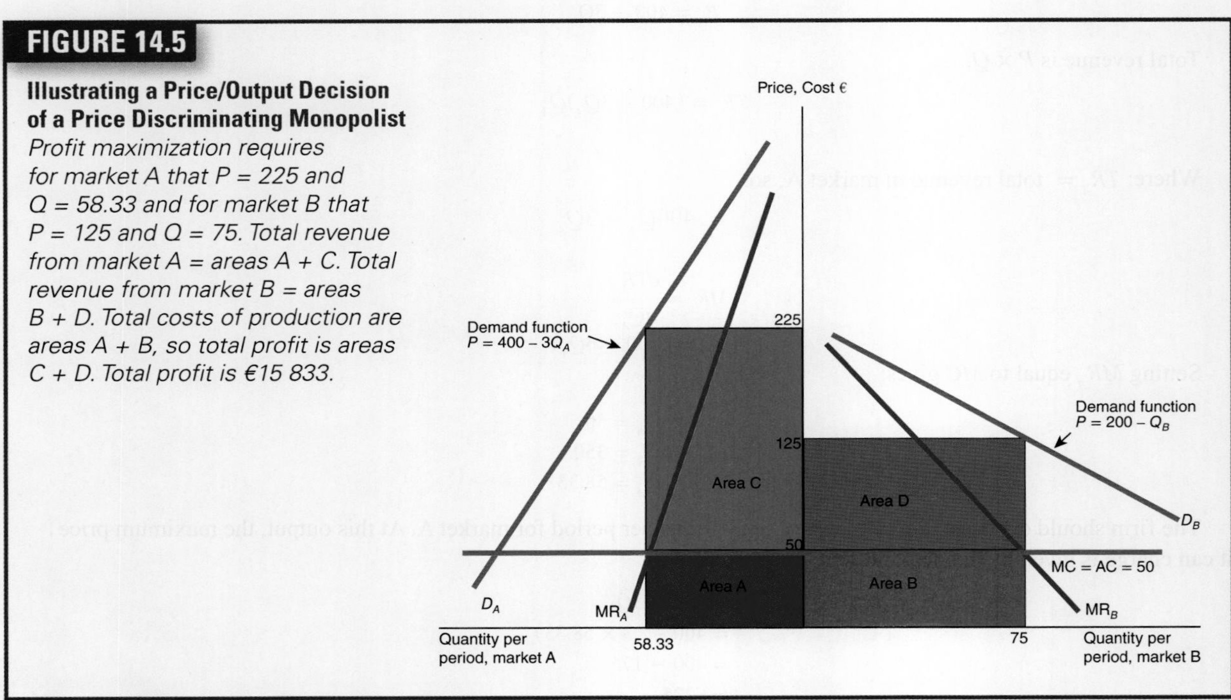

FIGURE 14.5

Illustrating a Price/Output Decision of a Price Discriminating Monopolist

Profit maximization requires for market A that P = 225 and Q = 58.33 and for market B that P = 125 and Q = 75. Total revenue from market A = areas A + C. Total revenue from market B = areas B + D. Total costs of production are areas A + B, so total profit is areas C + D. Total profit is €15 833.

Profit for the Price Discriminator

We will now find out how much profit the firm is able to make. Profit, π, will be the total revenue in each market, TR_A and TR_B respectively less total production cost, TC. That is:

$$\pi = (TR_A + TR_B) - TC$$

Let's first find TR_A:

$$\begin{aligned} TR_A &= Q_A \times P_A \\ Q_A &= 58.33 \\ P_A &= 225 \\ TR_A &= 58.33 \times 225 \\ &= €13\,124.25 \end{aligned}$$

This is represented by area A plus area C in Figure 14.5.

Now let's find TR_B:

$$TR_B = Q_B \times P_B$$
$$Q_B = 75$$
$$P_B = 125$$
$$TR_B = 75 \times 125$$
$$= €9375$$

This is represented as area B plus area D in Figure 14.5.

Thus total revenue for the two markets combined is:

$$€13\,124.25 + €9375 = €22\,499.25$$

This is represented as area A plus area C plus area B plus area D in Figure 14.5.

Having found the total revenue, we next need to find total cost given that $TC = 50Q$.

Here Q is the chosen output for market A plus the chosen output for market B

$$58.33 + 75 = 133.33$$
$$TC = 50 \times 133.33$$
$$= €6666.50$$

This is area A plus area B in Figure 14.5.

Profit is given by: $\pi = TR - TC$

$$= €22\,499.25 - €6666.50$$
$$= €15\,832.75$$

Total profit is €15 832.75.

Looking at Figure 14.5 this is represented by area A plus area C plus area B plus area D less area A, less area B. That is, total profit is shown as area C plus area D.

The Benefit to the Firm from Price Discrimination

Now let us suppose that price discrimination had not been possible but that demand and cost conditions were otherwise the same. We can calculate how much profit could then have been made and so discover just how much extra profit was the result of price discrimination.

If price discrimination is impossible we must find the total market demand curve by summing the demand curves of the two markets, A and B. We can do this in the way that we summed individual demand curves in Chapter 7. We have for market A: $P_A = 400 - 3Q_A$, and for market B, $P_B = 200 - Q_B$.

These are inverse demand curves. We find the demand curves by rearranging the equations with Q on the left-hand side. For market A:

$$P_A = 400 - 3Q_A$$
$$3Q_A = 400 - P_A$$
$$Q_A = 133.33 - \frac{1}{3}P_A$$

For market B:

$$P_B = 200 - Q_B$$
$$Q_B = 200 - P_B$$

Now we can sum these two functions to give us the total demand for the whole market:

$$\left(133.33 - \frac{1}{3}P_A\right) + (200 - P_B)$$
$$Q = 333.33 - \frac{4}{3}P$$

Now we can find the inverse demand curve for the whole of the market by rearranging with P on the left hand side:

$$\frac{4}{3}P = 333.33 - Q$$

$$P = \left(\frac{3}{4} \times 333.33\right) - \frac{3}{4}Q$$

$$P = 250 - \frac{3}{4}Q$$

Now we have an expression for a demand function for the whole combined market. To find the total revenue function for the combined market:

$$TR = P \times Q$$

$$= \left(250 - \frac{3}{4}Q\right) \times Q$$

$$= 250Q - \frac{3}{4}Q^2$$

$$MR = \frac{dTR}{dQ}$$

$$= 250 - \frac{3}{2}Q$$

Having found MR, and knowing that $MC = 50$ we can now find the profit maximizing price and output when the monopolist cannot price discriminate. First find the output level, Q.

$$MR = MC$$

$$250 - \frac{3}{2}Q = 50$$

$$\frac{3}{2}Q = 200$$

$$Q = 133.3$$

We can find the single profit maximizing price by substituting $Q = 133.33$ into the demand equation.

$$P = 250 - \frac{3}{4}Q$$

$$= 250 - \left(\frac{3}{4} \times 133.33\right)$$

$$= 250 - 100$$

$$= 150$$

Profit maximization when price discrimination is not possible means selling 133.33 units per period at the common price of €150. The amount of profit the monopolist makes under these circumstances is found by:

$$\pi = TR - TC$$

$$TR = 133.33 \times 150 = 19\,999.50$$

$$TC = 50Q \text{ where } Q = 133.33$$

$$= 50 \times 133.33$$

$$= €6666.50$$

$$\pi = €19\,999.50 - €6666.50$$

$$= 13\,333$$

Profit without price discrimination is €13 333. With price discrimination we calculated profit as €15 833. The benefit to the monopolist from being able to price discriminate is thus €15 833 – €13 333 = €2500 per period.

Monopoly power will often be such as to enable the firm to make a monopoly profit. Where the conditions for price discrimination are present, monopoly profit will always be larger.

PROBLEMS AND APPLICATIONS

1 Imagine you are a monopolist and have a known demand curve of:

$$P = 50 - 2Q$$

a. Develop the formula for the marginal revenue (MR) and draw MR and the price function (AR curve) in a diagram.
b. Explain why the downward slope of the MR curve is twice that of the AR curve.
c. Assume you have a short-run total cost schedule (STC) given by: $STC = 4 + 0.5Q^2$. What is your profit maximizing quantity and price?
d. Draw the MC curve in the diagram above.
e. Calculate your total profit.
f. What would be your price and output in the case of perfect competition?
g. Calculate the deadweight loss.
h. Compute the elasticity for the monopolistic case and the case of perfect competition.

2 A monopolist is confronted with the demand function $P(Q) = 1500 - 15Q$ where x is the quantity of the good bought by consumers at the price P. Total cost to produce any quantity x for the monopolist is given by the cost function $C(x) = 0.1Q^3 - 4,5Q^2 + 600Q + 5600$.

a. Calculate the revenue function of the monopolist.
b. Show the demand function in the graph below.
c. Derive the marginal revenue function and draw it in the graph below.
d. Calculate the functions for marginal cost and average total cost.
e. Marginal cost, average total cost, and average variable cost are depicted in the graph below. It appears that the marginal cost function is intersecting the average cost functions in their respective minimum. Is this a chance event or is this always the case? (Support your answer with analytical reasoning – based on the graph – or mathematically.)
f. Find the profit maximizing output quantity for the monopolist by calculation or graphically; in either case, explain what you are doing.
g. At which price is the monopolist selling and is he making a profit? (Again, you can choose between the graph and a calculation.)

FIGURE 14.6

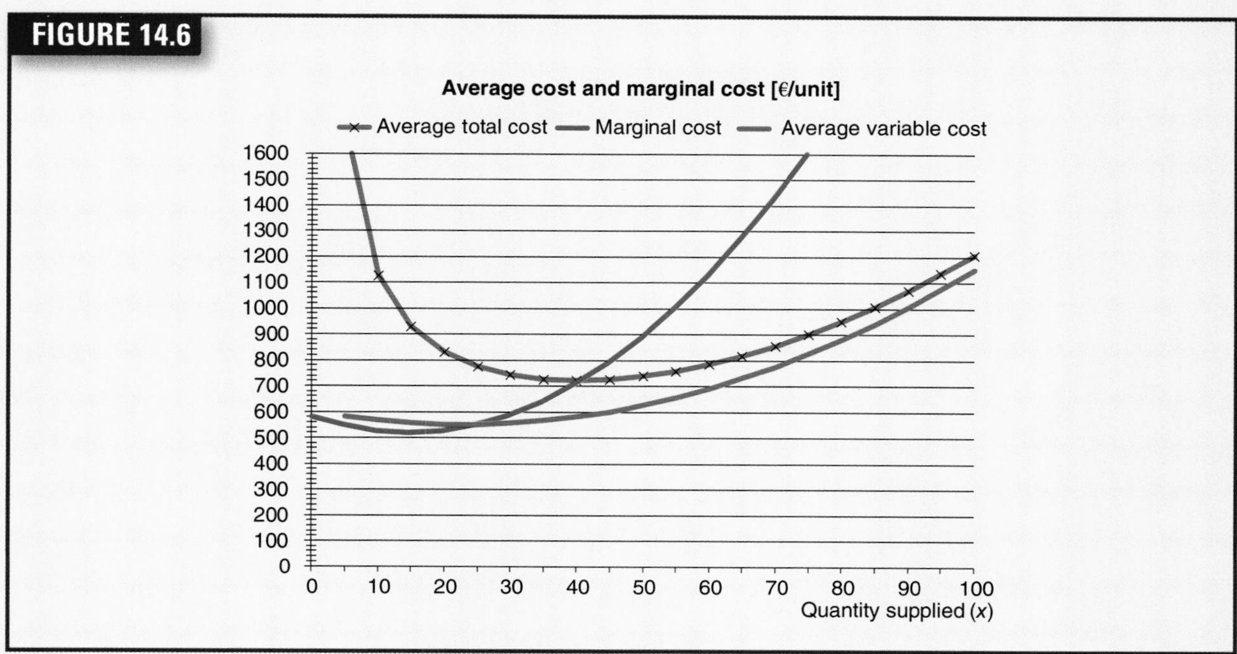

3 For a producer in perfect competition and a monopolist profit is revenue minus cost $\pi = TR - TC$. The first order condition for a maximum of profit in both cases is $\frac{d\pi}{dQ} = \frac{dTR}{dQ} - \frac{dTC}{dQ} = MR - MC = 0 \Leftrightarrow MR = MC$. Looking at this formula, where is the difference between a monopolist and a supplier in perfect competition?

4 A monopolistic producer of t-shirts knows that the price elasticity of his products is −3 for a current price of 7.5. How much additional revenue will he generate if he sells one t-shirt more? Assuming his marginal cost (MC) is at 6, will he expand the output?

5 Imagine you are a designer of dresses. Your clothes are so unique that your position is considered monopolistic. Furthermore you are able to sell your products on two different markets (A and B). Arbitrage between those two markets is not possible. The markets have given demand curves of:

$$P_A = 800 - 10Q$$
$$P_B = 600 - 4Q$$

Your total costs (TC) can be calculated as:

$$TC = 100 + 20Q \text{ (Q in thousands)}$$

a. Check if there are two different price elasticities on the two markets. Use a fictional price of 50.
b. Find the profit maximizing price on each of the two markets.
c. How much profit will you be able to make?
d. How much benefit do you earn by using price discrimination?

15 MARKET STRUCTURES II: MONOPOLISTIC COMPETITION

Having considered perfect competition and monopoly it can be seen that the structure of a market affects firm behaviour. One aspect of an industry's market structure is the number of firms and how much power this gives them over price. It is usually argued that, *ceteris paribus*, the fewer the firms the greater the market power.

The extent to which market power is concentrated is known as seller concentration. However, there are various ways in which this concentration can be measured so we will give over this chapter to looking at this topic. We will focus on just four measures of seller concentration. These are: the concentration ratio, a measure based on the Lorenz curve, the Herfindahl index and the average value of the cumulative concentration curve. Finally, we consider a somewhat different way of looking at this issue by considering the Lerner index.

MEASURING MARKET CONCENTRATION

In perfect competition there are many firms and no one firm can influence the market price, which is determined by the forces of supply and demand. At the opposite end of the spectrum is the monopolist. As the sole seller in the market the monopolist can generally exert considerable control over price, subject, of course, to the constraints of the demand curve. In monopolistic competition there are still many firms but each has the ability to differentiate their product which gives the individual firm some limited power over price. The question of market concentration and how to measure it is important, because in the view of many economists, seller concentration will be important in determining how prices are set in an industry, how much output is produced and how much profit is made. It may well also influence other things such as how advertising behaviour is determined, and how much research and development activity takes place. Measures of seller concentration will help us decide whether we should analyze an industry using our model of perfect competition, monopoly, monopolistic competition or oligopoly.

The Concentration Ratio

There are various ways of measuring market concentration and the first and the simplest way is based on what is called the *cumulative concentration ratio* from which we derive the cumulative concentration curve. This is the most commonly used measure of concentration in Europe.

It is defined as:

$$CR_r = \frac{\sum_{i=1}^{r} S_i}{\sum_{i=1}^{n} S_i} \times 100$$

Where:
CR_r = the concentration ratio of r firms
S_i = sales of the each of the firms in turn
r = some arbitrary number of firms
n = all firms in the market.

You can read the top line of the formula as 'the cumulated sum of the sales of the largest firms from one to r. The bottom line of the formula can be read as the cumulated sum of the sales of all n firms in the particular industry in question where n will vary between industries.

In other words we are looking at the largest firms and asking what share of the total market the largest firms have. For the UK it is usual to look at the top three or the top five. Consider the sales of groceries in Great Britain. The largest firms and their market share are given in Table 15.1. We have not included the smaller firms in the industry. We do not have the value of sales for each firm, but we can use their percentage share of the market, since we know that the whole market must sum to 100 per cent.

TABLE 15.1 **Share of GB Grocery Market, June 2015**

Firm	Market Share, by Sales (%)
Tesco	28.6
Asda	16.6
Sainsbury's	16.5
Morrisons	10.9
The Co-operative	6.0
Aldi	5.4
Waitrose	5.2

Source: Kantar

We might summarize this information into a single figure by looking at the share of the top three (CR_3), which is the proportion of sales of the top three cumulated. So here we have the cumulated share of Tesco, Asda and Sainsbury's, which equals 28.6 + 16.6 + 16.5 = 61.7. The biggest three have 61.7 per cent of the total market. Alternatively, we might look at the share of the top five (CR_5), which is the proportion of sales of the top five cumulated. So here we have the cumulated share of Tesco, Asda, Sainsbury's, Morrisons and the Co-operative, which equals 28.6 + 16.6 + 16.5 + 10.9 + 6.0 = 78.6. The biggest five have 78.6 per cent of the total market. When making industry comparisons it is usual in the US to look at the CR_4.

From the concentration data we can construct a concentration curve. For the market above it will look like Figure 15.1. Along the horizontal axis we measure the number of firms in the industry, cumulated from the largest. The vertical axis measures the proportion of the industry's output. In this case we do not have information about each individual firm in the industry. However, a concentration ratio can still be produced because industry sales must total 100 per cent.

FIGURE 15.1

Concentration Curve for the GB Grocery Market, June 2015

The concentration curve is a visual representation of industry concentration. Along the horizontal axis we measure the number of firms in the industry, cumulated from the largest. The vertical axis measures the proportion of the industry's output. The curve slopes upwards but at a diminishing rate because firms are cumulated from the largest.

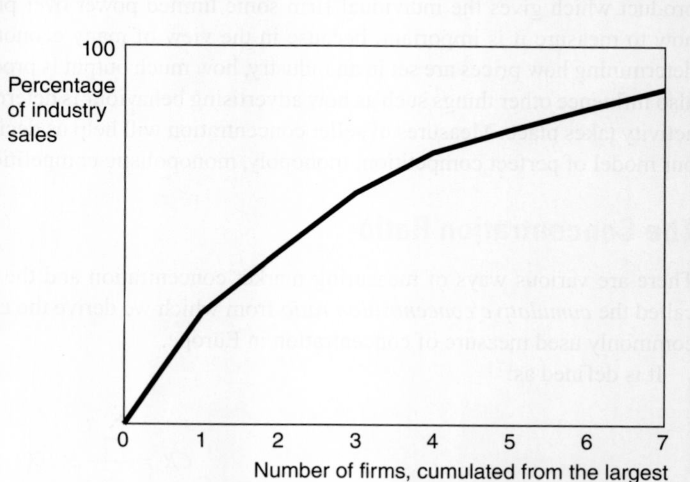

Notice the concentration curve slopes upwards, but at a diminishing rate because it is cumulated from the largest to the smallest firms.

When using this simple ratio we need to be aware of a number of problems with it. The first is that the arbitrary choice of firm number can lead to an oversimplified conclusion. Suppose we wish to compare the degree of market power in two industries A and B whose market shares are given in Table 15.2. Which is the more concentrated industry where power to raise price above the social optimum is most likely?

TABLE 15.2 **Concentration Data for Two Industries**

Firm, Ranked by Percentage Size of Sales	Industry A (percentage of sales)	Industry B (percentage of sales)
1	60	20
2	10	20
3	5	20
4	5	20
5	5	20

The CR_3 for industry A is 75 per cent but only 60 per cent for industry B. Industry A is more concentrated. If we had chosen the CR_5 as our measure, we have for industry A a figure of 85 per cent and for industry B a corresponding figure of 100 per cent. Now industry B appears to be more concentrated. Alternatively expressed, if we plot the industries' cumulative concentration curves they cross over at some point. There is a degree of arbitrariness about this measure.

Another issue when using concentration data is that we are using a measure of the concentration of market power when we might think that its dispersal is more appropriate. Refer back to Table 15.2. In industry A, power is heavily concentrated into the hands of one large firm. In industry B, power is dispersed more evenly. This might lead to different firm behaviour but the concentration ratio will not necessarily pick this up. We shall return to this issue shortly.

There is also the question of imports as a source of competition. A CR_5, say, of 70 per cent for example, will mean that the five largest firms in the industry produce 70 per cent of UK production. However, the total market may be much larger if there is a significant volume of imports. In this case the industry may be very competitive even if concentration levels appear high. If one is aware of the problem and the data is available, one can adjust the formula accordingly. As we shall see, the presence of exports may also affect market power.

The Trade Adjusted Concentration Ratio

Following the formula above we define:
S_r = Sales of the top r firms in the sector, where we shall assume that r is 5.
S_n = Total sales of all firms in the sector.
Then we have characterised CR_5 as a percentage:

$$CR_5 = \frac{S_5}{S_n} \times 100$$

Now let us consider the effect of imports in the sector, which we shall describe as M. A proportion of these imports may be undertaken by the top 5 firms themselves, i.e. they are intra-firm, and as such do not compete with the firm's own sales. Such imports are described as "non-competitive."

For our purposes here, it simplifies matters if we ignore such non-competitive imports and assume that all imports are competitive, i.e. they compete directly with the sales of the top 5.

If we treat all imports in the sector as competitive, then CR_5 adjusted for such imports, again expressed as a percentage, becomes:

$$CR_{5A} = \frac{S_5}{S_n + M} \times 100$$

where:
CR_{5A} = the concentration ratio adjusted for imports.
Hence if we compare industry sectors C and D in Table 15.3, it appears that there is more competition in sector D because the domestic firms must compete with competitive imports. Hence CR_5 in sector C is 80 per cent, but in sector D it is:

$$\frac{80}{120} \times 100 = 66\%$$

We have thus shown industry D to be less concentrated than industry C after the adjustment for the effect of imports.

TABLE 15.3 **The Effect of International Trade on the Concentration Ratio**

Industry	Cumulative Sales of Top five Firms (€ millions)	Total Domestic Sales (€ millions)	CR_5 (%)	Imports (€ millions)	Exports (€ millions)	Modified CR_5 (%)
C	80	100	80	0	0	80
D	80	100	80	20	0	67
E	80	100	80	20	50	57

Readjusting concentration data for imports will be very important for some industries and for some countries where trade is very open. One might also argue that we should take exports into account in that these are not part of the domestic market.

Next then, let us consider the effect of exports, which we shall call X. Again a complication arises because we need to consider the proportion of the total exports, which arises from the top 5 firms themselves.

Now clearly in theory this proportion can be anywhere between 0% and 100%. If we term this unknown proportion β, then the concentration ratio for the top 5 firms adjusted for both imports and exports, expressed as a percentage, becomes:

$$CR_{5A} = \frac{S_5 - \beta X}{S_n + M - X} \times 100$$

where:

$0 \leq \beta \leq 1$

For the sake of simplicity in the example, let us assume that $\beta = 0.8$.

So that for industry sector E in Table 15.3:

$$CR_{5A} = \frac{80 - 0.8 \times 50}{100 + 20 - 50} \times 100$$

$$= \frac{40}{70} \times 100$$

$$= 57\%$$

The CR_5 modified to take into account the presence of both imports and exports, that is CR_{5A}, is 57 per cent[1].

The Gini Coefficient

A second way to measure concentration is to use what is called the Lorenz curve and from that Lorenz curve to develop what is known as the Gini coefficient. In contrast to the concentration curve, in order to be able to construct a Lorenz curve, we need information about all firms in the industry. Consider Figure 15.2.

Along the horizontal axis is plotted, not the number of firms, but the percentage of firms in the industry, cumulated from the largest. On the vertical axis is plotted the percentage of total industry sales. Clearly the curve is going to start from the bottom left corner, since 0 per cent of the firms have 0 per cent of the output, and it will always finish in the top right corner, since 100 per cent of the firms will have 100 per cent of the output. If we have an industry where all firms are of the same size, then we have the line of absolute equality: 20 per cent of the firms will have 20 per cent of the output, 50 per cent of the firms will have 50 per cent of the output and so on. Suppose now we have an industry where all firms are not of the same size, then we have a Lorenz curve which bends away from the line of absolute equality. For example, Figure 15.2 shows an industry which we will call industry F, where the largest firm has 70 per cent of the market and three other firms each have ten per cent of sales. The more uneven the size distribution of firms, the further from the line of absolute equality the Lorenz curve for a given industry will be drawn.

This idea of focusing on the extent of inequality of firm size is in essence what the Lorenz curve is all about. We can now develop from the Lorenz curve a summary measure of an industry's market power. This is called the Gini coefficient.

From Figure 15.2, the shaded area A represents the extent to which the Lorenz curve has departed from the line of absolute equality. If we take area A as a proportion of the whole triangle, A plus B, then we have a measure of how uneven firm size is. That we refer to as the Gini coefficient. If we have a monopoly industry, so that one firm has all the industry's output, then that area, A, would cover the whole triangle and there would be no Area B.

[1] For further information about trade adjusted concentration ratios see Kumar, M. S. (1985). International Trade and Industrial Concentration. Oxford Economic Papers, New Series, Vol.37, Number 1, 125–133.

FIGURE 15.2

Lorenz Curve and Gini Coefficient for Industry F

The largest firm in industry F has 70 per cent of the market and three other firms each have ten per cent of sales. The further away from the line of absolute equality the Lorenz curve goes, the more uneven is the distribution of firm size. The green shaded area A shows how far the Lorenz curve has departed from the line of absolute equality. Area A as a proportion of the whole triangle, A plus B, gives us a measure of how uneven firm size is. This is the Gini coefficient.

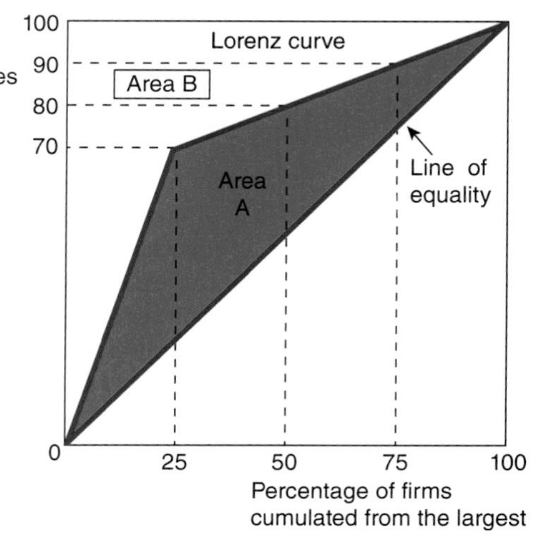

If all firms are of the same size, then area A is 0. So the Gini coefficient is always between 0 and 1. The more uneven is the distribution of power in the industry, the closer the Gini coefficient is to 1.

Area A is 45 per cent of Area A + B. Since the Gini coefficient is usually taken as having a value between zero and one we can divide by 100 and say that the Gini coefficient is 0.45.

This is how we calculate the Gini coefficient:

$$G = \frac{1}{N}\sum_{i=1}^{N}(N - 2i + 1)ms_i$$

Where:
G = Gini coefficient
N = number of firms in the industry
ms_i = market share of each firm in turn
Then we have:

$$\begin{aligned} G &= \frac{1}{4}[(4-2+1)\times 70 + (4-4+1)\times 10 + (4-6+1)\times 10 + (4-8+1)\times 10] \\ &= \frac{1}{4}(210 + 10 - 10 - 30) \\ &= \frac{1}{4}\times 180 \\ &= 45 \end{aligned}$$

Dividing by 100 gives 0.45.

The Gini coefficient comes directly from the idea of a Lorenz curve. Remember that in order to be able to use a Lorenz curve and thus develop a Gini coefficient, we will need information about all the firms in the industry, not just the larger ones.

We will meet the Gini coefficient again in Chapter 18 and will use a formula to calculate its value in that chapter.

There is an important point to note about what the Gini coefficient is saying and how differently from the concentration ratio it views market power. Imagine that there are five firms in a particular industry. The largest three have 25 per cent of the market each, the fourth largest firm has 15 per cent of the market and the smallest firm in the market has 10 per cent. Now the two smallest firms merge. How much of an increase in market power has taken place? If we look at, say, the CR_4, we can see that before the merger took place the top four firms had 90 per cent of the market between them. The CR_4, as a result of the merger, has increased to 100 per cent. The merger has increased concentration.

If we now look at the Gini coefficient, it gives an indication of how evenly sized firms were. By this measure, as a result of the merger of the two small firms, all firms in the industry are the same size. The Gini coefficient has actually been reduced to zero. According to this measure we have a decrease because the merger evened up the size of the firms in the market. Perfect competition and an industry of two firms with 50 per cent of the market each both give the same Gini coefficient. With the first measure, it is the concentration of power in which we are interested. However, in the case of the Gini coefficient it is the dispersal of power on which we have focused.

The Herfindahl–Hirschmann index

The Herfindahl Hirschmann index (HHI) is another measure of the degree of market concentration in an industry. In the view of some, one of the problems about the concentration ratio is that it does not give enough emphasis to the larger firm. Consider industry F. The large firm might be able to dominate a market, and have the power to set whatever price it chooses, constrained only by the demand curve. Other firms will then follow their lead and set price accordingly. The amount of power in the hands of that large firm is out of proportion to that which is implied by the concentration ratio. In the view of the proponents of the HHI, we need to emphasize the importance of the large firms. The HHI does that by squaring the market shares of each firm in the industry. By squaring the market shares of all firms, the larger firm is given a much greater prominence in the data.

The formula for the HHI is given as:

$$HHI = \sum (ms_i)^2$$

Where:

ms_i = market share of each individual firm

Consider an industry where two firms share the market equally. Then:

$$\begin{aligned} HHI &= 50^2 + 50^2 \\ &= 5000 \end{aligned}$$

Now consider a market where four firms share sales equally. Unlike the Gini coefficient, this will not give the same answer as the two-firm industry just considered.

$$\begin{aligned} HHI &= 25^2 + 25^2 + 25^2 + 25^2 \\ &= 2500 \end{aligned}$$

Now we look at an industry where one firm dominates the market, whilst not having a monopoly. Let's consider a market where one firm has 80 per cent of the market and two other firms have 10 per cent each.

$$HHI = 80^2 + 10^2 + 10^2 = 6600$$

What is the HHI for monopoly, and what is the index for perfect competition? For monopoly, if there is one firm with 100 per cent of the market, 100^2 squared gives us 10 000. For perfect competition, where each firm is infinitely small, then squaring many infinitely small amounts and adding them will give 0. As a result, the HHI in these two cases lies somewhere between 0 and 10 000. The key to understanding the number's significance is that the formula is emphasizing the significance of the larger firms.

The HHI is the basis for US antitrust policy. The American authorities look at large mergers to decide whether they think they are in the public interest. The most important thing that they consider is whether a merger will increase market power. Will it give a more concentrated industry, and would the increase in concentration be significant enough to have a detrimental effect on consumers? The basis for that decision is what would happen to the HHI. If the number is between 0 and 1000, this is regarded as an industry that is unconcentrated, and so a merger between two firms will be unchallenged. If the index lies between 1000 and 1800, this is regarded as a moderately concentrated industry and the authorities then look to see, as a result of the merger, whether the HHI is raised by more than 100 points. If it is, then the merger will be challenged. If the index in the industry is already above 1800, then a merger will be challenged, even if it raises the index by as little as 50 points.

HHI can also be seen as a measure of dispersion. We can write:

$$HHI = \frac{c^2 + 1}{n}$$

Where:

n = the number of firms in the industry

c = coefficient of variation of firm size

$$c = \frac{standard\ deviation}{arithmetic\ mean}$$

This is an equivalent approach giving the same result. To illustrate let's use the industry described in Table 15.4, where industry output is shared among four firms, A, B, C and D.

TABLE 15.4 **Illustrative Industrial Structure for an Industry Using the Herfindahl Index**

Firm by size rank	Market share, x	Square of market share, x^2
A	40	1600
B	20	400
C	20	400
D	20	400

First we calculate *c*.

$$c = \frac{standard\ deviation}{arithmetic\ mean,\ AM}$$

Standard deviation SD is given as:

$$SD = \sqrt{\frac{\sum x^2}{n} - \bar{x}^2}$$

Where:
x = market share of firms
$\bar{x}$ = arithmetic means of market shares

here in this example we have:

The arithmetic mean is $\frac{40 + 20 + 20 + 20}{4} = 25$, therefore:

$$SD = \sqrt{\frac{1600 + 400 + 400 + 400}{4} - 25^2}$$

$$= \sqrt{\frac{2800}{4} - 625}$$

$$= \sqrt{75}$$

$$\frac{SD}{AM} = \frac{\sqrt{75}}{25}$$

$$\text{Then: } HHI = \frac{c^2 + 1}{n}$$

$$= \frac{(\sqrt{75} / 25)^2 + 1}{4}$$

$$= \frac{75 / 625 + 1}{4}$$

$$= 0.28$$

If we find HHI by our first formula we have:

$$HHI = \sum (MS_i)^2$$

$$= 0.16 + 0.04 + 0.04 + 0.04$$

$$= 0.28$$

By either formula the Herfindahl index for the industrial structure described in Table 15.4 is 0.28.

The Average Value of the Cumulative Concentration Curve

This measure is one that includes data on the size distribution of all firms on the concentration curve but emphasizes the share of the largest firms. The formula is given as:

$$B_r = (1/rn\bar{s}) \sum_{i=1}^{r} (r - i + 1) Si$$

Where:
n = the number of firms on the concentration curve
r = the largest firms in the industry, where that number is arbitrarily chosen
$\bar{s}$ = average value of sales of the n firms
S_i = sales of each of the largest r firms in turn
i = each firm in turn

We will illustrate its use with four industries. In each case calculating the degree of concentration using this measure will show us something about interpreting the meaning of it. The industries we will use are given in the columns in Table 15.5. In each case we have information about the top four firms, that is, n = 4. Assume that market sales for the total industry amount to €100 million in each case except industry Q where it is €200 million. To analyze we choose some arbitrary spot on the curve. In each case we will choose three firms. That is, we will set r = 3.

TABLE 15.5 **Illustrating the Average Value of the Cumulative Concentration Curve**

Market Share (%)	Industry P	Industry Q	Industry R	Industry S
Firm One	40	40	10	20
Firm Two	20	20	10	20
Firm Three	10	10	10	20
Firm Four	10	10	10	20

We begin by calculating the value for industry P. Let's work out the average value of sales of the n firms, s̄. The first firm has 40 per cent of industry sales of €100 million. That is, Firm One has €40 million. Similarly, the second firm has 20 per cent of total industry sales, which is €20 million. The third and fourth firms each have values of €10 million. Therefore, we have:

$$\frac{40 + 20 + 10 + 10}{4} = €20 \textit{ million}$$

Our formula gives:

$$\frac{1}{3 \times 4 \times 20} \times [(3 - 1 + 1) \times 40 + (3 - 2 + 1) \times 20 + (3 - 3 + 1) \times 10]$$

$$= \frac{1}{3 \times 4 \times 20} \times (120 + 40 + 10)$$

$$= \frac{1}{240} \times 170$$

$$= 0.7083$$

This is the average value of the cumulative concentration curve for industry P.

For industry Q, sales are €200 million; the largest firm has 40 per cent of €200 million, which is €80 million. Similarly, Firm Two has 20 per cent of €200 million = €40 million. Firms Three and Four have €20 million each. This gives an average value of sales for n firms (s̄) of €40 million. Using the formula we have:

$$\frac{1}{3 \times 4 \times 40} \times (240 + 80 + 20)$$

$$= \frac{1}{480} \times 340$$

$$= 0.7083$$

We have the same value for industry Q as for industry P. That is, the measure uses an average value of sales but the value obtained is independent of the size of the industry.

Now look at industry R. The value we obtain is:

$$\frac{1}{3 \times 4 \times 10} \times (30 + 20 + 10)$$

$$= \frac{1}{120} \times 60$$

$$= 0.5$$

Finally, we calculate the value for industry S:

$$\frac{1}{3 \times 4 \times 20} \times (60 + 40 + 20)$$

$$= \frac{1}{240} \times 120$$

$$= 0.5$$

We obtain the same value as for industry R.

This is despite the fact that industry S is more concentrated than industry R. The formula is a measure of dispersion.

We have considered just some of the measures of market concentration. It is not the case that there is a measure of concentration that is 'right' or even necessarily better. Rather we need to think through what any particular measure is showing, and then decide which is the most appropriate.

THE LERNER INDEX

One further problem about the use of concentration data to consider is whether we are interested in the potential power of firms to raise prices or should the focus be on the extent to which they choose to use this power? Are we looking at what it is possible for firms to do by raising prices above costs or are we more interested in what they actually do? When we look at concentration data we are considering potential power.

An alternative way of looking at market power is to consider the actual market power that firms use. How might we do that? One measure is the Lerner Index. Think about a perfectly competitive industry. Here price does not exceed marginal cost but reflects the marginal cost of production. When we considered the monopolistic firm we saw that it will charge a price in excess of marginal cost. Consider Figure 15.3.

FIGURE 15.3

The Lerner Index

The Lerner Index is a measure of monopoly power. It is given as $\frac{P - MC}{P}$. We take the distance AB. Then we express that as a proportion of the price, P. The index will always take a value between 0 and 1, with perfect competition taking a value of 0.

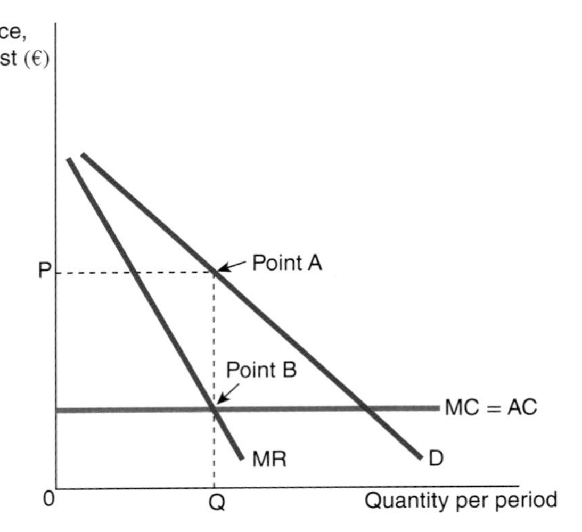

Here we have assumed for simplicity that the marginal cost and the average cost are constant so that $MC = AC$. The profit maximizing firm produces where $MC = MR$ at output Q. We have shown on the diagram the monopoly price as P. The price charged is in excess of marginal cost. The Lerner Index attempts to measure this excess in order to give an idea of how much power the firm is actually using. The formula is:

$$\frac{P - MC}{P}$$

Where:
P = Price charged
MC = Marginal Cost
In other words we take the difference between price and marginal cost, the extent to which the firm raises price above marginal cost (shown as AB in Figure 15.3). This is sometimes called the *monopoly mark-up*. Then we express that as a proportion of the price, P.

If a firm's marginal cost is €10 and the price it charges is €30, the Lerner Index is:

$$\frac{30 - 10}{30}$$

$$= 0.67$$

The index will always take a value between 0 and 1, with perfect competition taking a value of 0.

What the Lerner Index is measuring is the extent to which firms actually use their power to raise prices. This is different from measures such as the concentration ratio, which measure the extent to which firms have the power to raise price above marginal cost. However, there are considerable problems in obtaining the data on cost and demand conditions that will enable the Lerner Index to be calculated. In particular, although a firm will generally have a clear idea of its costs at its current level of output, it is difficult to gain an accurate estimate of its costs should it change its output. Similarly, although a firm knows its level of sales at its current price, it is not easy to discover what its sales would be at a different price. We saw this in chapter four in relation to the UK newspaper industry.

PROBLEMS AND APPLICATIONS

In the text, market concentration was calculated based on total sales values (turnover) of the firms in the market. In some markets you can also measure the concentration when looking at the sales volumes, the number of products sold by each firm. In the problems for this chapter we look at the number of passenger cars and light vehicles sold by different manufacturer groups in the European market. The data used are provided by the European Automobile Manufacturers Association, however, they were rearranged to suit us better for practicing the calculation of concentration indices. Among other things, the categories Domestic Producers and Imports were introduced and non-European brands were placed in the import category, even though, this does not do the complexity of today's value creation chains in the industry justice. For example, Toyota has large manufacturing facilities in Europe, whereas some of the vehicles under the General Motors brands are assembled in Asia. (Since these problems involve quite a few calculations, you could use a spreadsheet software to find the results more quickly.)

1 Use the data from Figure 15.4 of sales of passenger cars to calculate measures of concentration of the industry.
   a. Record the ranking of the groups of sellers of passenger cars by sales volume, first without imports and second including imports.
   b. Calculate the market shares for each group excluding and including the imported cars sold in the European market. (This is quite a bit of work; however, you will use these numbers in some of the other problems down below as well.)
   c. Determine the concentration ratio of the largest three, five and ten manufacturers by their sales among the domestic producers and for the European sales of all manufacturers.
   d. Graph the concentration curve for the European manufacturers of passenger cars and light vehicles.

2 How does the concentration curve relate to the Lorenz curve for the sales of passenger cars from domestic producers in Europe?

3 Compare the concentration of the automobile industry in passenger cars versus light vehicles.

a. Are sales from domestic manufacturers in the passenger car sector or the sector of light vehicles more concentrated, when judging by the concentration ratios for the largest three and the largest five manufacturers?
b. Explain some of the problems of your above analysis.

4 Again, use only the data for sales of European manufacturers in the following analysis.

a. Draw a Lozenz curve for passenger car sales.
b. Calculate the Gini coefficient based on the market shares relative to total sales of domestic manufacturers.
c. Evaluate the Herfindahl–Hirschmann index for European passenger car sales by European manufacturers.
d. Compare the Lorenz curve for passenger car sales with the curve for the sales of light vehicles. Comment on your findings regarding the concentration of the two segments of the automobile market.
e. Use the Gini and Herfindahl–Hirschmann indices to evaluate the market concentration for light vehicle sales by European manufacturers. Compare the concentration in the passenger car and the light vehicle market segments.

5 Calculate the average value of the concentration curve for the light vehicles sales of all manufacturers (domestic manufacturers and imports), using the five largest firms.

FIGURE 15.4

New registrations in European Union and EFTA
(full year 2015)

GROUP	BRANDS	Passenger cars	Total light vehicles up to 3.5t (excluding passenger cars)	Rank Passenger cars	Rank light vehicles
Domestic Producers		**11 461 709**	**1 651 555**		
ASTON MARTIN	ASTON MARTIN	1 594	0		
B.M.W.	B.M.W., MINI	935 624	1 028		
DAIMLER	MERCEDES, SMART	839 158	162 048		
FIAT	ALFA ROMEO, FIAT, LANCIA, JEEP	870 689	171 982		
FORD	FORD	1 031 158	263 829		
G.M.	OPEL, CHEVROLET	943 439	102 152		
IVECO	IVECO	622	50 316		
JAGUAR LAND ROVER	JAGUAR, LAND ROVER	178 435	22 495		
PORSCHE	PORSCHE	68 163	61		
PSA	CITROEN, DS, PEUGEOT	1 480 294	353 612		
RENAULT	DACIA, RENAULT	1 349 918	298 301		
VOLKSWAGEN AG	AUDI, SEAT, SKODA, VOLKSWAGEN	3 447 948	216 203		
OTHERS	SAAB, VOLVO, Others	314 667	9 528		
Imports		**2 727 225**	**135 221**		
CHINA	GREAT WALL, LANDWIND	143	956		
JAPAN	Total Japan	1 858 320	129 344		
of which	MAZDA	211 278	497		
	NISSAN	554 488	49 415		
	SUZUKI	180 465	522		
	TOYOTA	603 309	41 227		
	HONDA, MITSUBISHI, SUBARU, Others	308 780	37 683		
KOREA	HYUNDAI, KIA, Others	868 762	4 921		
TOTAL		**14 188 934**	**1 786 776**		

European Automobile Manufacturers Association
Source: Association Auxiliaire de l'Automobile

16 MARKET STRUCTURES III: OLIGOPOLY

In this chapter we will examine oligopoly theory from several different perspectives. First we consider a model where we assume that firms seek to maximize profits. The particular one that we consider is called the Cournot model. Second we will examine possible oligopolistic output decisions based on goals other than profit maximization. Then we consider the idea that firms do not attempt to find $MC = MR$, but rather that they work out costs and add on a mark-up to determine price. We will then see whether this gives a different price and output decision from equating MC with MR. Finally, we will examine an example problem that enables us to check our understanding of some of the key principles surrounding pricing.

THE COURNOT MODEL

Oligopoly is a market structure dominated by a few large firms. There are many models of oligopolistic behaviour, one of which is the Cournot model. In oligopoly firms are interdependent. The decision of one firm will have a direct effect on other firms in the market. Most firms will have a reasonable idea of the size of the market in which they operate and what position they hold in that market. For ease of analysis, we assume a duopoly, that is there are only two firms. We also assume high barriers to entry in the industry and so the two firms are not unduly worried by new entrants. Thus the number of firms in the industry is fixed.

Now we consider a market with two firms, A and B. Assume that Firm A has conducted research which shows that the size of the market it operates in is 1 000 000 units or a value of €1 million a year. We will also assume that marginal cost is constant.

Figure 16.1 illustrates this situation. If Firm A were the only producer in the market it would produce where the MR_1 curve cuts the MC curve and supply the whole 1 million units at Q_1. However, Firm A knows that Firm B also

FIGURE 16.1

RESIDUAL DEMAND

If Firm A supplied the whole market (i.e. it assumes Firm B produces nothing) then the profit maximizing output would be Q_1. If Firm A assumes Firm B produces 20 per cent of the market (shown by demand curve D_2) then its new profit maximizing output will be Q_2 where the MR curve associated with the residual demand curve D_2 cuts the MC curve. If Firm B were assumed to produce 40 per cent of the market output then Firm A would produce where MR_3 associated with residual demand D_3 cuts the MC curve at output Q_3.

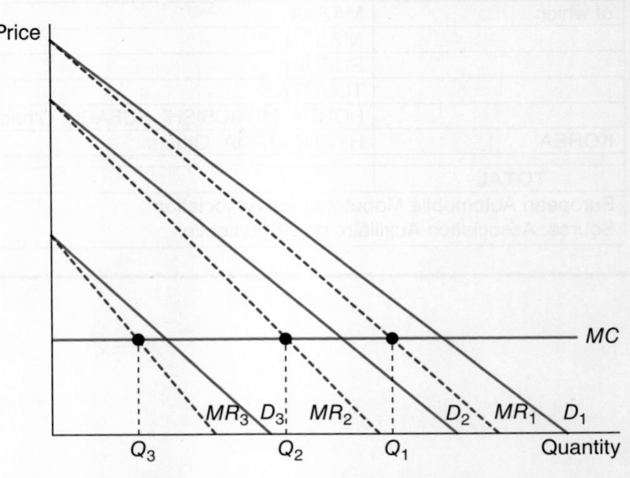

operates in the market and supplies 20 per cent of the market. The demand curve it faces is thus not D_1 but D_2, which is referred to as a residual demand curve. Residual demand is defined as the difference between the market demand curve and the amount supplied by other firms in the market. D_2 has an associated marginal revenue curve MR_2. Firm A's profit maximizing output is now Q_2 where MR_2 cuts the MC curve. The residual demand curve depends on the output decision of the other firms in the market. Firm A might expend some time and effort trying to find out, or at the very least estimate, what this output level might be. In other words, Firm A needs to have some idea of the residual demand curve it faces or risk producing an output which would drive down the market price it faced. If, for example, it produced 1 million units and Firm B produced 200 000 units then there would be excess supply and the price it faced would fall. Knowing what your rival is planning to do is important in adopting the right strategy to ensure profit maximizing output. If Firm B supplied 60 per cent of the market then Firm A would face a different residual demand curve D_3, and would set output at Q_3 where MR_3 cuts the MC curve. It would be possible to conceptualize a situation where Firm A could map all possible outputs by Firm B and thus how it would react to these output levels.

The result of this analysis by Firm A would give it its 'reaction function'. The reaction function shows the preferred strategies of one firm in relation to a particular issue which is dependent on the strategies adopted by its rival/s on that same issue. The reaction function, therefore, could outline the profit maximizing output for a firm given the simultaneous output decisions of its rivals.

Firm B will also have a reaction function derived from its analysis of how it would react to the output decisions of Firm A. The respective reaction functions show how Firm A would react if Firm B changed its output decisions and vice versa. This model of oligopoly was developed by Augustin Cournot in 1838. Cournot assumed that given two firms in a duopoly, each firm determines its profit maximizing output on the assumption of the output of the other firm and that the decision of the other firm will not change in a given time period. The strategy each firm adopts, therefore, is based on setting the quantity of output. If we assume that both firms are profit maximizers then the question will arise as to what the profit maximizing output will be for Firm A given the output by Firm B?

In a given time period, Firm A, for example, could alter its output decision and its rival would not react. However, Firm B makes its decision under the same assumptions. This simultaneous decision making whereby each firm is trying to increase its profits but assuming its rivals will not react over different time periods eventually leads to an equilibrium position.

We can represent this equilibrium in Figure 16.2. Firm A's output is on the vertical axis and Firm B's output on the horizontal axis. If Firm A assumed Firm B would produce zero then it would supply the whole market and take all the profits given by point C_1. If Firm B produced all the market output then Firm A would produce nothing indicated by point C_2. All other points in-between show combinations of output for Firm A given a corresponding output decision by Firm B. The red line is Firm A's reaction function. The further away the output level from the whole market output the lower the firm's profits (and vice versa).

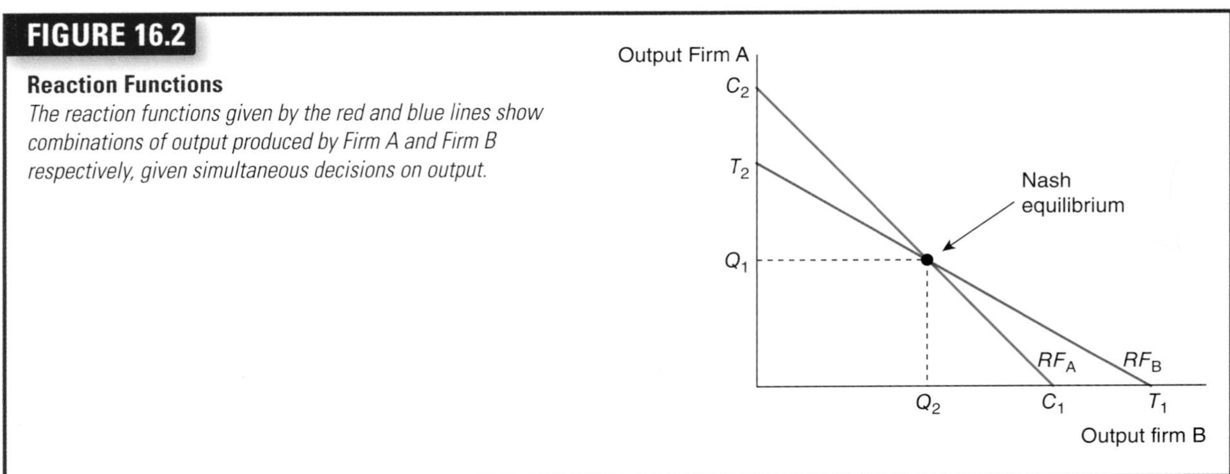

FIGURE 16.2

Reaction Functions

The reaction functions given by the red and blue lines show combinations of output produced by Firm A and Firm B respectively, given simultaneous decisions on output.

We can graph Firm B's reaction function in the same way and it will be the symmetrical opposite of Firm A's. If Firm A produces all the market output, Firm B will produce nothing (point T_2) and if Firm A produced nothing Firm

B would produce all the market output (point T_1). Connecting these points gives Firm B's reaction function indicated by the blue line.

If Firm A assumed Firm B will produce all the output in the market, it produces zero shown by the horizontal intercept C_1. If Firm B produced nothing, Firm A will act as a monopolist and produce all the output shown by the vertical intercept C_2. The points in-between show the various combinations of output Firm A would produce given Firm B's reaction and gives Firm A's reaction function RF_A.

If Firm A produced nothing, Firm B would act as the monopolist and produce all the output shown by the horizontal intercept T_1. If Firm A produced all the output, Firm B would produce nothing, as shown by the vertical intercept T_2. The points in-between give Firm B's reaction function shown by RF_B. If either firm produced off its reaction function at different time periods there would be an incentive for the other to change its output in subsequent time periods until equilibrium was reached at Q_1, Q_2. This represents a 'Nash equilibrium'. Nash equilibrium occurs when the optimal outcome is one such that no participant has any incentive to deviate from its chosen strategy given the choice of its opponent. Both firms make optimum decisions based on what its rivals are doing and a change in strategy by either firm would result in a less than optimum outcome.

Let's illustrate the Cournot equilibrium with a mathematical example.

The Mathematics of the Cournot Model

We saw in Chapter 14 that a monopolist's output is smaller than the output from a perfectly competitive market. The monopolistic price is higher than the one obtained in perfect competition. As you might expect, two firms competing against each other will have a lower price than the monopoly price and a higher output than the monopoly output. However, they will have a higher price and a lower output than the perfectly competitive outcome. Now we illustrate this with Cournot assumptions.

The market demand curve is:

$$Q_D = 960 - P$$
$$Q_D = q_A + q_B$$

Where:

q_A = output of firm A
q_B = output of firm B
Marginal cost, MC, is given as:

$$MC = 120$$

Each firm is a profit maximizer setting $MC = MR$.

Now we find the equilibrium output for each of the duopolists. The inverse demand curve for the market is:

$$P = 960 - Q_D$$

Or:

$$P = 960 - q_A - q_B$$

Next we find a total revenue function, TR, for each of the two firms. Consider firm A first:

$$\begin{aligned} TR &= P \times q_A \\ &= (960 - q_A - q_B)q_A \\ &= 960q_A - q_A^2 - q_A q_B \end{aligned}$$

Now consider firm B:

$$\begin{aligned} TR &= P \times q_B \\ &= (960 - q_A - q_B)q_B \\ &= 960q_B - q_A q_B - q_B^2 \end{aligned}$$

We can now find marginal revenue, MR, for each firm by differentiation and set it equal to marginal cost.

$$TR_A = 960q_A - q_A^2 - q_A q_B$$
$$\frac{dTR_A}{dq_A} = MR_A = 960 - 2q_A - q_B = 120$$

Similarly:

$$TR_B = 960q_B - q_Aq_B - q_B^2$$
$$\frac{dTR_B}{dq_B} = MR_B = 960 - q_A - 2q_B = 120$$

We have two equations and two unknowns:

$$960 - 2q_A - q_B = 960 - q_A - 2q_B$$

In our example each firm faces the same MC curve, thus each firm finishes up producing the same level of output, so that $q_A = q_B$. Thus we can write:

$$\begin{aligned} 960 - 2q_A - q_B &= 960 - q_A - 2q_B = 120 \\ 960 - 3q_A &= 120 \\ 3q_A &= 840 \\ q_A &= 280 \\ q_B &= 280 \\ Q &= 560 \end{aligned}$$

In equilibrium each firm produces 280 units and the total sales in the market are 560 units. We can now find the equilibrium price by substitution.

$$\begin{aligned} P &= 960 - Q_D \\ &= 960 - 560 \\ &= 400 \end{aligned}$$

We can now compare this equilibrium with that given by perfect competition and monopoly with the same demand and cost conditions.

In perfect competition equilibrium output is where $MC = D$.

$$\begin{aligned} P &= 960 - Q_D \\ MC &= 120 \\ 960 - Q_D &= 120 \\ Q_D &= 840 \end{aligned}$$

Now we find the equilibrium price in perfect competition:

$$\begin{aligned} P &= 960 - Q_D \\ &= 960 - 840 \\ &= 120 \end{aligned}$$

Let's now establish the equilibrium output for a monopolist. The monopolist maximizes profit where $MC = MR$.

$$\begin{aligned} TR &= P \times Q \\ TR &= (960 - Q) \times Q \\ &= 960Q - Q^2 \end{aligned}$$

$$\begin{aligned} MR &= \frac{dTR}{dQ} \\ &= 960 - 2Q \end{aligned}$$

Thus $MC = 960 - 2Q$.

$$\begin{aligned} 120 &= 960 - 2Q \\ 2Q &= 840 \\ Q &= 420 \end{aligned}$$

Now we find the monopolist's price:

$$\begin{aligned} P &= 960 - Q_D \\ &= 960 - 420 \\ &= 540 \end{aligned}$$

We have summarized the results of the comparison between oligopoly, perfect competition and monopoly in diagrammatic form in Figure 16.3.

FIGURE 16.3

Cournot Equilibrium in a Duopoly Compared with Perfect Competition and Monopoly

Cournot Equilibrium is at P = 400 and Q = 560. This is a lower output and a higher price than the perfectly competitive equilibrium of P = 120 and Q = 840. However, it is a higher output and a lower price than the monopolistic equilibrium of P = 540 and Q = 420.

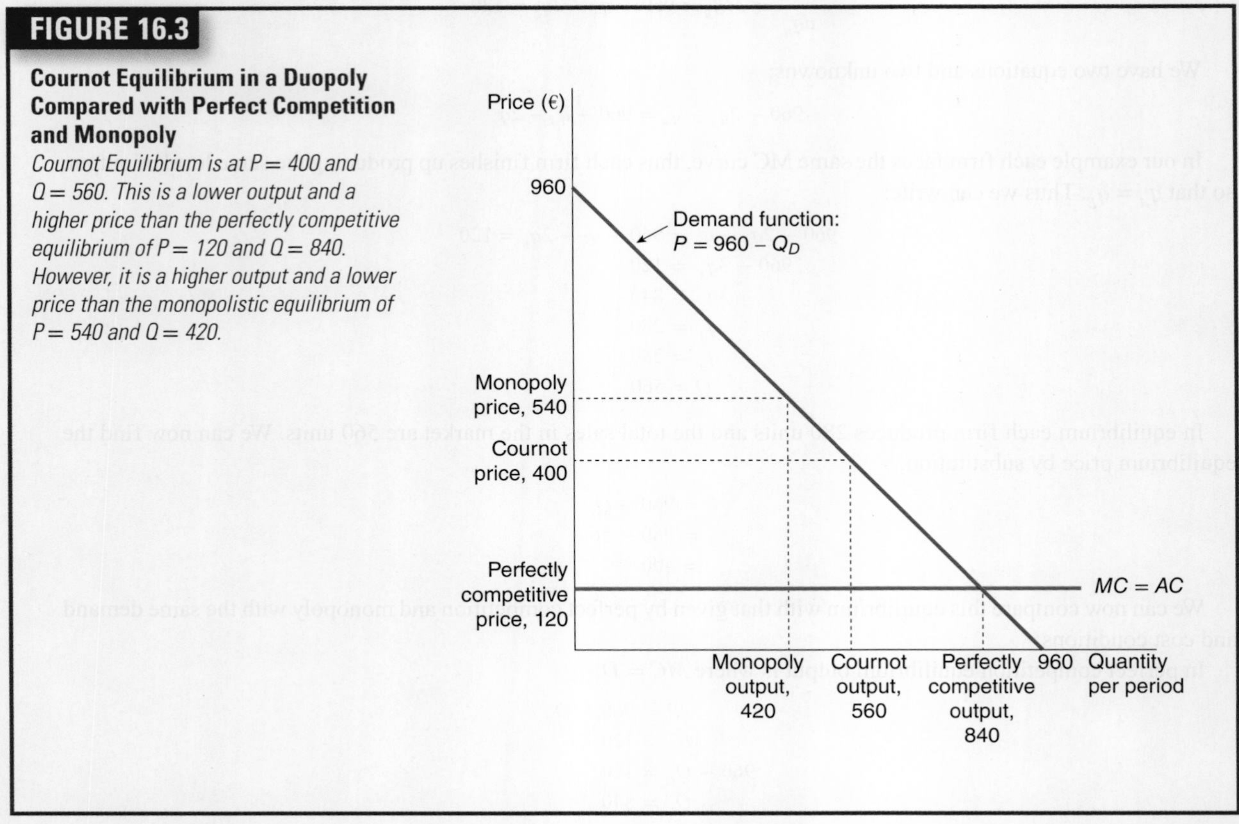

The diagram show the duopoly output of the Cournot model to be greater than the monopoly output but less than the perfectly competitive market.

SALES REVENUE MAXIMIZATION AND POTENTIAL CONFLICTS OF INTEREST

There are many models of oligopolistic behaviour. This is because there are many plausible assumptions about how rival firms will respond to the behaviour of the competition. Some of these models assume that firms attempt to maximize profits. Now we will focus on models which assume that firms do not necessarily attempt to maximize profits but rather have alternative goals. This model is usually referred to as the sales revenue maximization model.

Imagine that you are a shareholder in a company which has some monopoly power. The company may be a monopolist but quite possibly there are a few other firms in the market so that your company is better classified as an oligopolist. Your company has a sufficiently differentiated product and there are sufficiently high entry barriers that goals other than profit maximization are possible. You may wish the company to take into account a concern for the environment or the wider social interest. Alternatively, you may wish the company to maximize profits, for it is out of those profits that you will be paid an income in the form of a dividend. However, the management may have other goals. One such goal might be to maximize sales revenue rather than profit, if, for example the management wishes the company to grow regardless of the effect of that growth on profit.

If the objective is sales revenue maximization, this will lead to a higher output and a lower price than profit maximization. This must be so because sales revenue maximization occurs where marginal revenue is zero. If it is currently producing any smaller level of output it must increase sales revenue to expand output because marginal revenue is positive. Alternatively expressed, if the demand function is negatively sloped and linear, then sales revenue maximization occurs where demand elasticity is unitary. Marginal revenue has to be zero at the sales revenue maximization output. We will use the demand function from Chapter 14 to illustrate this and then compare it with the profit maximizing output and price we found there. We had a demand function given by:

$$P = 288 - 3Q_D$$

And a short-run marginal cost function of:

$$SMC = 1.2Q$$

The profit maximizing output was 40 units per week at a price of €168 per unit. The total short-run profit was €5720 per period.

If the aim of the firm is sales revenue maximization, it is anticipated that there will be a larger output, a lower price and a smaller total profit. Let us see if this turns out to be the case. We calculated *MR* to be:

$$MR = 288 - 6Q$$

To find the output at which sales revenue is maximized, we set $MR = 0$.

$$\begin{aligned} 288 - 6Q &= 0 \\ 6Q &= 288 \\ Q &= 48 \end{aligned}$$

The level of output that maximizes sales revenue is 48 units of output per period, compared with 40 for profit maximization. The price at this level of output is:

$$\begin{aligned} P &= 288 - 3Q \\ &= 288 - (3 \times 48) \\ &= 288 - 144 \\ &= €144 \end{aligned}$$

The price that maximizes sales revenue is €144 per period, compared with €168 for profit maximization. Now we can calculate the profit being made at this output level. In Chapter 14 we showed that the profits function, given the demand and cost conditions, is given as:

$$\pi = 288Q - 3.6Q^2 - 40$$

Substituting $Q = 48$ into the above gives:

$$\begin{aligned} \pi &= (288 \times 48) - (3.6 \times 48^2) - 40 \\ &= 13\ 824 - 8294.4 - 40 \\ &= €5489.60 \end{aligned}$$

Short-run profit is now €5489.60 per period. This, as we predicted, is less than the €5720 per period when the profit maximizing output and price are chosen. The results of this comparison are given in Table 16.1. Clearly the extent to which the sales revenue maximization results diverge from the profit maximizing results depends upon the cost and revenue functions but the direction of the results is exactly what one would expect.

TABLE 16.1 **A Comparison of Price/Output Decisions with Monopoly Power**

Policy	Output (units)	Price (€)	Profit (€)
Profit Maximization	40	168	5720
Sales Revenue Maximization	48	144	5489.60

An Illustration of Potential Conflict

To illustrate the point here, we are going to take an example of the publishing industry. Imagine that an author of crime novels wants to maximize income from their work. The author thinks that this can best be achieved by selling the books at a low price to encourage high sales. The publisher, however, prefers to sell fewer units, but at a higher price, to maximize profit. This presents a conflict of interest between the author and the publisher about the price at which to sell the author's book. Now assume that both publisher and author share the same views about demand and cost conditions. The publisher wishes to maximize profit. This is where $MC = MR$. This is shown in Figure 16.4 as π_{max}.

The author wants a price and output that will maximize sales revenue. This is where $MR = 0$. This would require a higher level of output, in this case of books sold. In Figure 16.4 this is shown as SRM_{max}. The author's wish is for a higher level of output and therefore, given a downward sloping demand curve, a lower price. The conflict arises because the contract almost always pays the author a fixed percentage of revenue, not a percentage of profit.

It might seem that a simple way to resolve the conflict is for the contract to specify a percentage of profit. However, it is hard in practice to determine how much profit a particular title makes. Many of the costs are spread over a number of titles so the profit on any particular title is hard to quantify. This means that contracts continue to be based on sales revenue.

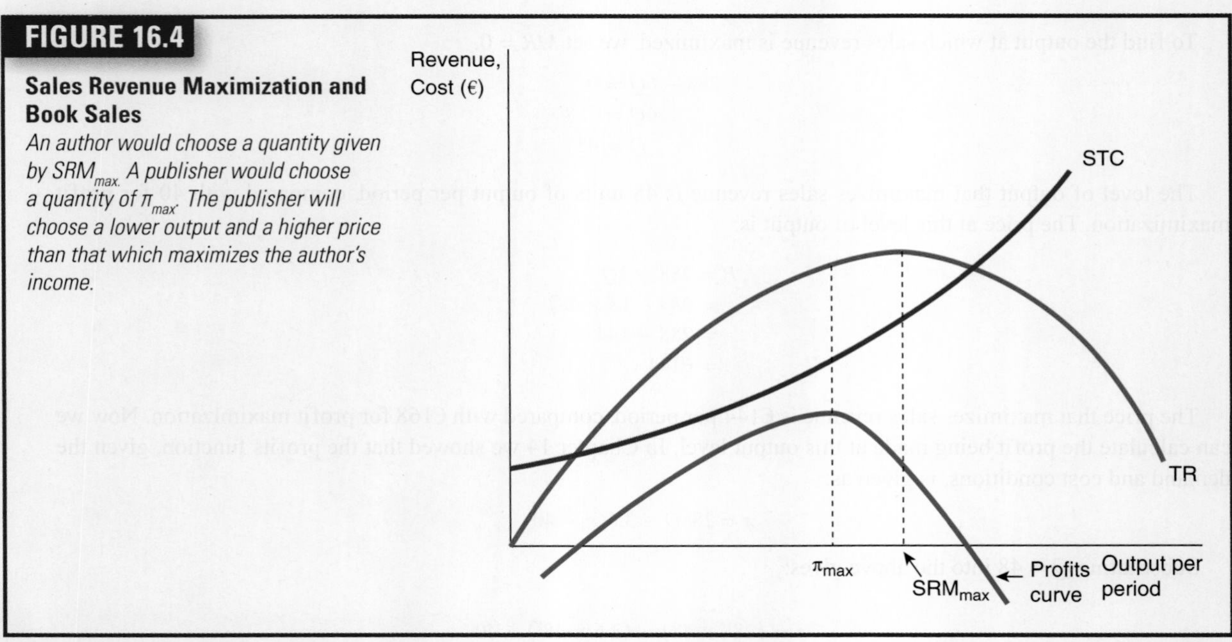

FIGURE 16.4

Sales Revenue Maximization and Book Sales

An author would choose a quantity given by SRM_{max}. A publisher would choose a quantity of π_{max}. The publisher will choose a lower output and a higher price than that which maximizes the author's income.

Sales Revenue Maximization with a Profit Constraint

It is quite possible that at the output which maximizes revenue profits could be too low to be acceptable to the shareholders. In this case management might wish to maximize sales revenue but subject to a profit constraint. We have illustrated the point diagrammatically in Figure 16.5.

Revenue maximization occurs at the output SRM_{max} where total revenue is maximized. If the profit constraint is at PC_1 then the firm maximizes revenue and makes sufficient profit to keep the shareholders happy. If the profit constraint is at PC_2 the firm cannot maximize sales revenue. It must produce less output at a higher price. It will produce at the constrained output, SRM_{con}.

Now we will use our previous example of the monopolist and illustrate the effect of an effective profit constraint:

$$\pi = TR - STC$$

where:

π = profit per period.

FIGURE 16.5

Constrained Sales Revenue Maximization

It may not be possible to maximize sales revenue. Shareholders require a minimal level of profit. If the profit constraint is PC_1, the profit constraint is irrelevant. If it is PC_2, the sales revenue maximizer is constrained by it. Thus it will produce a smaller level of output than that which maximizes sales revenue.

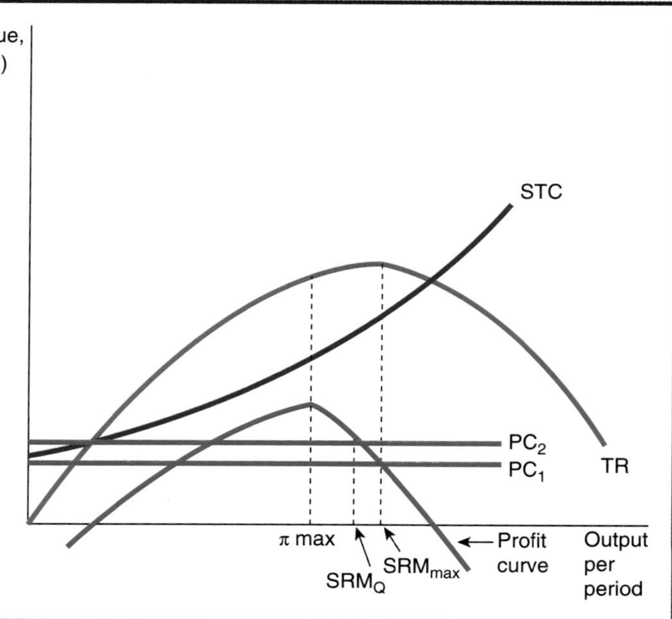

Using our total revenue and total cost functions we found that profit is given as:

$$\pi = 288Q - 3.6Q^2 - 40$$

Now let us suppose that the profit constraint is €5600 per period. What level of output gives this level of profit? To calculate this, substitute the profit constraint into the profit function and solve for Q.

$$5600 = 288Q - 3.6Q^2 - 40$$

Rearranging we get:

$$-3.6Q^2 + 288Q - 5640 = 0$$

By rearranging the terms in this way we get a quadratic equation. Remember that a quadratic equation has a higher power in it and takes the form:

$$y = ax^2 + bx + c$$

Here in our case the values are:

$$a = -3.6$$
$$b = 288$$
$$c = -5640$$

We solve using the standard formula. For $ax^2 + bx + c = 0$, where the value of x is given by:

$$x = \frac{-b \pm \sqrt{b^2 - 4ac}}{2a}$$

In this example, the solutions are:

$$x = \frac{-288 \pm \sqrt{288^2 - 4(-3.6)(-5640)}}{2(-3.6)}$$

$$= \frac{-288 \pm \sqrt{82\,944 - 81\,216}}{-7.2}$$

$$= \frac{-288 \pm 41.57}{-7.2}$$

$$= \text{either } \frac{-246.43}{-7.2} = 34.23$$

$$\text{Or } \frac{-329.57}{-7.2} = 45.77$$

A profit of €5600, sufficient to meet the profit constraint, will be made at 34.23 units of output per period or at 45.77 units.

Two levels of output solve our equation, when we look for an output level where profit is €5600 per period. Which of these two values is the one we need for our firm? Remember that the decision is to maximize total revenue subject only to the profit constraint. Figure 16.6 makes it clear. We have redrawn Figure 16.5 removing PC_1, and focussed on the two possible output levels we have found. Unconstrained sales revenue maximization would give an output level of 48 units per period. Since revenue is still rising until beyond 45.77 units the firm will choose the larger of the two outputs that solve our equation.

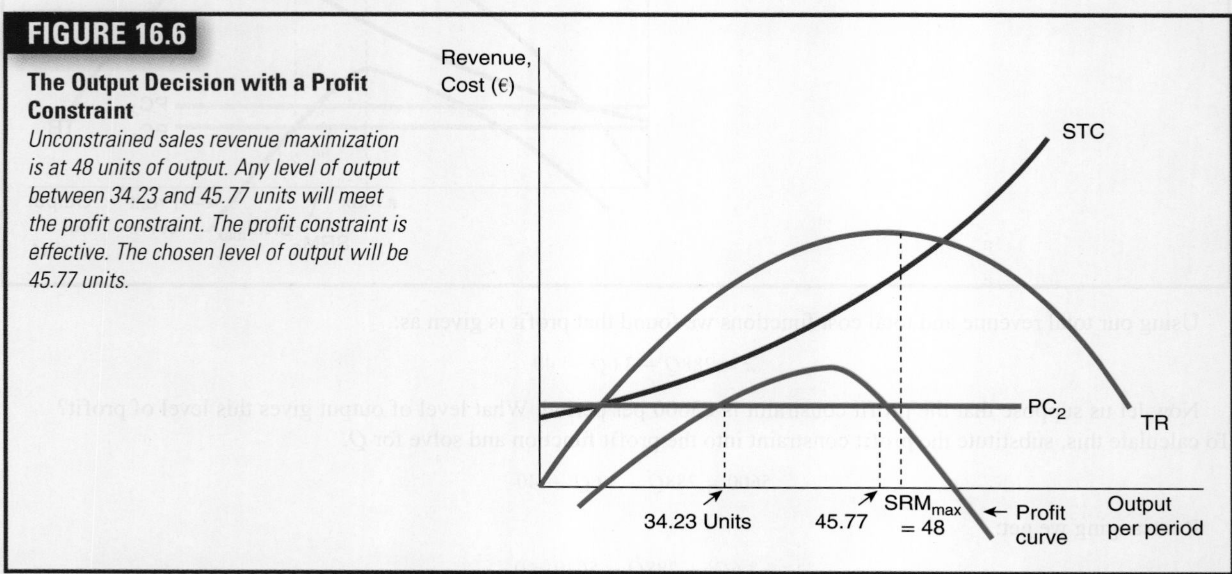

FIGURE 16.6

The Output Decision with a Profit Constraint

Unconstrained sales revenue maximization is at 48 units of output. Any level of output between 34.23 and 45.77 units will meet the profit constraint. The profit constraint is effective. The chosen level of output will be 45.77 units.

A Full Cost Pricing Approach

In surveys of firm behaviour, managers often say, *inter alia*, three things. First, they believe average costs to be constant over a large range of output. Second, they do not try to set output where $MC = MR$. Rather they take the full average cost of production and add on a mark-up to determine price, selling whatever they can at that chosen price level. Third, the size of the mark-up is determined by demand conditions. In other words they have a good idea about the demand curve including the elasticity of demand.

Diagrammatically this is described in Figure 16.7. When average cost becomes horizontal we have constant average cost and marginal cost is equal to average cost. The firm chooses a price by taking average cost, adding the mark-up as shown and arriving at the price P. The price P means that Q is sold, with the amount of sales constrained by the demand curve.

Now we show that under the circumstances described, this full cost pricing approach leads to the same result as setting output where $MC = MR$.

Recall from Chapter 14 that for a firm with monopoly power:

$$MR = P\left(1 + \frac{1}{E}\right)$$

Where:
MR = marginal revenue
P = price
E = price elasticity of demand

Since by assumption the firm is a profit maximizer it will set $MC = MR$ so we can rewrite as:

$$MR = P\left(1 + \frac{1}{E}\right)$$

FIGURE 16.7

Mark-up Pricing

MC = AC when AC is horizontal. Mark-up pricing means taking average cost and adding a mark-up for profit. Here the chosen mark up on average cost gives a price of P. Given the demand curve output will be Q.

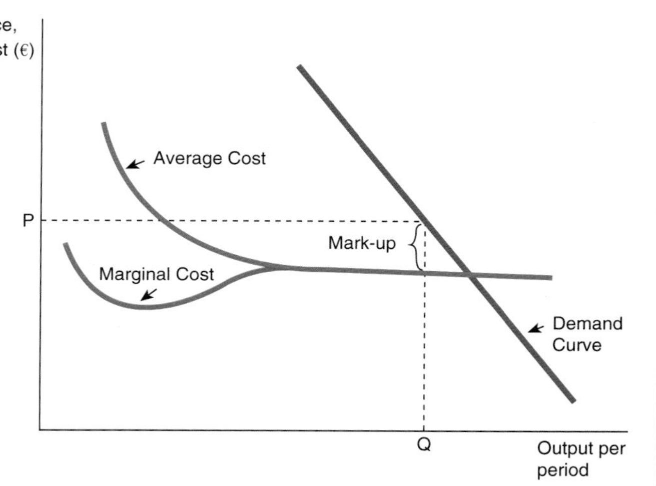

Where MC = marginal cost.
We can rewrite this as:

$$MC = P\left(\frac{E}{E} + \frac{1}{E}\right)$$

Then:

$$MC = P\left(\frac{E+1}{E}\right)$$

Dividing through by the term in the brackets gives:

$$\frac{MC}{\left(\frac{E+1}{E}\right)} = P$$

$$P = MC\left(\frac{E}{E+1}\right)$$

By assumption average costs are constant, so $MC = AC$. We can write:

$$P = AC\left(\frac{E}{E+1}\right)$$

Where AC = average cost.
We can rearrange this in the following way:

$$\begin{aligned} P &= AC\left(\frac{(E+1)-1}{E+1}\right) \\ &= AC\left(\frac{E+1}{E+1} - \frac{1}{E+1}\right) \\ &= AC - AC\left(\frac{1}{E+1}\right) \end{aligned}$$

This equation enables us to work out the appropriate mark up on costs to maximize profit. For example, suppose demand elasticity is -3, we can substitute into the formula:

$$\begin{aligned} P &= AC - AC\left(\frac{1}{-3+1}\right) \\ &= AC - AC\left(-\frac{1}{2}\right) \\ &= AC + \frac{1}{2}AC \end{aligned}$$

The mark-up on average cost is 1/2 or 50 per cent.

Table 16.2 gives some other optimal mark-ups for different degrees of price elasticity of demand. You can work any others out for yourself, but notice two things. First, the more elastic is demand the lower is the optimal mark-up. Second, if the firm is a profit maximizer with a known demand elasticity, then choosing an optimal mark-up gives the same price/output combination as setting $MC = MR$.

TABLE 16.2 **The Relationship between Demand Elasticity and the Optimal Mark-up on Costs**

Degree of Price Elasticity	Optimal % Mark-up on Costs
−2	100
−3	50
−4	33.33
−5	25
−10	11.1

Price and Output for a Theatre: Illustrating a Pricing Decision

We conclude this part of the book on pricing in non-competitive markets by looking at a problem that illustrates some of the principles we have been examining.

Imagine that you are the manager of a theatre which has a capacity of 250 seats. There will be a single, one-off performance of a play and you have to decide a price to charge for it. All tickets must be sold at the same price. You cannot engage in price discrimination. Experience of past performances means that demand for tickets can be estimated at:

$$P = 50 - 0.2Q_D$$

Where:

P = the price of a ticket in euros

Q = the quantity of seats sold

All costs are fixed. In other words, the performers, staff, lighting, heating, etc. are all given and must be met regardless of the number of tickets sold. Total fixed costs are €2000. You are considering three possible prices.

First, what is the maximum price you could charge and fill the theatre? This is the option preferred by the performers who prefer to play to a full house. Second, what price would you charge to maximize revenue from the performance? Third, what price would you charge to maximize profit from the performance?

Let's consider the first option.

Our particular demand curve has the form:

$$P = 50 - 0.2Q_D$$

To find the price at which you can sell 250 tickets, set $Q_D = 250$.

$$P = 50 - (0.2 \times 250)$$
$$P = 0$$

Given the demand function and that you cannot price discriminate, you would have to give the tickets away to fill the theatre.

Now consider the second option.

The demand function, the average revenue function, is of the form:

$$P = a - bQ$$

Total revenue is:

$$\begin{aligned} TR &= P \times Q \\ &= Q(a - bQ) \\ &= aQ - bQ^2 \end{aligned}$$

To find marginal revenue we differentiate the total revenue function with respect to Q:

$$\frac{dTR}{dQ} = a - 2bQ$$

The slope of $AR = -b$.
The slope of $MR = -2b$.
Our particular demand curve has the form:

$$P = 50 - 0.2Q_D$$

Multiplying through by Q gives:

$$TR = 50Q - 0.2Q^2$$

Differentiating the TR function gives:

$$MR = 50 - 0.4Q$$

Maximizing revenue means picking a level for Q where $MR = 0$. Thus:

$$\begin{aligned} 50 - 0.4Q &= 0 \\ 0.4Q &= 50 \\ Q &= 125 \end{aligned}$$

To sell 125 tickets:

$$\begin{aligned} P &= 50 - 0.2Q \\ P &= 50 - (0.2 \times 125) \\ &= 50 - 25 \\ &= €25 \end{aligned}$$

Maximizing revenue means setting a price of €25 per ticket and selling 125 tickets. Note that pursuing this pricing strategy leaves the theatre partly empty with 125 unsold seats. Total revenue is:

$$\begin{aligned} P \times Q &= 25 \times 125 \\ &= €3125 \end{aligned}$$

Now consider the third possibility, which is to maximize profit. If all costs are fixed, additional costs (the marginal costs arising from increasing the number of seats sold) are zero. $MC = 0$. At the point of profit maximization, when $MR = MC$, we have $MR = 0$ again. So the total revenue is still €3125.

How much profit is achieved? Profit, π, is revenue minus total fixed cost, TFC:

$$\begin{aligned} TR - TFC &= 3125 - 2000 \\ &= €1125 \end{aligned}$$

Total profit on the performance is €1125.

We show these options diagrammatically in Figure 16.8.

Finally, let's change one of the assumptions. Suppose that with the same known demand function and with the same cost conditions you can perfectly price discriminate. You wish to maximize profits. What price do you charge? How many seats do you sell? How much producer surplus will there be? How much consumer surplus will there be?

Since you can perfectly price discriminate you can charge a different price to each customer so that price will vary from €50, the choke price, to zero. You will sell all 250 seats and gain the entire producer surplus. In Figure 16.8, the whole area under the demand curve is producer surplus.

Producer surplus is the amount a seller is paid for a good over and above the (marginal) cost of production. As before we use the formula for any triangle:

$$A = \frac{hb}{2}$$

Where A = area
h = height
b = length of base

FIGURE 16.8

The Pricing of Theatre Tickets
Given the demand and cost functions only a zero price fills the theatre. Maximizing revenue requires a price of €25, filling only 125 of the 250 seats. Since MC = 0, the theatre maximizes profit at this same price and output.

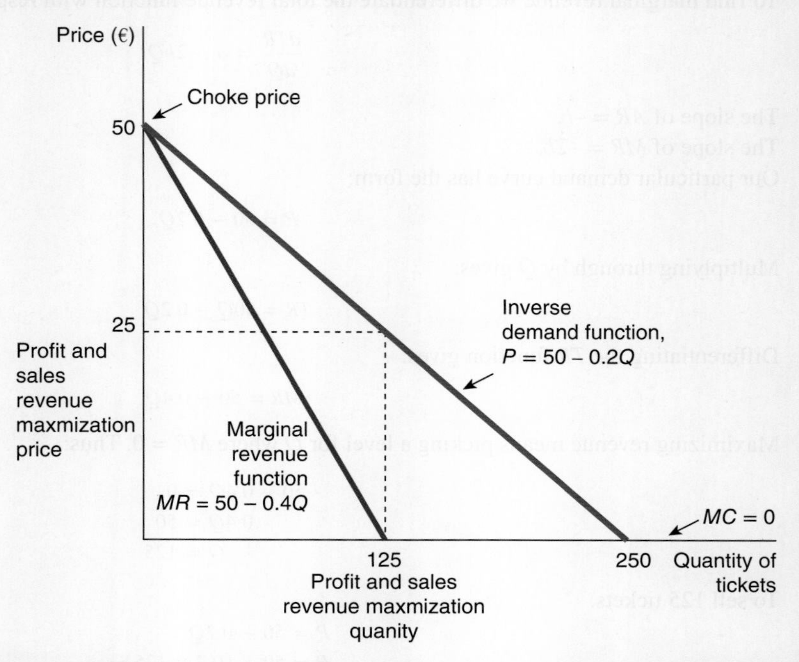

$$A = \frac{50 \times 250}{2} = €6250$$

The total value of producer surplus is €6250 for the performance. This is how much over and above the marginal cost of production you will receive.

Now we are ready to find consumer surplus. This is the area showing the value consumers place upon the good in excess of what they have to pay. Since you have perfectly price discriminated all theatre goers are paying the maximum they are willing to pay. You have extracted the entire consumer surplus. Consumer surplus is zero.

PROBLEMS AND APPLICATIONS

1 Consider a market with a demand function $Q_D = 92 - 0.05P_D$ and a supplier with a cost function $TC(Q) = 0.05Q^3 - 5Q^2 + 400Q + 6000$.

a. Rearrange terms to present the inverse demand function and the revenue function if there is only one firm supplying the market.
b. Calculate the marginal revenue function and the marginal cost function.
c. How large is the profit maximizing quantity for the monopolist and what price would the producer charge?
d. Find the quantity that will maximize the revenue of the firm. At which price will this revenue be sold?
e. Compare the profit of the firm when it maximizes revenue to the maximum profit.

2 Stay with the demand function $Q_D = 92 - 0.05P_D$ and the cost function $TC(Q) = 0.05Q^3 - 5Q^2 + 400Q + 6000$ from the previous problem. Continue assuming that the firm is maximizing revenues, however, now with a minimum required level of profit.

a. The firm's owners demand a profit level of at least €22 350. Will this change the firm's decision described in the previous problem?
b. Do the revenue maximizing managers have to adjust their decisions if the owners require €23 881.25 or more in profit?

3 Start from a very general inverse demand function $P_D = f(Q)$ so that total revenue can be written as $TR = P_D \times Q = f(Q) \times Q$ and show the relationship between the price elasticity of demand and marginal revenue for a monopolist.

4 A monopolist is faced with the inverse demand function $P_D = 1840 - 20Q_D$. Over the relevant range of output marginal costs are a flat function at €600 per unit.

a. Find the profit maximizing output.
b. How large is the mark-up of price over marginal cost?
c. Show the price elasticity of demand as a function of the quantity Q for the above demand schedule.
d. How high is the price elasticity of demand at the profit maximizing output? Compare your results to the mark-up.
e. Assume the firm has incomplete knowledge of the demand function and it is pricing at 80 per cent over marginal cost. Calculate the price, the quantity sold and the profit made.
f. How large is the producer surplus at a mark-up of 80 per cent and how large is it at the profit maximizing quantity?
g. Calculate the producer surplus at the quantity and price that maximize the profit and at the mark-up of 80 per cent.

PART 7 FACTOR MARKETS

17 THE ECONOMICS OF FACTOR MARKETS

We begin this chapter by linking the idea of profit maximization to that of the optimal employment of labour. Then we consider how to measure the amount of transfer earnings and economic rent in a labour market. Finally, we look at the mathematics of disequilibrium in labour markets, particularly with regard to minimum wage legislation.

THE RELATIONSHIP BETWEEN PROFIT MAXIMIZATION AND OPTIMAL LABOUR EMPLOYMENT

In this section we will be assuming that firms are perfectly competitive. Recall that a feature of perfect competition is that when a firm sells its output $MR = AR$. If a competitive firm expands its output it does not have to reduce price in order to sell the additional units produced. What, then, is the value to the firm of the output of an additional worker that the firm might hire?

In perfect competition this value is the number of additional units produced multiplied by the price. This we call 'the value of the marginal product', or VMP. Recall, however, that a monopolist has to reduce price to sell more output. When an additional worker is hired, the extra revenue per unit generated cannot be the number of units produced multiplied by the current price. It is the number of units produced multiplied by the marginal revenue of the output generated. This we call 'marginal revenue product', or MRP. However, in perfect competition, since $MR = AR$ it follows that VMP and MRP are the same. When we assume a perfectly competitive industry, we can use VMP and MRP as interchangeable terms.

We have seen that a profit maximizing firm, whether in perfect competition or not, will produce an output at which $MC = MR$. It is always worth expanding output until the additional cost, marginal cost, is equal to the extra revenue obtained from that unit. We have also discovered that in the short run when capital is fixed, the profit maximizing firm will hire additional labour until the wage rate the firm must pay is equal to the value of the marginal product that unit of labour produces. That is the firm will employ labour until $VMP = W$, where:

$$VMP = \text{the value of the marginal product}$$
$$W = \text{wage rate}$$

These are 'two sides of the same coin' which we will show with a little calculus.

$$VMP = P \times MP_L$$

Where MP_L = marginal product of labour.

P = price of the product

MP_L is the increase in the quantity of output, Q, with respect to the change in the quantity of labour employed, L. That is:

$$MP_L = \frac{dQ}{dL}$$

The VMP is the output multiplied by the marginal revenue from selling it:

$$VMP = \frac{dQ}{dL} \times MR$$

Profit maximization requires that the firm hires labour until the wage rate is equal to the VMP, that is where:

$$W = \frac{dQ}{dL} \times MR$$

This equation can be rearranged to give the requirement for profit maximization:

$$\frac{W}{dQ/dL} = MR$$

If we now assume that the only additional cost to the firm in expanding output in the short run is the cost of the labour, then:

$$MC = \frac{W}{dQ/dL}$$

Thus profit maximization requires that $MC = MR$.

CALCULATING TRANSFER EARNINGS AND ECONOMIC RENT

Transfer earnings are the minimum reward required to keep labour in its present employment. Economic Rent is the earnings received in excess of transfer earnings. Assuming an upward sloping supply for labour function, the total labour earnings, (the wage bill paid out by the industry), is the sum of transfer earnings and economic rent. The value of these will depend upon the nature of the supply and demand curves for labour, which will vary between occupations. We will show how to find these values. We begin with a labour market with the following demand and supply curves for labour:

$$Q_D = 4000 - 10W$$
$$Q_S = 1000 + 2W$$

Where:
Q_D = quantity of labour demanded by firms
W = the wage rate in euros per week
Q_S = quantity of labour supplied

Rather than find now the equilibrium quantity of labour supplied and demanded and the equilibrium wage for the industry, we will find the inverse supply and demand curves which will enable us to show this labour market diagrammatically.

To find the inverse demand curve:

$$Q_D = 4000 - 10W$$
$$10W = 4000 - Q_D$$
$$W = 400 - \frac{1}{10}Q$$

This is our inverse demand for labour function that we have plotted in Figure 17.1.

The inverse supply curve is:

$$Q_S = 1000 + 2W$$
$$2W = -1000 + Q_S$$
$$W = -500 + \frac{1}{2}Q_S$$

This is our inverse supply of labour function that we have also plotted in Figure 17.1. Now we find the equilibrium quantity of labour services for this market. In equilibrium:

$$Q_S = Q_D = Q$$
$$-500 + \frac{1}{2}Q = 400 - \frac{1}{10}Q$$
$$\frac{6}{10}Q = 900$$
$$Q = 1500$$

The equilibrium quantity of labour services in the market is 1500 units of labour. To find the price of labour services, that is, the wage rate, we substitute $Q = 1500$ into either the supply or demand for labour function. Using the supply function we get:

$$W = -500 + \frac{1}{2}Q_S$$
$$= -500 + \frac{1}{2} \times 1500$$
$$= €250$$

FIGURE 17.1

A Labour Market with an Inelastic Supply Curve for Labour

With a labour demand function of $W = 400 - \frac{1}{10}Q_D$ *and a labour supply function of* $W = -500 + \frac{1}{2}Q_S$ *the equilibrium quantity of labour is 1500 and the equilibrium wage rate equals €250. Total factor earnings are €375 000 of which transfer earnings are €62 500 and economic rent is €312 500.*

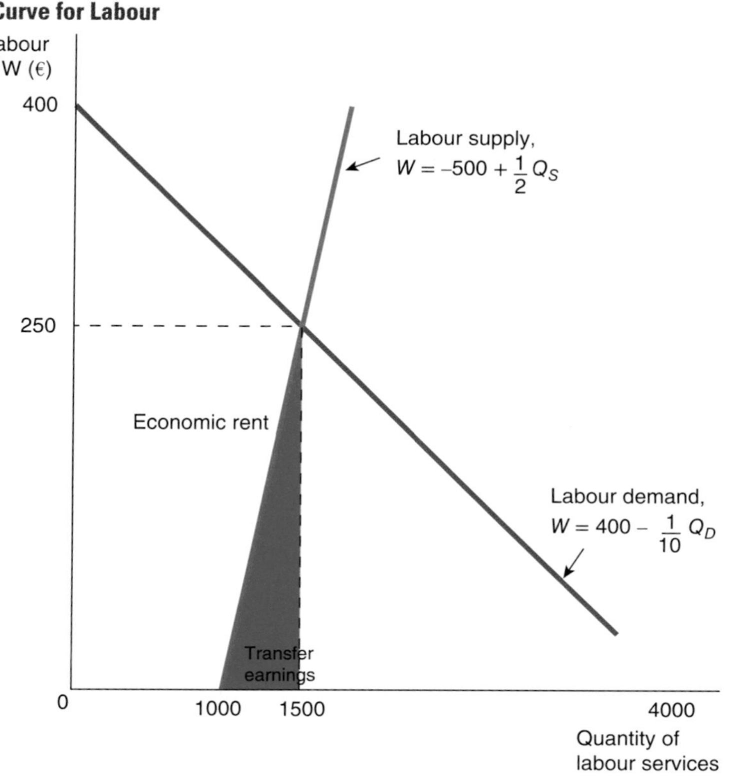

This is the equilibrium weekly wage. The model suggests that someone can get a job provided they are willing to accept a wage of €250 per week. Similarly, a firm can employ a person provided that firm is willing to offer a wage of €250 a week. We have shown both the equilibrium quantity of labour and the equilibrium wage rate in Figure 17.1. Now we can calculate transfer earnings and economic rent. We know that the labour supply curve is inelastic. Remember that if the supply curve cuts the horizontal axis, it must be inelastic. That makes it easier to calculate transfer earnings first, because given the linear supply function we have a triangular area to calculate. You can see in Figure 17.1 that the supply curve cuts the horizontal axis at 1000 units of labour. The supply function is $Q_S = 1000 + 2W$, so when $W = 0$, $Q_S = 1000$.

$$A = \frac{hb}{2}$$

Where A = area
h = height
b = length of base

$$A = \frac{250 \times (1500 - 1000)}{2} = €62\,500$$

The total value of transfer earnings is €62 500 per week.
Total factor earnings are:

$$250 \times 1500 = €375\,000$$

Economic rent, therefore, is: €375 000 – €62 500 = €312 500 per week.

If the supply of labour function is elastic it will be easier to calculate economic rent first. Let's illustrate. Suppose we keep the demand for labour function the same but we have a different supply of labour function. Assume the labour supply function to be:

$$Q_S = -500 + 5W$$

The inverse supply curve is:

$$Q_S = -500 + 5W$$
$$5W = 500 + Q_S$$
$$W = 100 + \frac{1}{5}Q_S$$

This is our new inverse supply of labour function that we have plotted in Figure 17.2, which also includes the unchanged demand for labour function. To find the equilibrium quantity of labour services for this market, we set $Q_S = Q_D$:

$$Q_S = Q_D = Q$$
$$W = 100 + \frac{1}{5}Q_S$$
$$W = 400 - \frac{1}{10}Q_D$$
$$100 + \frac{1}{5}Q = 400 - \frac{1}{10}Q$$
$$\frac{3}{10}Q = 300$$
$$\frac{1}{10}Q = 100$$
$$Q = 1000$$

The equilibrium quantity of labour in this market is 1000 units. We can find the equilibrium wage rate using the demand function:

$$W = 400 - \frac{1}{10}Q_D$$
$$= 400 - 100$$
$$= €300$$

The equilibrium wage rate in the market is €300 per week. The equilibrium quantity of labour and the equilibrium wage rate is shown in Figure 17.2.

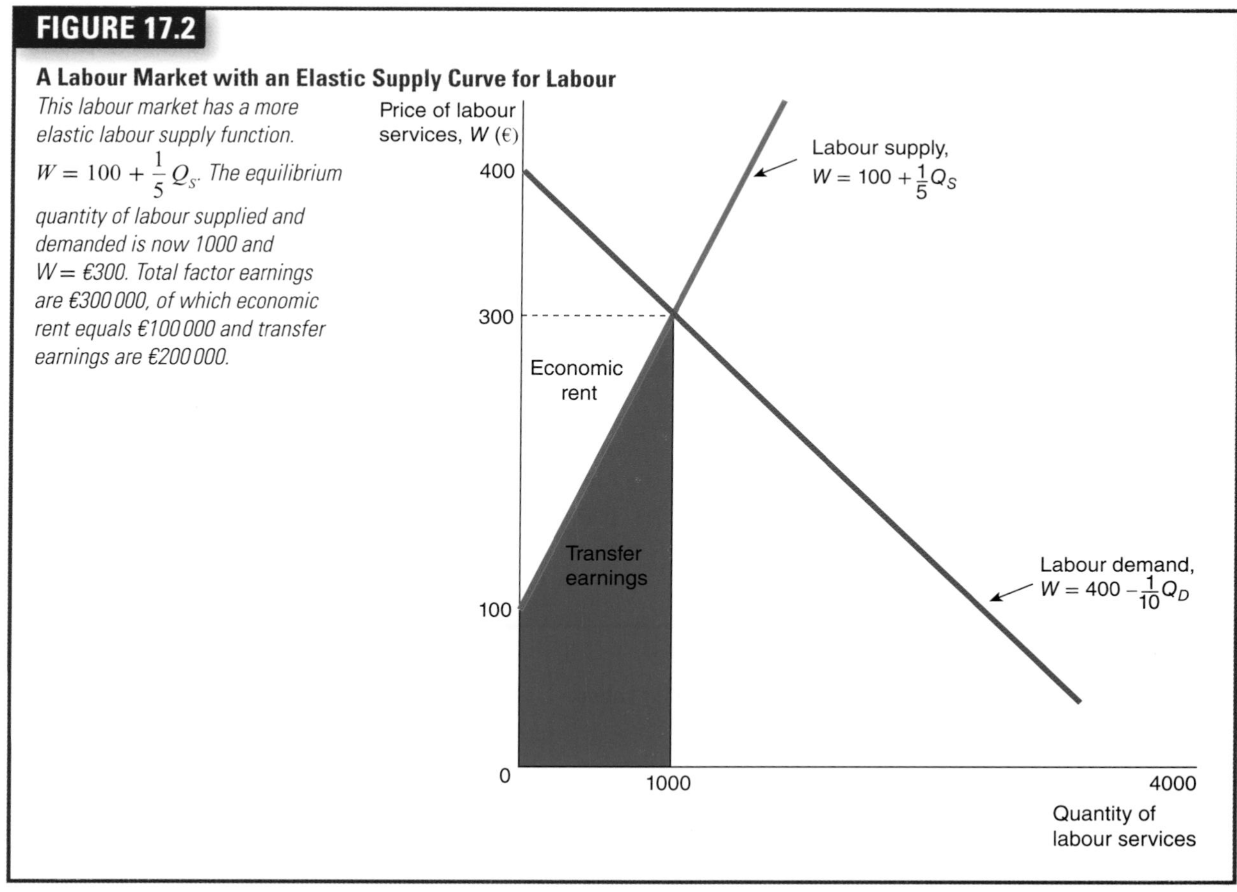

FIGURE 17.2

A Labour Market with an Elastic Supply Curve for Labour

This labour market has a more elastic labour supply function. $W = 100 + \frac{1}{5}Q_S$. The equilibrium quantity of labour supplied and demanded is now 1000 and W = €300. Total factor earnings are €300 000, of which economic rent equals €100 000 and transfer earnings are €200 000.

We are now in a position to calculate transfer earnings and economic rent. The labour supply curve is elastic. Remember that if the supply curve cuts the vertical axis, the supply curve must be elastic. So it's easier to calculate economic rent first because given the linear supply function we have a triangular area to calculate. In Figure 17.2, the supply curve cuts the vertical axis at 100. The supply curve is $Q_S = -500 + 5W$, so when $Q_S = 0$, $0 = -500 + 5W$. Therefore $W = 100$.

$$A = \frac{1000 \times (300 - 100)}{2} = €100\,000$$

The total value of economic rent is €100 000 per week.

Total factor earnings are:

$$300 \times 1000 = €300\,000.$$

Transfer earnings, therefore are: €300 000 – €100 000 = €200 000 per week.

When the supply curve is unit elastic, half of the total factor earnings are economic rent and half are transfer earnings. We illustrate with a unit elastic labour supply curve and the same labour demand function. Our illustrative labour supply function is:

$$Q_S = 10W$$

The inverse supply function is:

$$W = \frac{1}{10}Q_S$$

In equilibrium:

$$Q_S = Q_D = Q$$

$$W = \frac{1}{10} Q_S$$

$$W = 400 - \frac{1}{10} Q_D$$

$$\frac{1}{10} Q = 400 - \frac{1}{10} Q$$

$$\frac{2}{10} Q = 400$$

$$Q = 2000$$

We can now find the equilibrium wage rate using the supply function:

$$W = \frac{1}{10} Q_S$$

$$= \frac{1}{10} \times 2000$$

$$= €200$$

We have plotted these relationships in Figure 17.3. It should now be clear that the area represented by transfer earnings is the same as that represented by economic rent.

FIGURE 17.3

A Labour Market with a Unitary Elastic Supply Curve for Labour

If the labour supply is of unit elasticity transfer earnings equal economic rent. For example, if the labour demand function is $W = 400 - \frac{1}{10} Q_D$ and the labour supply function is $W = \frac{1}{10} Q_S$, the equilibrium quantity of labour is 2000 and the equilibrium wage rate is €200. Total factor earnings are therefore €400 000, of which €200 000 is transfer earnings and €200 000 is economic rent.

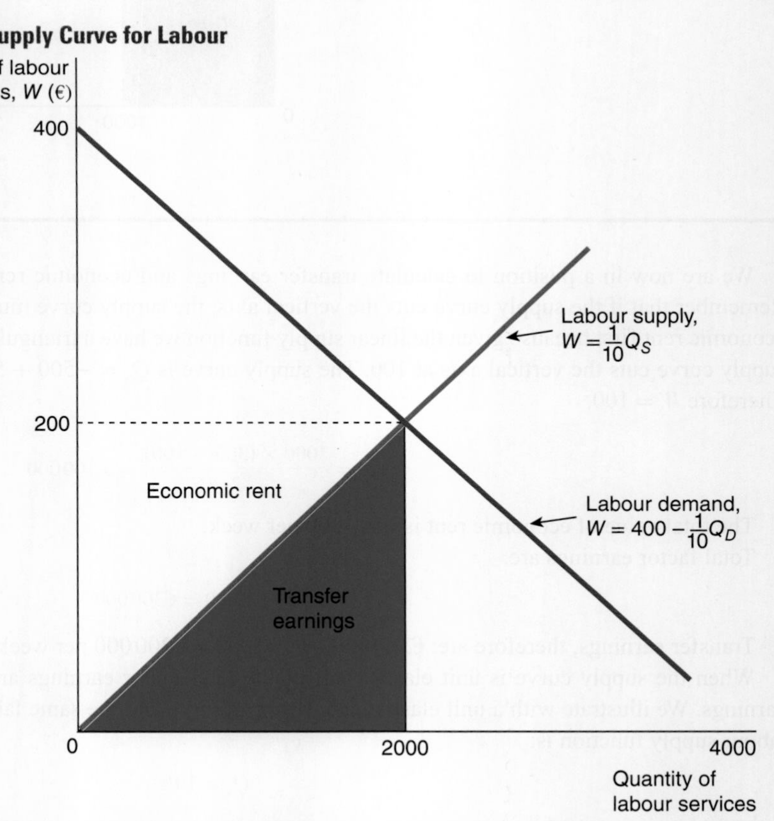

Total factor earnings are:

$$200 \times 2000 = €400\,000$$

Both transfer earnings and economic rent are:

$$€400\,000/2 = €200\,000$$

In general we would expect that, *ceteris paribus*, the more inelastic the labour supply, the greater the proportion of total earnings that is economic rent.

MINIMUM WAGES AND THE LABOUR MARKET

Sometimes a government may set a minimum legal wage above the market wage rate. We now look at some possible effects of such a decision in competitive labour markets. We will use the labour market equations used earlier in the chapter: $W = 100 + \frac{1}{5}Q_S$ and $W = 400 - \frac{1}{10}Q_D$

Given these functions, equilibrium is:

$$Q = 1000 \text{ and } W = €300$$

Assume a government introduces an effective and binding minimum wage which leads to an increase of €30 per week to €330. This creates market disequilibrium, as both suppliers and buyers of labour react. First consider the effect on quantity demanded.

$$W = 400 - \frac{1}{10}Q_D$$

If W = 330:

$$330 = 400 - \frac{1}{10}Q_D$$

$$\frac{1}{10}Q_D = 70$$

$$Q_D = 700$$

The quantity demanded as a result of the higher wage rate has been reduced from 1000 to 700 units. Now consider the effect on suppliers of labour services of the minimum wage of €330 per week.

$$W = 100 + \frac{1}{5}Q_S$$

$$330 = 100 + \frac{1}{5}Q_S$$

$$\frac{1}{5}Q_S = 230$$

$$Q_s = 1150$$

The quantity supplied as a result of the higher wage rate has been increased from 1000 to 1150 units.

There will now be an excess labour supply in the market of 1150 – 700 = 450 as illustrated in Figure 17.4. This would equate to the number of workers unemployed in the industry which results from the minimum wage.

The unemployment is comprised of two parts. First, there are those who had a job before who will no longer be employed; this number is 300. Second there are those who are now willing to work at the higher wage rate who are unable to secure work. This amounts to 150 workers.

FIGURE 17.4

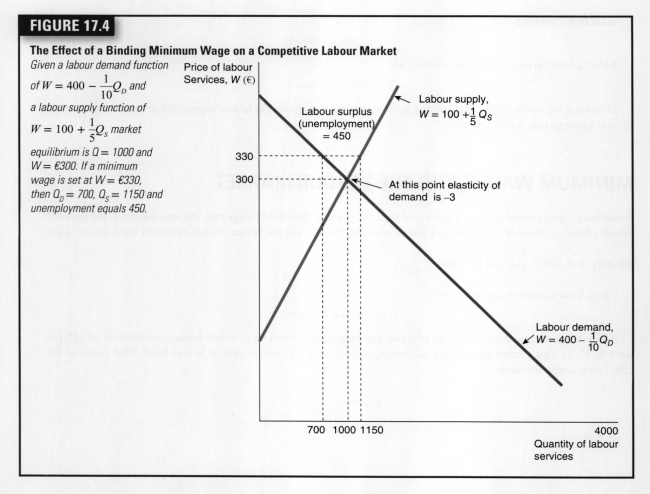

The Effect of a Binding Minimum Wage on a Competitive Labour Market

Given a labour demand function of $W = 400 - \frac{1}{10}Q_D$ and a labour supply function of $W = 100 + \frac{1}{5}Q_S$ market equilibrium is $Q = 1000$ and $W = €300$. If a minimum wage is set at $W = €330$, then $Q_D = 700$, $Q_S = 1150$ and unemployment equals 450.

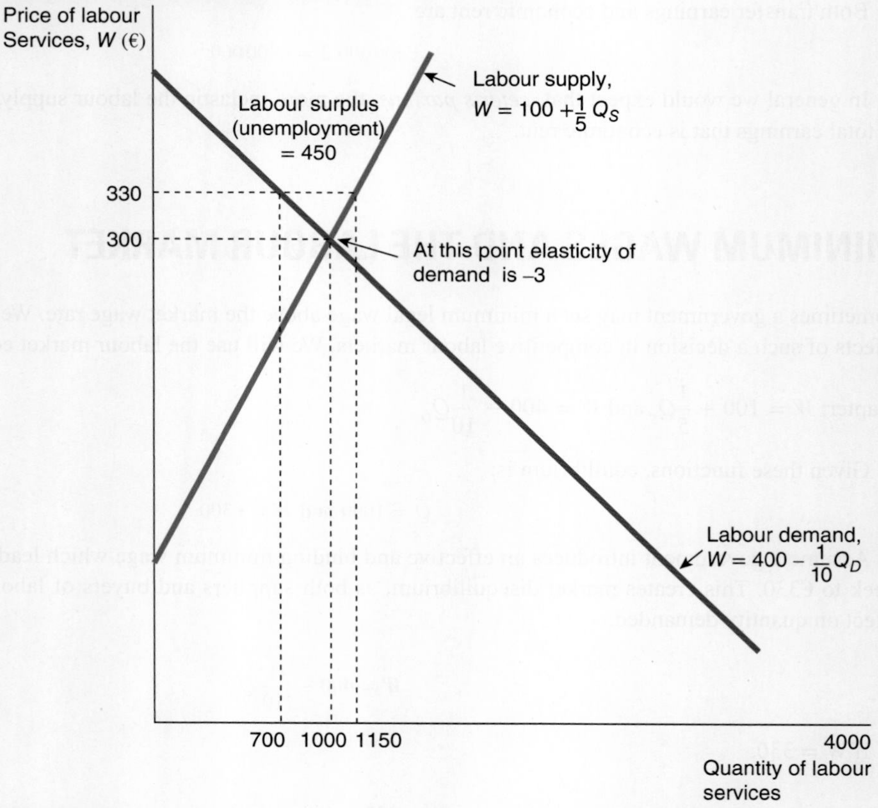

For any given supply curve for labour the degree of unemployment created by a binding minimum wage in a competitive labour market is determined by the elasticity of demand for labour. The more elastic the labour demand, the greater will be the unemployment created. We will now illustrate this by looking at a labour market with the same supply curve but with a more elastic demand curve. Let us suppose the labour demand curve is given by:

$$W = 400 - \frac{1}{20}Q_D$$

Equilibrium would now be found as:

$$100 + \frac{1}{5}Q_S = 400 - \frac{1}{20}Q_D$$

$$\frac{1}{4}Q = 300$$

$$Q = 1200$$

The equilibrium quantity of labour is 1200 units. To find the wage rate at this quantity, substitute $Q = 1200$ into the labour supply function:

$$\begin{aligned} W &= 100 + \frac{1}{5}Q_S \\ &= 100 + (\frac{1}{5} \times 1200) \\ &= 100 + 240 \\ &= €340 \end{aligned}$$

The equilibrium wage rate is €340.

Now we will introduce a minimum wage of €370, an increase of €30 as before. Consider first the effect on labour demand.

$$W = 400 - \frac{1}{20}Q_D$$

$$370 = 400 - \frac{1}{20}Q_D$$

$$\frac{1}{20}Q_D = 30$$

$$Q_D = 600$$

Labour demand is now 600 compared to 1200 workers before the introduction of the minimum wage. Now look at the effect on labour supply.

$$W = 100 + \frac{1}{5}Q_S$$

$$370 = 100 + \frac{1}{5}Q_S$$

$$\frac{1}{5}Q_S = 270$$

$$Q = 1350$$

Unemployment is now 1350 – 600 = 750 as shown in Figure 17.5 workers, a larger volume of unemployment than previously.

FIGURE 17.5

The Effect of Binding Minimum Wage on a Competitive Labour Market with Elastic Labour Demand

Given a supply curve of labour, unemployment created by a binding minimum wage above equilibrium is greater when labour demand is more elastic.

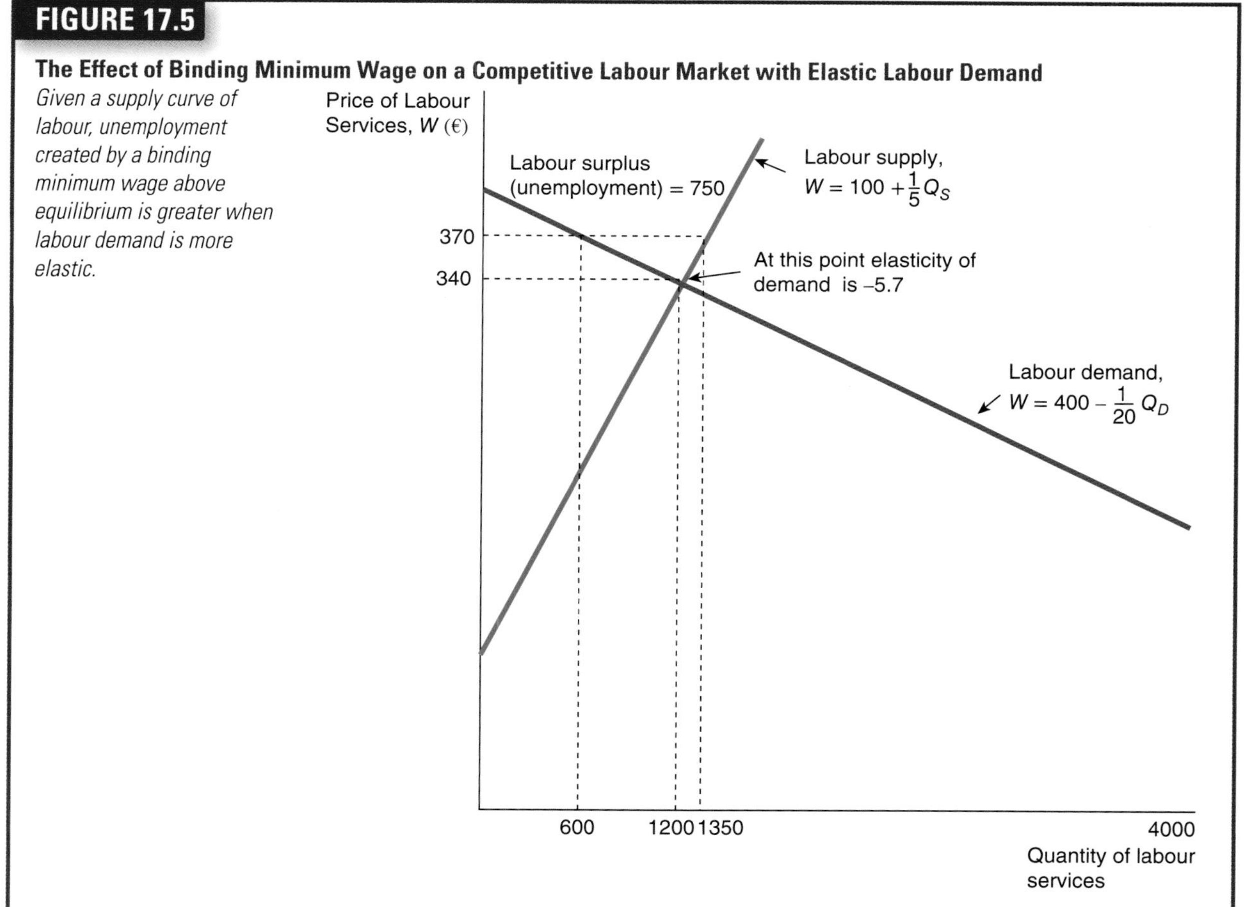

To check that demand is more elastic than in our previous example, take the original demand function:

$$W = 400 - \frac{1}{10}Q_D$$

This is an inverse demand function. The demand function, is:

$$Q_D = 4000 - 10W$$

To find the value of demand elasticity at equilibrium, we use the formula:

$$ped = \frac{dQ}{dP} \times \frac{P}{Q}$$

Where:
Q = quantity demanded
P = Price
We can use this formula, but remember that price in this case is the price of labour services. As a result we write the formula as:

$$ped = \frac{dQ}{dW} \times \frac{W}{Q}$$

Where:
W = the wage rate
Now we will calculate point elasticity where $W = 300$ and the quantity of labour, $Q = 1000$. Given that our demand function is:

$$Q_D = 4000 - 10W$$

Then:

$$\frac{dQ}{dW} = -10$$

$$-10 \times \frac{300}{1000} = -3$$

Elasticity can be calculated with the second demand function in the same way. The inverse demand curve is:

$$W = 400 - \frac{1}{20}Q_D$$

The demand curve, therefore, becomes:

$$\frac{1}{20}Q_D = 400 - W$$

$$Q_D = 8000 - 20W$$

Then:

$$\frac{dQ}{dW} = -20$$

The equilibrium wage rate is W = €340 and the equilibrium quantity of labour = 1200

$$ped = \frac{dQ}{dW} \times \frac{W}{Q}$$

$$= -20 \times \frac{340}{1200}$$

$$= -5.7$$

In the first case, the elasticity of demand is −3. In the second case demand elasticity is −5.7. In the second case demand is more elastic and the introduction of the minimum wage resulted in greater unemployment. This result holds true in general, so that the more elastic the demand for labour is in a market, *ceteris paribus*, the higher the unemployment which results from the introduction of a minimum wage will be.

PROBLEMS AND APPLICATIONS

1 A firm thinks about hiring a new employee. This new employee will possibly be able to produce 400 products a month, which the firm can sell for €10 each. What is the maximum monthly wage rate the firm will pay the employee?

2 Note the demand and supply curves for a specific labour market, where W = weekly earnings:

$$Q_D = 5000 - 8W$$
$$Q_s = 200 + 4W$$

a. Draw a diagram for the labour market and show the transfer earnings and the economic rent.
b. Calculate the equilibrium quantity of labour services and wage rate.
c. Compute the transfer earnings and the economic rent.

3 a. Calculate the economic rent and the transfer earnings for the following labour demand and supply curves. What is the difference from Problem 2?

$$Q_D = 5000 - 8W$$
$$Q_s = -200 + 2W$$

b. Considering the results of Problem 17.2 c): How does the elasticity of the supply curve influence the relationship between the economic rent and transfer earnings?

4 Given are the following (inverse) curves for supply and demand in a labour market:

$$W_S = 30 + \frac{1}{3}Q$$
$$W_D = 600 - \frac{1}{6}Q$$

a. Calculate the equilibrium.
b. Compute the elasticity of the labour demand curve at the equilibrium.
c. Now the government decides to introduce a minimum wage of €500. What are the effects on the quantities of labour supply and labour demand? What is the excess labour supply and therefore unemployment?
d. Assume another demand curve for labour has an elasticity of −5 at the equilibrium. In which of the both cases will unemployment be greater?

PART 8 INEQUALITY

18 INCOME INEQUALITY AND POVERTY

In this chapter we will consider the distribution of income and use the Gini coefficient as an indicator. We will show how the Gini coefficient can be calculated for discrete data either before or after taxes and benefits. Then we will use logs to explore the relationship between income and recorded happiness.

In considering poverty, we will use the Gini coefficient to show that although the distribution of income and poverty are related, they are not identical concerns. Finally, we will consider the concept of median income which is central to ideas about poverty.

CALCULATING THE GINI COEFFICIENT

We met the idea of a Lorenz curve and a Gini coefficient in the context of the dispersion of power between firms in Chapter 15. We can also use these concepts in the context of the distribution of wealth or income. Here we look at the cumulative distribution function of income where household incomes are ordered from least to greatest. Each (x, y) point on the curve shows the bottom x per cent of households receives y per cent of that society's total income.

Whereas firms' market share is usually shown as cumulated from the largest, income is shown as cumulated from the smallest. In Figure 18.1 we show two Lorenz curves for a typical country. Lorenz curve A is the distribution of gross household income before tax and before various social security payments. These will tend to redistribute income towards equality but still leave the distribution of income as uneven. This will give a distribution such as Lorenz curve B. Recall that the Gini coefficient will lie between 0 and 1. In the context of income distribution, 1 is the most unequal distribution, where one household has all the income, and 0 is the most equal, every household having an equal share of income. The Gini coefficient for Lorenz curve B will be positive but smaller than for Lorenz curve A.

As an example, the pre-redistribution Gini coefficient is thought to be around 0.65 and the post-redistribution figure is believed to be around 0.47.

Some data that you will see has been equalized. That is, adjustment has been made to reflect that different sizes of households will have different needs.

FIGURE 18.1

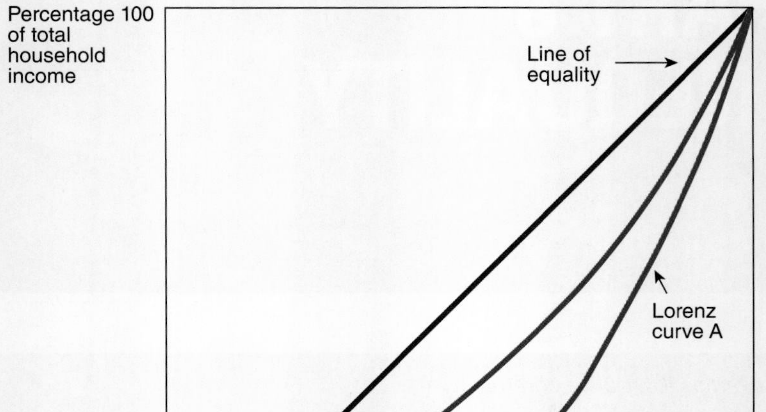

Lorenz Curves before and after Government Redistribution of Income
Lorenz curve A shows a typical distribution of income before tax and social security payments. Lorenz curve B shows a typical distribution after such an allowance is made. Lorenz curve B is closer to the line of equality, showing the effect of tax and social security payments is to redistribute income towards equality.

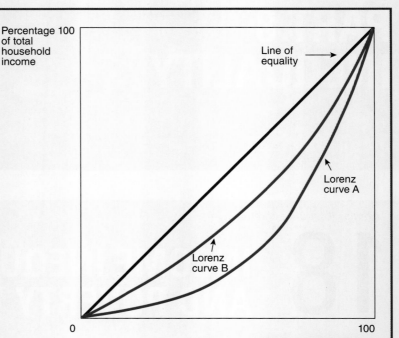

Recall that the Gini coefficient is the area between the income distribution curve, the Lorenz curve, and the line of equality, expressed as a proportion of the lens-shaped segment under the equal distribution curve. One reason for measuring the Gini coefficient is to see how much government policy redistributes income.

We shall now show how this area can be calculated. In Figure 18.1 we showed the Lorenz curve as a continuous function. Almost always we have only grouped data. We may know the proportion of incomes received by each quintile or decile of the population, not the incomes of every household. When cumulating from the smallest, the appropriate formula is:

$$G = \frac{n+1}{n} - \frac{2\sum_{i=1}^{n}(n+1-i)x_i}{n\sum_{i=1}^{n}x_i}$$

Where:
G = Gini coefficient
n = the number of household groupings
x_i = household income in each grouping in turn

We will illustrate its application with a small economy of four households whose details are given in Table 18.1. Total income per week is €20. Of this total income, Amanda's household earns €2 per week, or 10 per cent of the economy's income. Boris' household earns €3 per week, 15 per cent of total income in the economy. The cumulative share of Amanda and Boris' household together is 10 + 15 = 25 per cent. Figure 18.2 shows the information as a Lorenz curve. We calculate G, that is area A, as a proportion of A + B. That is:

$$G = \frac{A}{(A+B)}$$

Alternatively we can express this as:

$$G = \frac{2A}{10000}$$

since the area of the whole square is equal to 100 × 100 = 10 000, so A + B = 100 × 100/2.

TABLE 18.1 **Distribution of Household Income in a Small Community**

Household	Weekly Household Income (€) (x_i)	Percentage of Total (%)	Cumulative Share of Total (%)
Amanda	2	10	10
Boris	3	15	25
Carlos	5	25	50
Dorothea	10	50	100

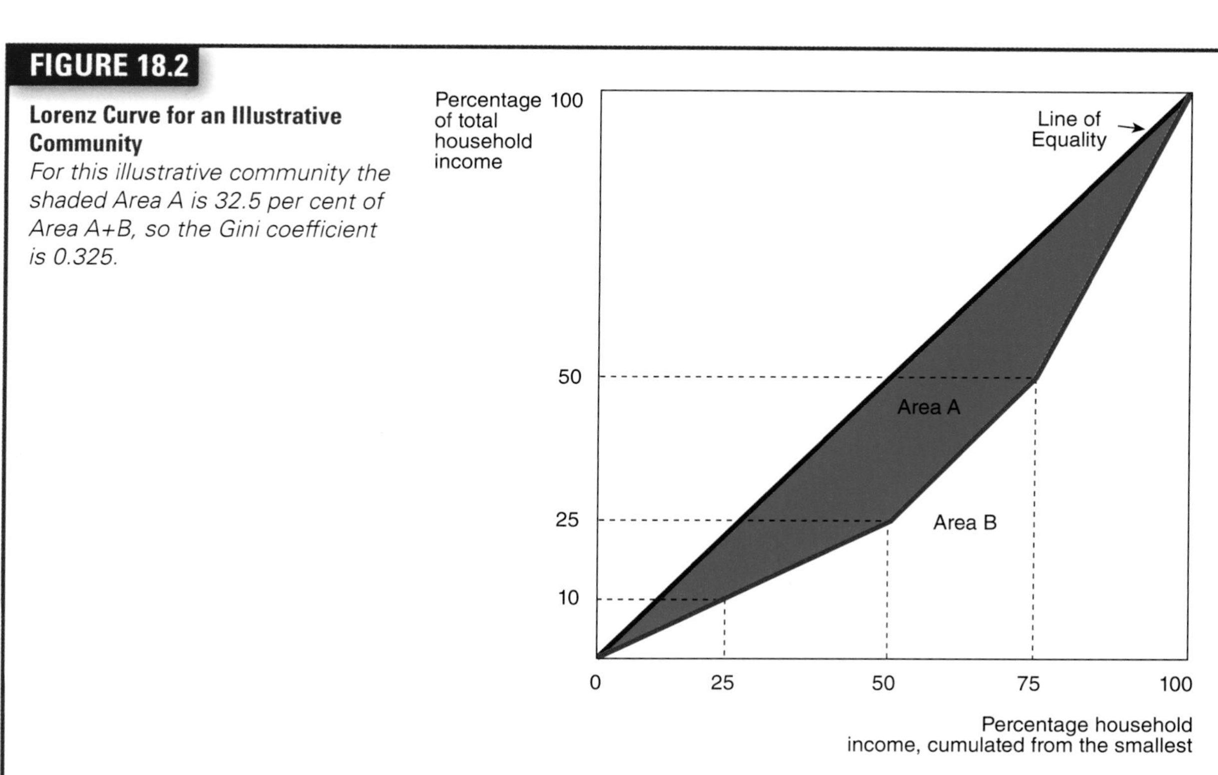

FIGURE 18.2

Lorenz Curve for an Illustrative Community

For this illustrative community the shaded Area A is 32.5 per cent of Area A+B, so the Gini coefficient is 0.325.

We can use the following formula to calculate the Gini coefficient.

$$2\sum_{i=1}^{n}(n+1-i)x_i$$

For our small economy, $n = 4$, I = the cumulative number of households from smallest upwards and x_i is the weekly household income given in Table 18.1.This gives:

$$\begin{aligned}
&2 \times [(4+1-1)\times 2 + (4+1-2)\times 3 + (4+1-3)\times 5 + (4+1-4)\times 10] \\
&= 2 \times 37 \\
&= 74
\end{aligned}$$

Having calculated this part of the formula, we can substitute 74 into the whole formula:

$$\begin{aligned}
G &= \frac{4+1}{4} - \frac{74}{4 \times 20} \\
&= 1.25 - 0.925 \\
&= 0.325
\end{aligned}$$

Our Gini coefficient is 0.325. In other words Area A in Figure 18.2 is 32.5 per cent of the area A + B.

Income and Recorded Happiness

What would you expect to be the relationship between a person's level of income and the extent to which that person regards him/herself as happy? Surveys have been done in many societies to establish this general relationship. The pattern of answer is quite consistent. We sketch the typical result in Figure 18.3.

FIGURE 18.3

Relationship between Self-Reported Satisfaction and Income

As income rises self-reported satisfaction increases but at a diminishing rate.

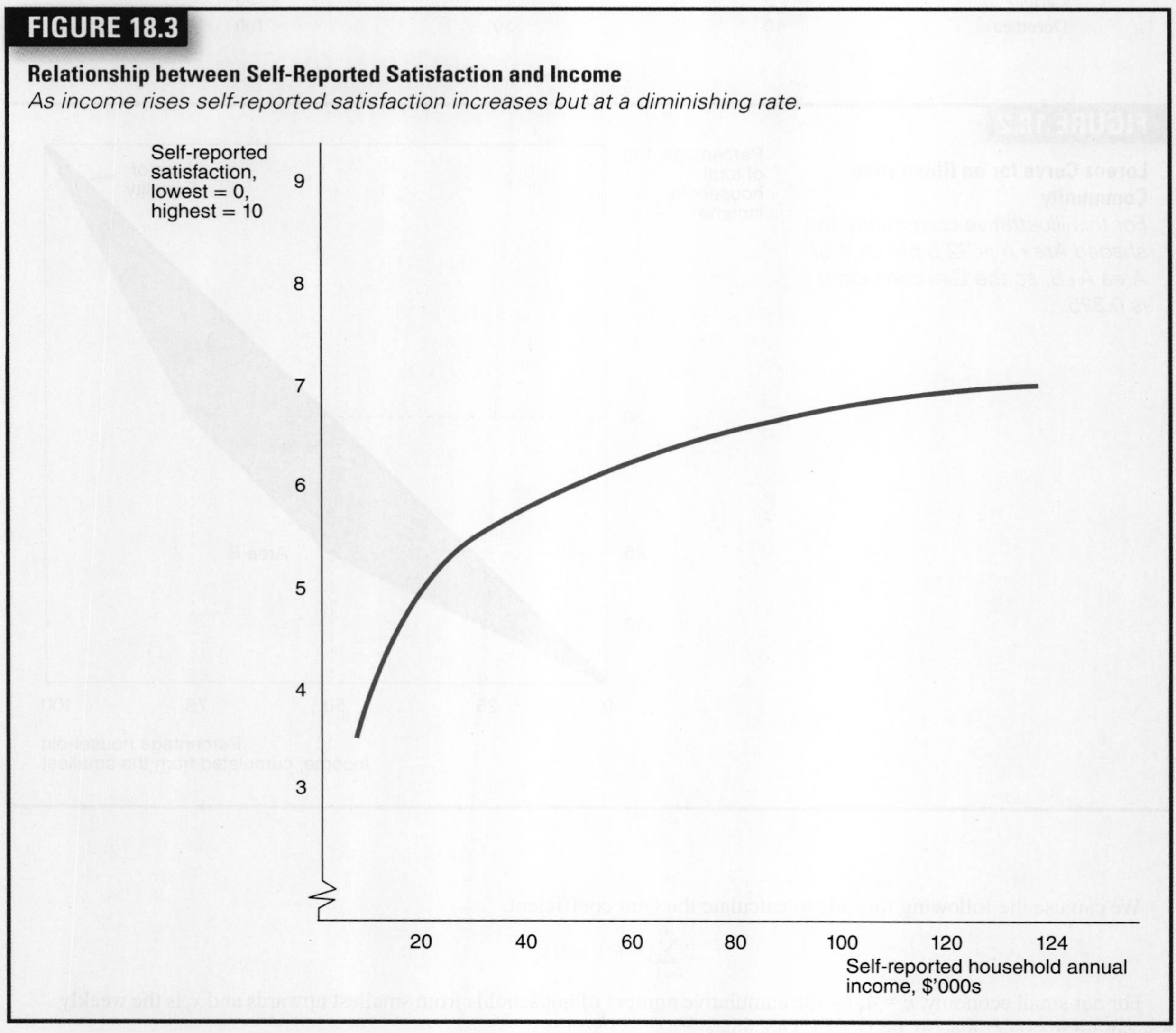

As income increases, reported happiness increases. People prefer to have more income than less. However, the relationship becomes much weaker beyond a relatively low level of income. Research suggests this happens at an annual income of somewhere between $8000 and $25 000 a year.[1] This may be explained by the concept of diminishing marginal returns. For a typical good there is a diminishing marginal utility; there appears to be a diminishing marginal utility of income also.

This is an important conclusion because it is widely used to argue a case for redistributing income towards equality. Take some income from a high-income household and its level of well-being is reduced but not by much. Redistribute it to a low income household and that household's well-being rises by an appreciable amount. Thus redistributing income towards equality raises total society well-being.

[1] See, for example, B Stevenson and J Wolfers (2013) 'Subjective Well-being and Income: Is there Any Evidence of Satiation?' NBER Working Paper 18992.

There are various objections to this view and we consider one of them here. When a group of people negotiates a pay rise, perhaps a trade union for its members, the rise will typically be a percentage increase. The absolute pay increase will be smaller for the lower income member. So what would happen if we sketched the relationship from Figure 18.3 but showed the annual income on a log graph? This is what we do in Figure 18.4 which shows proportionate increases in income. If we consider proportionate increase in income, recorded happiness goes on rising at the same rate. If you have forgotten the significance of a log scale, refer back to Chapter 2.

FIGURE 18.4

Relationship between Self-Reported Satisfaction and Income, Log Scale

As the log of income rises self-reported satisfaction increases at a constant rate.

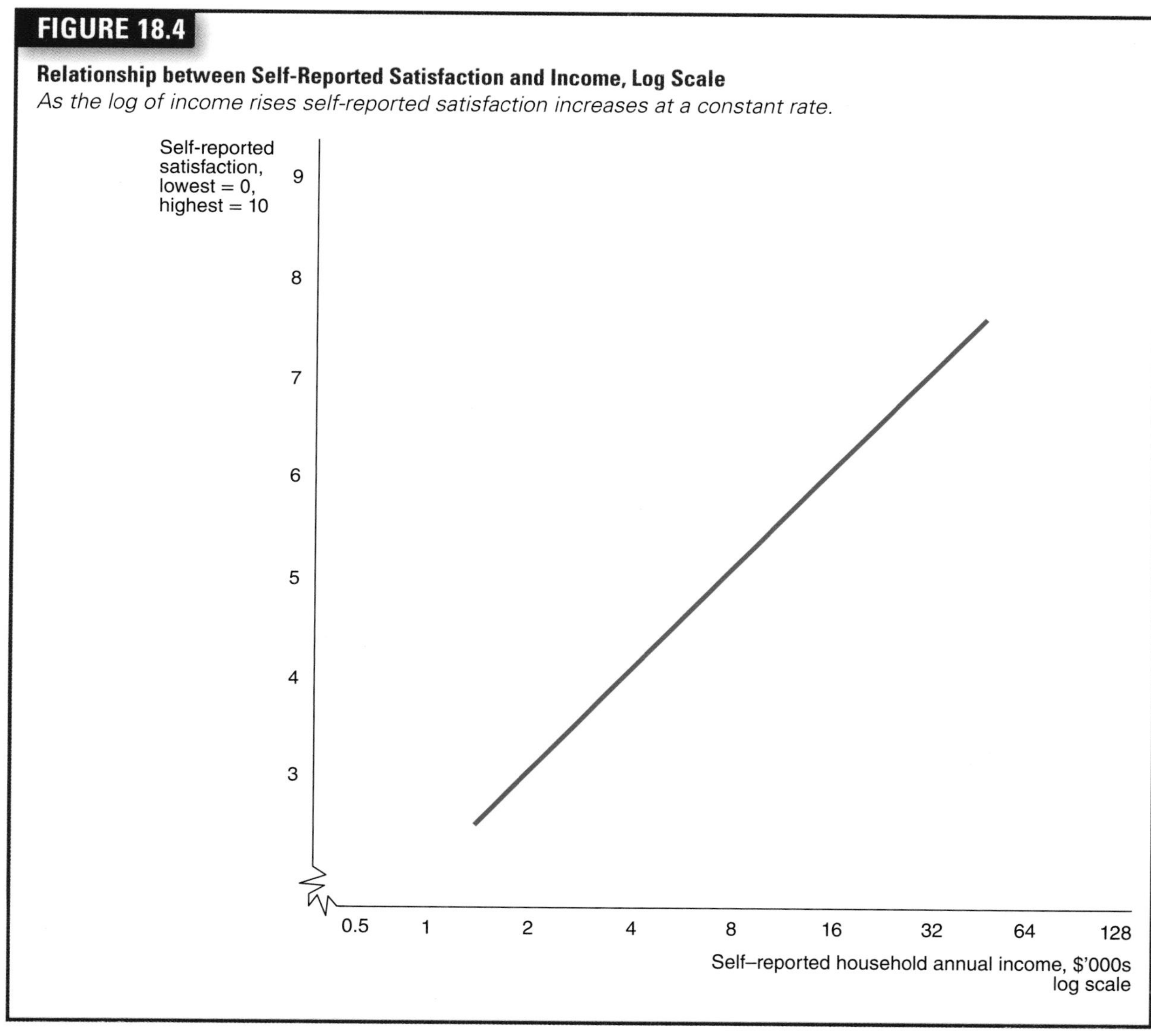

This in no way settles the question of what is the 'right' distribution of income but it does show how valuable logs are in giving information in order to help form a judgement.

Income Distribution and Poverty

Income distribution and poverty are clearly linked issues but they are also separate issues. We will use our concept of the Gini coefficient to illustrate. Table 18.2 shows two different societies, each with three individuals. In each society total weekly income is €100 but it is distributed differently. Which society has the fairer distribution of income? Most people choose Society X. Do you agree?

We have plotted the Lorenz curves in Figure 18.5. As the curves cross, it isn't easy to compare the Gini coefficients. Below, we calculate the Gini coefficients for each society to make things clear.

TABLE 18.2 **Possible Alternative Income distributions**

	Society X	Society Y
Heidi	16	20
Hayden	42	20
Henrik	42	60

FIGURE 18.5

Comparing Income Distributions in Two Societies

Lorenz curves for different societies may cross. However, it is still possible to compare income distributions by calculating their Gini coefficients.

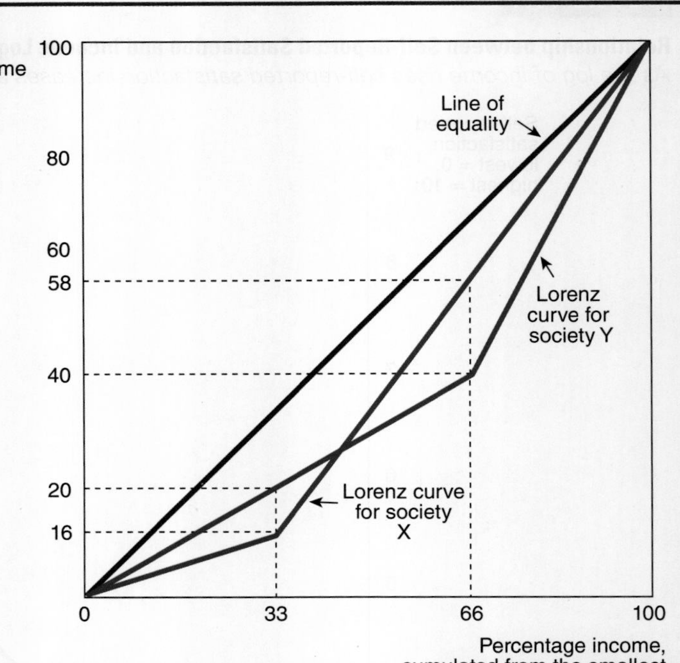

The Gini coefficient for Society X is given by:

$$G = \frac{n+1}{n} - \frac{2\sum_{i=1}^{n}(n+1-i)x_i}{n\sum_{i=1}^{n}x_i}$$

As in our earlier example, we focus first on the second part of the formula:

$$2\sum_{i=1}^{n}(n+1-i)x_i$$

This gives:

$$\begin{aligned} &2 \times [(3+1-1) \times 16 + (3+1-2) \times 42 + (3+1-3) \times 42] \\ &= 2 \times 174 \\ &= 348 \end{aligned}$$

Substituting into the whole formula:

$$\begin{aligned} G &= \frac{3+1}{3} - \frac{348}{3 \times 100} \\ &= 1.33 - 1.16 \\ &= 0.17 \end{aligned}$$

The Gini coefficient for Society X is 0.17. Now let's compare this with Society Y.

The Gini coefficient for Society Y is:

$$\begin{aligned} &2 \times [(3 + 1 - 1) \times 20 + (3 + 1 - 2) \times 20 + (3 + 1 - 3) \times 60] \\ &= 2 \times 160 \\ &= 320 \end{aligned}$$

Substituting into the whole formula:

$$\begin{aligned} G &= \frac{3 + 1}{3} - \frac{320}{3 \times 100} \\ &= 1.33 - 1.067 \\ &= 0.26 \end{aligned}$$

The Gini coefficient for Society Y is 0.26, a higher coefficient than for Society X. We can conclude that income is more evenly distributed in Society X.

We might therefore argue that Society X has a fairer distribution of income. However, now look at Heidi, the lowest income person. Heidi is 25 per cent better off in Society Y, the society with the more unequal distribution of income as measured by the Gini coefficient. It is true that some at the bottom of the income distribution might prefer to be in Society X because they are better off relative to other members, but in an absolute sense Heidi is substantially better off in Society Y.

Median Income with Grouped Data

Now we return to the idea of the median that we first mentioned in Chapter 2. The median in the context of income is an important idea. As we saw in Chapter 2, the mean can be a misleading guide for an average. Sometimes the median is a better guide. For example, income distribution is often skewed and a more realistic guide to poverty is sometimes thought to be how a household's income relates to median income rather than mean average income. A number of countries define a 'poverty line' where a household has less than 60 per cent of median income. Of course this is not necessarily ideal. As the higher income groups get better off over a period of time, more people would be deemed to live in poverty, even though their income may also have risen during this time. We will now see how the median income is sometimes calculated.

In Chapter 2 we defined the median as the middle value when we rank in ascending order. However, often it won't be as easy to estimate the median as this sounds. Sometimes we have grouped data and the groups may well be of different size classes.

In this case we can use a formula to calculate the median. The formula we will use is given as:

$$\text{Median} = x_i + (x_u - x_i)\left(\frac{\frac{N+1}{2} - F}{f}\right)$$

Where:

X_i = lower limit of the class interval containing the median
X_u = upper limit of this class interval
N = number of observations, in this case the number of households
F = cumulative frequency of the class intervals up to but not including the one containing the median
f = frequency of the class interval containing the median

As an example of how this might be used let's consider a small island economy where we have some information on income distribution for its 200 households. The data is shown in Table 18.3.

TABLE 18.3 **Income Distribution in a Small Illustrative Island Economy**

Range of weekly income (€)	Frequency (number of households)	Cumulative Frequency
0–10	30	30
11–40	50	80
41–100	50	130
101–200	40	170
201–	30	200
Total	200	

Now we need to find the median income, the income of the middle household, which in our case is the 100th by rank. Our table shows that this household has an income of between €41 and €100 per week because the households by rank from 80–130 all lie within that range. To estimate the income of the 100th household we use the formula below.

The class interval is the range of weekly income for that class. We know that our median income lies within this range. This means that $x_i = 41$ and $x_u = 100$. The number of observations is the number of households which means $N = 200$. The cumulative frequency of the class interval up to but not including the mean is 30 + 50 = 80, thus $F = 80$ and the frequency of the class interval containing the mean (41 – 100) is 50; f = 50. Substituting these figures into the formula gives:

$$\text{Median} = 41 + \left\{(100 - 41)\left(\frac{\frac{201}{2} - 80}{50}\right)\right\}$$

$$= 41 + \left\{59\left(\frac{20.5}{50}\right)\right\}$$

$$= 41 + 24.19$$

$$= €65.19$$

The median household has a weekly income of €65.19 in our island economy.

As noted in Chapter 2, one measure of an average is not necessarily better than another but one may be more illuminating than another in a given context. The use of the median when examining income distribution data is often thought to be the most valuable measure of the average.

PROBLEMS AND APPLICATIONS

1 In a medium sized town there are five supermarkets. They have the following daily earnings: Market one: 20 000, Market two: 16 000, Market three: 48 000, Market four: 7000 and Market five: 9000.

a. Draw the Lorenz Curve.

b. Calculate and interpret the Gini coefficient.

2 Imagine there are two different countries (A and B) with three inhabitants each. The table shows the income distributions.

Person	A	B
1	20	30
2	90	30
3	90	140

a. Calculate the Gini coefficient for both countries.

b. Why is it difficult to say which income distribution is more 'fair'?

3 Imagine there are 300 people living in a small town. Their weekly income is summarized in the table below.

Income	Frequency
1–20	70
20–50	80
50–100	100
>100	50

a. Compute the cumulative frequency and the median.

In a town nearby live 400 people. Their income distribution is slightly different:

Income	Frequency	Cumulative Frequency
1–10	140	140
10–50	100	240
50–100	80	320
100–200	70	390
>200	10	400

b. Calculate the median.

c. In which of the two towns is the income distribution 'better'?

PART 9 TRADE

19 INTERDEPENDENCE AND THE GAINS FROM TRADE

In this chapter we begin to look at international trade. We start by considering welfare in the trading of one good within each of two countries but where there is no trade between those countries, a situation called autarky. Then we examine the welfare effects of opening up trade between the countries. Finally, we consider the effects on welfare in an importing country when its government introduces a tax on imports.

EQUILIBRIUM WITH AUTARKY

We begin by looking at trade in a single homogeneous commodity where there are no transport costs and no government imposed restrictions. We will also assume that the countries concerned have a common currency, the euro. In this section we first find the equilibrium price with autarky, both at home and in the rest of the world. Then we will work through the effects of allowing free trade to take place.

We assume the following supply and demand functions at home.

$$Q_{Dh} = 100 - 2P_h$$
$$Q_{Sh} = P_h + 10$$
$$Q_{Sh} = Q_{Dh}$$

Where:
Q_{Dh} = Quantity demanded at home
Q_{Sh} = Quantity supplied at home
P_h = Price in the home market
Given these functions, the equilibrium price will be:

$$P_h + 10 = 100 - 2P_h$$
$$3P_h = 90$$
$$P_h = €30$$

The equilibrium quantity at home can be found by substituting $P_h = 30$ into either the home supply or home demand equation. Using the home demand equation we get:

$$\begin{aligned} Q_{Dh} &= 100 - 2P_h \\ &= 100 - (2 \times 30) \\ &= 40 \end{aligned}$$

We can check our answer by substituting into the home supply equation:

$$\begin{aligned} Q_{Sh} &= P_h + 10 \\ Q_{Sh} &= 30 + 10 \\ &= 40 \end{aligned}$$

The autarky price at home is €30 and the autarky quantity at home is 40. We can show this result diagrammatically but to do this we need to calculate the inverse supply and demand functions. First we find the inverse demand function.

$$\begin{aligned} Q_{Dh} &= 100 - 2P_h \\ 2P_h &= 100 - Q_{Dh} \\ P_h &= 50 - \frac{1}{2}Q_{Dh} \end{aligned}$$

Next we find the inverse supply function:

$$\begin{aligned} Q_{Sh} &= P_h + 10 \\ P_h &= Q_{Sh} - 10 \end{aligned}$$

In Figure 19.1 we plot these two functions and show the equilibrium price.

FIGURE 19.1

Home Market Equilibrium without International Trade

Given a home demand function of $P_h = 50 - \frac{1}{2}Q_{Dh}$ and a home supply function of $P_h = Q_{Sh} - 10$, the no-trade equilibrium is $P =$ €30 and $Q = 40$.

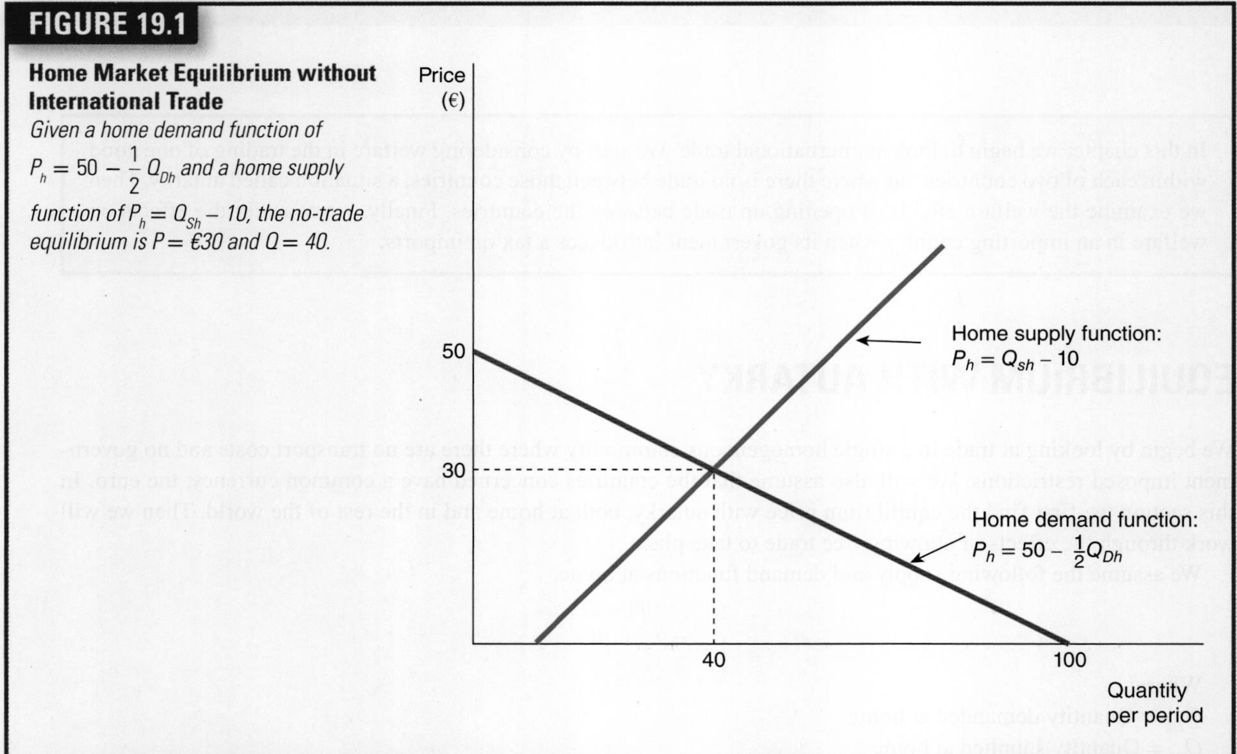

Now consider the rest of the world, which has a different demand and a different supply function:

$$\begin{aligned} Q_{Df} &= 300 - 2P_f \\ Q_{Sf} &= 10P_f + 60 \end{aligned}$$

Where:

Q_{Df} = the quantity demanded in the rest of the world
Q_{Sf} = the quantity supplied in the rest of the world
P_f = the foreign price, the price in the rest of the world

Using these functions, the equilibrium world price will be:

$$Q_{Sf} = Q_{df}$$
$$10P_f + 60 = 300 - 2P_f$$
$$12P_f = 240$$
$$P_f = €20$$

As above, we can find the equilibrium quantity by substitution. Using the demand equation we get:

$$Q_{Df} = 300 - 2P_f$$
$$= 300 - (2 \times 20)$$
$$= 260$$

We can check our answer with the supply equation:

$$Q_{Sf} = 10P_f + 60$$
$$= (10 \times 20) + 60$$
$$= 260$$

Price and quantity in the rest of the world are different from the home price and quantity. The rest of the world price is lower, at €20 rather than €30, and the equilibrium quantity is higher, 260 rather than 40. We can show this result diagrammatically but to do this we need to calculate the inverse supply and demand functions for the foreign market. First we find the inverse demand function:

$$Q_{Df} = 300 - 2P_f$$
$$2P_f = 300 - Q_{Df}$$
$$P_f = 150 - \frac{1}{2}Q_{Df}$$

Now we find the inverse supply function:

$$Q_{Sf} = 10P_f + 60$$
$$10P_f = Q_{Sf} - 60$$
$$P_f = \frac{1}{10}Q_{Sf} - 6$$

Using these inverse functions, we have plotted the foreign market equilibrium in Figure 19.2.

FIGURE 19.2

Foreign Market Equilibrium without International Trade

The foreign demand and supply functions may be different from the home market functions. With a foreign demand function of $P_f = 150 - \frac{1}{2}Q_{Df}$ and a foreign supply function of $P_f = \frac{1}{10}Q_{Sf} - 6$, the foreign market equilibrium is $P =$ €20 and $Q = 260$. The foreign market price before trade is lower than in the home market.

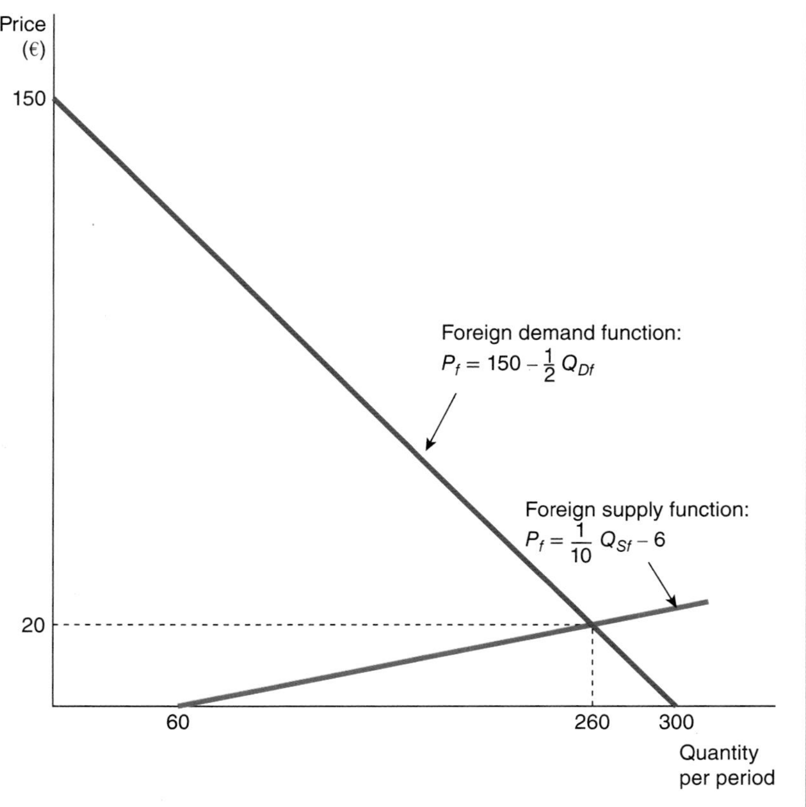

FREE TRADE EQUILIBRIUM

Let us now suppose that trade can take place between the two countries, that the markets are competitive and there are no transport costs. We will also assume that each country uses the same currency, the euro. For now we will also assume no government restrictions on trade, an assumption we will drop shortly. The law of one price tells us that under these conditions the market will bring about a common price. The price will rise in the country with the lower pre-trade price and fall in the country with the higher pre-trade price. The country with the lower pre-trade price will export the good. The country with the higher pre-trade price will import it. In our example, the home country has the higher pre-trade price.

What will be the new equilibrium price? How much will be exported from the foreign country and how much will be imported into the home country?

The difference between foreign supply and foreign demand will be exported. This must equal the difference between home demand and home supply – home imports. Excess supply in the foreign country, that is exports, equals excess demand in the home country, that is imports.

In our example we have in the home country:

$$\begin{aligned} Q_{Dh} - Q_{Sh} &= 100 - 2P_h - (P_h + 10) \\ &= 100 - 3P_h - 10 \\ &= 90 - 3P_h \end{aligned}$$

This is the expression for excess demand at home. Notice that if price were to remain the same at €30, we would have:

$$\begin{aligned} Q_{Dh} - Q_{Sh} &= 90 - 3P_h \\ &= 90 - (3 \times 30) = 0 \end{aligned}$$

There would be no excess demand. Now we consider excess supply in the foreign country which is:

$$\begin{aligned} Q_{Df} - Q_{Sf} &= 10P_f + 60 - (300 - 2P_f) \\ &= 10P_f + 60 - 300 + 2P_f \\ &= 12P_f - 240 \end{aligned}$$

This is the expression for excess supply in the foreign country. If price were to remain the same at €20, we would have:

$$\begin{aligned} Q_{Df} - Q_{Sf} &= 12P_f - 240 \\ &= (12 \times 20) - 240 = 0 \end{aligned}$$

There would be no excess supply.

For the post-trade equilibrium, we need foreign exports to be equal to home imports, that is, foreign excess supply = home excess demand. Therefore, we have:

$$90 - 3P_h = 12P_f - 240$$

but P_f and P_h will be equal so we can write:

$$15P = 330$$

Where P = the price common to both countries:

$$P = €22$$

At this common price the level of home imports is:

$$\begin{aligned} &90 - 3P_h \\ &90 - (3 \times 22) \\ &= 24 \end{aligned}$$

We can check that this is the level of foreign exports:

$$\begin{aligned} &12P_f - 240 \\ &(12 \times 22) - 240 \\ &= 24 \end{aligned}$$

The post-trade equilibrium will be a common price of €22 per unit with foreign exports of 24 units per period and home imports of the same amount. We show this post-trade equilibrium in Figure 19.3. The diagram also shows home supply, home demand, foreign supply and foreign demand. We have calculated these values from the appropriate functions as follows. In the home market:

$$\begin{aligned} Q_{Dh} &= 100 - 2P_h \\ &= 100 - (2 \times 22) \\ &= 56 \\ Q_{Sh} &= P_h + 10 \\ &= 22 + 10 \\ &= 32 \end{aligned}$$

This confirms our calculation of home excess demand, imports of:

$$56 - 32 = 24$$

In the foreign market:

$$\begin{aligned} Q_{Df} &= 300 - 2P_f \\ &= 300 - (2 \times 22) \\ &= 256 \\ Q_{Sf} &= 10P_f + 60 \\ &= (10 \times 22) + 60 \\ &= 280 \end{aligned}$$

This confirms our calculation of foreign excess supply, exports, of:

$$280 - 256 = 24$$

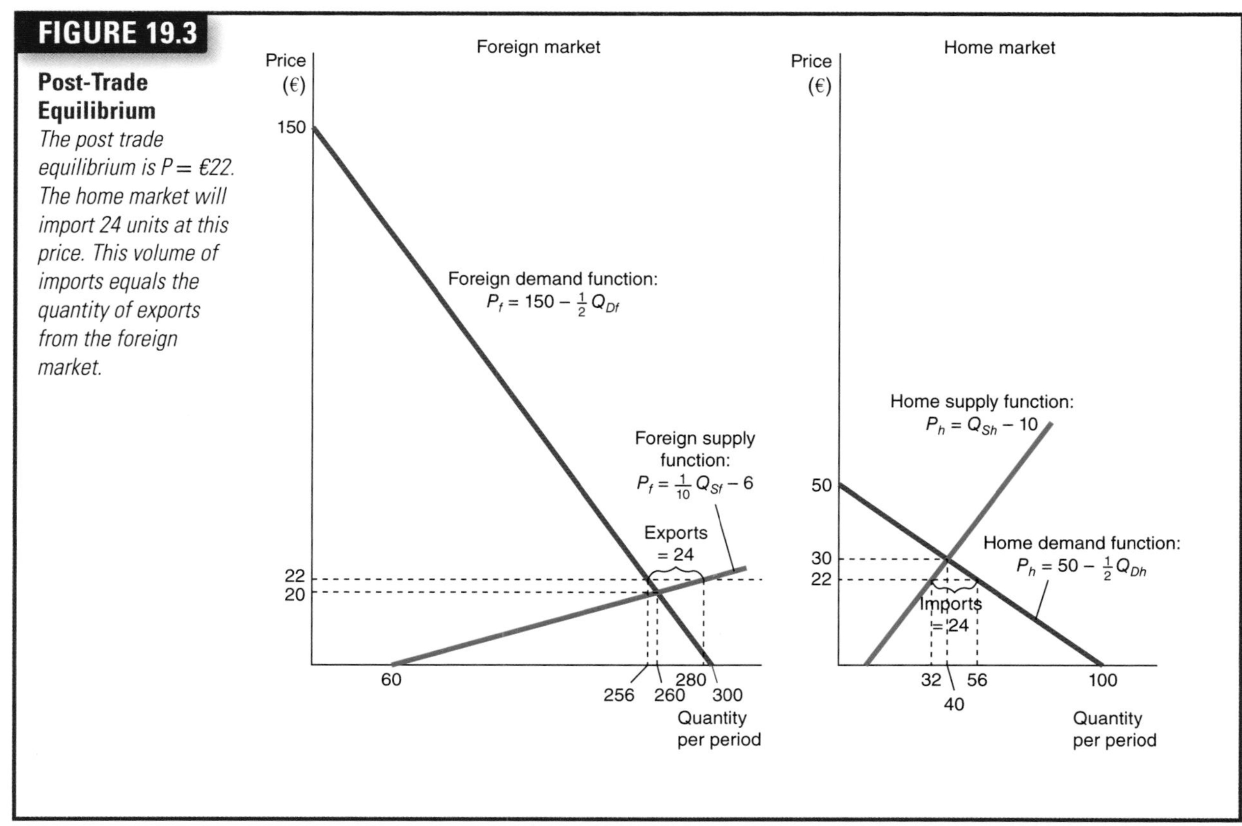

FIGURE 19.3

Post-Trade Equilibrium

The post trade equilibrium is P = €22. The home market will import 24 units at this price. This volume of imports equals the quantity of exports from the foreign market.

Gains and Losses from International Trade

We will now use this example to illustrate the gains from trade. Both home and foreign countries gain as a result of trade. We will look at each of the markets in turn to calculate the size of the gains. First consider the exporting country. Figure 19.4 shows that when the world price rises from €20 to €22, producers are better off. Producer surplus rises from area C to areas B + C + D. Buyers in the foreign country are worse off. Consumer surplus falls from areas A + B to area A. Thus trade has raised welfare by area D. We can calculate the size of the net welfare gain, then the producer gain, then the size of consumer loss welfare loss.

FIGURE 19.4

Welfare Gain in the Foreign Market

Trade improves foreign welfare. Producer surplus increases from C to B + C + D. This is a gain of €540. Consumer surplus falls from A + B to A. This is a loss of €516. The net welfare gain is thus 540 – 516 = €24.

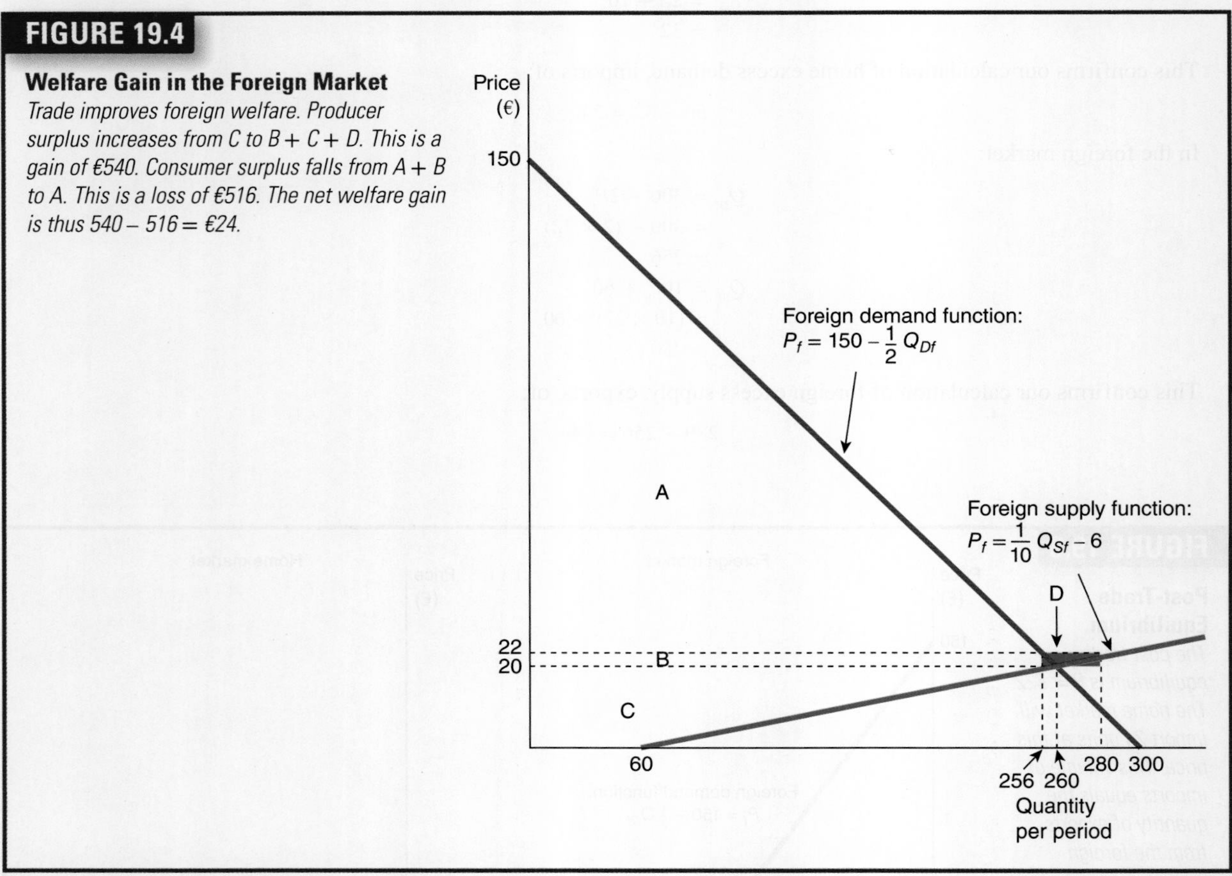

First we find the net welfare gain, area D using the formula for calculating the area of a triangle.

$$= \frac{(280 - 256) \times 2}{22 - 20}$$

$$= \frac{24 \times 2}{2} = 24$$

The net welfare gain is €24 per period. However, there is a redistribution of income from consumers to producers. The loss of consumer welfare is Area B. The simplest way to calculate this is to calculate A + B, then calculate A, then find the difference in the two amounts.

We have shown the demand curve cutting the vertical axis at a price of €150. This is the choke price.

$$P_f = 150 - \frac{1}{2}Q_{Df}$$

Therefore when $Q = 0$:

$$P_f = 150 - 0$$
$$= €150$$

Using the formula for calculating the area of a triangle, we have:

$$\begin{aligned} A + B &= \frac{(150 - 20) \times 260}{2} \\ &= \frac{130 \times 260}{2} \\ &= €16\,900 \\ A &= \frac{(150 - 22) \times 256}{2} \\ &= \frac{128 \times 256}{2} \\ &= €16\,384 \end{aligned}$$

Then area B:

$$€16\,900 - €16\,384 = €516$$

Consumer welfare is reduced by €516 per period. Now we find the welfare gain for producers. This is area B + D. We have already calculated both B and D.

$$516 + 24 = €540$$

Producers gain €540 per period, consumers lose €516 per period. The net welfare gain is:

$$\begin{aligned} &€540 - €516 \\ &= €24 \textit{ per period} \end{aligned}$$

Now we turn our attention to the home market, using Figure 19.5. First we find the net welfare gain, area D.

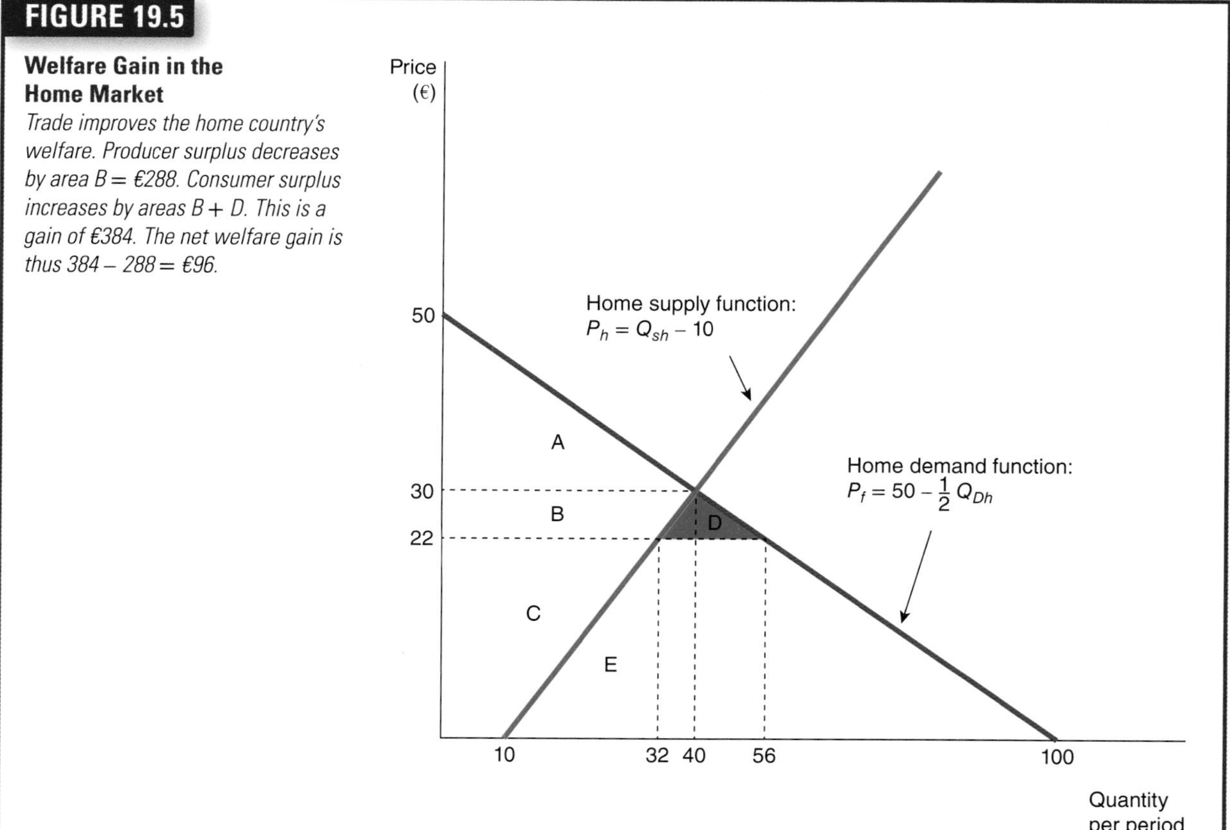

FIGURE 19.5

Welfare Gain in the Home Market

Trade improves the home country's welfare. Producer surplus decreases by area B = €288. Consumer surplus increases by areas B + D. This is a gain of €384. The net welfare gain is thus 384 – 288 = €96.

For the triangle, Area D, the fall in price is €8. The base of the triangle is 56 – 32 = 24. So we have:

$$D = \frac{8 \times 24}{2} = €96$$

The net welfare gain is €96 per period. However, there is a redistribution of income, this time from producers to consumers. The gain in consumer welfare is Area B + D. The simplest way to calculate this is to calculate A + B + D, then calculate A, then find the difference in the two amounts.

$$\text{Area A} + B + D = \frac{(50 - 22) \times 56}{2} = €784$$

$$\text{Area A} = \frac{(50 - 30) \times 40}{2} = €400$$

$$\text{Area B} + D = €784 - €400 = €384$$

The consumer welfare gain is €384 per period.

Now consider the producer welfare loss. This is area B. We can calculate this by measuring the area A + B + D, then subtracting areas A and D.

$$A + B + D = €784$$
$$A = €400$$
$$D = €96$$
$$€784 - €400 - €96 = €288$$

The producer welfare loss is €288 per period.

The net gain to the home market community is:

$$€384 - €288 = €96 \textit{ per period.}$$

Both countries are net gainers from free trade. Some will lose, some will gain but the sum of gains is greater than the sum of losses in each community.

THE WELFARE EFFECTS OF TARIFFS

Despite the apparent benefits of free trade, governments often impose barriers to trade such as import taxes, or tariffs. This can be because producers, who are losers under free trade, have sufficient political influence with governments. Let us assume that the government of the home, importing country imposes a tariff. Given a free trade price of €22, the imposition of a tariff of €8 will raise the home price to €30 and eliminate trade entirely.

Let's see what happens if the government imposes a tariff of €4, raising price in the home market to €26. The effect is shown diagrammatically in Figure 19.6.

What we have shown in the diagram, but not explained mathematically, is the values of 48 and 36 respectively for the new level of quantity demanded and the new level of quantity supplied at the higher, post-tariff price. Let us now show this result in mathematical form. These values were calculated by reference to the appropriate functions.

First consider the new quantity demanded.

$$Q_{Dh} = 100 - 2P_h$$

The new price = €26 so:

$$Q_{Dh} = 100 - (2 \times 26)$$
$$= 48$$

The higher price has caused marginal consumers to withdraw from the market and quantity demanded is lower. Now consider the new quantity supplied:

$$Q_{Sh} = P_h + 10$$

The new price = €26 so:

$$Q_{Sh} = P_h + 10$$
$$Q_{Sh} = 26 + 10$$
$$= 36$$

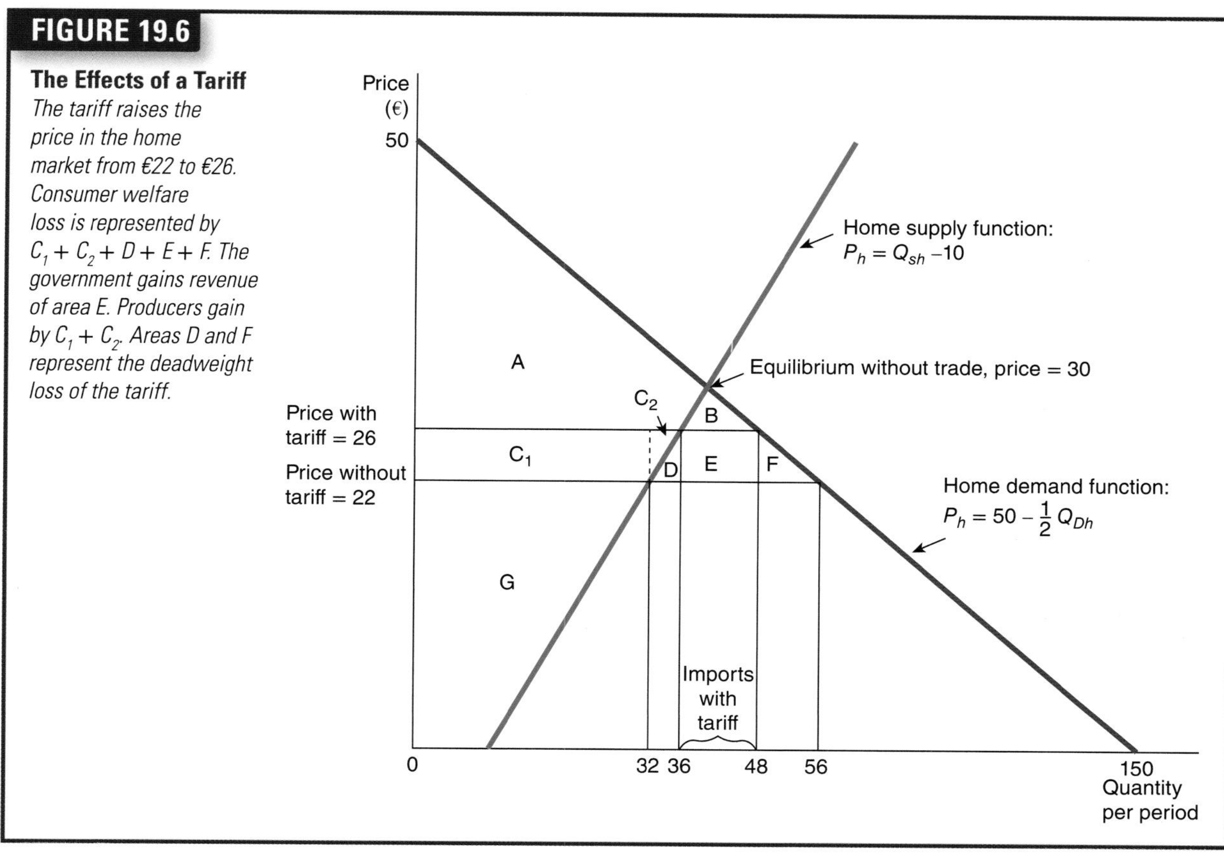

FIGURE 19.6

The Effects of a Tariff
The tariff raises the price in the home market from €22 to €26. Consumer welfare loss is represented by $C_1 + C_2 + D + E + F$. The government gains revenue of area E. Producers gain by $C_1 + C_2$. Areas D and F represent the deadweight loss of the tariff.

The higher price has caused marginal producers to expand production and the market quantity supplied is higher. The difference between home demand and home supply, 48 – 36 = 12, is the new level of imports.

Now we can find the change in welfare with reference to Figure 19.6. We begin with area E. This represents income to the government as a result of the tax. There are 12 units of imports per period and on each unit there is a €4 per unit tax.

$$\textit{Area } E = 12 \times €4 = €48 \textit{ per period.}$$

Society has benefited because government income is higher. With regard to producer surplus, producers have also gained. Previously producer surplus was area G, income in excess of opportunity cost. Now it is G + C_1 + C_2 so the gain is C_1 + C_2. Area C_1 is the increase in producer surplus to existing producers. They were willing to supply at a price of €22 but now receive a price of €26. So the total is:

$$32 \times (26 - 22) = €128$$

Area C_2 is the surplus to the more efficient of the new producers, the income in excess of opportunity cost to them. We calculate the area of this triangle as:

$$C_2 = \frac{(36 - 32) \times (26 - 22)}{2}$$
$$= \frac{4 \times 4}{2}$$
$$= €8$$

$$\textit{Area } C_1 + C_2 = 128 + 8 = €136.$$

Producer welfare has risen by €136.

Now look at consumer welfare. Consumer surplus is reduced by the higher price. Previously it was A + B + C_1 + C_2 + D + E + F. Now it is A + B. So we need to find the size of the area given by C_1 + C_2 + D + E + F.

We have already calculated $C_1 + C_2$, and area E, so now we need D and F. D is given as:

$$= \frac{4 \times 4}{2} = €8$$

And F is given as:

$$F = \frac{(56 - 48) \times (26 - 22)}{2}$$

$$= \frac{8 \times 4}{2}$$

$$= €16$$

$$C_1 + C_2 + D + E + F = 128 + 8 + 8 + 48 + 16 = €208$$

Consumer welfare has been reduced by €208. This is partially offset by an increase in producer welfare of €136, and an increase in government welfare of €48. Net welfare loss equals:

$$€208 - €136 - €48 = €24$$

This net loss is areas D and F. This is the deadweight loss of the tariff. Just as free trade increased total welfare but redistributed income within the country, so tariffs reduce total welfare but redistribute income within the country.

Summary

We have examined the effects of a tariff on international trade. However, the effects of a tariff are in many ways similar to the effects of transport costs. In both cases costs are raised that will be spread between consumers and producers. One estimate is that every day goods are in transit adds a cost equivalent to a tariff of between 0.6 and 2.1 per cent.[1]

PROBLEMS AND APPLICATIONS

1 Imagine you live in a country called 'Happyland' (H). At first Happyland does not trade any goods with the rest of the world (F). Rather, it focuses only on the domestic economy. Assume there are the following supply and demand curves for H:

$$Q_{Dh} = 300 - 5P_h$$
$$Q_{Sh} = -50 + 2P_h$$

The rest of the world has different functions for demand and supply:

$$Q_{Df} = 300 - 4P_f$$
$$Q_{Sf} = 20 + P_f$$

a. Calculate the equilibria for both markets (H and F).
b. Show the curves and equilibria in two different diagrams.
Happyland now opens its borders in order to trade with the rest of the world.
c. Will there be an excess demand or an excess supply in H?
d. Show the formulas for the excess from c and the excess for F.
e. Calculate the post trade equilibrium. Does H export or import new goods?
f. Confirm the results of e by computing the amounts for demand and supply in both H and F.
g. Show the new price, the new producer surplus, the new consumer surplus and the welfare gain in the both diagrams from b.
h. Calculate the welfare gain for H and F.
i. Compute the changes of consumer and producer welfare for H.
j. Confirm the results of h with the results of i.

2 You are still considering countries H and F from Problem 19.1. Assume F implements a tariff of €1.50.

a. Under the assumption that the world market price does not change with the imposition of a tariff, the new price in F is €54. Show the effects of this tariff for the foreign county in a diagram and calculate the loss of welfare.
b. You may want to develop a second scenario in which the world market price adjusts to the tariff. This implies that not only the foreign market but also the home market are affected by the tariff on the foreign countries' imports. Who is bearing the burden of the tariff now?

[1] D Hummels and G S Chauer (2013), 'Time as a Trade Barrier', *American Economic Review*, Vol 103, No 7, December, pp. 935–59

PART 10 THE DATA OF MACROECONOMICS

20 MEASURING A NATION'S WELL-BEING

In this chapter we are going to use some basic mathematics to explore the difference between equations and identities and illustrate the distinction in the context of GDP, explore the components of GDP via a simple problem, develop the meaning of GDP and its relationship to GNP and illustrate the use of real GDP and money GDP. Then we examine another alternative measure to GDP as a measure of welfare, the Human Development Index, HDI.

DISTINGUISHING EQUATIONS AND IDENTITIES

It is essential for understanding national income accounts and indeed for many other purposes, to distinguish between an equation and an identity. Let's begin with the meaning of an equation.

An equation is characterized by having two sides separated by an equals sign. Whatever the sum of the value of the terms depicted on the left-hand side (LHS), the ultimate value of the terms on the right-hand side (RHS) will be equal to it. The equation $2 + 2 = 4$ tells us that when we add the two numbers on the LHS, the result is the same as that on the RHS. Most of the equations you will come across in economics will contain unknown quantities. For example:

$$x + y = 6$$

Here the values of x and y are unknown. For the equation to be true, whatever values x and y take, when added together these values must add up to 6.

Equations can be true for some particular values of x and y but not for others. It is true if x is 4 and y is 2. It is also true if x is 5 and y is 1. However, for other values it is <u>not</u> true. It is not true, for example, if x is 5 and y is 3.

An *identity,* on the other hand, is something that is always true for any values of the variables involved. An example of an identity would be:

$$3(x + y) \equiv 3x + 3y$$

If any pair of values for x and y are substituted, then the LHS of this identity will give the same value as the RHS. Note that identities cannot be 'solved' since they are always true. For example, let's try it for $x = 5$ and $y = 3$. If we substitute these values into the identity we have:

$$3(5 + 3) = 3 \times 5 + 3 \times 3$$
$$3 \times 8 = 15 + 9$$
$$24 = 24$$

If you are unsure whether this would really be true for any values of x and y, pick a few numbers as values in the above identity and check this out for yourself. Notice that we should distinguish between an equation and an identity by denoting an equation as '=' with two bars. We denote an identity by writing it with 3 bars, '≡'. In practice this is not always done because the context of whether we are dealing with an identity or an equation is usually clear.

Let's consider the idea of an identity in relation to national income accounting. GDP is the measure of the value of output of a country over a period. GDP can measure two things at once. It can measure output or it can measure the income derived from producing the output.

The total value of all output of final goods and services is GDP. Whenever some part of the GDP is made, someone earns an income in producing it. This income might be in the form of wages, profit, interest or rent. Then all these 'factor incomes' taken together will have the same value as the GDP. This income recorded in the national income accounts is called Gross Domestic Income, or GDI.

A third method of calculating the value of output produced is to examine *expenditure* on that output. Since all output is purchased by some person or agent, the value of national output must be equal to the value of gross domestic expenditure, GDE.

So we might write:

$$GDP \equiv GDI \equiv GDE$$

This is a National Income Identity. Whatever value we have for GNP we will have the same value for GNI and GNE.

Now let's consider an equation through looking at GDP in a little more detail.

Planned and Actual Expenditure: Identities or Equations?

Since output, GDP, is equal to the expenditure upon it and the elements of expenditure are consumption demand, investment demand, government demand and net exports, we have:

$$GDP \equiv C + I + G + NX$$

Where:
C = Consumption
I = Investment
G = Government Expenditure
NX = Net Exports, Exports, X, minus imports, M.

This is true by definition. However, it is only true in an *ex post* sense, not in an *ex ante* sense.

The term *ex ante* means 'before the event', whereas the term *ex post* refers to the actual outcome (or 'after the event').

Look up any set of national income accounts and the identity holds. You are observing in those accounts what actually happened. They are *ex post* accounts. However, this may not have been the outcome that people wanted. The combined wishes of consumers, firms making investment decisions, governments and net exporters may have been to purchase more than was being produced. Output was not enough to satisfy their demands. That is:

$$Y < C + I + G + NX$$

where $Y = GDP$.

Alternatively, their demands may have been less than firms produced. Firms had intended to sell all they produced but aggregate demand was less than anticipated and they ended the year with unplanned stock rises. That is:

$$Y > C + I + G + NX$$

Ex ante, output was not equal to the demands made upon it. So we might write:

$$Y_a \equiv C_a + I_a + G_a + NX_a$$

and:

$$Y_p = C_p + I_p + G_p + NX_p$$

Where the subscript $_a$ refers to actual (*ex post*) and the subscript $_p$ refers to planned (*ex ante*). We write it like this because *ex post* we have an identity but *ex ante* it will be true for some values but not others.

We will explore the significance of this for an economy in a later chapter but for now notice that *ex post*, we have an identity and for *ex ante* we do not.

Exploring the Components of GDP

We have established the major components of GDP. However, the proportions of GDP represented by each are not fixed. They can vary between countries. For example, the proportion of GDP represented by government spending, G, is noticeably higher in some countries than in others.

Furthermore, the proportions can change over time within a given country. For example in countries where international trade is very important, net exports (NX) will vary from year to year. Furthermore, NX is partly determined by what is happening within an economy. We can explore this idea by working through the problem below.

Let us assume that the actual level of national income in some society is 500 and that $C = 200$, $I = 100$, $G = 100$ and $NX = 100$. The society's national accounts for last year show some changes on the previous year. Households' expenditure (C) has risen by 5 per cent, gross investment (I) (including stocks) has risen by 2 per cent, and the government current spending (G) has risen by 5 per cent. Exports are unchanged and GDP has remained unchanged also. What has happened to the country's trade balance?

We can begin with our identity. It's an identity because we are looking at the accounts ex post.

$$Y_a \equiv C_a + I_a + G_a + NX_a$$

Where NX_a is the trade balance.

$$NX_a \equiv (X - M)$$

$$500 = 200 + 100 + 100 + 100$$

After the changes described above we have:

$$C = 200 \times 105\% = 210$$
$$I = 100 \times 102\% = 102$$
$$G = 100 \times 105\% = 105$$

Then:

$$500 = 210 + 102 + 105 + NX$$
$$500 = 417 + NX$$
$$NX = 83$$

This tells us that net exports have fallen from 100 to 83. The country must be importing more than it is exporting and as a result the trade balance has worsened by 17 per cent. As ever, if we have an equation or identity with only one unknown, we can in principle find the unknown value.

Developing the Meaning of GDP

GDP is the sum of all the values added for all industries. This means not just manufacturing and construction. It includes service industries, whether state or private, and also industries producing for export. Value added is the total output of an industry minus inputs from other industries whether they are home industries or whether the inputs have been purchased from abroad.

Having established the meaning of GDP we now turn to seeing the difference between GDP and Gross National Product, GNP.

Summing the values added of all industries in an economy gives us GDP, but you may well have heard reference to the GNP. What is the difference between the two concepts and does it matter much? As we shall see in a moment, it matters a great deal for some economies.

GDP represents the value of output produced within the borders of an economy for a given year. Some of this output is produced by its resources that are located overseas. Some oil, for example, is extracted in various parts of the world, using UK-owned oil rigs. As a result there is an inflow into the UK of profits, dividends and interest which represents the value of UK output even though the capital which produced it was not located in the UK.

Similarly, some of the output within an economy's borders is produced with foreign-owned resources. Japanese resources are used to manufacture cars in the UK. Part of this output is UK output because UK workers contributed to its manufacture, but part of the output of cars is Japanese. This is seen in the outflow of profits, dividends and interest from the UK to Japan.

For any country there will be an outflow and an inflow of such income. The net flow we might call 'Net Property Income' (NPI).

$$GDP + NPI \equiv GNP$$

Or:

$$NPI \equiv GNP - GDP$$

We have another identity.

The difference between the two amounts is quite small for some economies but for others it can be substantial. For example, the Irish GDP is much greater than its GNP since Ireland has attracted substantial foreign investment. However, only some of the output produced as a result of that investment goes to Irish citizens; the rest is property income that leaves the country. For the UK and the US the difference between the two measures is much smaller.

Take care also that you note what time period you are considering for an economy. For Kuwait the ratio of GNP to GDP has varied in the last 40 years between 75 and 150 per cent.

For the UK the GNP is higher than GDP. Does this mean that the UK has more assets overseas than foreigners have in the UK? Well not necessarily. It isn't just the volume of assets but their productivity that's important. Here we are not measuring the stock of overseas capital but the flow of profits dividends and interest that flow from it. Returns to capital in the form of profits, dividends and interest can vary considerably.

Here's a problem for you to check out your understanding and significance of the difference between GDP and GNP. When you have had a try yourself we will solve it for you and answer the question.

GDP and GNP: A Problem

Country A has overseas assets worth 10 per cent of its GDP and the average rate of return on these investments is 5 per cent. Foreign owned assets represent 5 per cent of its GDP and foreigners earn an average of a 10 per cent rate of return.

1. How does country A's GDP compare with its GNP?
2. If rates of return are currently higher on assets in country A than elsewhere, what might be expected to happen over time and why?

Let's look at part (1).

Country A earns 5 per cent on its 10 per cent of overseas assets. 5 per cent of 10 per cent gives a flow of income of $0.05 \times 0.1 = 0.005$ per cent of GDP earned in profits, dividends and interest.

The outflow from returns to foreign investment will be 10 per cent of the 5 per cent that foreigners own, namely $0.1 \times 0.05 = 0.005$ per cent of country A's GDP. So the outflow is equal to the inflow. The net flow is zero. GDP = GNP. This is an equation. In our case GDP = GNP, but it is often not the case.

This illustrates an important point. Whether the net property income flow is positive or negative depends only partly on the extent to which a country has assets abroad and has foreign-owned assets within its borders. It depends also on the productivity of those assets.

Now look at the second part of the question. If the rate of return on assets in one country is high relative to other countries it will attract further investment. Against this, the more investment a country makes the lower the return on the additional investment is likely to be. This will depress the average rate of return so over time the rate of return will tend to move towards the average for all countries.

If this is not clear, recall what we saw in an earlier chapter. If more labour is added to a given volume of capital, the marginal product of labour will decline. This will reduce the average productivity and therefore its earning (wages). In a similar way, if we add more capital, the productivity of the marginal investment will fall and so will average productivity. Capital's earning, interest, will therefore fall.

Illustrating the Measurement of Real and Money GDP

It is very important that we understand the distinction between nominal and real GDP, and that we know the basis of calculation for each. The key point to remember is that nominal variables are variables measured in monetary units (such as the prices of goods and services) and real variables are measured in physical units such as output. Here we work through a simple example to illustrate the difference.

Modelia has just two kinds of production, manufactures and services. Total output and prices (in Modelian Roubles) for each of these kinds of production are given in Table 20.1 for years 1, 2 and 3.

TABLE 20.1 **Output and Prices for Three Consecutive Years in Modelia**

Year	Quantity of Manufactures (M)	Price of Manufactures (P_m)	Quantity of Services (S)	Price of Services (P_s)
1	100	2	50	4
2	200	2	100	4
3	200	4	100	8

The task involves four steps. Compute:

1. Nominal GDP for each of the three years.
2. Real GDP using year one as the base year.
3. The percentage change in nominal GDP in years two and three from the preceding year.
4. The percentage change in real GDP in years two and three from the preceding year.

Calculating Nominal GDP for Each of the Three Years

This is the sum of each of the kinds of output multiplied by its price in the current year:

Year 1: $(100 \times 2) + ((50 \times 4) = 400$

Year 2: $(200 \times 2) + (100 \times 4) = 800$

Year 3: $(200 \times 4) + (100 \times 8) = 1600$

From this calculation we can see that nominal GDP has been rising sharply in Modelia over the period from 400 in Year 1 to 1600 in Year 3.

Computing Real GDP using Year One as the Base Year

In order to draw comparisons we have to have a base year against which to make the comparison. Real figures refer to changes in output and so we have to multiply the output of manufactures and services in each year by the price in the base year. In our example, the price of manufactures in the base year (Year 1) is 2 and the price of services, 4. This results in the following:

Year 1: $(100 \times 2) + (50 \times 4) = 400$

Year 2: $(200 \times 2) + (100 \times 4) = 800$

Year 3: $(200 \times 2) + (100 \times 4) = 800$

We now get a different picture of the changes in the Modelia economy. Between Year 1 and Year 3, real GDP rose sharply from 400 to 800 but notice that between Year 2 and Year 3, real GDP was constant.

Computing the Percentage Change in Nominal GDP in Years 2 and 3 from the Preceding Year

To calculate the percentage change, we use the formula:

$$\frac{\textit{Change in nominal GDP}}{\textit{Base year nominal GDP}} \times 100$$

From Year 1 to Year 2, nominal GDP changed from 400 to 800. The percentage change, therefore, is:

$$\frac{800 - 400}{400} \times 100 = 100\%$$

From Year 2 to Year 3, nominal GDP changed from 800 to 1600. The percentage change in nominal GDP, therefore, is:

$$\frac{1600 - 800}{800} \times 100 = 100\%$$

We now have a measure of the extent to which nominal GDP has risen over the period. Our calculations tell us that nominal GDP rose by 100 per cent (or doubled) in each of the Years 2 and 3.

Between Year 1 and Year 3, the change in nominal GDP would be:

$$\frac{1600 - 400}{400} \times 100 = 300\%$$

Nominal GDP rose by three times over the period from Year 1 to Year 3.

Computing the Percentage Change in Real GDP in Years Two and Three from the Preceding Year

To arrive at the change in real GDP, we use the formula:

$$\frac{\textit{Change in real GDP}}{\textit{Base year real GDP}} \times 100$$

Substituting in the figures for real GDP, we get:

From Year 1 to Year 2: $\frac{800 - 400}{400} \times 100 = 100\%$

From Year 2 to Year 3: $\frac{800 - 800}{800} \times 100 = 0\%$

This presents a very different picture to that shown by nominal GDP. Between Year 1 and Year 2, the increase in real GDP was the same as nominal GDP, 100 per cent. However, the change in real GDP between years 2 and 3 was zero whereas the change in nominal GDP was 100 per cent. The reason for the change in nominal GDP was purely due to a doubling of the prices of manufactures and services from 2 and 4 respectively, to 4 and 8. Notice that the output between Years 2 and 3 did not change, staying at 200 and 100.

THE HUMAN DEVELOPMENT INDEX

The Human Development Index (HDI) is an alternative measure of welfare for a country that seeks to take into account the size of national output plus measures of the country's education and health. It has an advantage in that it picks up things that GDP tends to ignore. However, as we shall see, it also has its weaknesses.

HDIs vary hugely between countries. We will choose one country to illustrate its calculation. One country which by this measure has a 'high', but not very 'high', ranking is Bulgaria. We will calculate Bulgaria's HDI but remember, the HDI is not static. It gets recalculated every year because things change. For example, one country that has experienced rapid growth in recent years is China. If output is rising faster than the population, output per head rises and people's real incomes will rise. This will affect HDI in other ways. Higher incomes can mean a longer life expectancy. It can also mean that more resources are devoted to education which further affects HDI. Now let's see how the data is arrived at.

In Chapter 2 we defined a 'mean'. The mean is a calculated central value of a set of numbers. To calculate it we just add up all the numbers in the set, then divide by how many numbers there are. This can be termed the 'arithmetic mean'. HDI uses a different average known as the 'geometric mean'.

Here the numbers in a set are multiplied and then the *n*th root (where *n* is the count of numbers in the set) of the resulting product is taken. For instance, the geometric mean of two numbers, say 2 and 8, is just the square root of their product (the product of any set of numbers is the total when multiplied together), that is:

$$\sqrt{2 \times 8} = 4$$

As another example, the geometric mean of the three numbers 4, 1, and 1/32 is the cube root of their product (1/8), which is $\frac{1}{2}$; that is:

$$\sqrt[3]{\frac{4 \times 1 \times 1}{32}} = \frac{1}{2}$$

Armed with this understanding we can see how the HDI is measured using Bulgaria as an example.

The first step is to create sub-indices, one for each of the three 'dimensions' or chosen factors, national output, health and education. We will then be able to combine them into a single index.

For each of the sub-indices we need to set minimum and maximum values (or goalposts) so that we can transform the indicators into indices between 0 and 1. The minimum values are set at 20 years for life expectancy, 0 for both education variables and at \$100 for per capita Gross National Income, GNI.[1] The maximum values are set to the actual observed maximum values of the indicator. Once we have the minimum and the maximum values we have to calculate each of the sub-indices using the following formula:

$$Index = \frac{Actual\ Value - Minimum\ Value}{Maximum\ Value - Minimum\ Value}$$

For Bulgaria we show the (2014) data in Table 20.2 that we can use to create the HDI.

TABLE 20.2 **Bulgarian Welfare Indicators**

Indicator	Value
Life expectancy at birth (years)	74.2
Mean years of schooling (years)	10.6
Expected years of schooling (years)	14.4
GNP per capita (PPP US\$)	15 596

Step 1: Calculate The Health Index. The Health Index is based upon life expectancy at birth. The justification for the minimum value of 20 for life expectancy is that no country in the 20th century had a life expectancy of less than 20 years. The use of 85 as a maximum value is that 85 years can be seen as a reasonable 'aspirational' goal for a society. Thus we have in Bulgaria's case:

$$Health\ Index = \frac{74.2 - 20}{85 - 20} = 0.834$$

Step 2: Calculate The Education dimension index. This comprises two parts. The Mean Years of Schooling Index and the Expected Years of Schooling Index. The minimum value of 0 reflects the fact that societies can exist with no formal education at all and the maximum value of 15 is the projected maximum of this indicator for 2025.

$$Mean\ Years\ of\ Schooling\ Index = \frac{10.6 - 0}{15 - 0} = 0.707$$

The maximum of 18 for expected years of schooling is used because it is the equivalent of achieving a masters' degree in most countries.

$$Expected\ Years\ of\ Schooling\ Index = \frac{14.4 - 0}{18 - 0} = 0.800$$

[1] Gross National Income is similar to Gross Domestic Product. Remember that Gross is before depreciation. As we explained earlier in the chapter, 'Domestic' is similar to 'National' but whereas 'Domestic' is output produced within the borders of the economy, 'National' takes account of earnings on assets overseas. Remember also that 'Product' is the same as 'Income'.

The Education Index is now found by taking the mean of the Mean Years of Schooling Index and the Expected Years of Schooling Index:

$$\text{Education Index} = \frac{0.707 + 0.800}{2} = 0.754$$

Step 3: Calculate The Income index. The minimum value for Gross National Income per capita is set at $100, which is chosen because it takes into account subsistence and non-market production in low income societies. The maximum of $75 000 reflects the views of some economists who have argued that there is virtually no gain in well-being at income levels beyond that amount. Hence we have for Bulgaria:

$$\text{Income Index} = \frac{\ln(15\,596) - \ln(100)}{\ln(75\,000) - \ln(100)} = 0.762$$

Notice that we use logs for the income index. As we explained in Chapter 2, the effect of using logs is that changes in income are expressed in proportional rather than absolute amounts. In other words an increase in income from, say, 400 to 800 would be the same as an increase from 800 to 1600. Although the absolute change is bigger from 800 to 1600, the proportionate change is the same as from 400 to 800. In each case it has doubled.

Step 4: Calculate Human Development Index

The actual HDI score is a geometric mean of the indices for the three dimensions, each sub-index having an equal weight:

$$\begin{aligned} \text{HDI} &= \sqrt[3]{0.834 \times 0.754 \times 0.762} \\ &= 0.782 \end{aligned}$$

This number for Bulgaria puts it somewhat below the very highest countries in the rankings but well above many less developed nations. In Table 20.3 we give a few other countries' rankings for comparison.

TABLE 20.3 **Selected HDI Rankings**

HDI Rank	Country	Life Expectancy at Birth	Expected Years of Schooling	Mean Years of Schooling	Gross National Income per Head (2011 PPP ($)	HDI Value
1	Norway	81.6	17.5	12.6	64 992	0.944
8	United States	79.1	16.5	12.9	52 947	0.915
14	United Kingdom	80.7	16.2	13.1	39 267	0.907
39	Saudi Arabia	74.3	16.3	8.7	52 821	0.837
59	Bulgaria	74.2	14.4	10.6	15 596	0.782
90	China	75.8	13.1	7.5	12 547	0.727
116	South Africa	57.4	13.6	9.9	12 122	0.666
188	Niger	61.4	5.4	1.5	908	0.348

Source: United Nations Development Report, 2015

You may think that HDI is an improvement on national income statistics as an indicator of welfare, but there are problems in using it. The most important of these is that it is still an arbitrary measure. Why choose this particular weighting system rather than a different one? There is no particular logic in attaching equal significance to each part of the index. Nevertheless, improvements continue to be made. For example, there is a more sophisticated measure than the one we have calculated, which takes account not only of a country's income but its distribution.

SUMMARY

We have spent some time examining the issues around the national income accounts but our understanding of the economy will be made much clearer as a result of the time we have spent in this chapter.

PROBLEMS AND APPLICATIONS

1 Are the following terms equations or identities?

a. $2x\ (y - x) = 2y - (-(-2x))$

b. $3y^3 + x = 3y^2 \times (y + x)$

c. $5x - y = (-5) \times \left(\frac{1}{5}xy - x\right)$

d. $28xy^2 = 7x\ (4x \times 4y)$

2 Assume you live in a country with the following data:

Households' expenditure (C):	300
Gross Investments (I):	400
Government current spending (G):	100
Exports (X):	500
Imports (M):	300

a. Compute the GDP.

b. Now imagine that next year C will rise by 5 per cent, whereas I and G both drop by 10 per cent each. Imports and the GDP itself will remain constant. What will happen to the trade balance?

3 Country A owns assets in oversea worth 10 per cent of its GDP. These assets have an average rate of return of 20 per cent. Furthermore, foreign countries own assets in A worth 30 per cent of its GDP but the rate of return of these assets is only at 7 per cent. Which is higher: GDP or GNP?

4 You live in a country called Motoria (M). Motoria produces only two products: Cars and Motorcycles. The Output and Prices of these goods are shown in the following table:

Year	Output (Cars)	Price (Cars)	Output (Motorcycles)	Price (Motorcycles)
2014	300	1000	70	200
2015	300	2000	80	500
2016	500	2500	100	550

a. Calculate the nominal GDP for all three years.

b. Compute the annual growth of the nominal GDP.

c. Calculate the real GDP in 2015 and 2016 using the previous year as the base year.

d. Compute the annual growth rate of real GDP.

5 Calculate the geometric mean of: 2, 5, 6, 10 and of the growth rate of nominal and real GDP from Problem 4.

6 Imagine you live in a third world country. The life expectancy in this country would be at 34 (Rest of the world: Maximum: 85; Minimum: 20), the mean years of school would be at 1.5 (Rest of the world: Maximum: 15; Minimum: 0), the expected years of schooling at 4 (Rest of the world: Maximum: 18; Minimum: 0) and your GNP per capita at €250 (Rest of the world: Maximum: 75 000; Minimum: 100). The Maximum Education Dimension Index in the rest of the world has a maximum of 0.951 and a minimum of 0. Calculate the HDI.

21 MEASURING THE COST OF LIVING

In this chapter we focus on the use of index numbers as a means of dealing with price changes over time. We will explain the Laspeyres index as a means of measuring price changes, the Paasche Index as an alternative, and the Fisher index. Then we look at index points, explain how to re-base index numbers, calculate a chain index, and finally see how index numbers can be used to link wages to reveal the distinction between nominal and real variables.

INTRODUCTION

Index numbers seek to sum up a complex situation in a single number or series of numbers. The process of making this possible is called aggregation, that is, the combining of several elements. A key function of most index numbers is to facilitate comparisons over time. By reference to a starting or base period they show how things have changed. In this chapter we are only concerned with index numbers in the context of price changes over time. The focus is not upon how the price of one good or service has been changing but how some average of many prices has changed.

When aggregating many price changes into a single index there is need for a weighting system. Changes in the price of some goods matter to consumers more than changes in the price of others. Not including a weighting system implies that all goods are of equal importance to consumers. We will see this in three index numbers of prices, the Laspeyres index, the Paasche index and the Fisher Index. We begin with the Laspeyres index.

THE LASPEYRES INDEX

Imagine a simple economy with just four goods purchased. This is the 'basket' of goods from which we construct an index of prices. Table 21.1 shows the prices and quantities purchased of these four goods over a period of three years. An index needs a base year against which comparisons in price movements can be made. The index for the base year will invariably be 100. In this example, we are going to assume Year 2 is the base year. We will construct a Laspeyres Index for year three. The quantities purchased are needed to give us an idea of the relative importance of different goods in the minds of consumers. These have changed over the period, partly reflecting changes in tastes but partly reflecting changes in the relative prices of the goods. Consumers tend to substitute, at the margin, out of the relatively dear goods and into the relatively cheap goods.

TABLE 21.1 Price and Quantity Data for an Illustrative Small Economy

Units of:	Year 1 Prices (€)	Year 2 Prices (€) (Base Year)	Year 3 Prices (€) (Current Year)	Year 1 Quantity	Year 2 Quantity	Year 3 Quantity
Clothing	1	2	3	2	3	6
Drink	0.5	1	2	4	6	4
Food	1	2	2	3	3	7
Chocolate	3	4	4	2	3	3

The Laspeyres Index is given as:

$$I_L = \frac{\sum P_n Q_0}{\sum P_0 Q_0} \times 100$$

Where:
I_L = the Laspeyres Index
P_n = the price of goods in a given year
P_0 = the price of goods in the base year
Q_0 = the quantity of goods in the base year
Substituting the figures from Table 2.1 into the formula gives the index of prices in Year 3:

$$\begin{aligned} I_L &= \frac{(3 \times 3) + (2 \times 6) + (2 \times 3) + (4 \times 3)}{(2 \times 3) + (1 \times 6) + (2 \times 3) + (4 \times 3)} \times 100 \\ &= \frac{9 + 12 + 6 + 12}{6 + 6 + 6 + 12} \times 100 \\ &= \frac{39}{30} \times 100 \\ &= 130 \end{aligned}$$

The index of prices in Year 3 = 130. There was a 30 per cent increase in the price level between years 2 and 3.

The index requires relatively little information. It only needs data on how each of the prices has changed. It assumes that people buy the same quantities so one only needs information about quantities for the base year. However, this is also a weakness, known as a substitution bias. The law of demand tells us that, when the price of a good or service increases, its quantity demanded decreases, and vice versa, *ceteris paribus*.

Suppose there is a price increase for a good that has a high weight and at the same time the price of another with a lower weighting falls or remains the same. There is a change in relative prices. Consumers then substitute out of the relatively dear and into the relatively cheap good. As a result inflation is overstated with a Laspeyres index. This is a substitution bias.

We therefore consider an alternative measure, the Paasche index.

THE PAASCHE INDEX

The formula for this index is given as:

$$I_P = \frac{\sum P_n Q_n}{\sum P_0 Q_n} \times 100$$

Where:
I_P = the Paasche Index
P_n = the price of goods in a given year
P_0 = the price of goods in the base year
Q_n = the quantity of goods in a given year
Using the data from Table 21.1 we calculate the Paasche index of prices in year as:

$$\begin{aligned} I_P &= \frac{(3 \times 6) + (2 \times 4) + (2 \times 7) + (4 \times 3)}{(2 \times 6) + (1 \times 4) + (2 \times 7) + (4 \times 3)} \times 100 \\ &= \frac{18 + 8 + 14 + 12}{12 + 4 + 14 + 12} \times 100 \\ &= \frac{52}{42} \times 100 \\ &= 123.81 \end{aligned}$$

The index of prices in Year 3 according to the Paasche index = 123.81. There was a 23.81 per cent increase in the price level between Years 2 and 3. This change in the price level is lower than that using the Laspeyres index because it allows for changes in quantity consumed over time. It requires more information than the Laspeyres index because we must know quantity as well as price changes. However, as Laspeyres tends to overstate inflation, Paasche tends to understate it.

THE FISHER INDEX

The failure to correct for quantity changes is known as substitution bias. An attempt to correct for this is the Fisher index, which uses baskets from both the base and the current period. It is the geometric average of the Laspeyres index, which as we have seen, uses just the base period basket, and the Paasche index, which just uses the current period basket. The formula is:

$$I_F = \sqrt{\frac{\sum P_n Q_0}{\sum P_0 Q_0} \times \frac{\sum P_n Q_n}{\sum P_0 Q_n} \times 100}$$

However, since the first term is the Laspeyres index and the second term is the Paasche index, we could write it as:

$$I_F = \sqrt{I_L \times I_P}$$

In the base year when the Laspeyres index and the Paasche index are both 100, the Fisher index is:

$$\begin{aligned} I_F &= \sqrt{100 \times 100} \\ &= \sqrt{100000} \\ &= 100 \end{aligned}$$

Using the example of the data from Table 21.1 we calculated for Year 3 that $I_L = 130$ and $I_P = 123.8$. Substituting these figures into the Fisher index formula gives:

$$\begin{aligned} I_F &= \sqrt{130 \times 123.8} \\ &= \sqrt{16094} \\ &= 126.86 \end{aligned}$$

We have now looked at three possible formulae. All three assume that the items in the shopping basket remain the same over time. Most governments will modify the index to allow for changes in the choice of goods as well as in the quantities they buy.

The preferred one of the three measures we have examined will often be determined by what data is available. The Fisher index requires more data than either Laspeyres or Paasche.

INDEX POINTS

The main use of index numbers is to show changes over time. This is done by expressing an index relative to its value in the base period. For convenience the base period is almost always given the number 100. One exception to this rule is the Financial Times Stock Exchange Index (FTSE), known as the 'Footsie', where the base was set at 1000. By choosing a base of 100 it makes calculating percentage changes straightforward but care is still needed. Consider the series in Table 21.2 showing inflation data for an imaginary economy. Here 2016 is the base year, so the index number for that year is 100.

TABLE 21.2 **Inflation Data over a Period of Time**

Year	Price Index
2016	100
2017	116
2018	132

Prices in each period are shown relative to the base period. In the table the base period is 2016. The Index for 2017 is:

$$I_{2015} = \frac{Price\ Index\ 2017}{Price\ Index\ 2016} \times 100$$
$$= \frac{116}{100} \times 100$$
$$= 116$$

By 2017 a weighted average of prices has increased by 16 per cent since 2016. Similarly:

$$I_{2016} = \frac{Price\ Index\ 2018}{Price\ Index\ 2016} \times 100$$
$$= \frac{132}{100} \times 100$$
$$= 132$$

By 2018 a weighted average of prices has increased by 32 per cent since 2016.

However, care must be taken when comparing 2018 and 2017 prices. Changes in an index are sometimes quoted in terms of 'points'. Between 2017 and 2018 the index rose from 116 to 132, an increase of 132 – 116 = 16 points. This is not a percentage rise. Over this period the percentage rise in the index was:

$$= \frac{132 - 116}{116} \times 100$$
$$= \frac{16}{116} \times 100$$
$$= 13.79\%$$

Whilst the economy experienced inflation, the rate of increase in the price level actually slowed.

This can also be understood in terms of scale factors. From 2016 to 2017, prices rose by a factor of 1.16, whilst from 2016 to 2018 prices rose by a factor of 1.32 which is the product of two factors, 1.16 and the factor for the change from 2017 to 2018. Let's call this z. Then:

$$1.16z = 1.32$$
$$z = 1.1379$$

This represents an increase of 13.79 per cent as we show above.

Scale Factors

We may want to see what has happened to inflation over a longer period than a year. As we have just seen we can think of percentage changes in the price level in terms of a scale factor. If the price level rises by 5 per cent in Year 1 and then by 10 per cent, then at the end of Year 2 the price level is:

$$P_2 = P_0(1.05)(1.10) = 1.155P_0$$

where:

P_0 = price index in year 0

P_2 = price index in year 2

Since we want the change in the price level over the two years, we multiply 1.155 by 100. This gives 115.5 as the index of prices in year 2.

Now we subtract the original price level of 100. This gives us the change in the price level, which is therefore 15.5 per cent. Prices have risen by 15.5 per cent over those two years. Note that this is not 15 per cent, since we apply a 10 per cent rise to an increase of price level at the end of Year 1, not 10 per cent of the original price level.

If we wish to go forwards over time we multiply by the appropriate scale factor and if we wish to go back in time we divide. We know that the price index in year 2 is 115.5. We know that last year prices rose by 10 per cent and in the previous year by 5 per cent. What was the price level in year 0?

$$P_0 = \frac{P_2}{(1.05)(1.10)}$$
$$= \frac{P_2}{1.155}$$
$$= \frac{1.155}{1.155} \times 100$$
$$= 100$$

So far we have assumed that prices are rising. It is possible that the price level can also fall. Suppose the price level index, P, rises by 5 per cent in Year 1 and then drops by 10 per cent in Year 2. Using the scale factor, we have:

$$P_2 = P_0(1.05)(0.9) = 0.945$$

Prices have fallen by 5.5 per cent over the two years.

Re-basing the Index

Since the purpose of the index is to make a comparison with the base period, the choice of the base period is important. However, with long-running indices such as the price level, the base period needs to be adjusted from time to time. Comparisons of the current price level with that of, say, 30 years ago, may be historically interesting but is not particularly useful for current economic policy. For this reason the base year is reassessed every five years or so. We show how to do undertake this process with some fictional data over a nine-year period recorded in Table 21.3. We take the inflation data with a base of 2010 and rebase it to 2015.

TABLE 21.3 **Rebasing the Index of Inflation**

Year	Inflation Index, 2010 = 100	Inflation Index, 2015 = 100
2010	100	66.67
2011	112	74.67
2012	124	82.67
2013	138	92.00
2014	145	96.67
2015	150	100.00
2016	155	103.33
2017	158	105.33
2018	162	108.00

We divide each value of the index base 2010 by the value of the index in 2015. Let's start by making 2015 the new base year where the number must be 100. The inflation index with a base of 2010 has a value of 150 in 2015. This needs to be rebased to 100. Thus:

$$I_{2015} = \frac{\textit{Price Index } 2015}{\textit{Price Index } 2015} \times 100 = \frac{150}{150} \times 100 = 100$$

We now have a new base of 100 as our inflation rate for 2015. Now we calculate the inflation rate for 2016 with the new 2015 base.

$$I_{2016} = \frac{\textit{Price Index } 2016}{\textit{Price Index } 2015} \times 100 = \frac{155}{150} \times 100 = 103.33$$

For 2017 we get:

$$I_{2017} = \frac{\textit{Price Index } 2017}{\textit{Price Index } 2015} \times 100 = \frac{158}{150} \times 100 = 105.33$$

And finally for 2018:

$$I_{2018} = \frac{\textit{Price Index } 2018}{\textit{Price Index } 2015} \times 100 = \frac{162}{150} \times 100 = 108$$

The purpose of re-basing is to keep the comparison with the base reasonably up to date. However, should we wish, we can calculate the inflation data for an earlier period using the more recent base. This we have shown in Table 21.3. So, for example, the new index for 2010 becomes:

$$I_{2010} = \frac{\textit{Price Index } 2010}{\textit{Price Index } 2015} \times 100 = \frac{100}{150} \times 100 = 66.67$$

A Chain Index

A chain index does not have a fixed base period. The preceding period is always the base year. Thus, assuming an annual index, for the year 2018 the base year would be 2017, for 2017 it would be 2016 and so on. In other words the base is continually changing.

It is sometimes expressed as:

$$P_{n-1},_{n} = \frac{Pn}{Pn-1} \times 100$$

Where:

$P_{n-1},_{n}$ = a 'price relative', the ratio of the price level in period n, relative to the price level in period $n-1$, expressed as a percentage

P_n = price index for the current period

P_{n-1} = index for the previous period

Using the data from Column 3 of Table 21.3 we calculate a chain index as follows. First for the year 2016:

$$I_{2016} = \frac{Price\ Index\ 2016}{Price\ Index\ 2015} \times 100 = \frac{103.33}{100} \times 100 = 103.33$$

Between 2015 and 2016 the price level rose by 3.33 per cent.

For 2017:

$$I_{2017} = \frac{Price\ Index\ 2017}{Price\ Index\ 2016} \times 100 = \frac{105.33}{103.33} \times 100 = 101.94$$

Between 2016 and 2017 the price level rose by 1.94 per cent.

And for 2018:

$$I_{2018} = \frac{Price\ Index\ 2018}{Price\ Index\ 2017} \times 100 = \frac{108}{105.33} \times 100 = 102.53$$

Between 2017 and 2018 the price level rose by 2.53 per cent.

We can also calculate a chain index for years previous to the base year using the same formula. For example, for 2011:

$$I_{2011} = \frac{Price\ Index\ 2011}{Price\ Index\ 2010} \times 100 = \frac{74.67}{66.67} \times 100 = 112$$

Between 2010 and 2011 the price level rose by 12 per cent.

TABLE 21.4 **A Chain Index**

Year	Inflation Index, 2015 = 100	Chain Index, 2015 = 100
2010	66.67	-
2011	74.67	112.00
2012	82.67	110.71
2013	92.00	111.29
2014	96.67	105.08
2015	100.00	100.00
2016	103.33	103.33
2017	105.33	101.94
2018	108.00	102.53

We have filled in the value for the other years using the same principle in Table 21.4.

There are certain advantages in a chain index but there are two in particular. First, the price relative of a year can be immediately compared with the price level of the preceding year. Recall what we said about index points. We cannot do this with a series that is not a chain index. For example for 2018, using the chain index in column three of Table 21.4 the price level rose by:

$$102.53 - 100 = 2.53\ per\ cent$$

Using the series that is not a chain index, column 2 of Table 21.4, to find the same result we must express the change in the index as a proportion:

$$\frac{108}{105.33} \times 100 = 102.53$$

That is, the price level rose by 2.53 per cent.

The second advantage is that the chain index series can include changes in the basket of items used in its construction whereas the other price indices we have discussed cannot do so.

Index Linking

It is common for some changes in wage rates, pensions and other incomes to be linked to a price index, which allows us to see what happens to pay, etc. over time. We can consider what happens to the money wage and also what happens to the real wage. The money wage is simply the number of euros or pounds (or any other currency) earned per year. The real wage is what that money wage buys, that is, how it relates to the price level. To illustrate we will use the inflation data given in column two of Table 21.4.

Two people in 2016 had a salary of €40 000 per annum. Anton's wage for the next two years was index linked. His pay increase was determined by the price index. Natalie's deal is that she will get an increase of 4 per cent per annum for the next two years. Let's compare how their salaries change. First consider Anton.

In 2017 he receives:

$$\frac{\textit{Price Index } 2017}{\textit{Price Index } 2016} \times \text{Salary } 2016 = \frac{105.33}{100} \times 40\,000 = €42\,132$$

In 2018 he receives:

$$\frac{\textit{Price Index } 2018}{\textit{Price Index } 2017} \times \text{Salary } 2017 = \frac{108}{105.33} \times 42\,132 = €43\,200$$

Now consider Natalie's position.

In 2017 she receives:

$$= \frac{104}{100} \times 40\,000 = €41\,600$$

In 2018 she receives:

$$= \frac{104}{100} \times 41\,600 = €43\,264$$

When there is any inflation in the system, index-linked pay like Anton's keeps his money wage rising but his real wage constant. Non-index-linked pay like Natalie's is subject to uncertainty. Her real wage may rise or fall. In this case she has received a real wage increase by 2018 but by how much? To calculate the real rise in her salary we must compare her 2018 salary with that of 2016 using the same money values. Taking her 2018 salary we get:

$$\frac{\textit{Price Index } 2016}{\textit{Price Index } 2018} \times 43\,264$$

$$= \frac{103.33}{108} \times 43\,264 = €41\,393.23$$

Her money increase in salary was from €40 000 to €43 264. Her real salary increase has been from €40 000 to €41 393.23.

Had we only been interested in the salary positions at 2018 we could have shortened the calculations using scale factors. For Anton:

$$40\,000 \times 1.08 = €43\,200$$

For Natalie:

$$40\,000 \times (1.04)(1.04) = €43\,264.$$

Finally, we can use an inflation index to compare a salary with the equivalent spending power in an earlier period. Natalie earned €43 264 per annum in 2018. What would that sum have been worth in 2010? In other words, what would its equivalent spending power have been?

$$Equivalent\ 2010\ Value = Value\ 2016 \times \frac{Price\ Index\ 2010}{Price\ Index\ 2018}$$

$$= 43\,264 \times \frac{66.67}{108}$$

$$= €\,26\,708$$

€43 264 in 2108 buys the same amount of goods and services as €26 708 would have bought in 2010.

PROBLEMS AND APPLICATIONS

TABLE 21.5

Prices and Quantities of Fruit

	Apples		Kiwis		Bananas		
Period (t)	**Quantity [kg]**	**Price [€/kg]**	**Quantity [kg]**	**Price [€/kg]**	**Quantity [kg]**	**Price [€/kg]**	**Expenditure [€]**
2012	527	1.90	250	2.25	945	2.15	3595.55
2013	589	1.80	262	2.50	930	2.50	4040.20
2014	595	1.90	278	2.60	938	2.52	4217.06
2015	622	1.98	288	2.65	942	2.76	4594.68
2016	625	1.99	302	2.65	950	2.89	4789.55
2017	632	2.10	310	2.72	952	2.95	4978.80

The table below shows the prices of thee staple fruits for several years and the annual consumption of these fruit.

1 Calculate the Laspeyres price index for the years 2014 and 2015 with the base year 2012.

2 How high was the inflation rate of fruit prices between the years 2014 and 2015? How much higher have prices in 2015 risen since 2012?

3 Calculate the Paasche price index for the years 2014 and 2015 with the base year 2012.

4 Calculate the rate of inflation in fruit prices according to the Paasche index from 2014 to 2015. How much higher have prices in 2015 risen since 2012?

5 Compare the inflation rates according to the Laspeyres and the Paasche formulae.

6 Calculate the Fisher index for the years 2014 and 2015 and the respective inflation rate.

7 Fill in the missing values in the table Table 21.6 using scale factors.

TABLE 21.6

Indices and Inflation Rates

Period (t)	Laspeyres price index (2012 = 100)	Inflation rate (y-o-y)
2012	100.00	5.00%
2013		9.47%
2014		2.45%
2015		
2016	123.55	2.97%
2017	127.23	

8 Use the rebasing method to find the index values in the empty cells of the table Table 21.7

TABLE 21.7

Rebasing ndex Series

Period (t)	Index (2010 = 100)	Index (2012 = 100)	Index (2016 = 100)
2012		100.00	
2013	122.60	109.47	
2014			90.78
2015			97.12
2016		123.55	
2017		127.23	

9 Calculate the chain index series and the missing value for the original index in 2012 from the data in Table 21.8.

TABLE 21.8

Period (t)	Index (2015 = 100)	Chain Index
2007	88.98	
2008	91.83	
2009	87.24	
2010	90.90	
2011	92.45	101.70
2012		101.80
2013	96.18	
2014	98.45	
2015	100.00	
2016	116.20	
2017	123.09	

PART 11 THE REAL ECONOMY IN THE LONG RUN

22 PRODUCTION AND GROWTH

In this chapter we focus on economic growth. We will introduce the idea of compounding. Then we will use this principle to see how an economy's national income over time is related to the rate at which it can grow. Then we will look at the factors which determine a country's growth rate and the limits to growth using the Solow model of economic growth. Finally we will briefly consider the idea of endogenous growth.

COMPOUNDING

Imagine that Aaron has a sum of money saved. Compounding occurs when a savings account's interest is added to the principal. As a result, he now has a larger base on which to accumulate future earnings. Assume that Aaron deposited €1000 in a bank at an interest rate of 2 per cent. The interest earned in the first year, I_1, is:

$$I_1 = 1000 \times 2/100 = 1000 \times 0.02 = €20$$

The interest is added to the original deposit so he will now have €1020 on which to earn interest. Interest in the second year, I_2, is:

$$I_2 = 1020 \times 2/100 = 1020 \times 0.02 = €20.40$$

The total amount Aaron now has in his account is:

$$1000 + 20 + 20.4 = €1040.40$$

We can now generalize to produce a formula that allows us to calculate the amount in the account after n years. Interest after one year is:

$$I_1 = P \times r$$

Where:
P = the principal, the amount initially deposited
r = the interest rate earned.
The interest is added to the original deposit so the accumulated sum, A_1 is:

$$P + I_1 = P + P \times r = P(1 + r)$$

Interest earned in year two, I_2, is:

$$I_2 = P(1 + r) \times r$$

And so the accumulated sum A_2, is now:

$$\begin{aligned} A_2 &= P(1 + r) + I_2 \\ &= P(1 + r) + P(1 + r)r \\ &= P(1 + r)(1 + r) \\ &= €1040.40 \end{aligned}$$

In Aaron's case:

$$P = 1000, r = 0.02, n = 2, \text{ so:}$$

$$\begin{aligned} A_2 &= P(1 + r)^2 \\ &= 1000 \times (1 + 0.02)^2 \\ &= €1040.40 \end{aligned}$$

In general, after n periods we have:

$$A_n = P(1 + r)^n$$

Had Aaron managed to find an account paying 4 per cent and had he left the account untouched for ten years then $P = 1000$, $r = 0.04$, $n = 10$, so with compound interest the sum in his account after ten years would be:

$$\begin{aligned} &1000 \times (1 + 0.04)^{10} \\ &= €1480 \end{aligned}$$

This formula is the basis for a number of different calculations where we need to use compounding. We will consider some in Chapter 25. Here we can use these principles to see how a country's national income grows over time.

Compounding and Economic Growth

Over time most countries' output rises. The rate at which they grow has a crucial effect on their citizens' welfare. Here we consider the relationship between the growth rate and the size of national income. We will use the basis of the compounding formula above. The formula here is:

$$Y_n = Y_c \times r^n$$

Where:
Y_n = the level of national output in some future time period, n
Y_c = the current level of national output
r = the scale factor
n = the number of years over which we are compounding

The scale factor is the annual growth rate. It is the equivalent of the rate of interest when we compounded Aaron's savings growth. It is the annual rate at which national output is growing. If national income is €100 billion and the country grows at 2 per cent per annum, i.e. the scale factor is 1.02, then after four years national income will be:

$$\begin{aligned} Y_n &= Y_c \times r^n \\ Y_n &= 100 \times (1.02)^4 \\ &= €108.2 \text{ billion} \end{aligned}$$

If national income is €100 billion and the country grows at 4 per cent per annum, that is, the scale factor is 1.04, then after 50 years national income will be:

$$\begin{aligned} Y_n &= Y_c \times r^n \\ Y_n &= 100 \times (1.04)^{50} \\ &= €710.7 \text{ billion} \end{aligned}$$

We give some other examples in Table 22.1.

We have assumed a number of different growth rates because historically countries have grown at very different rates. You will notice that although a small difference in the assumed growth rate makes relatively little difference over a period of a few years, the effect of compounding is to make a considerable difference in the longer term.

TABLE 22.1 The Level of National Income at Different Growth Rates

End of Year	NY at 2% Growth Rate (€bn)	NY at 4% Growth Rate (€bn)	NY at 8% Growth Rate (€bn)
0	100	100	100
1	102	104	108
2	104	108.2	116.6
3	106.1	112.5	126
4	108.2	117	136.1
10	121.9	148	215.9
50	269.2	710.7	4690.2
100	724.5	5050.5	219976.1

Doubling Output and the Rule of 70

The 'rule of 70' is a useful way of estimating how long it takes for a country to double its output. Clearly, this will depend upon the growth rate. We use the formula that we introduced earlier in the chapter:

$$Y_n = Y_c \times r^n$$

Suppose the growth rate is 2 per cent. For our purposes it doesn't matter what the original level of income, Y_c is. We will set the current level of income, Y_c, at 1 and see how long it takes for the level of output to be 2. Now we will need logs to find the answer to the problem. We need to solve for:

$$2 = r^n$$

Then:

$$\ln 2 = \ln(r^n)$$

We can now use a law of logs that says:

$$\ln a^b = \mathrm{b}(\ln a)$$

Then:

$$\ln 2 = n \ln r$$

Now we can rearrange this expression to find the unknown value, n.

$$n = \ln 2 / \ln r$$

If the growth rate is 2 per cent, then r = 1.02.

$$\ln 1.02 = 0.0198$$

$$\ln 2 = 0.6931$$

$$n = 0.6931/0.0198$$
$$= 35$$

Given our assumptions output will double in 35 years.

The Rule of 70

It is a close approximation that the number of years taken to double output can be found as 70 / Growth Rate. In the case we have just examined:

$$70/2 = 35$$

With a growth rate of 5 per cent:

$$70/5 = 14$$

And so on. This is the rule of 70.[1]

[1] The same principle applies to the accumulation of debt. For example, suppose you borrow on a credit card at, say, $r = 1.28$, that is, 28 per cent APR, the annual percentage rate. Your debt doubles in just 2.5 years according to the rule of 70, although done more precisely it is 2.8 years. 70 / 28 = 2.5. In ten years your debt will be approximately 12 times greater than the amount you borrowed. Our advice is never to borrow on a credit card!

The growth rate in a country is not always positive. Countries experience declines in output as well as rises. We shall return to the mathematics of negative growth in Chapter 31.

THE SOLOW MODEL

What explains a country's economic growth? We can begin to answer by looking at an aggregate production function. Here we look at total output in the economy, not the output of one particular firm or industry. This might take the form:

$$Y/L = f(K/L, H/L, T)$$

Where:

Y/L = output per worker, that is output divided by the number of units of labour
K/L = the amount of physical capital per worker
H/L = the amount of human capital per worker
T = the given state of technique, or technology
Output depends upon the volume of each of the inputs.

To simplify we assume that H/L and T are constant. Further, we will think of the total capital stock, K, rather than capital per worker. Finally we will think of output rather than output per worker, so that we just have an aggregate production function of:

$$Y = f(K)$$

In order to explain the Solow model we need that this function has two characteristics. One is that the relationship is positive. More K leads to more Y. The other is that there are diminishing marginal returns to *K*. Just as labour is subject to diminishing returns, so is capital. To illustrate the Solow model we will assume a function of the form:

$$Y = \sqrt{K}$$

This production function can be represented graphically as in Figure 22.1 with output (Y) on the vertical axis and the capital stock, K, on the horizontal axis. When the capital stock, K = 100, national output is:

$$Y = \sqrt{100} = 10$$

When K = 200:

$$Y = \sqrt{200} = 14.14$$

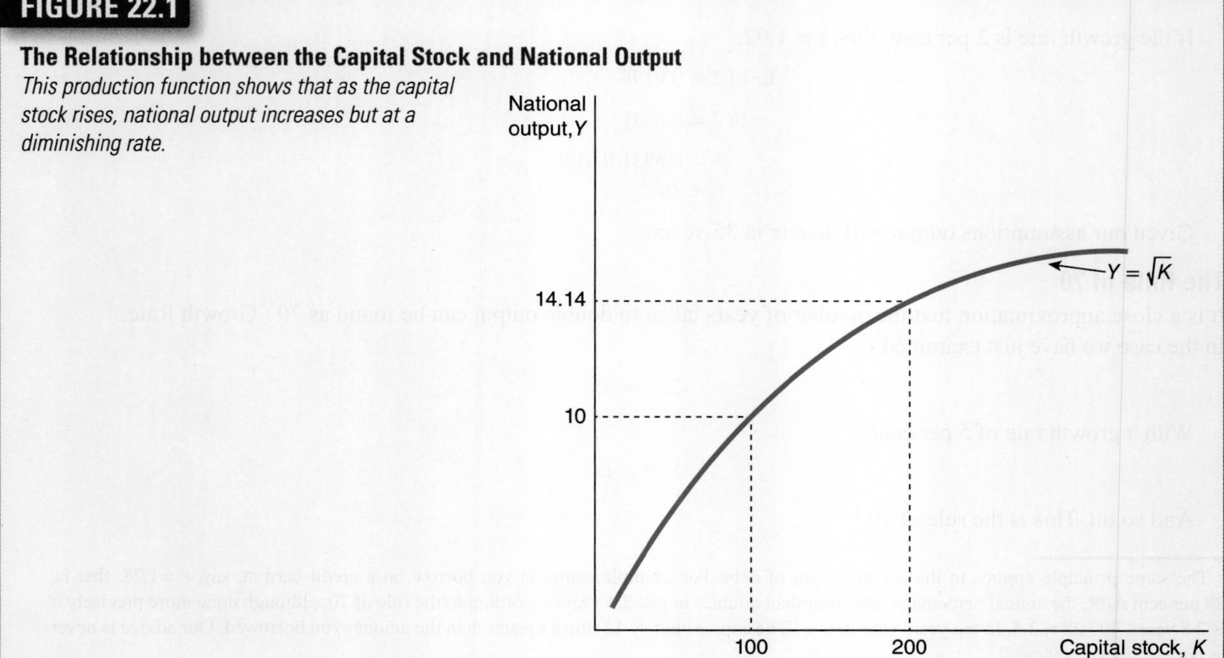

FIGURE 22.1

The Relationship between the Capital Stock and National Output

This production function shows that as the capital stock rises, national output increases but at a diminishing rate.

How much capital a society invests will vary between countries but we will assume that a country either consumes what it produces or invests it. It either produces consumption goods or investment goods. There is an opportunity cost of investment, foregone current consumption. Its choices are shown in Figure 22.2, where the opportunity cost of investment increases. It will operate somewhere around the opportunity cost curve (production possibility curve). For example, if the country operates at point Z it enjoys OC'_t current consumption. The country forgoes current consumption of C'_tX, enabling C'_{t+1} consumption next period. How societies make such a decision we will reflect on in a future chapter. However in our simplified economy we can see that the answer is that funds to invest come from savings.

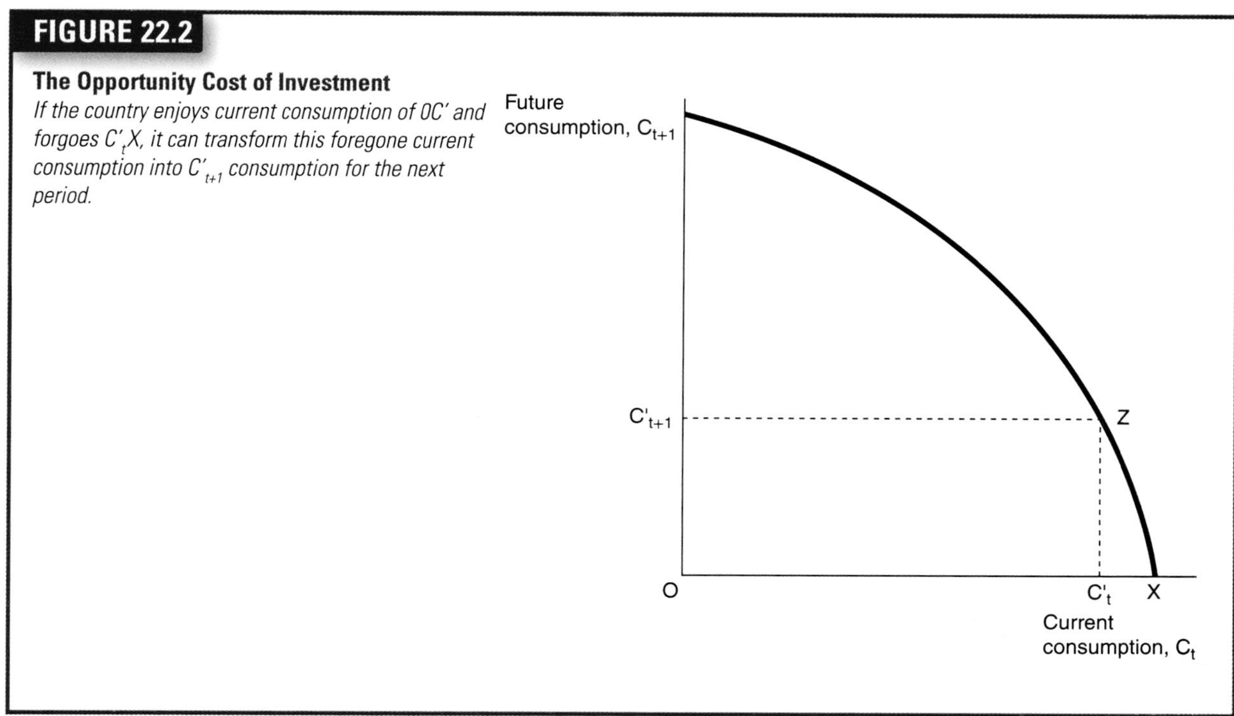

FIGURE 22.2

The Opportunity Cost of Investment

If the country enjoys current consumption of OC′ and forgoes C'_tX, it can transform this foregone current consumption into C'_{t+1} consumption for the next period.

In a simple economy we consume or save our income.

$$Y = C + S$$

Where:
Y = Income or output
C = Consumption
S = Saving
Output is either consumed or invested:

$$Y = C + I$$

Where:
I = Investment
Then:

$$S = I$$

Here we will assume that our society sets aside a given proportion of its output as investment for future consumption. We will assume that this proportion is ½. For example, if the capital stock = 64, national output is:

$$Y = \sqrt{64} = 8$$

Of which half is consumption goods = 4 and half is investment goods = 4. We show this in Figure 22.3.

FIGURE 22.3

The Relationship between the Capital Stock, Investment and National Output

The diagram illustrates the effect of a society's decision to set aside half of its output as investment goods to enable it to produce output in the future.

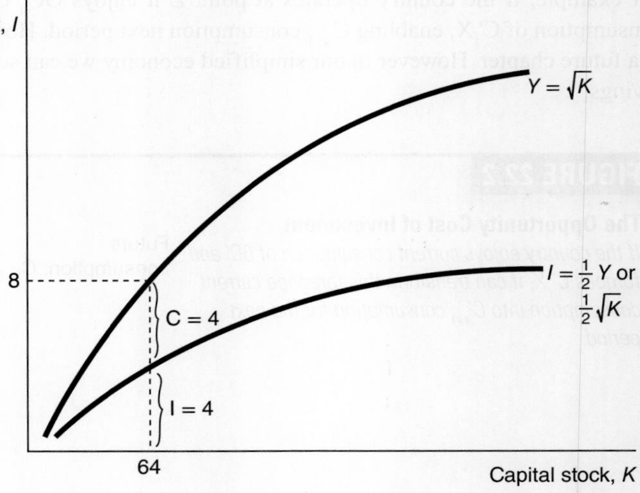

The Problem of Depreciation

More investment in a given year does not necessarily mean that the capital stock rises. The capital stock depreciates with time; machinery wears out and buildings decay. A distinction is made between gross investment and net investment. If gross investment = I_t and the capital stock now is K_t, and depreciation = δ, then there is no change in the capital stock if:

$$K_t = K_{t-1} + I_t - \delta$$

i.e. when gross investment = depreciation.

We will assume that depreciation is greater when the capital stock is higher and we will assume that it is a constant proportion of K. This gives us a linear function which we will assume is:

$$\delta = 0.04K$$

For every €100 worth of capital stock the annual depreciation is €4. Now we can calculate the level of capital stock where investment is just sufficient to cover depreciation and keep the capital stock constant.

$$\frac{1}{2}\sqrt{K} = 0.04K$$

$$\frac{\sqrt{K}}{2} = 0.04K$$

$$\sqrt{K} = 0.08K$$

$$K = 0.0064K^2$$

$$0.0064K^2 - K + 0 = 0$$

Now we have a quadratic equation. We solve using the standard formula. For $ax^2 + bx + c = 0$, the value of x is given by:

$$x = \frac{-b \pm \sqrt{b^2 - 4ac}}{2a}$$

Here:

$$
\begin{aligned}
a &= 0.0064 \\
b &= -1 \\
c &= 0 \\
&= \frac{-(-1) \pm \sqrt{(-1)^2 - 4(0.0064)(0)}}{2(0.0064)} \\
&= \frac{1 \pm \sqrt{1 - 0}}{0.0128} \\
&= \frac{1 \pm \sqrt{1}}{0.0128} \\
&= \text{either } \frac{2}{0.0128} = 156.25 \\
&\quad \text{or } \frac{0}{0.0128} = 0
\end{aligned}
$$

We can eliminate from our consideration the zero value. The level of the capital stock has to be positive. We are left with a unique meaningful value of 156.25.

Alternatively, we can find the answer without the use of a quadratic equation:

$$\frac{1}{2}\sqrt{K} = 0.04K$$

Multiply both sides by 100:

$$\frac{100}{2}\sqrt{K} = 4K$$

Dividing by 4 gives:

$$12.5\sqrt{K} = K$$

We can present K as equal to $\sqrt{K} \times \sqrt{K}$:

$$12.5\sqrt{K} = \sqrt{K} \times \sqrt{K}$$

Now divide by $\sqrt{K}$:

$$12.5 = \sqrt{K}$$

Now square both sides:

$$(12.5)^2 = (\sqrt{K})^2$$

$$K = 156.25$$

The capital stock at which investment is just sufficient to cover the replacement of worn out capital is 156.25.

At this level of capital stock national output is:

$$
\begin{aligned}
Y &= \sqrt{K} \\
&= \sqrt{156.25} \\
&= €12.5
\end{aligned}
$$

We show these results in Figure 22.4.

This level of capital stock is sometimes called the 'steady state'.

We can now see the crucial conclusion of the Solow model. From Figure 22.4, note that when the capital stock is less than the steady state level, the capital stock is bound to be rising. Investment is greater than depreciation. However, when the capital stock is greater than the steady state level, the capital stock is bound to be falling. Investment is less than depreciation. If all investment is needed to replace worn out capital, the capital stock is not increasing. Investment at that point cannot be the driving force of economic growth. We must look elsewhere for this.

FIGURE 22.4

The Capital Stock and Depreciation

If the capital stock is 156.25, then investment is just sufficient to replace capital depreciation.

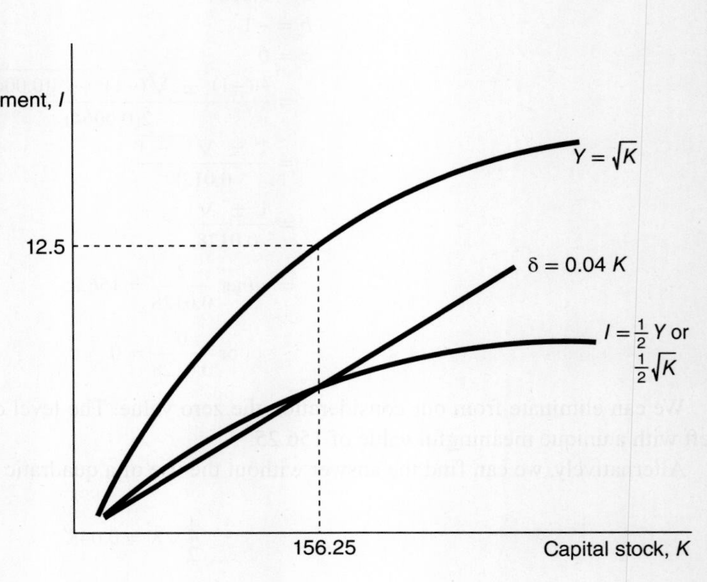

If an economy reaches this steady state, where further accumulations of capital alone cannot increase Y, increases in Y can still take place. Let's return to our aggregate production function:

$$Y/L = f(K/L, H/L, T)$$

To simplify our model we worked on a total output basis rather than on a per capita basis. Similarly, we worked on a capital basis rather than capital per unit of labour but in principle this is the same function that we used for the model. We can now see that sustained increases in output must come from one of these other items in the production function. Increases in human capital are still a form of capital so ultimately it will have to come from improvements in technology. If T rises, that is, there is an improvement in technology, the whole of the productivity curve will shift upwards.

For simplicity we have been focusing on income but income per head would be a better measure of welfare. We have also been assuming that the whole population is working. Clearly this is a simplification too as there are many in a population who are unable to or choose not to work. When we take these factors into account we can decompose average income per head to give:

$$\frac{Y}{Pop} = \frac{Y}{N} \times \frac{N}{Pop}$$

Where:

N = the number working

$\frac{Y}{Pop}$ = income per head

$\frac{Y}{N}$ = average labour productivity, output per person employed

$\frac{N}{Pop}$ = proportion of the population working

That is, real GDP per head must equal average labour productivity multiplied by the proportion of population employed. If there are reasons why the proportion of the population working cannot increase, then, to increase GDP per head, average labour productivity must rise. In the Solow view it will eventually be necessary for this productivity rise to come from improvements in technology.

ENDOGENOUS GROWTH THEORY

The Solow model has formed the basis of growth theory for many years. However, it has not gone unchallenged. Any model is only as good as the validity of its assumptions. One possible criticism of the Solow model is that of endogenous growth theory which challenges the Solow model on at least two grounds. The first is that there is no necessarily diminishing marginal product of K. The second is that there is a significant role for government in encouraging research to increase technical knowledge and in making investment in human capital, in the form of training and education. In the Solow model, technology is exogenous. In endogenous growth theory, the state of technology is not a given. It becomes endogenous, with the state taking a key role in raising long run growth.

PROBLEMS AND APPLICATIONS

1 Imagine you got €2000 in your bank account. Every year you will get 4 per cent interest.
   a. How much money will you have after 4 years?
   b. What will be the interest payment in year 3?
   c. Assume you have another bank account with €3000. The interest rate on this account is not fixed. In the first year you get 2 per cent, in the second year 5 per cent and in the third year 4 per cent. How much money do you have on this account after 3 years?

2 Assume there are 3 different countries A, B and C. A has a GDP of 100 and an annual growth of 10 per cent. B has a GDP of 2000 and an annual growth of 2 per cent. C has a GDP of 100 000 but its economy shrinks each year by 5 per cent.
   a. Which country will have the largest GDP in 50 years?
   b. How long will it take country A to double its output? How long will it take country B?
   c. Apply the 'Rule of 70' to check your answer.

3 The capital stock of a certain country is at 256. Assume the relationship between capital and output is $Y = \sqrt{K}$.
   a. What will be the national output, according to the Solow model?
   b. Imagine one quarter of the output will be invested. The depreciation of the capital stock can be calculated as $0.01K = D$. What will be the capital stock in the next period?

4 In another country, one third of the national output will be invested. The depreciation in this country can be described as $0.02K = D$.
   a. At which capital stock is the investment just sufficient to reach a steady state?
   b. Describe why the capital stock cannot be the driving force of economic growth.
   c. So if not the capital stock, which factor can increase the productivity of an economy?

23 UNEMPLOYMENT

There are many explanations that have been offered for unemployment. In this chapter we focus on just two of them. First, we consider the role of trade union activity as a possible contributing factor. Second, we examine an aspect of the problem of imperfect information and consider the extent to which this can also create unemployment.

UNEMPLOYMENT AND TRADE UNION ACTIVITY

We will examine the effect of trade union activity assuming that the market for labour is otherwise competitive. We begin by looking at a market for labour where no union activity is present and use this as a comparison with a situation in which a powerful trade union is able to impose its own preferences on employers. Before looking at trade union behaviour, we illustrate a market where the equilibrium quantity of labour is determined and where there is therefore no unemployment at all.

Our assumed competitive labour market has the following demand and supply functions.

For the demand curve:

$$W = 800 - 0.08Q_D$$

Where:
W = the price of labour services, the weekly wage rate
Q_D = the quantity of that labour demanded by firms each week.
And for the supply curve:

$$W = 40 + 0.02Q_S$$

Where:
Q_S = the quantity of that labour supplied to the market each week.
In equilibrium and with no trade union activity the quantity of labour supplied and demanded is found as:

$$\begin{aligned} 800 - 0.08Q &= 40 + 0.02Q \\ 0.1Q &= 760 \\ Q &= 7600 \end{aligned}$$

So, 7600 people will be employed in the industry. Now we can find the wage rate that will clear the market. Using the supply curve for labour we substitute $Q = 7600$ in the labour supply function thus:

$$\begin{aligned} W &= 40 + 0.02Q_S \\ &= 40 + (0.02 \times 7600) \\ &= 40 + 152 \\ &= €192 \end{aligned}$$

The equilibrium wage rate is €192 per week for each employee.

We can find the same result using the labour demand curve:

$$\begin{aligned} W &= 800 - 0.08Q_D \\ &= 800 - (0.08 \times 7600) \\ &= 800 - 608 \\ &= €192 \end{aligned}$$

We show this result diagrammatically in Figure 23.1.

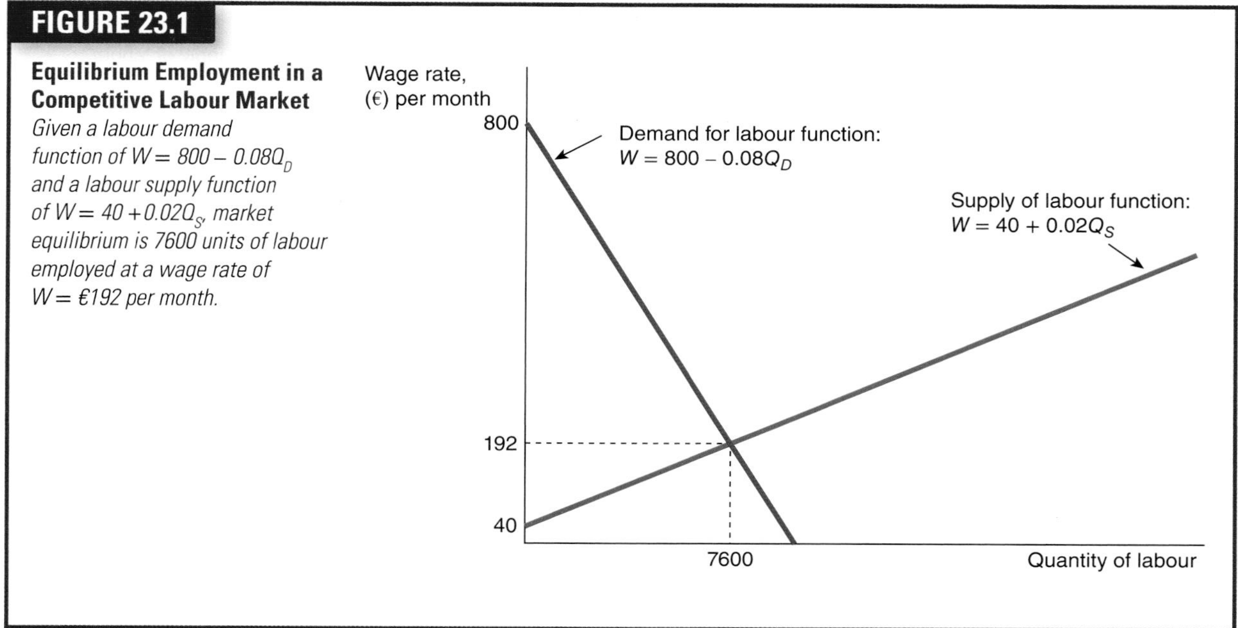

FIGURE 23.1

Equilibrium Employment in a Competitive Labour Market
Given a labour demand function of $W = 800 - 0.08Q_D$ and a labour supply function of $W = 40 + 0.02Q_S$, market equilibrium is 7600 units of labour employed at a wage rate of $W = €192$ per month.

Trade Union Objectives

How might a trade union alter this outcome? If the union has sufficient power it may wish to use its power to raise the wage rate, subject to the constraint of the labour demand curve.

This is illustrated in Figure 23.2. The union would prefer to have both higher wages and also a larger membership. However, it must work within the constraint imposed by the demand for labour. It must trade off its preferences which are shown in the set of indifference curves, IC_0, IC_1 and IC_2. If it accepts the competitive outcome it has a utility associated with IC_0 but it can do better than this. It can achieve a higher level of utility. The highest indifference curve it can reach, subject to the constraint of the labour demand curve, is IC_1. This means seeking a wage of W_u, which is above the equilibrium wage, W_e, and accepting a level of employment of L_u, below the equilibrium level of employment, L_e.

To what extent does this create unemployment? At first sight it may seem that unemployment can be seen as $L_e - L_u$. This will be determined by the elasticity of demand for labour. However, it can be argued that the higher wage increases the quantity of labour supplied to the market to L_s and as a result, unemployment created by the union activity is $L_S - L_U$. The extent to which the higher wage creates an increase in quantity supplied is determined by the elasticity of supply of labour.

Given its preference, the extent to which the union can achieve its goal depends upon its strength in the labour market. In what follows we will assume that the union does have sufficient power to achieve its goals although this is far from inevitable. It may be entirely or just partly successful.

Possible Trade Union Policy: 1

The first union policy we shall consider is the policy of maximizing the income of its members. In an earlier chapter we considered the possibility that a monopolist might aim to maximize sales revenue. That is, the goal was

FIGURE 23.2

Possible Union Preferences in a Labour Market

The union trades off its preferences shown in the indifference curves. The competitive outcome gives it a utility associated with IC_0, but, subject to the constraint of the labour demand curve, it can reach IC_1. This means seeking a wage of W_u, and a level of employment of L_u.

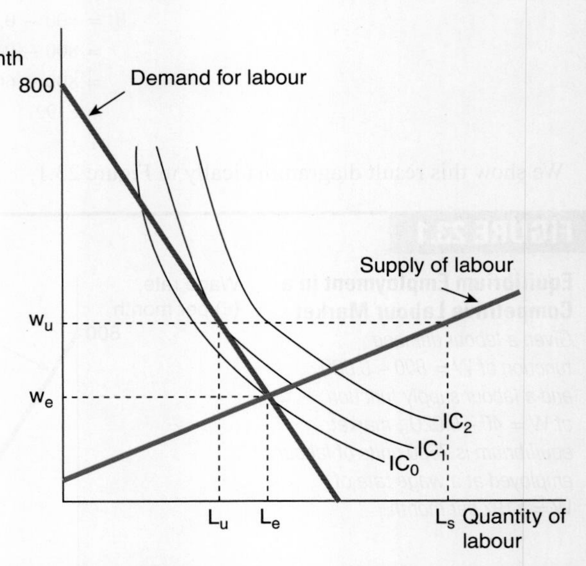

not profit maximization but sales revenue maximization. The powerful union's presence can turn this otherwise perfectly competitive industry into one where it will attempt to act as a monopolist. It might then adopt a similar policy to the sales revenue maximizer, aiming to maximize income to its members. We saw that for a firm to achieve this goal it would produce where total revenue is maximized. Alternatively expressed, it would produce where marginal revenue (MR) = 0. Now let's assume that the trade union behaves in a similar way and see what level of employment results. To do this we take the labour demand function, and use it to find a total revenue function, TR. Then we can differentiate the TR function to find MR. Where MR = 0, TR is maximized. If this were the demand curve for a firm's product, TR would be the total revenue from selling the product. Here TR = total income received by the workers in the industry.

$$W = 800 - 0.08Q$$
$$\text{TR} = (800 - 0.08Q)Q$$
$$= 800Q - 0.08Q^2$$

Differentiating TR with respect to labour demand we have:

$$\frac{dTR}{dQ} = MR = 800 - 0.16Q$$

Setting this to zero gives:

$$800 - 0.16Q = 0$$

Therefore:

$$0.16Q = 800$$
$$Q = 5000$$

The level of employment that maximizes income to the trade union members is 5000 units of labour.

We can now find the wage rate that is the highest possible for the union to achieve if 5000 units of labour are to be employed. The demand for labour is:

$$W = 800 - 0.08Q_D$$

So substituting for $Q_D = 5000$ we have:

$$W = 800 - 0.08 \times 5000$$
$$= 800 - 400$$
$$= 400$$

Union policy is to have a wage rate of €400 per month and 5000 units of labour to be employed. If the union is successful in negotiating this wage how much unemployment is created? We can find this by looking at the quantity of labour supplied and demanded at a wage rate of €400 per month. Consider first the supply of labour.

$$W = 40 + 0.02Q_S$$

With a wage of €400 per month, quantity of labour supplied is found as:

$$\begin{aligned} 400 &= 40 + 0.02Q \\ 0.02Q &= 360 \\ Q &= 18\,000 \end{aligned}$$

At a wage rate of €400 per month the quantity supplied of this particular kind of labour is 18 000.
We have established that the quantity of labour demanded is 5000 so unemployment in this industry is:

$$18\,000 - 5000 = 13\,000$$

This figure of 13 000 is the unemployment, the excess supply of labour. Part of this increased quantity of labour supplied is because of the higher wage rate. If we move from the original equilibrium to this new equilibrium, the number of workers laid off will be:

$$7600 - 5000 = 2600$$

We have shown the effect of trade union activity with this kind of policy in Figure 23.3.

FIGURE 23.3

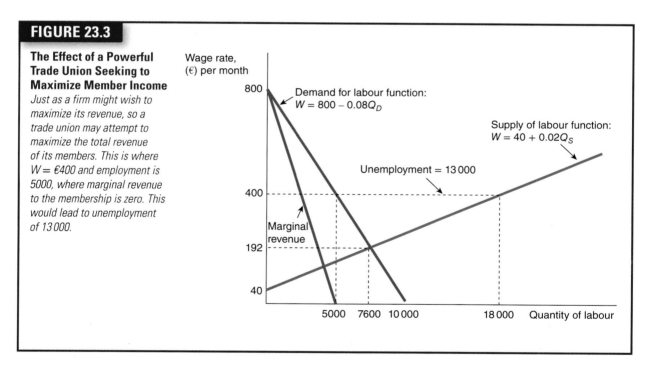

The Effect of a Powerful Trade Union Seeking to Maximize Member Income
Just as a firm might wish to maximize its revenue, so a trade union may attempt to maximize the total revenue of its members. This is where W = €400 and employment is 5000, where marginal revenue to the membership is zero. This would lead to unemployment of 13 000.

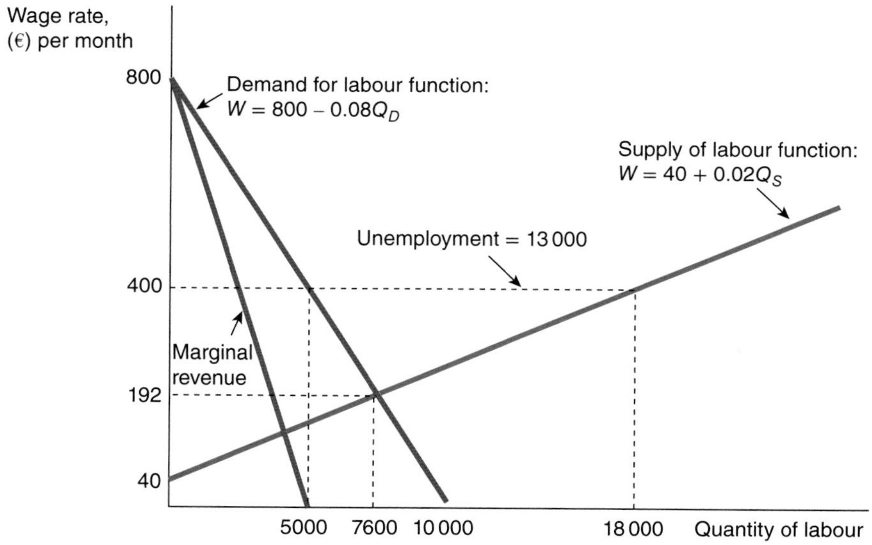

Given a demand for labour function of:

$$\begin{aligned} D &= 800 - 0.08Q \\ 0.08Q &= 800 - D \\ Q &= 10000 - 12.5D \end{aligned}$$

When $D = 0$, $Q = 10\,000$
Recall from Chapter 14 that the slope of MR is twice that of AR. As a result, MR cuts the horizontal axis at 5000, half the quantity (10 000) when $D = 0$.

Possible Trade Union Policy: 2

Now we consider the effect of an alternative union policy. What would maximize union welfare if the policy was to gain the maximum income above opportunity cost for its members? We have considered before the behaviour of a monopolist that seeks to maximize profits for its shareholders. It seeks a price that maximizes revenue. Alternatively expressed, it seeks to maximize income in excess of opportunity cost of resources. The trade union might adopt the same goal for its members. It aims to set the price of labour, the wage rate, where:

$$MC = MR$$

As we have seen previously MC = the supply curve. Here it is:

$$W = 40 + 0.02Q_S$$

We have already calculated MR in looking at trade union behaviour with policy one.

$$\text{MR} = 800 - 0.16Q$$

Setting MC = MR gives:

$$\begin{aligned} 40 + 0.02Q &= 800 - 0.16Q \\ 0.18Q &= 760 \\ Q &= 4222.22 \end{aligned}$$

The optimum number of workers employed to achieve this policy is 4222.22 workers.

Now we can find from the labour demand curve the wage rate that corresponds to this level of employment:

$$\begin{aligned} W &= 800 - 0.08Q_D \\ &= 800 - (0.08 \times 4222.22) \\ &= 800 - 337.78 \\ &= €462.22 \end{aligned}$$

The wage rate will be €462.22 per month. If the union is successful in negotiating this wage how much unemployment is created? First we find the quantity of labour supplied at this wage rate.

$$W = 40 + 0.02Q_S$$

With a wage of €462.22 per month:

$$\begin{aligned} 462.22 &= 40 + 0.02Q \\ 0.02Q &= 422.22 \\ Q &= 21\,111 \end{aligned}$$

The quantity of labour offered at a wage rate of €462.22 is 21 111.

We have already established that the quantity of labour demanded = 4222.22.

Therefore unemployment is:

$$21\,111 - 4222.22 = 16\,888.78$$

This is the excess supply of labour. Part of this increased quantity of labour supplied is because of the higher wage rate. If we move from the original equilibrium to this new equilibrium, the number of workers laid off will be:

$$7600 - 4222.22 = 3377.78$$

This result is shown diagrammatically in Figure 23.4.

To reiterate, the extent of the unemployment created by trade union activity depends partly upon its policy preferences and partly upon its strength to fulfil its objectives. However, we can say that it is likely that the trade union would choose a higher wage rate and a lower quantity of labour employed than one would expect to find in a competitive labour market. Having considered one possible source of unemployment we now look at one other source, that of imperfect information.

FIGURE 23.4

The Effect of a Powerful Trade Union Seeking to Maximize Member Income in Excess of Opportunity Cost

Here the union seeks to maximize income above opportunity cost. This involves seeking a wage of €462.22 and therefore a level of employment of 4222.22. This policy, if successful, creates unemployment of 16 888.88.

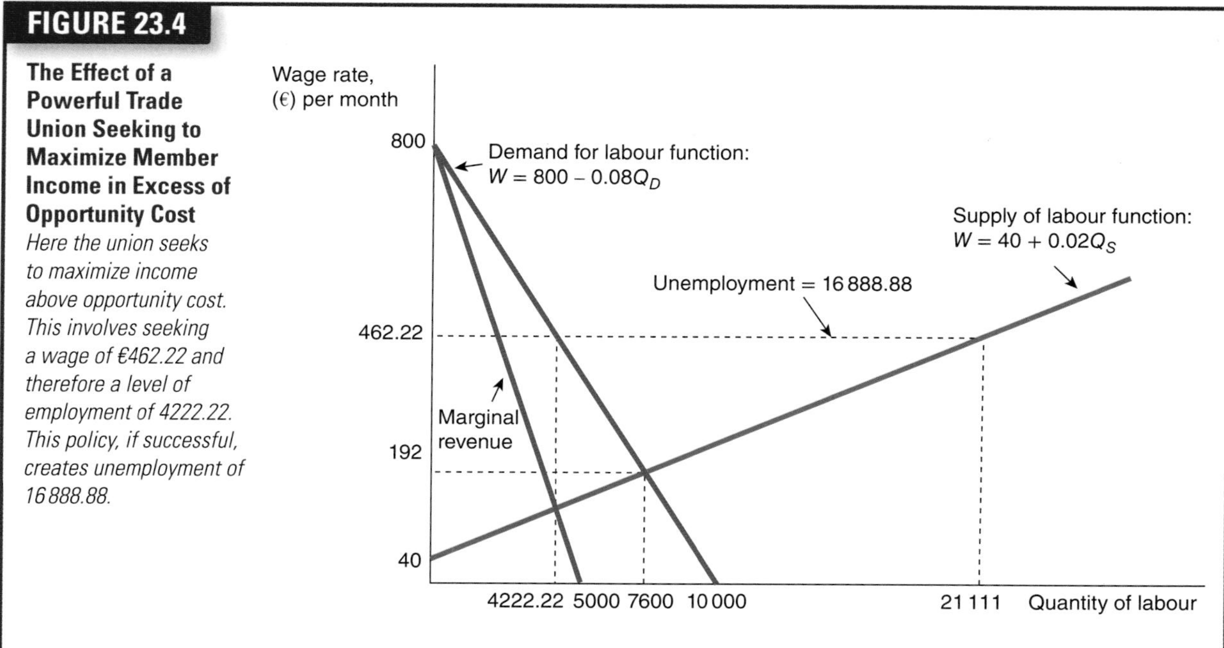

UNEMPLOYMENT AND IMPERFECT INFORMATION

One kind of unemployment experienced by all economies is frictional unemployment, also called transitional unemployment. This is unemployment relating to labour market turnover. A typical example of a frictionally unemployed worker might be one who is temporarily out of a job until a new one begins. A proportion of frictional unemployment is voluntary in that the decision to be unemployed is made by the employee rather than the employer choosing to end the contract.

Why does frictional employment exist at all? Won't a worker hold on to the current job until a new one is available? The benefit of doing so is clear, but one would expect a worker to consider all costs and all benefits in the decision to change jobs. It may be that the expected benefit of a new job outweighs the cost of temporary unemployment. We look at a simple model to explore idea that the decision is made with reference to costs and benefits. We will see that it gives insights as to the factors that affect the level of frictional unemployment.

First, what are the potential benefits of choosing to become temporarily unemployed? The first factor is the additional income the new job will pay. We can include non-pecuniary (money related) benefits in this calculation. This benefit is:

$$B_p = W^* - W$$

Where:

B_p = Benefit of becoming temporarily unemployed
W^* = the potential new wage
W = the current wage

However, at the point the worker gives up the current wage there is no guarantee that W^* will be forthcoming. Information concerning the future wage is uncertain. The worker must estimate the probability, P. Then the benefit of giving up the job becomes:

$$P \times (W^* - W)$$

Where:

P = probability of obtaining the job with the higher wage.

If a worker currently earns €10 000 and estimates that there is a 50 per cent chance of getting a job with a wage of €15 000, then the benefit of becoming temporarily unemployed in order to try for the job is:

$$B_p = 0.5(15\,000 - 10\,000)$$
$$= €2500$$

Often there is not one possible job available but a series of them. In this case we can use a weighted average to estimate the expected gain. Suppose there are four possible jobs with different wages offered. Table 23.1 summarizes these and also shows the probability of obtaining each one.

TABLE 23.1 **The Probability of Obtaining Possible Job Offers**

	Job A (€)	Job B (€)	Job C (€)	Job D (€)
Wage, W*	12 000	15 000	18 000	20 000
W* – W	2000	5000	8000	10 000
Probability, P	0.7	0.5	0.3	0.1

Then:

$$\begin{aligned} B_p &= 0.7(12\,000 - 10\,000) + 0.5(15\,000 - 10\,000) + 0.3(18\,000 - 10\,000) + 0.1(20\,000 - 10\,000) \\ &= 0.7(2000) + 0.5(5000) + 0.3(8000) + 0.1(10\,000) \\ &= €7300 \end{aligned}$$

The expected benefit of getting a job with a higher wage is €7300.

We can now see why during a recession frictional unemployment declines. A worker fears to leave the current job because the chance of getting a better one is reduced. The job offers available are less, the wage offered tends to be smaller, but the estimated probability of getting another job is also lower.

Until now we have assumed that the new job only lasts for one year. In most cases it will last longer. We now need to ask how long this higher wage will be earned. How long will the new job last? It is likely to last for some years but even if it is only for, say, two to three years, it will mean that a future job will pay more because of the improved CV. However, we can't simply add the benefits over many years. As we have seen before in Chapter 10 a sum of money received in the future is worth less than the same sum of money received now. The 'present value' of a future stream of earnings is given by:

$$PV = (W^* - W)_1\left(\frac{1}{1+r}\right) + (W^* - W)_2\left(\frac{1}{1+r}\right)^2 + (W^* - W)_3\left(\frac{1}{1+r}\right)^3 + \ldots + (W^* - W)_n\left(\frac{1}{1+r}\right)^n$$

Where:
PV = present value
r = the rate of interest

The sum received in a year's time is 'discounted' by $\frac{1}{1+r}$, where r is the rate of interest. For a sum of W* – W its value in a year's time is only $W^* - W\left(\frac{1}{1+r}\right)$

For example, if you expect to receive an additional wage of €10 000 in a year's time and assume an interest rate of 10 per cent:

$$W^* - W\left(\frac{1}{1+r}\right) \text{ gives } 10\,000\left(\frac{1}{1+0.1}\right) = €9091$$

This is the present value of the €10 000 received in one year's time. The greater the rate of interest, the less a future stream of earnings is worth. Using r enables us to calculate the future value of a different job even if it lasts for some time.

So far we have considered the benefit of being temporarily unemployed. However, there are costs. The cost, apart from the lost earnings from the current job, is the search costs of finding job opportunities, preparing CVs, writing letters, attending interviews, etc.. It may be that we need to subtract from that any unemployment benefit to which the worker may be entitled. If the expected benefit of being unemployed exceeds the costs, some will be voluntarily unemployed and add to frictional unemployment.

Frictional unemployment, then, according to our model, is a function of the extent to which a different job offers a higher wage, the estimated probability of getting a different job, the rate of interest, the size of the search costs and the level of unemployment benefit payable.

PROBLEMS AND APPLICATIONS

1 The mayor of a town nearby gives you the demand and supply curves for the competitive labour market in his town:

$$W_D = 600 - 0.04Q_D$$
$$W_S = 80 + 0.01Q_S$$

a. Calculate the equilibrium wage and quantity and draw both curves in a diagram.
b. The mayor tells you that a powerful trade union is now being established in his town. It wishes to maximize the income of its members. Find out at which quantity and which wage income maximization will be achieved.
c. How much unemployment is created if the trade union aims for income maximization? Draw the new wage rate and the unemployment in the diagram of a.
d. Imagine the policy of the trade union was not only to maximize the income, but to maximize the income in excess of opportunity costs. What would be the wage rate in this case?
e. Compute the unemployment for problem d and show it in the diagram.

2 In your current job you earn €20 000 per annum, but there is a 70 per cent chance that you can get a new, better paid job which offers €40 000 each year.

a. What is the benefit of becoming temporarily unemployed, assuming all jobs mentioned last one year?
b. If you have to be 9 months unemployed to get this possibility, would you do it?
c. Now imagine additional to the possible job above there are 3 other possible jobs available. The first one offers €50 000 with a probability of 50 per cent, the second one offers €70 000 with a probability of 30 per cent and the last one offers €100 000 with a probability of 10 per cent. Calculate the expected benefit of being temporarily unemployed.

3 You get a job offer in which you can earn €30 000 per annum more than in your current job over the next three years. Assume the interest rate is at 10 per cent. Compute the present value of the benefits of this job.

PART 12 INTEREST RATES, MONEY AND PRICES IN THE LONG RUN

24 SAVING, INVESTMENT AND THE FINANCIAL SYSTEM

In this chapter we focus on saving and investment. In particular, we will contrast bonds and stocks as financial instruments, and explain the inverse relationship between bond prices and interest rates. Then we work out how the market places a value on bonds. Next we consider how risk affects the valuation of bonds. Finally, we will explain how stocks and shares can be compared with bonds as financial instruments.

INTRODUCTION: BONDS AND STOCKS CONTRASTED

Let's begin by reminding ourselves of the similarities and differences between bonds and stocks. A stock is a claim to partial ownership in a firm. A bond is a certificate of indebtedness. They are similar in that both are financial instruments used by companies to raise money for investment purposes, both can be traded, and the returns to both are normally subject to tax.

However, they are also different in a number of important ways. First, the bond normally pays interest, sometimes called a coupon. This is a fixed payment determined at the time the bond is issued. In contrast a stock or share pays a dividend. This is a share of a firm's profits, meaning the dividend is variable and its size depends upon the firm's profitability.

Second, bonds, with a few exceptions, have a fixed time before they mature. By contrast a stock never matures.

Third, if a company becomes bankrupt, the holders of bonds get paid out of whatever assets remain before the stockholders. Therefore, stockholders take greater risks. As a result of this risk bearing, shareholders will normally be compensated with a higher return than bondholders.

Finally, not all bonds are issued by companies. Many are issued by governments that need to borrow. A government would not normally issue shares.

Both shares and bonds are financial instruments of considerable importance, but bonds are more useful in understanding the role of money and interest in an economy so we will focus now upon understanding how bond prices are determined.

The Inverse Relationship between Bond Prices and Interest Rates

A bond states on it what it will pay to the purchaser. We will begin our discussion by assuming that there are no risks attached to purchasing bonds. It is certain that the issuer will honour its obligation. This is an assumption that we will drop later in the chapter.

Let's begin by taking a government bond that has a nominal value of €100. It offers a coupon of 5 per cent of its nominal, par, value, that is, €5 at the end of year one and another coupon of €5 at the end of year two. At this time the bond matures and the government promises to pay back the par value, the €100 it has borrowed from the purchaser. Is it a good deal to buy this bond? Assume that current interest rates in the economy are 5 per cent. The purchaser of the bond will get approximately 5 per cent on their money if they pay the face value for the bond. Since this is what could also be obtained by putting the funds into a bank account when interest rates are 5 per cent, the value of a bond represents the price that people will be willing to pay for it.

Suppose that you buy this bond and immediately there is a change of interest rates in the economy. Suppose the government raises interest rates to 7 per cent. You are not stuck with this bond for two years. Bonds are tradable. You can go the market and sell it. However, you are not guaranteed to get €100, the par value of the bond. You will get whatever someone is willing to pay you for it. Given that interest rates have increased, the market value of the bond will be less than €100. If you sell at €100 the purchaser gets a 5 per cent return. Why would they do this if they can get 7 per cent interest in a bank deposit account? They will pay you whatever amount enables them to make a 7 per cent return. This will be less than €100. When interest rates rise the market value of existing bonds falls.

Suppose now interest rates had fallen to 3 per cent after you purchased the bond. Selling it at a price of €100 represents a great deal for the buyer who would get 5 per cent as against 3 per cent in the bank account. Competition for your bond would push up the price you get above its par value. We can conclude that there is an inverse relationship between bond prices and interest rates; as interest rates fall bond prices rise and vice versa.

Establishing the Market Value of a Bond

To calculate the market price of a bond, we will begin with an example of a 'zero coupon' bond. This is a bond that pays no interest at all. The return has an implied interest rate. Suppose a bond is issued with a face value of €100. The bond matures in 3 years' time when the bond issuer pays out the face value of the bond. At that time, it will pay out €100 but in the meantime it pays out nothing. It is a zero coupon bond. Purchasing such a bond is still attractive but the price will have to be at a discount to par. When the bond matures in 3 years' time, they receive the full €100 and will have earned an implied interest rate. Suppose interest rates are currently 5 per cent. What might someone offer for the bond? The price will be:

$$P(1 + r)(1 + r)(1 + r) = 100$$

Where:
P = the price of the bond
r = the current interest rate
In this case:

$$P(1 + 0.05)(1 + 0.05)(1 + 0.05) = 100$$

Or:

$$P(1 + r)^3 = 100$$
$$P(1 + 0.05)^3 = 100$$
$$P = \frac{100}{(1 + 0.05)^3}$$
$$P = \frac{100}{1.158}$$
$$= €86.36$$

The market price of the bond at issue is €86.36. At this price the implied interest rate is 5 per cent for the next three years, the equivalent of the return earned putting the money into a deposit account at 5 per cent.

Had market interest rates been higher, say 7 per cent, the market value of the bond at issue will be:

$$P(1 + r)^3 = 100$$
$$P = \frac{100}{(1 + 0.07)^3}$$
$$P = \frac{100}{1.225}$$
$$= €81.63$$

At 7 per cent the market value of the bond at issue will be €81.63. With higher interest rates the value of the bond will be lower.

Finally consider the bond price with lower interest rates, say, at 3 per cent.

$$P(1 + r)^3 = 100$$
$$P = \frac{100}{(1 + 0.03)^3}$$
$$P = \frac{100}{1.093}$$
$$= €91.49$$

At 3 per cent the market value of the bond at issue will be €91.49. With lower interest rates the value of the bond will be higher.

We have now established the inverse relationship between bond prices and interest rates. Next we will look at the determination of a bond price's value when a coupon is paid throughout the bond's life to maturity.

The Market Price of Bonds with a Coupon

Many bonds pay a coupon annually or every six months until maturity. How do we calculate the market value of such bonds? We use the same principles as above. We write down the payments to be received and then discount them at some appropriate rate of discount. Let's take an example. Company B has a €1000 bond outstanding that matures in three years with a coupon of 10 per cent (€100 annually). If interest rates enable a yield of 10 per cent what is the market value of this bond?

$$MV = A_1\frac{1}{1 + r} + A_2\frac{1}{(1 + r)^2} + A_3\frac{1}{(1 + r)^3} + B_3\frac{1}{(1 + r)^3}$$

Or:

$$MV = \frac{A_1}{1 + r} + \frac{A_2}{(1 + r)^2} + \frac{A_3}{(1 + r)^3} + \frac{B_3}{(1 + r)^3}$$

Where:
MV = market value of the bond
A = stream of coupon payments
r = the rate of interest
B = the par value of the bond

We have 'discounted' the revenue stream at some appropriate rate of interest to find the present value of this stream of revenue but then at maturity the company pays back the par value of the bond. Since the bondholder must wait until maturity to receive it this must also be discounted. This explains the last term of the formula.

So, using the alternatively expressed formula, the market value of this bond is:

$$\frac{100}{1 + 0.1} + \frac{100}{(1 + 0.1)^2} + \frac{100}{(1 + 0.1)^3} + \frac{1000}{(1 + 0.1)^3}$$
$$= \frac{100}{1.1} + \frac{100}{1.21} + \frac{100}{1.331} + \frac{1000}{1.331}$$
$$= 90.909 + 82.645 + 75.131 + 751.315$$
$$= €1000$$

The market value of the bond is €1000. This is what we would expect. The value of the bond is the discounted value of the income that it generates. The company expects to be able to sell the bond at its par value because it offers a 10 per cent rate of return when interest rates in the market are 10 per cent.

Now let's take a different example where we have a different interest rate and a different number of years to maturity. Company C has a bond that pays €105 in annual interest, with a €1000 par value. The bond matures in 10 years. Interest rates are 8 per cent. Now let's calculate the value of the bond.

If we discount each of the annual payments appropriately and then discount the par value of the bond at maturity we have:

$$MV = \frac{105}{1.08} + \frac{105}{(1.08)^2} + \frac{105}{(1.08)^3} + \frac{105}{(1.08)^4} + \frac{105}{(1.08)^5} + \frac{105}{(1.08)^6} + \frac{105}{(1.08)^7} + \frac{105}{(1.08)^8} + \frac{105}{(1.08)^9} + \frac{105}{(1.08)^{10}} + \frac{1000}{(1.08)^{10}}$$
$$= \frac{105}{1.08} + \frac{105}{1.1664} + \frac{105}{1.2597} + \frac{105}{1.3605} + \frac{105}{1.4693} + \frac{105}{1.5869} + \frac{105}{1.7138} + \frac{105}{1.8509} + \frac{105}{1.999} + \frac{105}{2.1589} + \frac{1000}{2.1589}$$
$$= 97.22 + 90.02 + 83.35 + 77.18 + 71.46 + 66.17 + 61.27 + 56.73 + 52.53 + 48.64 + 463.20$$
$$= €1167.77$$

This bond has a long time to maturity so the calculations could be tedious. However, if the coupon is the same over the life of the asset there is a way to reduce the volume of calculations. We can sum the 'discount factors' and then multiply by the annual coupon payment. Then we must add the discounted value of the par value of the bond that will paid out at maturity. This gives us:

$$\frac{1}{1.08} = 0.9259$$

$$\frac{1}{(1.08)^2} = 0.8573$$

and so on. The series of discount factors at 8 per cent that we then sum from years 1 through 10 gives:

$$0.9259 + 0.8573 + 0.7938 + 0.7350 + 0.6806 + 0.6302 + 0.5835 + 0.5403 + 0.5002 + 0.4632 = 6.71$$

Now multiply the sum of the discount factors, 6.71, by the annual cash flow:

$$6.71 \times 105 = 704.55$$

Now find the discounted value of the bond at maturity:

$$1000 \times 0.4632 = 463.20$$

Finally add together the value of the cash flow and the discounted value of the bond:

$$704.55 + 463.20 = €1167.75$$

This is the same answer that we had above, subject to a small rounding error. The principle we have explained is the basis of an "annuity". By purchasing an annuity at the market price the investor receives a fixed payment, often annually, for a fixed period of years.

Perpetual Bonds

Some bonds are perpetual. There is no redemption date. If you buy such a bond you cannot hold it to maturity to get your money back. You will have to go the market and sell it. How does this affect the price of such a bond? We have an infinite series where each successive term gets smaller. The coupon remains the same but its discounted value gets ever smaller. The sum converges to:

$$MV = \frac{C}{r_r}$$

Where:
MV = market value of the bond
C = coupon payment
r_r = required rate of return, the comparable interest rate

As an example, a government issues a perpetual bond with a par value of €1000. The bond pays 5 per cent of par value as an annual coupon. The marginal investor looks at current interest rates and requires a 7 per cent rate of return. Then the investor will pay:

$$MV = \frac{C}{r_r}$$

$$MV = \frac{50}{0.07}$$

$$= €714.29$$

The market value of the bond is €714.29. If interest rates had been 9 per cent, the required rate of return would have been higher and the bond price lower:

$$MV = \frac{50}{0.09}$$

$$= €555.56$$

The marginal investor would pay less. Once again, a higher interest rate means a lower bond price.

Risk and The Valuation of Bonds

So far we have assumed that there is no risk in buying financial instruments such as bonds. Now we take into account that bonds have risks attached to them. Companies may become insolvent before they pay out the coupon or return the par value of the bond at maturity. Financial investors will build in a risk factor to allow for the probability of default.

Suppose there is a bond that you can buy from Company D. It costs €100 and promises to pay 7 per cent one year from now. You estimate the probability that it will not default, and so honour its promise at $P = 0.8$, i.e. there is an 80 per cent chance that the firm will not default on its payment. Your expected return can be found as:

$$ER_D = (7\% \times P) + (0\% \times (1 - P))$$

Where:

ER_D = expected return on company D's bond

P = probability

Had there been the choice of a reduced, but still positive payment, we would multiply that payment by $(1 - P)$. However in this case we are assuming that either the full payment is made or no payment is made at all. Hence the term $0\% \times (1 - P)$. The estimated return therefore, is calculated as:

$$\begin{aligned} ER_D &= (7\% \times 80\%) + 0 \\ &= 5.6\% \end{aligned}$$

Your estimated return will be 5.6 per cent. This is what you will compare with a zero risk form of saving such as a deposit account in a commercial bank when the government guarantees a payout in the event of a bank default.

Suppose now that you are faced with a choice of two bonds. A government bond costs €100 and promises to pay €4 one year from now. There is also on offer a private company bond from firm E. This bond is also priced at €100 and promises to pay €6 one year from now. The risks inherent in these two bonds are different. The government has never defaulted on its debt so you can treat the promise as a certainty. Company E may become insolvent and be unable to pay. If P = the probability that you will get your money, how is the probability calculated?

$$ER_G = 4\%$$

Where:

$$\begin{aligned} ER_G &= \textit{Expected return from the government bond} \\ ER_E &= (6\% \times P) + (0\% \times (1 - P)) \\ &= (6\% \times P) \end{aligned}$$

Where:

ER_G = Expected return from the government bond

ER_E = Expected return from Company E

Unless you get an equivalent return from Company E you will not buy its bond so it must have an expected gain of 4 per cent. This will be the case when:

$$\begin{aligned} (6\% \times P) &= 4 \\ P &= \frac{4}{6} \\ &= 0.66 \end{aligned}$$

Unless you assess the probability of a payout from firm E of at least 0.66, it is preferable to buy the government bond.

Assessing the probability is possible because there is a history associated with defaults of different companies in different industries. One can also look at companies and assess the size of their assets compared with their liabilities, future trading prospects and so on. Thus P can reasonably be estimated. Even with government bonds, some are riskier than others. For example, there has been concern in recent years that some European countries' governments have such large debts relative to GDP that there is a risk that they might default. Therefore, the market expects higher rates of return to compensate additional risk even with some government bonds.

Figure 24.1 can be thought of as a set of indifference curves for a typical investor. Indifference curves are generally negatively sloped as a consumer trades off two goods. Here the investor is trading off a 'good' (the return), and a 'bad' risk, and as a result the curves are positively sloped. The investor has the same utility anywhere along R_1, where increased risk is compensated with increased returns. However anywhere along R_2 shows a higher level of utility than anywhere along R_1. Similarly, R_3 is associated with a lower level of utility.

FIGURE 24.1

Trading off Risk and Return

A typical investor has indifference curves that are positively sloped, trading off a 'good', the return on financial investment, and a 'bad', the risk associated with the investment. Utility is the same anywhere along R_1, where increased risk is compensated with increased returns. R_2 shows a higher level of utility than R_1. R_3 is associated with a lower level of utility.

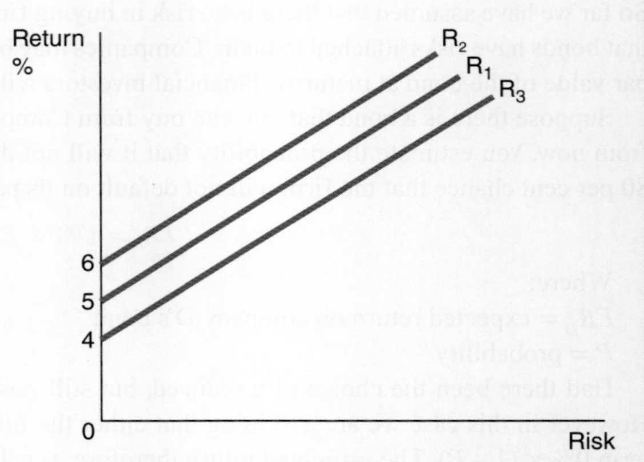

As with consumers of goods, not everyone has the same preferences. For example, an investor who is risk averse can choose safer alternatives by accepting a lower rate of return.

Risk Assessment between Shares and Bonds

Shares have typically made higher returns than bonds but are more risky. How might the market assess the risks? We will illustrate the way in which the market is able to do this by comparing an illustrative set of shares and a set of bonds.

Most people do not buy bonds and stocks directly, but use financial intermediaries. These are institutions which include commercial banks, building societies and mutual funds. They take funds from savers and purchase financial instruments in large quantities, so reducing the transactions costs. If you save through such an intermediary you are effectively buying a small part of many shares or bonds. Suppose that you wish to save with either a shares fund or a bond fund. How do you assess the risk? You can begin by looking at the performance of these funds over recent years and use this as a guide. Table 24.1 illustrates two funds' performance records over a ten-year period. The assessment might be done in the following way. We showed this procedure in a different context in Chapter 2.

TABLE 24.1 **Computing the Risks of Shares and Bonds: Average Percentage Annual Returns over Ten Years**

Year	One	Two	Three	Four	Five	Six	Seven	Eight	Nine	Ten
Fund S (Shares) Return (%)	16	8	10	−8	16	−6	12	15	13	4
Fund B (Bonds) Return (%)	6	8	6	7	9	5	4	5	4	6

First find the mean average return, $\bar{x}$. We do this by summing all the returns and dividing by the number of years. For fund S:

$$\bar{x}_S = \frac{(16 + 8 + 10 - 8 + 16 - 6 + 12 + 15 + 13 + 4)}{10} = 8$$

For fund B:

$$\bar{x}_B = \frac{(6 + 8 + 6 + 7 + 9 + 5 + 4 + 5 + 4 + 6)}{10} = 6$$

The average return for fund S, the shares, over the last ten years is 8 per cent and the average return for fund B, the Bonds, is 6 per cent.[1] Clearly the bond fund has returned less, on average, over the period. However the potential investor needs some way of assessing the relative risk. One way to do this is to find the standard deviation of returns. First we do this for fund S, recording the results in Table 24.2.

Now we work out the difference between each of the observations and the mean, $(x - \bar{x})$. For the first recorded observation the return was 16 per cent and the mean was 8 per cent so $(x - \bar{x}) = 16 - 8 = 8$ per cent. We have done this for all ten years and recorded the result in column 3. Now we square these differences to get the square of difference, $(x - \bar{x})^2$. For the first year:

$$8^2 = 64$$

[1] As an alternative one could use a geometric mean, as explained in Chapter 20.

TABLE 24.2 Assessing the Risk of a Shares Fund

Individual Return, (x) (%)	Mean Average Return, ($\bar{x}$) (%)	Difference, ($x - \bar{x}$)	Square of Difference, $(x - \bar{x})^2$
16	8	8	64
8	8	0	0
10	8	2	4
−8	8	−16	256
16	8	8	64
−6	8	−14	196
12	8	4	16
15	8	7	49
13	8	5	25
4	8	−4	16

We have done this calculation for all years and recorded the results in column 4. If we now sum the values in column 4 we get 690.

We now find the mean average of the sum of the squared differences, the variance:

$$\frac{\sum(x - \bar{x})^2}{n}$$

Where n = the number of observations, in our case 10.

$$\frac{690}{10} = 69$$

Now we take the square root of the variance to get the standard deviation, which we will call s.

$$s = \sqrt{\frac{\sum(x - \bar{x})^2}{n}}$$

The square root of 69 = 26.27

The standard deviation of the shares fund is 8.31

Now we work out the standard deviation for the bond fund. We show the calculations in Table 24.3.

TABLE 24.3 Assessing the Risk of a Bond Fund

Individual Return, (x) (%)	Mean Average Return, ($\bar{x}$) (%)	Difference, ($x - \bar{x}$)	Square of Difference, $(x - \bar{x})^2$
6	6	0	0
8	6	2	4
6	6	0	0
7	6	1	1
9	6	3	9
5	6	−1	1
4	6	−2	4
5	6	−1	1
4	6	−2	4
6	6	0	0

If we now sum the values in column 4 we get 24.

We now find the mean average of the sum of the squared differences, the variance:

$$\frac{\sum(x - \bar{x})^2}{n}$$

Where n = 10:

$$\frac{24}{10} = 2.4$$

Now we take the square root of the variance to get the standard deviation, which we will call s.

$$s = \sqrt{\frac{\sum(x - \bar{x})^2}{n}}$$

The square root of 24 = 1.55

The standard deviation of the bond fund is 1.55, compared with 8.31 for the shares fund.

However, remember that a larger standard deviation may reflect not larger variations but larger numbers.

It's the proportionate variations that are important, not the absolute number. We calculate the proportionate variations by calculating the coefficient of variation, that is:

Standard deviation/mean

For the shares fund we have:

$$\frac{8.31}{8} = 1.04$$

For the bond fund we have:

$$\frac{1.55}{6}$$

$$= 0.26$$

The coefficient of variation is much lower for the bond fund, which suggests that the bond fund is safer although the return over a period tends to be lower. These calculations enable savers in the market to choose between financial instruments based on their willingness to accept risk.

PROBLEMS AND APPLICATIONS

1 A large corporation issues a zero (coupon) bond with a nominal value of €50 million which is to be repayed in ten years.

a. How much can the corporation expect as a pay-out for the debt it incurs if the market interest rate currently is at 3.5 per cent?

b. How much will the bond issue return at a market interest rate of 8 per cent.

c. Assume an interest rate of 5 per cent. The financing need of the corporation is €40 million. How much in nominal debt does the firm need to issue?

d. The firm has been able to issue a nominal value of €100 million in nominal debt with a yield of 5 per cent for €37.69 million. How long is the maturity of this zero coupon paper?

e. The firm has borrowed a nominal amount of €81.21 million for eight years to finance an investment of €50 million. What is the interest rate on the bond?

2 You have just learned in the text that a coupon bond essentially can be viewed as consisting of two parts. There is the outstanding nominal amount of debt repaid at maturity (B_n= par value or principal amount) after n years and secondly the annual coupon payments of A_t for all the years from $t = 1, 2, \ldots n$. With a nominal interest rate i printed on the bond, you can easily calculate the annual coupon of $A_t = i \times B_n = A$, since we assume a constant nominal coupon interest rate i we can drop the time index t on the annual coupon payments. To distinguish in the nominal interest rate of the coupon we write the market interest rate as r in the problems below.

In other parts of the book you have learned that $\frac{1}{(1+r)}, \frac{1}{(1+r)^2}, \frac{1}{(1+r)^3}, \ldots, \frac{1}{(1+r)^{n-1}}, \frac{1}{(1+r)^n}$ is a geometric progression. Writing $q = 1 + r$ and using the formula for a sum of the geometric progression we therefore get:

$$\sum_{t=1}^{n} \frac{1}{q^n} = = \frac{1}{q} + \frac{1}{q^2} + \ldots + \frac{1}{q^n} = \frac{1}{(1+r)} + \frac{1}{(1+r)^2} + \ldots + \frac{1}{(1+r)^n}$$

$$= \frac{1}{q^n}\frac{q^n - 1}{q - 1} = \frac{1}{(1+r)^n}\frac{(1+r)^n - 1}{(1+r) - 1} = \frac{(1+r)^n - 1}{(1+r)^n r} = \frac{(1+r)^n}{(1+r)^n r} - \frac{1}{(1+r)^n r} = \frac{1}{r} - \frac{1}{(1+r)^n r}$$

$$= \frac{1}{r} - \frac{\frac{1}{(1+r)^n}}{r} = \frac{1 - \frac{1}{(1+r)^n}}{r} = \frac{1-(1+r)^{-n}}{r} = \frac{1-q^{-n}}{r}.$$

This is very useful for calculating the sum of the present values of the cupon payments A:

$$\sum_{t=1}^{n} A\frac{1}{q^n} = \frac{A}{q} + \frac{A}{q^2} + \ldots + \frac{A}{q^n} = A\left(\sum_{t=1}^{n} \frac{1}{q^n}\right) = A\left(\frac{1}{q} + \frac{1}{q^2} + \ldots + \frac{1}{q^n}\right).$$

a. How large is the present value of a coupon bond with a nominal outstanding amount of €100, a nominal interest rate of 8 per cent per year and 3 years to maturity. Assume the market interest rate currently is at $r = 3.5$ per cent.

b. What is the bond's price at a market interest rate of $r = 10$ % with $I = 8$ % and $n = 3$?
c. Assume a government issues a very long-term coupon bond with a maturity of 30 years and a principal amount of €100. The nominal interest rate is 4 per cent; however, the market interest rate on this maturity has fallen to just 2 per cent. Calculate the price of the bond.

3 A perpetual bond with a nominal (par) value of €100 has a nominal coupon interest rate of 7 per cent annually. Determine the market value of the bond at the market interest rates of 5 per cent and 10 per cent.

4 You're looking at a bond issued by a medium-sized company that is promising to pay a coupon of 10 per cent and the repayment of them nominal amount of €100 one year from now. You estimate the probability that the firm will default on the payments at 8 per cent. In case of default the firm will not pay the interest due and you will only be able to recover half of the principal amount in the insolvency proceedings. How much money do you expect to receive from the bond in a year?

5 You are using the average annual returns on stocks and bonds of the last 10 years to assess the riskiness of an investment in these two asset classes. Calculate the coefficient of variation for stocks and bonds from the annual average returns given in Table 24.4 and make a comparison. (Most calculators have a special statistics function to calculate means and standard deviations, alternatively you could use a spreadsheet software again.)

TABLE 24.4

Year	Shares (X_i)	Bonds (Y_i)
1	−2.80%	2.20%
2	8.30%	2.60%
3	12.40%	5.20%
4	2.80%	3.20%
5	7.30%	2.80%
6	1.40%	4.80%
7	9.70%	4.30%
8	8.80%	3.60%
9	−4.60%	5.10%
10	12.70%	2.90%

25 THE BASIC TOOLS OF FINANCE

In this chapter, we further develop the concept of the time value of money. Then we examine in some detail how a private company can use this concept, plus an analysis of risk to make the most profitable investment choices, using the techniques we refer to as investment analysis.

Finally, we see how governments and other state bodies can incorporate these principles in making investment choices in the public sector. This is referred to as Cost Benefit Analysis.

INTRODUCTION TO INVESTMENT ANALYSIS: THE TIME VALUE OF MONEY

Imagine that you are on the board of directors of a large company. A number of investment projects are before you and you now have to decide whether to give the go-ahead or not. We will look at one example project shortly. It's a tiny project with very small numbers that we can consider in order to establish the principles, but if it helps to make it more realistic you can think of the numbers we use as being in millions of euros. We will look at some other projects a little later.

As with all investment projects money has to be found now but there will be a delay before the project produces a saleable product and the money invested starts to generate returns. Recall that money earned further into the future is worth less than money received sooner. The earlier a firm gets its money back the more it is worth because it can be invested and produce some interest. How much less the future cash flows are worth depends upon when they are received and on the rate of interest that can be currently earned. Reducing the size of the cash flows to allow for this is called discounting.

Preparing to Make an Investment Decision

The analysts have presented to you Project A. They have laid out for you the capital cost of the project and given you their best estimates of the expected cash flows, or revenue streams, the project is expected to earn. The revenue stream is the revenue from the sale of the product over time minus the costs of materials, labour, etc. In the capital cost estimates the analysts have taken into account any investment allowances the government may be offering. The revenue stream takes into account any taxes to be paid on the profits. Depreciation is expected to be such that at the end of the project's life the machinery has no resale value. The project is presented in summary in Table 25.1.

TABLE 25.1 Cash Flow for Potential Investment Project A

Year	0	1	2	3	4
Cash Flow (€)	−31.7	10	10	10	10

In year 0, the capital cost must be met, €31.7, and since this is an outlay, a cost, we show it as a negative amount.

Methods of Discounting

There are various methods of discounting. We will examine three. They are:

1. The Net Present Value, NPV
2. The Internal Rate of Return, IRR
3. The Annual Capital Charge, ACC.

All use the same basic principle that money earned in the future is worth less than money earned sooner. First consider the NPV method of decision-making.

The Net Present Value Method

Recall that cash flows need to be discounted to recognize that the further into the future a sum is generated, the less it is worth. The basic formula for calculating NPV is:

$$NPV = P_1\frac{1}{1+r} + P_2\frac{1}{(1+r)^2} + P_3\frac{1}{(1+r)^3} \dots + P_n\frac{1}{(1+r)^n} - C$$

Where:

NPV = net present value
P = cash flows
r = the rate of interest
C = the capital cost

Suppose the current rate of interest is 10 per cent. We know now how much the cash flow for each year is worth to us.

The cash flow earned in a year's time is discounted by $\frac{1}{1+r}$ where r is the rate of interest. So in our case, assuming an interest rate of 10 per cent:

$$P_1\frac{1}{1+r} \text{ gives:}$$

$$10 \times \frac{1}{1+0.1}$$

$$= €9.1$$

This is the present value of the €10 in one year's time.

Translating this it means that if we had €9.1 now and we could invest it at a 10 per cent rate of interest, we could turn it into €10 in a year. This implies we are indifferent between €9.1 now or €10 in a year's time.

We can think of the interest rate, r, as the price we pay for loanable funds or the rate we receive for loaning funds ourselves. In practice there are many interest rates reflecting the risk to be borne, but since these rates all tend to move up and down together, we will simplify and refer to *the* interest rate. Also for simplicity we will assume that the rate of interest we must pay in order to borrow is the rate we would receive if we were lending funds.

What is €10 worth if we have to wait two years to receive it instead of just one? Following our formula we have:

$$P_2\frac{1}{(1+r)^2} \text{ gives:}$$

$$10 \times \frac{1}{(1+0.1)^2}$$

$$= €8.3$$

This is the present value of €10 received in two years' time. If we had €8.3 now we could invest it at 10 per cent and a year later we would have €9.1. If we invest the €9.1 for another year we would turn it into €10 in two years' time.

If we follow the same procedure to find the present value of €10 in three years' time we have:

$$P_3\frac{1}{(1+r)^3}$$

gives:

$$10 \times \frac{1}{(1 + 0.1)^3}$$

$$= €7.5$$

It should now be clear how to find the present value of €10 in 4 years' time.

$$P_4 \frac{1}{(1 + r)^4}$$

gives:

$$10 \times \frac{1}{(1 + 0.1)^4}$$

$$= €6.8$$

We can use this procedure to establish the value of a cash flow received for any number of years, n, into the future. We can now present, in summary form, our project in Table 25.2.

TABLE 25.2 **Discounted Cash Flow for Potential Investment Project A**

Year	0	1	2	3	4
Discounted Cash Flow (€)	−31.7	9.1	8.3	7.5	6.8

Summing the cash flows, we have a Gross Present Value (GPV) of 9.1 + 8.3 + 7.5 + 6.8 = €31.7

$$NPV = GPV - C$$

In this case GPV and C are equal so:

$$0 = 31.7 - 31.7$$

The proposal before the board involves spending €31.7 and getting back €31.7 in four years' time. There is no NPV. What firms will look for is a positive NPV as a determinant of whether a project is worth allocating investment funds.

- Definition: The NPV is the present value of an investment's expected cash flow less the cost of making the investment.
- Decision Rule: Invest only if the NPV of a project is positive.

What would a positive NPV mean? Consider another project, Project B, that has been put to the board and has a positive NPV; according to our decision rule, this project would go ahead. The project is summarized in Table 25.3.

TABLE 25.3 **Discounted Cash Flow for Potential Investment Project B**

Year	0	1	2	3	4
Cash Flow (€)	−10 000	5000	4000	3000	2000
Discounted Cash Flow (DCF) at 10 % (€)	−10 000	4545	3306	2254	1366

The sum of the discounted cash flows, $GPV = 4545 + 3306 + 2254 + 1366 = €11\,471$

$$NPV = GPV - C = €11\,471 - €10\,000 = €1471$$

How do we interpret this €1471? In order to get the cash flow shown above we could take €11 471 to the bank and deposit it. Given that $r = 10$ per cent, at the end of year one we would generate more than €10 000 (the cost of the investment) because it earns interest at 10 per cent. We will now have €10 000 multiplied by $(1 + r)$ where $r = 0.1$. Thus we have €11 000. We could now withdraw €5000, the cash flow in Table 25.3 at the end of year 1. We could leave the other €6000 to be invested for a further year earning 10 per cent interest. At the end of that year we could withdraw €4000 (Table 25.3, end of year 2) but leave the rest to accumulate more interest. At the end of the following year we could remove €3000 and leave the rest for a further year. At the end of year 4 we could take out €2000 and be left with nothing in the account. To achieve this cash flow requires €11 471. This project will yield the same cash flow for only €10 000, a 'saving' of €1471.

INTERNAL RATE OF RETURN

For the internal rate of return we use the following formula:

$$IRR = P_1\frac{1}{1+r} + P_2\frac{1}{(1+r)^2} + P_3\frac{1}{(1+r)^3} + \ldots + P_n\frac{1}{(1+r)^n} - C = 0$$

Where:
IRR = internal rate of return
P = cash flow, the subscript denoting the year
r = the interest rate which solves our equation
n = the number of years the project lasts
C = initial capital cost

We have an equation where the unknown for which we have to solve is r. In other words we are looking for the interest rate that will discount the cash flows just sufficiently so that their value is equal to the capital cost of the project. This will tell us the rate of return we are getting on the investment. We can then compare this rate of return with the cost of borrowing the funds needed to make the investment.

For example, consider another project before the board, Project C. Assume that the firm is able to borrow funds at r = 10 per cent. The project is expected to produce the following cash flows given in Table 25.4.

TABLE 25.4 **Cash Flow for Potential Investment Project C**

Year	0	1	2	3	4	5
Cash Flows (€)	–2000	500	500	600	600	440

When we examined the NPV method we discounted the cash flows at the market rate of interest to see whether this gave a positive or negative NPV. With IRR we find the value for r that discounts the cash flows to the capital cost. Without calculators or computers we would need some kind of iteration procedure but a computer programme will solve this for you. With a search engine you can find online calculators for IRR problems.

There you can enter the project capital cost in the appropriate box. Make sure you enter it as a minus. Underneath is a series of boxes for each year of the project's life. Enter the amounts. Make sure that all years after the project ends are entered as zero. Go the bottom of the column of boxes and press 'calculate' and the programme will give you the answer.

It turns out that Project C solves at 10 per cent. If the firm can borrow funds at 5 per cent it's a good project in which to invest. If funds costs 15 per cent to borrow the firm is likely to reject the project. If funds are available at ten per cent then it's a very marginal project.

- Definition: The IRR of an investment is the rate of interest at which the NPV of the investment cost equals the NPV of the cash flows of the investment.
- Decision Rule: Invest only if the IRR of a project exceeds the cost of borrowing.

Interpreting IRR

It would be easy to assume that the IRR tells us the rate of return on the whole of the investment cost for the whole of the project's life but this is not the case. It is the rate of return on the capital tied up while it is tied up. Over the project's life the capital cost is being returned in the cash flows. The IRR is the rate of return on the declining balance of funds tied up in the project. We cannot assume that as the funds are withdrawn from the project they can be reinvested at the project's solution rate.

Consider the following Project, D, summarized in Table 25.5, which involves investing €2000 for a cash flow over a period of 5 years. The size of the cash flows is laid out in the table, column 3. The project gives an IRR of 10 per cent. The firm invests €2000 for one year. The cash flow at the end of the year is €500. This represents the income from the sale of the product that the investment produces. This is €200 and represents interest at a 10 per cent rate of return on the €2000 invested. The other €300 is repayment of some of the money invested in the project, which is now withdrawn, (column 5). Only €1700 is left in the project (column 6).

If you put your money in the bank to earn some interest, you want the interest agreed but you also want your capital back at some point. This is the same for the firm. At the end of Year 1 it gets back €300 of its original €2000 investment.

In year two the firm earns 10 per cent, not on €2000 but on the €1700 still tied up in the project. Ten per cent of €1700 is €170. As Table 25.5 shows, the cash flow is €500 in Year 2.

€500 – €170 = €330. The €330 is a further repayment of the capital. The rest of the cash flow represents capital repayment. The process of withdrawing capital from the project and receiving interest on the remaining capital continues to the end of the project's life. At the end the firm has received its investment fund back plus10 per cent on the capital while it was tied up.

TABLE 25.5 **Cash Flow for Potential Investment Project D**

Year	Amount invested at beginning of year (€)	Cash Flow (€)	10 % interest on Capital outstanding (€)	Capital Repayment (€)	Amount outstanding as investment at year end (€)
1	2000	500	200	300	1700
2	1700	500	170	330	1370
3	1370	600	137	463	907
4	907	600	91	509	398
5	398	440	40	400	(2)

A Comparison of NPV and IRR

Except in relatively unusual circumstances, the two methods we have discussed are equivalent. Projects that yield a positive NPV will give an IRR in excess of the cost of borrowing. In unusual circumstances, for example where there are negative cash flows during the project's life, modifications may have to be made to the IRR formula.

THE ANNUAL CAPITAL CHARGE METHOD

The annual capital charge method (ACC) is best used for large projects with fairly even cash flows. The formula we use is:

$$ACC = \frac{I_r(1 + r)^n}{(1 + r)^n - 1}$$

Where:
ACC = annual capital charge in euros
I = cost of sum to be borrowed for investment
r = interest rate
n = number of years of the project's life

Project E involves investing €2000 for an annual cash flow of €850 for three years. In our example the annual capital charge is:

$$ACC = \frac{(2000 \times 0.10)(1.10)^3}{(1.10)^3 - 1} = €804$$

This sum tells us the cost of Project E, annualized to include interest on what is being borrowed. If the firm borrows €2000 at 10 per cent and wishes to pay it back in equal instalments over a given number of years this is the annual amount it must pay. The firm is borrowing €2000 for one year. At year end it pays interest on that €2000 plus some of the original capital sum borrowed. The firm borrows less than €2000 in the following year.

The formula establishes that three payments of €804 will be required to repay the capital plus interest on the declining amount borrowed.

Should you wish to take out a personal loan with a bank over several years, perhaps to buy a car, you must pay back the loan in equal instalments over an agreed number of years, so that you repay the loan plus interest on the money while you have borrowed it. This will be interest on a declining amount as you repay the sum borrowed. This is the kind of formula the bank manager will use to determine the size of your repayments.

To determine whether the project is worth pursuing, we compare the ACC with the annual cash flow. If the annual cash flow is greater than the ACC the project is profitable. In this case the annual cash flow of €850 exceeds the ACC of €804, so the project represents a worthwhile investment.

This is summarized in Table 25.6. Notice that we have a zero capital cost in year 0 because we have spread that cost (plus interest on the amount borrowed) over the life of the project.

TABLE 25.6 **Annual Capital Charge Method, ACC**

Year	0	1	2	3
ACC (€)	0	804	804	804
Cash Flow (€)	0	850	850	850

HANDLING RISK AND UNCERTAINTY

We have treated the assumed outcomes in our analysis as though they were certain events. Clearly, however, there is significant risk and uncertainty attached to the future whichever method of investment analysis is used. How can firms handle this? Often a sensitivity analysis is undertaken asking how sensitive the project is to the assumptions we are making about the future. Here we indicate very briefly just one way of handling this problem in order to indicate how it might be approached.

In our example the area of doubt surrounds the future demand for the good the firm intends to produce from the investment. There are a range of possible outcomes: A, B and C, representing low medium and high future demand respectively. We have three possible ways of handling the problem, X, Y and Z. These represent size of capital outlay: small, medium and high outlay, respectively. The possible outcomes are set out in Table 25.7. The numbers in the table represent the NPV in millions of euros for each of the nine possible outcomes. For example, if the firm only makes a small investment and then demand growth is high, its lack of capacity will lead to an inefficient means of meeting demand, causing a loss of €3 million. NPV will be negative. But if demand growth is high and the firm has undertaken the largest capital outlay it can expect a positive NPV of €6 million. What should the firm do?

TABLE 25.7 **NPV Under Different Possible Growth Scenarios**

	A (Low Demand Growth) (€)	B (Medium Demand Growth) (€)	C (High Demand Growth) (€)
X (Small Outlay)	4	2	−3
Y (Medium Outlay)	2	2	1
Z (Large Outlay)	−3	−1	6

We will consider three means of decision-making. The first can be used if it faces a situation of risk. Remember this means that although the future is not known, the probability of each possible outcome is known. In our case we can use the formula:

$$E(X) = X_A P(A) + X_B P(B) + X_C P(C)$$

Where:
$E(X)$ = Expected Value of X
X_A = NPV if outcome A occurs
X_B = NPV if outcome B occurs
X_C = NPV if outcome C occurs
$P(A)$ = The probability of outcome A occurring
$P(B)$ = The probability of outcome B occurring
$P(C)$ = The probability of outcome C occurring

$$= \Sigma_{i} XiP(i)$$

Now let's assume there's a 25 per cent chance of outcome A, a 50 per cent chance of outcome B and a 25 per cent chance of outcome C. Using the formula we have:

$$E(X) = \frac{1}{4} \times 4 + \frac{1}{2} \times 2 + \frac{1}{4} \times -3 = 1\frac{1}{4}$$

Repeating the procedure for an investment in Y, where of course, the probabilities of each outcome are given and remain the same, gives us:

$$\Sigma_{i\ YiP(i)}$$

$$E(Y) = \frac{1}{4} \times 2 + \frac{1}{2} \times 2 + \frac{1}{4} \times 1 = 1¾$$

Repeating the procedure for an investment in Z, again with these known probabilities, gives us:

$$\Sigma_{i\ ZiP(i)}$$

$$E(Z) = \frac{1}{4} \times -3 + \frac{1}{2} \times -1 + \frac{1}{4} \times 6 = ¼$$

The firm would then normally pick the project whose outcome has the highest expected value. In our case this would be project Y, the medium outlay.

The second means of decision-making can be considered if the firm is in a situation of uncertainty through use of the 'principle of insufficient reason'. This says that the firm has no sufficient reason for thinking that any one outcome is more or less likely than any of the others, so it attaches an equal weight to each possible outcome. In our case where we have three possible outcomes each one is given the weight of one third. So we would proceed as follows:

$$E(X) = \Sigma_{i\ XiP(i)}$$

$$= \frac{1}{3} \times 4 + \frac{1}{3} \times 2 + \frac{1}{3} \times -3 = 1$$

$$E(Y) = \Sigma_{i\ YiP(i)}$$

$$= \frac{1}{3} \times 2 + \frac{1}{3} \times 2 + \frac{1}{3} \times 1 = 1\frac{2}{3}$$

$$E(Z) = \Sigma_{i\ YiP(i)}$$

$$= \frac{1}{3} \times -3 + \frac{1}{3} \times -1 + \frac{1}{3} \times 6 = \frac{2}{3}$$

Investment Y would be chosen.

The third approach we can consider can also be used in the presence of uncertainty. It is known as the minimax regret criterion. The firm may choose an option that it later regrets. The idea is to choose the option that minimizes the extent to which one might regret the choice. The procedure is as follows. First we construct a regret matrix. This is done in Table 25.8. It tells us the maximum regret that we would have for each choice we make under each outcome. For example, let's see what happens if the actual outcome turns out to be A, low demand growth. If the firm's choice is X when the actual outcome is A, we achieve an outcome of NPV = €4 million. We know this by referring back to Table 25.7.

Outcome A, Scenario X:

NPV = €4 million

Regret = 0

You can see that the firm has no regrets in choosing X. It is *the best* possible outcome if we have A, low demand growth. Had it chosen Y or Z, the outcome would have been worse.

What is the regret if we choose Y and we get an outcome of A? From Table 25.7 a choice of Y with an outcome of A gives an NPV of €2 million. The firm will regret not choosing X, which would have given it €4 million.

Outcome A, Scenario Y:

NPV = €2 million

Regret = 4 – 2 = €2 million.

We have a regret of €2 million because we had an NPV of only two instead of the four, which was the maximum possible. This is the difference between what the firm could have had if it had chosen X, the best possible outcome and what it has now, having chosen Y.

Similarly, if the firm chooses the largest outlay, Z and the outcome is A it will have a regret of €7 million, an actual outcome of –3 instead of +4 that would have been possible if it had chosen X.

Outcome A, Scenario Z:

$$\text{NPV} = -€3 \text{ million}$$
$$\text{Regret} = 4 - (-3) = 4 + 3 = €7 \text{ million.}$$

Table 25.8 shows all possible regrets for all possible choices. The decision rule is now to choose the project that minimizes the maximum regret that the firm could have. The maximum regret if we choose X is 9. If we choose X and it turns out that there is high demand growth, we get −3, whereas had the firm chosen to make a large outlay, it would have had 6. The regret would be the difference between −3 and 6, that is 9. For a choice of Y the maximum regret is 5 and for Z it's 7. Under this decision rule we choose Y, the choice that minimizes the maximum possible regret.

Notice that the decision rule doesn't involve calculating the average regret, nor do we total all the regrets for each decision. We ask 'what is the highest possible regret associated with each of our three choices?' Then we pick the project that minimizes the maximum regret, in our case project Y.

TABLE 25.8 **A Minimax Regret Matrix**

	A (Low Demand Growth)	B (Medium Demand Growth)	C (High Demand Growth)
X (Small Outlay)	0	0	9
Y (Medium Outlay)	2	0	5
Z (Large Outlay)	7	3	0

In the face of risk and uncertainty there is no guarantee that any firm will choose the best outcome. Nevertheless this kind of analysis helps them to make a decision based on the best information.

We have treated this as an optimization problem. However, for some firms it might be a constrained optimization. For example they may have capital constraints which rule out larger projects or they may impose upon themselves decision rules such as never considering options that have any chance of making a loss. These constraints may well change the choice of project made.

Investment Analysis: A Summary

When choosing a project, whichever method is used, all of our three methods will generally suggest the same answer. The projects are worthwhile according to NPV will be worthwhile according to IRR and indeed ACC, although the result of using the ACC method will be more difficult to interpret if the cash flows are not consistently above or below the ACC across the project's life. We can reduce the risks of picking the wrong investments but we can never eliminate them.

COST BENEFIT ANALYSIS

We have focused so far on an understanding of investment decisions made by private firms. In principle, the same mathematical procedures can be adopted for analyzing the costs and benefits of projects that are undertaken by governments. Such procedures would normally include modifications to the analysis to allow for all costs and benefits that accrue to society at large. This might include, for example, modifying the cash flows to take into account damage to the environment or the value of time saved, things which tend to be ignored by private sector firms that are focusing only on costs and benefits that accrue to the firm. When such a project analysis is undertaken it is usually referred to as Cost Benefit Analysis (CBA).

The logic of an investment analysis is to make sure that a project is only undertaken if it is in the interests of the firm making the decision. More specifically, the benefits to the firm must outweigh the costs. Cost Benefit Analysis uses essentially the same approach to investments undertaken by the state or local authority. Do the social benefits of the project outweigh the social costs? The approach is similar to investment analysis but with some important differences and we will comment briefly on three main ones.

The Choice of Benefits and Costs

We must list all the costs and benefits. These include the tangible ones, that is the direct costs and benefits but also the intangibles, that is, the indirect costs and benefits. The costs and benefits of a planned new public airport, for example, will include not only the faster times for travellers but the noise pollution for those who will be living near the airport.

Some of this list can then be removed because they cancel each other out. For example, a new stretch of planned motorway may harm the business of a pub on the old road which will now be by-passed. However, people will not eat less, just eat somewhere else, perhaps at a new service station. So the overall effect of the motorway investment on the output of pub food is nil. These kinds of indirect costs and benefits can be cancelled out to produce 'net' costs and benefits.

The Valuation of Costs and Benefits

When a private company makes an investment analysis the valuation of costs and benefits is relatively straightforward. Market prices form the basis of the calculation. If a firm is investing in a new paint factory and has worked out expected sales volumes, it can multiply this volume by the price it expects to receive.

However, three additional difficulties occur when undertaking a CBA. First, using market prices ignores the value of consumer surplus. The benefit to society is not just price multiplied by quantity, but the surplus of value that we called consumer surplus when exploring this idea in Chapter 7. In principle, consumer surplus must be included. However, the problem of including it as a benefit is that we can only measure it to the extent that we know the demand function and this may be difficult or impossible to determine. As a result consumer surplus is often ignored in CBA.

The second difficulty is that the market price may not reflect social welfare. We examined this problem in Chapter 11. The policymaker can adjust price and use what is sometimes called a 'shadow price', that reflects the externality. The shadow price is the price that would prevail if the price reflected the true social costs and benefits. For example. Suppose the market price of some output is €10 per unit, but there are external costs of €2 per unit. Then the socially optimum price is 10 – 2 = €8. Thus, when finding the social value of this output, one should use a price of €8. This shadow price of €8 differs from the market price of €10. The policy maker has corrected for the externality by using a shadow price for the valuation of output.

The third and final difficulty to mention is deciding what to do about valuing costs and benefits when there is no market price. For example, a motorway will save business and leisure time, but valuing time saved is a problem because there is no market in time. There are various possibilities but the probably the most fruitful way to handle such difficulties is to imply a value from markets where there is a price. For example, houses close to airports have a lower market price than similar ones further away. The higher value of the more distant house can be seen to represent the capitalized value of avoiding airport noise.

The Distribution of Costs and Benefits

A somewhat controversial issue is the weighting of costs and benefits that accrue to different income groups. There is a case for saying that when a project's benefits are not evenly distributed we should weight benefits more heavily towards those on lower incomes. This might either be income groups within a country or between countries. For example, improved transport infrastructure can benefit everyone through lowering transport costs and hence the price of many goods, but some will gain more from this process than others. Or a hydroelectric dam scheme may distribute benefits widely through reduced electricity costs but some sailing facilities will be created that will largely benefit higher income groups.

Without such a weighting system we are implicitly saying that the only concern is to maximize total benefits to society. What is the case for a weighting system favouring lower income groups? It is the diminishing marginal utility of income that was discussed in the context of risk. Each additional euro of a person's income gains less utility.

Many possible weighting systems have been suggested which can be argued to reflect this view. We consider two. First we can weight all benefits by Y^1 / Y^2.

Where:

Y^1 = the average income of the whole society

Y^2 = the average income of the group receiving the benefit

If a society's average income is €20 000 per annum and a certain benefit of the project would go to people with an average income of €40 000, the weight to be attached to that benefit is:

$$\frac{y^1}{y^2} = \frac{20\,000}{40\,000} = 0.5$$

If in this society benefits accrue to people with an average income of €10 000 per annum we would have:

$$\frac{y^1}{y^2} = \frac{20\,000}{10\,000} = 2$$

The other system we mention is that which uses the inverse of the marginal tax rate. This alternative system of weights gives us a quite different set of numbers. Marginal tax rates tend to increase with income and this can be argued to reflect society's views about income distribution. So if a benefit of the project accrues to people who have a low marginal tax rate of 20 per cent the weight becomes

$$\frac{1}{0.2} = 5$$

If a benefit accrues to those with a marginal tax rate of 50 per cent those benefits are weighted at:

$$\frac{1}{0.5} = 2$$

Clearly such weighting systems favouring lower income groups are controversial but the decision maker has to decide first whether to adopt such weights and second, if so, what the weighting system will be.

SUMMARY

These modifications to the private investment analysis we discussed earlier are quite substantial but the principle of the time value of money remains when any investment is considered. Similarly, whatever kind of investment we examine there is risk or uncertainty involved. So although these problems are substantial, there are, as we have seen, means of handling them.

PROBLEMS AND APPLICATIONS

1 Imagine you are the chief executive officer (CEO) of a large company. Your analysts give you their estimates of the expected cash flows for several projects. The first one is project A.

a. Calculate the NPV of project A for an interest rate of 5 per cent.

Year	0	1	2	3	4	5
Cash Flow	–93	20	20	20	20	30

b. Interpret the NPV. Would you invest the company's money in this project?

2 The second project your analysts show you is project B. It has the following cash flow:

a. Compute the IRR.

Year	0	1	2
Cash Flow	–100	60	80

b. Assuming you could invest your money in another project which offers a return of 20 per cent. Which project would you choose?

3 Project C requires an investment of €1000. Your analysts tell you that C will earn fairly even returns over the next 5 years. The interest rate is still at 5 per cent.

a. Calculate the ACC.
b. Assume project C earns €250 each year. Would you do it?

4 You are considering the expected demand growth of a certain product you could produce with project D in order to estimate the best capital outlay. Your analysts gives you the following table of NPVs for several scenarios.

	A (low demand growth)	**B (medium demand growth)**	**C (high demand growth)**
X (small outlay)	5	1	−4
Y (medium outlay)	1	3	2
Z (large outlay)	−4	−1	8

a. Assume there is a 30 per cent chance for A, a 20 per cent chance for B and a 50 per cent chance for C. Calculate the expected value for each of the three outlays.
b. Compute the expected outcomes if you don't know the chances for the scenarios and you have to assume equal weights.
c. Use the minimax regret criterion to make a decision about the strategies W, Y, or Z.

26 ISSUES IN FINANCIAL MARKETS[1]

The financial crisis of 2007 had its roots in events which began well over a decade ago. However, its effects are still felt in the world economy. In this chapter we look at the role of the Credit Default Swap (CDS). We begin by explaining its meaning and the history of its development. Then we examine how the mathematics of the CDS played a major part in the financial crisis.

THE ROLE OF CDS IN THE FINANCIAL CRISIS

We begin by summarizing the chain of events which were central to the financial crisis of 2007–8, a crisis considered by many economists to have been the worst since the 1930s.

US Government policy in recent decades, and indeed that of the UK government, had sought to encourage business, partially through 'deregulation', including reduced oversight of the activity of banks and other financial institutions and reduced disclosure of information.

It seems that policymakers failed to appreciate the increasingly important role played by investment banks and the shadow banking system[2] in providing credit to the US economy. In total this may have become as important as that of the commercial banks, whilst not being subject to the same degree of regulation.

It is also important to consider the role of interest rates. During the past two decades real interest rates have become unusually low. These low interest rates have had several results. One result has been the sharp increase in consumption accompanied by rising household debt, and this has been mirrored in the housing market, with households taking on higher mortgages for bigger houses or second homes, leading to a sharp increase in house prices. In the US this was termed a 'real estate bubble'. Another result is that investors and fund managers may have been driven toward more risky investments in the search for higher yields on financial investments. Such investments may easily run into trouble during an economic downturn.

During the 1980s to mid-90s, the UK government had pursued a policy of encouraging wider home ownership. This also applied in the US, which had set up agencies attempting to expedite this change. The process was eased in the US by the changing nature of bank lending, and this leads us to distinguish between the classic mortgage lending model of 'lend-to-hold' and the more recent idea of 'lend-to-distribute'. Under the traditional model a mortgage bank would lend against the security of the home and retain the debt whilst receiving the repayments of interest and capital. However, under lend-to-distribute, the bank lends against the home but does not hold the debt. Instead, it sells off the debt, probably to some specialist financial institution which mixes the debt up with similar loans purchased from other mortgage providers into a parcel termed a Mortgage Backed Security (MBS). They may also be mixed up with other loans, credit cards, motor loans and indeed corporate borrowing into a bundle termed a Collateralized Debt Obligation (CDO), which is then sold onward as a security. This process is termed securitization, and the shadow banking system has been very active in creating and trading such securities.

It should be apparent that when the bank holds a loan under the traditional lend-to-hold model, it will be very circumspect about the credit worthiness of its customers and their ability to repay. Hence the bank will carry out a

[1] Our grateful thanks to Dr Peter Andrew who provided the essence of the material in this chapter.

[2] We use the term 'shadow banking system' or 'shadow financial system' to describe the range of non-depository financial institutions such as investment banks that operate with less regulation than the banking system itself.

careful diligence exercise on the borrower. But will the bank be so careful under the lend-to-distribute approach? The answer is that it will probably not. The lending discipline built up over many decades was seriously weakened.

In this resulting period of fierce competition between mortgage lenders for revenue and market share, and as the supply of creditworthy borrowers was obviously limited, mortgage lenders relaxed underwriting standards and approved riskier mortgages to less creditworthy borrowers. Mortgage standards declined and risky loans proliferated. Such 'subprime' lending expanded dramatically through 2004-6 to comprise around 20 per cent of the market.

One might expect institutions in search of yield to be concerned about the riskiness of their investments. However, during these years it seems that many of these investments were rated AAA by the ratings agencies[3] when arguably they were far more risky than that rating might suggest.

Between 2002 and 2005 US interest rates had been around 1–2 per cent. By 2007, they had suddenly jumped to 5 per cent. The result was that many 'sub-prime' borrowers, those with a poor credit history, and who were at the limits of their personal gearing in the first place, were unable to make payments to the lenders and began to default. Mortgage interest and capital repayments were no longer forthcoming, and these payments formed the income component of the MBS and part of the income component of the CDO. The market prices of these securities began to implode. To make matters worse, house prices also rapidly began to collapse, so that the buyers were often trapped in the situation known as negative equity, where the market value of the house is exceeded by the outstanding mortgage loan. Hence, holders of MBS were not able to recover the cost of the MBS by re-possession of the property.

At this point, financial institutions rapidly began to be less certain of solvency, to suspect each other of being in possession of large quantities of undisclosed liabilities in the form of such MBS/CDO, and were less willing to lend to each other. Liquidity began to dry up, and with it the confidence critical to the banking sector.

The Credit Default Swap

It is often argued that the root cause of the 2007 financial crisis was the incidence of defaults in the sub-prime housing market in the US. However, it is possible that the role of the CDS may have been more damaging still.

The essence of a CDS is that protection buyer A makes a series of payments to protection seller B under the condition that B will pay a cash sum to A if a third party C called the 'reference obligation' defaults on the payment of some capital instrument such as a bond or loan. The credit default could thus be non-payment of capital or interest on a loan arrangement in which neither A nor B have any direct concern.

Hence a CDS is not an option. With an option there is a right but not an obligation. With a CDS there is both a right and an obligation. A CDS is more akin to an insurance contract, but with the bizarre feature that A is able to insure itself with B against the default of C even though A is in no way involved with C and has no insurable interest.

Once written, CDS could be bought and sold in a secondary market, with the value of the CDS being a function of the likelihood that C would default.

FIGURE 26.1

The figure shows the essence of a CDS. Protection buyer A makes a series of payments to B under the condition that B will pay a cash sum to A if a third party C, termed the 'reference obligation', defaults on the payment of a bond or loan. The series of payments made half yearly or quarterly by the buyer to the seller up to the point at which the reference entity defaults, if at all, is called the premium leg. If the reference entity does not default, the premium leg will be paid until the completion of the contract.

If the reference entity does indeed default, the premium payments will cease and the seller B will deliver the agreed value less any recovery to A.

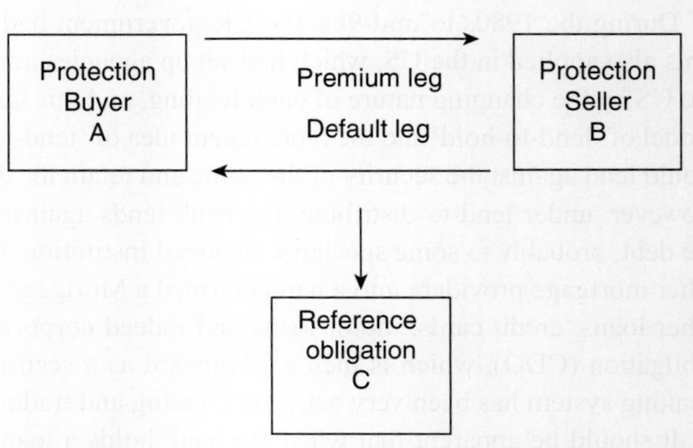

[3] The ratings agencies are credit-rating agencies, which assess the creditworthiness of large scale borrowers, whether companies or countries. These agencies have a marking system, with AAA as the top rating, which serve to indicate how likely the debt is to be paid back.

Hence the buyer makes a series of periodic payments to the seller and in return receives a pay-off if a default in the underlying asset occurs. The CDS will have a determined life, e.g. five years.

There are a number of aspects to CDS which render them a particularly toxic form of credit derivative, one of which is that neither party to the contract needs to be regulated. Hence the party required to pay out in the event of default is not required to set aside any provision to allow for such an event. The shadow banking system has therefore been particularly active in this sector.

Now if Hedge Fund[4] P actually *owned* debt in Company R, and purchased a CDS from Shadow Bank Q against default by R, that CDS could be termed a hedge. In contrast, if there is no insurable interest, the CDS would be pure speculation.

Potential Profits and Losses from Trading in CDS

We now give a number of examples of the potential profits and losses in trading CDS. The first one involves Hedge Fund P.

Example one

Suppose Hedge Fund P suspects that Company R is less solvent than it should be, and that it might, say within 5 years, default upon its debt.

Hedge Fund P purchases €50m of CDS from Shadow Bank Q for 5 years with Company R's debt as the reference. The 'spread' is the amount the buyer must pay the seller as a percentage of the nominal value of the CDS contract, and is stated in terms of 'basis points', each basis point being one hundredth of one per cent (i.e. 0.01 per cent).

In this case let the spread be 400 basis points, or 4 per cent.

So we have:

$$\begin{aligned} \textit{Nominal value of CDS} &= \text{€}50 \textit{ million} \\ \textit{Spread} &= 400 \textit{ basis point } (4 \textit{ per cent}) \\ \textit{Term} &= 5 \textit{ years} \end{aligned}$$

Hence P pays to Q:

$$4\% \times \text{€}50m = \text{€}2m \textit{ per year.}$$

If Hedge Fund P was wrong about the solvency of Company R, and R never did default upon its debt obligations, P would pay to Q over the life of the CDS contract a total of:

$$5 \times \text{€}2m = \text{€}10m$$

This is good business for Shadow Bank Q, but bad business for Hedge Fund P. Hence CDS are a zero-sum game.

However, if Company R did indeed default after say 3 years, then P would have paid 3 × €2m = €6m to Q, but Q would now have to pay the value of the CDS to P, namely €50m, hence Q would have made a loss on the deal:

$$50 - 6 = \text{€}44m$$

Q would lose €44 million.

A third possibility is that Hedge Fund P might sell the CDS on into the secondary market before it expires, and if it transpires that R looks more likely to default than it did when the CDS contract was first written, P will be able to sell the CDS for more than it has paid for it, and may turn a profit.

Example two

The second example concerns Hedge Fund A. Suppose that Hedge Fund A believes that Negligent plc may soon default on its debt. It buys €10 million worth of CDS protection for two years from Goodnessme Bank, with Negligent plc as the reference entity, at a spread of 500 basis points.

$$\begin{aligned} \textit{Nominal value of CDS} &= \text{€}10 \textit{ million} \\ \textit{Spread} &= 500 \textit{ basis point } (5 \textit{ per cent}) \\ \textit{Term} &= 2 \textit{ years} \end{aligned}$$

[4] A hedge fund is an investment vehicle that can invest in many types of financial securities. They are very lightly regulated and can therefore invest in a wider range of securities than mutual funds such as insurance companies and investment trusts. They are best known for engaging in relatively risky investments.

Hence A will pay 5% × 10 000 000 = €500 000 per annum to Goodnessme Bank.

If Negligent plc does indeed default after, say, one year, then Hedge Fund A will have paid €500 000 to the bank, but then receives €10 million, hence making a profit of €9.5m on the deal (assuming that Goodnessme Bank has the liquidity to cover the loss). The bank, and its investors, will incur a €9.5 million loss unless the bank has somehow offset the position prior to the default.

However, if Negligent plc does *not* default, then the CDS contract runs for two years, and Hedge Fund A ends up paying €1 million, without any return, thereby incurring a loss of €1m. Goodnessme Bank, by selling protection, has made 2 × 500 000 = €1 million without any capital investment.

Example three

Our third example continues with the above scenario, but now we note that there is a third possibility. Hedge Fund A could decide to liquidate its position after a certain period of time in an attempt to realize its gains or losses.

Suppose that after one year, the market now considers Negligent plc to be *more likely* to default, so its CDS spread has *widened* from 500 to 1500 basis points (or 15 per cent).

Hedge Fund A manages to *sell* €10 million worth of CDS for 1 year back to Goodnessme Bank at this spread. Hence over the two years the hedge fund pays the bank:

$$2 \times 5\% \times 10000000 = €1000000$$

However it receives:

$$15\% \times 10000000 = €1500000$$

This gives a total *profit* of €500 000.

This assumes that no default actually occurs.

Conversely, if after say one year the market now considers Negligent plc to be much *less likely* to default, its CDS spread may *tighten* from 500 to 250 basis points (2.5 per cent).

Again, Hedge Fund A may manage to *sell* €10 million worth of protection for 1 year to somebody, say Goodnessme Bank at this reduced spread. Hence over the two years Hedge Fund A pays the bank:

$$2 \times 5\% \times 10000000 = €1000000$$

This time it receives:

$$2.5\% \times 10000000 = €250000$$

This gives a total loss of €750 000. This loss is smaller than the £1 million loss that would have occurred if the second transaction had not been entered.

Example four

It is not only banks as lenders which hedge risk. Holders of corporate bonds, including pension funds and insurance companies may buy a CDS as a hedge. In our fourth example a pension fund owns five-year bonds issued by Reckless plc with par value of €10 million. To hedge the risk of loss if Reckless plc defaults on its debt, the pension fund buys €10m of CDS from Astronomicalbonus Bank at a spread of 200 basis points.

So we have:

$$\begin{aligned} \textit{Bonds par value} &= €10 \textit{ million} \\ \textit{Nominal value of CDS} &= €10 \textit{ million} \\ \textit{Spread} &= 200 \textit{ basis point (2 per cent)} \\ \textit{Term} &= 5 \textit{ years} \end{aligned}$$

The pension fund thus pays the spread of 2 per cent of £10 million = £200 000 per annum in quarterly instalments of £50 000 to Astronomicalbonus Bank.

If Reckless plc does *not* default on its bond payments, the pension fund makes quarterly payments to Astronomicalbonus Bank for 5 years and receives its £10 million back after five years from Reckless plc.

So the total CDS payments would be:

$$5 \times 2\% \times 10000000 = €1000000$$

Whilst the €1 million of CDS payments reduces investment returns for the pension fund, its risk of total loss due to Reckless plc defaulting on the bond is hedged. In this scenario, Astronomicalbonus Bank has made a profit of €1m on the CDS.

However, if Reckless plc *does* default on its debt three years into the CDS contract, the pension fund would stop paying the quarterly premium, and Astronomicalbonus Bank would refund the pension fund its loss of £10 million. For three years the bank would have received payments of:

$$3 \times 2\% \times 10\,000\,000 = €600\,000$$

The pension fund still loses the €600 000 it has paid over three years, but without the CDS contract it would have lost the entire €10 million. In this scenario, Astronomicalbonus Bank has made a loss of €9.4m.

Example five

Now consider a CDS buyer who purchases a 5-year €10m protection on an underlying entity with a spread of 300 basis points.

$$\begin{aligned} \textit{Nominal value of CDS} &= €10 \textit{ million} \\ \textit{Spread} &= 300 \textit{ basis point } (3 \textit{ per cent}) \\ \textit{Term} &= 5 \textit{ years} \end{aligned}$$

The buyer thus renders *quarterly* payments of:

$$0.25 \times 3\% \times 10\,000\,000 = €75\,000$$

Now assume that at some point the reference entity defaults, but that a recovery price of €45 per €100 of face is agreed.

The cash flows due to this event are as follows:

The CDS buyer is compensated by the seller for the loss on the face value of the asset, which is:

$$(100\% - 45\%) \times 10\,000\,000 = €5\,500\,000$$

The CDS buyer pays the accrued premium from the previous premium date to the time of the default event. So if the event occurs after three months, then the buyer pays:

$$3/12 \times 3\% \times 10\,000\,000 = €75\,000 \textit{ for the premium accrued.}$$

Hence the seller settles for €5 425 000.

THE VALUATION OF CDS

In order to price a CDS, we require knowledge of the probability of the default, when it is likely to occur and the recovery rate if the default occurs. The easiest way to obtain the probability of default is through observation of bond spreads. The government bond yield is normally assumed to be risk-free, that is, to represent the risk-free rate. Corporate bonds, however, are not risk-free, hence there is some probability of default, and lenders require some premium over and above the risk-free rate to compensate them for the possibility of default, and this is termed the 'bond spread'.

The spread is a function of a number of factors, including credit rating and term to maturity, as well as the more obvious supply and demand. The term to maturity is a significant factor, and lower quality bonds trade at higher spreads than, say AAs, and longer-dated bonds normally at higher spreads than shorter ones. For example, a 2-year AA might trade at a spread of 20 basis points, whilst a 5-year AA trades at a spread of 30 basis points.

A straightforward approach to the pricing of CDS is the 'market approach' first described by JP Morgan. This employs parameters observed in the market.

A CDS has two cash-flow 'legs', the fee premium leg plus the contingent cash-flow leg, which describes the cash-flows resulting from default. The second leg is the leg under which the seller settles, resulting from default. If we wish to determine the premium or par-spread, we must bear in mind that in accordance with the principle of zero-arbitrage, the expected net present value, termed the ENPV of the two legs must be zero, i.e. both legs must have the same value.

The essence of this is that the buyer of the CDS will make a series of payments over the life of the contract and that in all likelihood these payments will continue throughout the life of the CDS because, in theory at least, the probability that the reference entity will default is low.

The seller of the CDS, conversely, will only make a single payment in the event of default, and in theory the probability of this occurrence is low. Hence, the credit default 'swap' involves a swap of a high probability of a number of low payments for a low probability of a high payment. But let us not forget the boundary condition of no-arbitrage.

The fee-premium leg is simply a series of constant cash flows and could thus be resolved using the principles we developed in Chapter 24. However, let us consider a 5-year CDS with a 6-monthly premium, although in reality it would probably be quarterly. Suppose the discount rate applied to the bond is 5 per cent and that the probability of the underlying entity defaulting in any given period, derived from the spread, is 2 per cent. Assume a 30 per cent recovery rate.

Let us now consider the cash flows defining the no-default leg. Look at Table 26.1.

TABLE 26.1 **Assumed Cash flow of a no-default of a CDS**

Time (years)	5% DCFi	Prob Survival PSi	Expected PV
0.5			
1.0	0.9524	0.9800	0.9334
1.5			
2.0	0.9070	0.9604	0.8711
2.5			
3.0	0.8638	0.9412	0.8130
3.5			
4.0	0.8227	0.9224	0.7589
4.5			
5.0	0.7835	0.9039	0.7082
			Total 4.0846

We have met discounted cash flow techniques in earlier chapters. Now we use them to explain the value of the cash flow here. Column 1 shows the time period in years and column 2 the discount factors at 5 per cent. So for example, after one year at a discount rate of 5 per cent we have:

$$1/(1 + r) = 1/(1 + 0.05) = 0.9524$$

And after two years:

$$1/(1 + r)^2 = 1/(1 + 0.05)^2 = 0.9070$$

In the table we show all the discount factors to year 5.

The third column labelled 'Prob Survival Psi' is the probability of the underlying entity surviving, which we assumed to be 2 per cent. That is, after one year there is a 98 per cent chance of survival, 0.9800. The chance of survival after a second year is therefore:

$$0.9800 \times 0.9800 = 0.9604$$

The table shows all the probability factors to year 5.

The final column shows the expected present value, Expected PV. This is the present value of the cash flow multiplied by the probability of survival. Thus for each year we multiply the value in column 2 by the value in column 3. So, for example, for year 1, we have:

$$0.9524 \times 0.9800 = 0.9334$$

And for year 2:

$$0.9070 \times 0.9604 = 0.8711$$

We can now summarize the expected present value of the fee premium leg. This is the sum of all the expected present values for all five years.

$$0.9334 + 0.8771 + 0.8130 + 0.7585 + 0.7082 = 4.0842$$

Or in summary form:

$$\sum_{i=1}^{n} DCF_i \, PS_i = 4.0846$$

Now we add the accrual part of the premium payments, the premium payment which will accrue during the *part* of the year during which the default occurs. As we do not know at what point in the year the default will occur, if at all, we will assume that it is at the halfway, six-month point, and form a 6-month default probability PDj and a half yearly discount factor DCFj.

Now we can find the cash flows pertaining to the accrual leg which we summarize in Table 26.2.

TABLE 26.2 **Assumed Cash flow of an accrual leg of a CDS**

Time	Cum Prob Survival PSi	Prob Default in Year	Prob Default PDi	Half-year Default PDj	Half-year DCFj	Accrual EPV
0.5				1.00%	0.9759	0.009759
1.0	0.9800	2.00%	2.00%			
1.5				0.98%	0.9294	0.009108
2.0	0.9604	2.00%	1.96%			
2.5				0.96%	0.8851	0.008497
3.0	0.9412	2.00%	1.92%			
3.5				0.94%	0.8430	0.007924
4.0	0.9224	2.00%	1.88%			
4.5				0.92%	0.8029	0.007387
5.0	0.9039	3.00%	1.84%			
						Total 0.042675

Column 1 of Table 26.2 shows the time period in years and column 2 the probability of default.

This we have labelled 'Prob Default PD_i'. As before, the probability of default after one year is assumed to be 2 per cent so we record this value as 2.00. Then after two years the annual probability of default remains at 2%, but the probability of survival into Year 2 is 0.98, so that the probability of default during Year 2 is:

$$2.00 \times 0.98 = 1.96\% \textit{ and so on until year 5}$$

The 3rd column gives us the default probability values for half way through each year. Thus the probability of default halfway through the first year is:

$$0.5 \times 2.00 = 1\% \textit{ and so on}$$

Now look at column 4. Just as we have discount factors for whole years we have them for half years, such that the $(1 + r)$ factor is raised to a non-integer power, such as 1/2, 3/2 or 5/2. Hence the discount factor for six months is the square root of the one-year factor, which gives 0.9759 and the 18-month factor is the square root of the 3-year factor, which gives 0.9294. The discount factors for each half year to year 5 are given in Table 26.2. The expected present value for each of the relevant time periods is shown in the last column. As before, we multiply the probability of default by the appropriate discount factor to give the expected present value. Then if we sum these values for each year we get the sum 0.042615. That is:

$$\sum_{i=0.5}^{n-0.5} DCF_j PD_j = 0.042675$$

Then the expectation of the total premiums paid by the CDS buyer under our above assumptions is the sum of the two accrual legs:

$$\sum_{i=1}^{n} DCF_i PS_i + \sum_{i=0.5}^{n-1} DCF_j PD_j = 4.1273$$

Now we consider the expectation of the payment to be made by the CDS seller in the event of default, the "low probability high payment" referred to above.

We can tabulate the situation pertaining to the seller using Table 26.3.

Column 1 is again the time period under consideration. Column 2 shows the assumed probability of default as before. Column 3, labelled PDj(1 – R), is found as follows. We have an assumed recovery rate of 30 per cent. Thus we multiply the values in column 2 of Table 26.3 by 70 per cent, 0.7. So for example after six months, 0.5 of a year:

$$2.0 \times 0.7 = 1.4$$

And so on for the whole period.

The half year discount factors of column four are shown again as they were for Table 26.2.

Now consider the final column, column 5. We find these values by multiplying the probability of default in column three by the appropriate half-year discount factor in column 4. So, for example, after half a year:

$$1.4 \textit{ per cent} \times 0.9756 = 0.0136$$

TABLE 26.3 The situation of the Seller of the CDS

Time	Prob Default PDj	PDj(1 – R)	Half-Year DCFj	EPV
0.5	2.0%	1.40%	0.9759	0.01366
1.0				
1.5	1.96%	1.37%	0.9294	0.01273
2.0				
2.5	1.92%	1.34%	0.8851	0.01186
3.0				
3.5	1.88%	1.31%	0.8430	0.01104
4.0				
4.5	1.84%	1.29%	0.8029	0.01036
5.0				
				Total 0.05965

Repeating this for all half-years gives the values in column 5, the expected present value, EPV. The sum of these EPVs over the whole period is 0.05957. That is:

$$\sum_{i=0.5}^{n-0.5} PD_i(1-R)DCF = 0.05965$$

Now under our zero-arbitrage assumption, the discounted and probability-adjusted payments made by the buyer must balance the discounted, probability-adjusted payments made by the seller, so:

$$\sum_{i=1}^{n} DCF_i PS_i + \sum_{i=0.5}^{n-1} DCF_j PD_j = \sum_{j=0.5}^{n-05} PD_j(1-R)DCF_j$$

So that:

$$4.12723S = 0.05965$$
$$S = 0.01445$$
$$= 145 \text{ basis points or } 1.45 \text{ per cent}$$

What is the significance of this number? The spread is a percentage of the insured amount.

In this example, if the buyer had purchased €10m of CDS at 145 bps, i.e. 1.45 per cent, he would pay annually 1.45 per cent of €10m, or €145 000. In practical CDS this may be paid half yearly at €72 500 per 6 month, or even quarterly.

If the assumptions are invalid the assumed return is also invalid. If, for example, the recovery rate is much lower, as it proved to be when the market collapsed, the return that should have been looked for needed to be far higher. In the years leading up to the financial crisis it clearly was not!

The market for CDS

The market for CDS expanded dramatically in the decade or so before the financial crash. By 2001, the outstanding value of CDS was over US$630 bn, and growing to around US$55 Trillion in 2007. This figure is comparable to global GDP, although some of this was hedged.

Why did the CDS market grow so explosively? The answer appears to be once again the frantic search for yield. There was not enough sub-prime debt to go round. Once sub-prime debt has been sliced and diced into an MBS or CDO, it can only be sold once. The bankers were running out of risky assets. What made CDS so strikingly different was that CDS could be written on the same asset an indefinite number of times, that is, *there is no limit to the amount of CDS that can be written!* A major issue though, is that some CDS were being written against cash streams flowing from MBS / CDO.[5]

A possible analogy to CDS can be found in horse-racing. Here, the owner/breeder/trainer of the horse incurs cost to bring the horse to the race in the hope of possibly winning prize money. The jockey rides the horse for a fee and a share in the prize money, definitely risking his/her life in the process. However, the largest sums of money changing

[5] A good explanation of the explosive growth of the CDS market can be found in A. Buckley (2011) *Financial Crisis: Causes: Context and Consequences*. Prentice Hall.

hands in this matter are to be found with the bookmakers, who accept bets from gamblers on the *outcome* of the race. The quantity of money changing hands in this process bears no relationship to the prize money involved in the race, which it dwarfs hundreds or thousands of times over. Neither bookmaker nor gambler has any financial interest in the horse, trainer, jockey or their welfare. The most striking parallel between horse-racing and CDS is that there is no limit to the number or magnitude of the gambling transactions which can be agreed on the outcome of this horse running in this race. Nor, therefore, is there any limit to the profits and losses which can accrue to the bookmaker or punter, none of which in any way benefits the provider of the underlying asset.

Consider again Company R. It might have €50m of debt, and an equity market capitalization of €200m, hence a total entity value of €250m. However, CDS on Company R are not limited to €50m, or €500m, or €5bn or €50bn. The universe is the limit. There was literally no limit to the amount of speculation into which the shadow banking system could enter via CDS, and thus possibly no limit to the bonuses that bankers could create for themselves by creating and selling such products. Further, the addition of CDS into a MBS/CDO slice-dice package could actually improve its credit rating, because the CDS was in some cases *not correlated* with the MBS/CDO.

The unwinding

Let us now briefly reflect upon what happened when interest rates suddenly began to rise and the possibility of defaults on cash streams flowing from MBS/CDO securities began to loom.

The event, which it seemed that few involved in the sale of CDS had foreseen as possible, was that many of the underlying assets such as MBS/CDO whose defaults would trigger the contingent liabilities inherent in the CDS contracts began to default. The defaults rapidly snowballed. The point that many of these assets were in fact *not* AAA rated began to be realized. When a hedge fund or investment bank has sold a bundle of CDS on assets that now seem suddenly likely to default, it is faced with the prospect of paying out on all or many of them. Now, as we have seen, the sheer volume of this trade was colossal. Yet these unregulated entities were never obliged to lay aside any provision for such an event. Since many of these assets now had a zero value some institutions were effectively bankrupt.

As with so many things, an understanding of mathematics enables us to see how the financial crisis developed.

PROBLEMS AND APPLICATIONS

1 A protection buyer A (PBA) is purchasing a CDS from a protection seller B (PSB) with a nominal amount of €4 million for 4 years. The spread on the reference obligation C (ROC) is 50 basis points (bp) at the time of issue of the CDS. Premium payments are paid quarterly.

a. How much does the CDS cost the PBA quarterly and annually?

b. Assume the debtor of ROC fails to pay after $2\frac{1}{2}$ years and nothing can be recovered. Calculate the net financial position of PBA and PSB from the CDS instrument.

c. How are the profits and losses of PBA and PSB affected, if ROC fails on the debt obligation just two years into the contract but 60 per cent of the nominal amounts can be recovered from ROCs assets?

d. PBA would like to sell the CDS one year after the issuance, because the risk perceived in ROC has declined even further. The spread has fallen to 25 basis points. Over the three years of the remaining life of the CDS, how much does PBA win or lose, compared to holding onto the contract?

2 Walk through the steps of pricing a CDS with the price being the spread in per cent or per €1 of nominal value of the reference obligation. Use a discount rate of 4 per cent per annum in the valuation process. Assume that in each of the four years of the life of the CDS the probability of a default of the reference obligation is 3 per cent. If there is a default, 50 per cent of the nominal value of the reference obligation can be recovered from the assets of the borrower under the reference obligation, so the seller of the CDS will only pay 50 per cent of the CDS amount in the default leg. Premium payments are annual at the end of a year. In case of default, however, the premium is to be payed up to the end of the half year in which the default (event) occurs. (Again, it might be useful to do this using a spreadsheet software.)

a. Calculate the probabilities that the CDS event has not been triggered for each of the half years under the contract (probability of survival).
b. Find the factors to discount the cash flows for each of the four years.
c. Calculate the expected present values of the yearly premium payments the buyer of the CDS pays (under the assumption of no default).
d. Calculate the expected present values of the semi-annual premium payments the buyer will have to make, if the CDS-event occurs during the first half of the year for each of the four years.
e. Which amount can the seller of the CDS expect to pay under the contract?
f. Equate the expected payments of both parties in the contract and solve for the spread of the CDS.
g. What happens to the spread as the probability of default rises to 5 per cent or even to 20 per cent in each of the years?

27 THE MONETARY SYSTEM

We begin with a consideration of transactions costs. Money is valuable as a medium of exchange in that it reduces transaction costs compared with a barter economy. However, we show that there are benefits to minimizing transaction costs in a barter economy also. Then we look at the mathematics of series and finally we use this concept to examine the money multiplier.

BARTER, MONEY AND TRANSACTION COSTS

You may have seen adverts where a business claims that you can get the best value by dealing with them because by dealing directly with them you will 'cut out the middleman'. The middleman, it is implied, is a parasite contributing nothing useful to the economy. To examine this view we need to understand transaction costs, defined as: 'the costs that parties incur in the process of agreeing and following through on a bargain'.

Any business has costs which are directly related to the manufacturing process, but there are other costs too. Transaction costs are the costs associated with an exchange. Firms must produce price lists and advertise their products. Consumers have to spend time searching for the products they want. Sometimes disputes arise after a good has been purchased and there are legal costs sorting out the problems. These are the costs not directly associated with the production of the good. These are transactions costs.

Whenever people buy and sell they engage in an exchange. In an advanced economy they do it through the medium of money. For now, let's consider a simpler economy where there is only barter – the exchange goods without money. Imagine there are only two people on an island. David gathers coconuts, Gill grows mangoes. He wants some of her mangoes, she wants some of his coconuts so they exchange. However, there will be some transactions costs. They have to arrange to meet, agree a rate of exchange and so on. Each period there is one exchange. Now a third person joins the community, Jordana, who specializes in catching fish and wants to exchange her fish with the goods of the other two. How many exchanges are there on the island each period now? David exchanges with Jordana, he exchanges also with Gill, and Jordana exchanges with Gill so there are three exchanges, each one with the associated transactions costs. How many exchanges are there if a fourth person, Brian, joins and specializes in clothing, and then a fifth person, Megi, making shoes? Suppose the community grows to be a hundred, each specializing in some different product? How many exchanges will there be then, assuming each wants some of the product of all the others? The formula is as follows.

Let the number of people in the society be represented as N. Each wishes to exchange with everyone else, that is, with the $N-1$ people. So this would seem to give us a total amount of exchanges as:

$$N \times (N-1)$$

However, this would be double counting. For example, it includes David's exchange of coconuts for Gill's mangoes and also Gill's exchange of mangoes for David's coconuts. The correct total of exchanges is only half of the above. If we divide by two we have a formula of:

$$TE = \frac{N \times (N-1)}{2}$$

Where:
TE = total number of exchanges
N = the number of people in the society

Alternatively, we could express it as:

$$TE = \frac{N^2 - N}{2}$$

This tells us the total exchanges for any number of people on the island. The formula enables us to see how quickly the number of exchanges, and hence the amount of transaction costs, rises as the numbers in society increase. For example, with four people the number of exchanges will be:

$$TE = \frac{4 \times (4 - 1)}{2}$$
$$= 6$$

But with 100 people the number of exchanges rises to:

$$TE = \frac{100 \times (100 - 1)}{2}$$
$$= 4950$$

All these exchanges have transactions costs, absorbing scarce resources. Now imagine that one of the people on the island sets up a shop or trading post. Everyone brings their specialist goods and can exchange for some of all the other goods. Now everyone makes a trade with the person at the trading post. If each of the other members of our society can go and trade their produce for all other products, how many exchanges will there be? With 100 members of the society each one of the other 99 has to make just one trade with the person at the trading post so there are 99 exchanges. In general, the number of transactions is simply $N - 1$. We now have fewer transactions and therefore savings on transaction costs. The reduction in the number of exchanges is larger the larger the number of people. We can call the person operating the trading post a 'middleman'. We give some illustrative numbers in Table 27.1.

TABLE 27.1 **Transactions in an Economy with and without a Middleman.**

Number of people	Without a Trading Post	With a Trading Post
2	1	1
3	3	2
5	10	4
10	45	9
50	1 225	49
100	4 950	99
250	31 125	249

There's a widespread feeling that such a person is 'unproductive', not producing anything but living off the hard work of the other members of society. In fact, the middleman's contribution is the reduction in transaction costs. This transaction cost saving is why, for example, many supermarkets are successful. People get all the things they want and pay just once at the till so reducing transaction costs.

We now consider a society that uses money instead of barter. One of the key benefits of money as a medium of exchange is the further reduction in transaction costs.

The Use of Series

The amount of money in circulation is much greater than the amount of notes and coins. Most money is bank credit. Banks create money via the 'money multiplier'. Although a modern banking system is far more complex than this money multiplier suggests, it is an important explanation of the volume of money in circulation.

The money multiplier is the amount of money that the banking system generates with each unit of reserves. In order to examine the size of the money multiplier we need to be clear about summing a series.

Suppose we have a set of numerical values that follows a rule. The rule enables us to calculate each term by observing the preceding values. This is a 'sequence'. An example might be:

$$1, \frac{1}{2}, \frac{1}{4}, \frac{1}{8}, \ldots$$

where since each term is half of the previous one we know the value of the next term. If the series has a constant ratio or difference, it is referred to as a progression. An example of an arithmetic progression would be:

$$1, 3, 5, 7, 9, \ldots\ldots\ldots\ldots$$

The most useful in economics tend to be geometric progressions, where each term is a multiple of the previous one. The multiplying factor is called the 'common ratio'. For example:

$$3, 6, 12, 24, 48, \ldots\ldots\ldots\ldots$$

Is a geometric progression with a common ratio of 2.

Consider a sequence:

$$a,\ ar,\ ar^2,\ ar^3,\ ar^4,\ ar^5,\ \ldots\ldots$$

Then if $a = 4$ and $r = 2$ the geometric progression, GP, would be:

$$4, 8, 16, 32, 64, 128, \ldots\ldots\ldots\ldots$$

The formula for finding the sum of a GP to a given number of terms is:

$$S_n = \frac{a(1 - r^n)}{1 - r}$$

Where:

S_n = the sum of the series to n terms

a = the first term of the series

r = the ratio of the progression

For the above series, if we wish to know the value of the first six terms, we have:

$$\begin{aligned} S_6 &= \frac{4 \times (1 - 2^6)}{1 - 2} \\ &= \frac{4 \times (1 - 64)}{-1} \\ &= \frac{-252}{-1} \\ &= 252 \end{aligned}$$

i.e. the sum of 4, 8, 16, 32, 64 and 128.

In economics the common ratio, r, is often less than one. This is the case about the money multiplier, as we shall see. In the above example suppose we leave $a = 4$ unchanged, but change r, so that $r = 1/2$. The series then looks like this:

$$\begin{aligned} S &= 4 + \left(4 \times \frac{1}{2}\right) + \left(4 \times \frac{1}{2} \times \frac{1}{2}\right) + \left(4 \times \frac{1}{2} \times \frac{1}{2} \times \frac{1}{2}\right) + \ldots\ldots \\ &= 4 + 2 + 1 + \frac{1}{2} + \ldots\ldots \end{aligned}$$

Will the formula still work? It will. This time we will use the formula on the above series, but set n to just 3, so that it is easy to check that we have the right answer.

$$\begin{aligned} S_3 &= \frac{4 \times \left(1 - \frac{1}{2}\right)^3}{1 - \frac{1}{2}} \\ &= \frac{4 \times \left(1 - \frac{1}{8}\right)}{\frac{1}{2}} \\ &= \frac{4 \times \frac{7}{8}}{\frac{1}{2}} \\ &= \frac{3\frac{1}{2}}{\frac{1}{2}} \\ &= 7 \end{aligned}$$

That is, the first three terms in the series, 4, 2 and 1 sum to 7.

If a GP has a common ratio that is greater than one, then S increases without limit. The progression is divergent. However, if the common ratio of the GP is less than one, then each successive term is smaller, so that there must be a total which cannot be exceeded. If $-1 < r < 1$ then the resulting geometric progression is said to be convergent. It is summing to infinity. In economics, the condition $-1 < r < 1$ is true about most of the important series and the situation is straightforward. So consider our series:

$$4, 2, 1, \frac{1}{2}, \frac{1}{4}, \frac{1}{8}, \ldots\ldots\ldots\ldots$$

The first two terms sum to six, the first three to 7, the first four to $7\frac{1}{2}$ etc. The sum of the series converges to 8 but never quite reaches it.

With GPs with a common ratio of less than one, if we are adding more and more terms of the series we get a more accurate value of the total but never quite reach it. We refer to this as the limit of the process. If $-1 < r < 1$ the progression converges to the value:

$$\frac{a}{1-r}$$

Now consider the series:

$$27, 9, 3, 1, \frac{1}{3}, \frac{1}{9}, \ldots\ldots\ldots$$

This has a common ratio of 1/3 and the first term is 27. So:

$$S = \frac{27}{1 - \frac{1}{3}}$$

$$= 27 \times \frac{3}{2}$$

$$= 40\frac{1}{2}$$

Sometimes we may need to know the value of a particular term in a series. In this case we will need to use logarithms. Using logs (base 10) we illustrate, with the following sequence where we wish to know at what point the term becomes less than 1.

100, 50, 25, 12.5, …..

To do this we solve for:

$$100 \times 0.5^{(n-1)} < 1$$

$$0.5^{(n-1)} < 0.01$$

$$(n-1)\log 0.5 < \log 0.01$$

The inequality sign changed now changes because we divide by a negative ($\log 0.5 < 0$).

$$n - 1 > \frac{\log 0.01}{\log 0.5} = \frac{-2}{-0.301}$$

$$n - 1 > 6.64$$

Therefore: $n > 7.64$, or since n, the number of terms in the sequence, must be a whole number, then $n = 8$. In the above sequence the 8th term will be less than 1. If you want to check that this is really the case, you can continue the sequence, using $r = \frac{1}{2}$, then we have:

100, 50, 25, 12.5, 6.25, 3.125, 1.5625, 0.78125, ...

It is indeed the 8th term = 0.78125 that is the first one that has a value less than 1.

Series and the Money Multiplier

Assume a bank has received a deposit of €100 with a 10 per cent cash ratio which enables an eventual expansion of the money supply of €1000. This assumes that the credit created is re-deposited within the banking system. The bank lends out nine tenths of the €100 deposited, €91. If this €91 is re-deposited in the banking system, nine tenths of that is loaned out.

Further monetary expansion occurs so that if we add up all these rounds we get €1000 of money as shown in Table 27.2. This is a convergent geometric series with a constant ratio $r = 0.9$.

TABLE 27.2 **The Money Multiplier with a 10 Per Cent Cash Ratio**

Deposit	Amount of Money Created (€)	Explanation
Original Deposit	100	Deposited with the banking system
First European Lending	90	0.9 × €100 lent
Second European Lending	81	0.9 × €90 lent
Third European lending	72.9	0.9 × €81 lent
: : : : : :	: : : : : :	: : : : : :
: : : : : :	: : : : : :	: : : : : :
: : : : : :	: : : : : :	: : : : : :
Total Money Supply	1000	Expansion = 10 × Original Deposit

The banking system retains one tenth of what is deposited with it so the cash ratio = one tenth. The other nine tenths is lent out so r in this case is 0.9. Then using our formula, where:

$$a = 100, \ r = 0.9$$

We have a series: 100, 90, 81, 72.9...... and the eventual total expansion converges to:

$$= \frac{a}{1 - r}$$
$$= \frac{100}{1 - 0.9}$$
$$= \frac{100}{0.1}$$
$$= 10\,000$$

The money multiplier is 10.

If the government wishes to reduce the power of the banking system to create credit and it specifies a cash ratio of 20 per cent rather than 10 per cent we have a series:

$$100, 80, 64, 51.2.........$$

And the eventual total expansion converges to:

$$\frac{100}{1 - 0.8}$$
$$= \frac{100}{0.2}$$
$$= 500$$

The higher cash ratio reduces the money multiplier. Table 27.3 illustrates this.

TABLE 27.3 **The Money Multiplier with a 20 Per Cent Cash Ratio**

Deposit	Amount of Money Created (€)	Explanation
Original Deposit	100	Deposited with the banking system
First European Lending	80	0.8 × €100 lent
Second European Lending	64	0.8 × €80 lent
Third European lending	51.2	0.8 × €64 lent
: : : : : :	: : : : : :	: : : : : :
: : : : : :	: : : : : :	: : : : : :
: : : : : :	: : : : : :	: : : : : :
Total Money Supply	500	Expansion = 5 × Original Deposit

Should we wish, we can use one of our previous formulae to find out how far this monetary expansion has progressed after any number of rounds. We will use the example of an initial deposit of €100 and a cash ratio of 10 per cent and find the size of the expansion after four rounds.

Using the formula with $a = 100$ and $r = 0.9$:

$$S_n = \frac{a(1 - r^n)}{1 - r}$$

We have:

$$S_4 = \frac{100 \times (1 - 0.9^4)}{1 - 0.9}$$
$$= \frac{100 \times (1 - 0.6561)}{0.1}$$
$$= \frac{34.39}{0.1}$$
$$= 343.9$$

With a higher reserve ratio of 20 per cent and an initial deposit of €5000, after 6 rounds of monetary expansion we would have:

$$S_n = \frac{a(1 - r^n)}{1 - r}$$
$$S_6 = \frac{5000 \times (1 - 0.8^6)}{1 - 0.8}$$
$$= \frac{5000 \times (1 - 0.262144)}{1 - 0.8}$$
$$= \frac{5000 \times 0.737856}{0.2}$$
$$= \frac{3689.28}{0.2}$$
$$= €18\,446.40$$

After six rounds of monetary expansion an initial deposit of €5000 has become €18 446.40. The eventual expansion will be:

$$\frac{a}{1 - r}$$

gives:

$$\frac{5000}{1 - 0.8}$$
$$= \frac{5000}{0.2}$$
$$= €25\,000$$

Now suppose we wish to know how many rounds of credit creation it will take with an initial deposit of €100 and a cash ratio of 0.9 before the next round of credit expansion is less than €70.

$$A = 100, r = 0.9$$

We need to find which would be the first term less than 70.

$$100, 90, 81, \ldots.$$
$$100 \times 0.9^{(n-1)} < 70$$
$$0.9^{(n-1)} < 0.7$$
$$(n - 1) \log 0.9 < \log 0.7$$
$$n - 1 > \frac{\log 0.7}{\log 0.9} = \frac{-0.15}{-0.05}$$
$$n - 1 > 3$$

Therefore $n > 4$ or $n = 5$.
The 5th term in this sequence is the first one which is less than 70.
We can check this. The series is:

$$100, 90, 81, 72.9, 65, 61, \ldots.$$

The 5th round of expansion at €65.61 is the first round below 70.

SUMMARY

The banking system, then, is an important factor in determining the volume of money in circulation. However, no modern banking system operates independently of a central bank. In principle, the government, through the central bank, can influence the banking system's power to create credit. Governments feel it necessary to do this because the amount of money in circulation affects the real economy. We shall see this in more detail in later chapters.

PROBLEMS AND APPLICATIONS

1 Calculate the amount of transactions on an island (where everyone wants to have every product) for 20, 40 and 200 people with and without a trading post.

2 Calculate the sum of the following series using the formula $S_n = \frac{a(1 - r^n)}{1 - r}$

a. 5, 10, 20, 40 80
b. 11, 22, 44, 88
c. 7, 21, 63, 189, 567
d. 5, 25, 125, 625, 6125, 15 625
e. $6, 2, \frac{2}{3}, \frac{2}{9}, \frac{2}{27}$

3 To which term do the following series converge?

a. $50, 10, 2, \frac{2}{5} \ldots$
b. $63, 9, \frac{9}{7} \ldots$
c. 1331, 121, 11, 1 …

4 At which point do the following series become less than 1?

a. $300, 100, \frac{100}{3}, \ldots$
b. 81, 54, 36, 24, …

5 Assume a bank receives a €2000 cash deposit and has to retain 50 per cent of the amount.

a. What will be the money multiplier and the total amount of money supply?
b. How many rounds will it take until the additional credit expansion is less than €1?

28 MONEY, GROWTH AND INFLATION

In this chapter we focus on the relationship between the quantity of money in circulation, the level of output and the price level. We then consider the quantity theory of money and its significance. Then we look at the Cambridge version of the quantity theory of money. Finally, we illustrate how the quantity of money in circulation is affected by people's decisions about holding cash or demand deposits.

THE RELATIONSHIP BETWEEN MONEY, OUTPUT AND THE PRICE LEVEL

Imagine a desert island with just four people, each of whom specializes in the production of a commodity for exchange with other members of the community. Each produces three units of output per year, each of these 12 units being exchanged for €1. The GDP is thus €12. The number of units exchanged, which we will call Y, is 12. The average price of these units, P, is €1. Then:

$$\begin{aligned} GDP &= PY \\ &= 1 \times 12 \\ &= €12 \end{aligned}$$

The exchange process is facilitated by the use of money rather than barter, but to begin with we assume that all money is notes and coins. We will introduce bank deposits later. Here on the island there are only six €1 coins. Can all the trade take place? It can if the coins are used more than once during the course of the year. In fact, on average, each coin will have to be used twice to support the exchange of the €12 of output. The average amount of times a coin changes hands we call the velocity of circulation, V. It follows that the money stock, M multiplied by V must be equal to value of the island's GDP.

$$GDP = PY = MV$$

Here:

$$GDP = 1 \times 12 = 6 \times 2$$

This must hold for any economy, not just this small, simple island economy. This can be written as:

$$MV = PY$$

We find the velocity of circulation, V, by dividing through by M to give:

$$V = \frac{PY}{M}$$

This is useful because we cannot measure V directly. It might seem impossible to measure the velocity of circulation. How can we observe how often, say, a €10 note changes hands? We can now see that it is straightforward to establish the value of V because we can measure both M and PY.

Transactions Velocity and Income Velocity

We now need to distinguish 'Transactions Velocity' and 'Income Velocity'. The transactions velocity of circulation equals the value of all transactions in an economy divided by the money stock. The income velocity of circulation equals the value of national output divided by the money stock. Until now we have used these two terms interchangeably because on our island there was no intermediate output. All sales were to final consumers. The total value of transactions $PV = GDP$. Recall that intermediate inputs refer to the value of goods and services such as energy and raw materials, which are purchased by one industry from another as part of the production process. GDP, or the sum of all values added, excludes these intermediate inputs. As a result, the total number of transactions is considerably more than the number of final transactions. Because of this, we have two definitions of the velocity of circulation, the transactions velocity, which we will call V_T, and the income velocity which we will call V_Y.

The transactions velocity of circulation is given as:

$$V_T = \frac{PT}{M}$$

Where:
T = the number of transactions
Or:

$$PT = MV_T$$

The income velocity of circulation is given as:

$$V_Y = \frac{PY}{M}$$

Where:
Y = the number of final sales. Thus:

$$PY = MV_Y$$

Real Income and the Price Level

Before proceeding it will be useful to establish the relationship between real income/output and the price level. Y is real national output and can be defined as:

$$Y = \frac{\text{Nominal GDP}}{P}$$

where P = the price level
Just as we have a nominal and a real level of output, we have a nominal and a real money stock.

$$M_R = \frac{M}{P}$$

Where:
M_R = real money stock
M = nominal money stock
P = some suitable price index

As we saw in Chapter 21, there are various price indices that one could use. The important thing is that we choose one that is consistent.

The Quantity Theory of Money

Now we examine what is known as the quantity theory of money. We begin with one form of the equation of exchange:

$$MV_Y \equiv PY$$

We write this with three bars to remind ourselves that it is an identity, not an equation. This useful but non-controversial identity is the basis of a controversial argument called the quantity theory of money. The theory proceeds from this identity to make two critical assumptions. First, V_Y tends to be constant in the long run. Second, Y in the long run, will be the full employment level of output. When there is unemployment, there is, by definition, an excess supply of labour. This will depress the wage rate until all who want a job have one. Thus we can regard Y as the full employment level of Y.

Now consider an increase in M. With V_Y constant, there must be an equivalent rise in PY but by assumption Y cannot change. Thus any increase in M must lead to an equal increase in P.

Formally:

$$M\,dV_Y + V_Y\,dM = P\,dY + Y\,dP$$

However, by the argument above Y cannot change since it is at the full employment level and so $dY = 0$. If we further assume V_Y is constant, then $dV_Y = 0$ too. So now we have:

$$V_Y\,dM = Y\,dP$$

Thus any increase in M must lead to an equal increase in P.

We can now write this relationship as:

$$\frac{dP}{dM} = \frac{V_Y}{Y}$$

so that the ratio between changes in the money stock, M, and changes in the price level, P, is the same as between the income velocity of money and the nominal income. Referring back to our island economy, we had:

$$M = 6$$
$$P = 1$$
$$Y = 12$$
$$V_Y = 2$$

Now suppose that M doubles, i.e. the money supply rises by 6, from 6 to 12 so that the change in M i.e. dM = 6. What happens to the change in the price level?

$$\frac{dP}{dM} = \frac{V_Y}{Y}$$
$$\frac{dP}{6} = \frac{2}{12}$$
$$dP = 1$$

That is, the change in the price level is from 1 to $P + dP = 2$. The price level doubles. Thus, according to this model, increasing the money supply will cause inflation.

The Cambridge Version of the Quantity Theory

The Cambridge version is an important variant of the quantity theory. The quantity theory discusses the supply of money but the Cambridge version focuses on money demand. In the quantity theory money is used only as a medium of exchange. In the Cambridge version it also acts as a store of value. People will wish to hold some cash for this purpose. Some part, k, of the money supply is not used for transactions but for the benefits of having wealth as cash.

Then:

$$M_D = k \times PY$$

Where:

M_D = demand for money

Now assume the economy to be in equilibrium, that is:

$$M_D = M_S$$

Where:

M_S = money supply

Assume also that k, at least in the short run, is fixed. Then taking the money demand equation and dividing through by k gives:

$$M_D \times \frac{1}{k} = PY$$

The original equation of exchange was:

$$MV = PY$$

The two equations are identical with:

$$V = \frac{1}{K}$$

i.e. the velocity of circulation is the inverse of k.

Illustrating from our island economy, let's assume that $k = ¼$, i.e. ¼ of the island's money supply is held as a store of value.

$$M_D = \frac{1}{4} \times 12 = 3$$

Then we have an identity:

$$3 \times \frac{1}{\frac{1}{4}} \equiv 1 \times 12$$

If $k = \frac{1}{2}$, then:

$$M_D = 6$$

$$6 \times \frac{1}{\frac{1}{2}} \equiv 1 \times 12$$

The Quantity of Money and Demand Deposits

If an economy has a banking system we can use the equation of exchange to explore the effect when some part of the money supply is held as bank deposits. Suppose that in another, larger, island economy there are 3000 €1 coins.

Then if people there hold all money as currency, the quantity of money is €3000. If people hold all money as demand deposits, and banks maintain a 10 per cent reserve ratio, then using our analysis from the last chapter, we have a money multiplier of:

$$\frac{1}{0.10} = 10$$

Thus if the people on the island hold all money as demand deposits, the quantity of money is 10 × €3000 = €30 000.

Suppose now that people hold part of the currency as cash and part as demand deposits, how can we calculate the money supply? To illustrate we will again assume that banks maintain a reserve ratio of 10 per cent, and that one quarter of the currency is held as cash.[1] By definition three-quarters of the currency is held as demand deposits. Demand deposits are three times the size of cash, so:

$$D = 3C$$

Where:
D = demand deposits
C = cash
Or:

$$C = \frac{1}{3}D$$

[1] We can distinguish between the monetary base and the money supply. In contrast to the money supply the monetary base is only that part of the money supply that is highly liquid.

Using the money multiplier:

$$D = 10 \times (3000 - C)$$

But we have worked out that $C = \frac{1}{3}D$, so substituting this gives:

$$D = 10 \times \left(3000 - \frac{1}{3}D\right)$$
$$= 30\,000 - \frac{10}{3}D$$
$$\frac{13}{3}D = 30\,000$$
$$D = €6923.08$$

We have now established the size of D. To find the total money supply we now need to find C:

$$C = \frac{1}{3}D$$
$$= \frac{1}{3} \times (6923.08)$$
$$= 2307.69$$

Adding D and C together gives:

$$6923.08 + 2307.69 = 9230.77$$

Alternatively we can say that the total money supply is $\frac{4}{3} \times \text{D}$

$$\frac{4}{3} \times 6923.08$$
$$= €9230.77$$

As we saw in the last chapter, any change either in the proportion of the money stock held as demand deposits, or in the reserve ratio will alter the size of the money supply. Now we can see that any change in the proportion of currency held by the public will also change the size of the money supply.

SUMMARY

We have shown how the money supply is determined by the banking system and by decisions made by the public with regard to their preferences for holding their wealth in a liquid form. However, in practice it is generally determined also by the actions of the central bank. The most important way in which a central bank influences the size of the money supply is by open market operations.

If the central bank wishes to increase the money supply, it can purchase government bonds from the public and from the commercial banks. The central bank pays the bondholders who keep their funds in the banking system. Thus central bank purchasing of bonds increases the commercial banks' ability to lend more money, resulting in an increase in the money supply.

If the central bank wishes to lower interest rates but the demand for money function is such that an increase in the money supply has little effect on the equilibrium interest rate, it can engage in quantitative easing. In this case the central bank buys assets, usually government bonds, with money it has created electronically. It then uses this money to buy bonds from the public, banks or other financial institutions. Again this increases the money supply.

Should the central bank wish to reduce the money supply, it can sell government bonds to the public and to the commercial banks. When the public and the commercial banks pay the central bank for the bonds this reduces bank liquidity and therefore reduces the banks' ability to lend money. The result is a decrease in the money supply.

PROBLEMS AND APPLICATIONS

1 The quantity theory postulates a relationship between the money stock (M), the velocity (V), the price level (P) and the level of real output (Y). Rearrange the terms this relationship to calculate the missing values in the problems below.
   a. Money stock is 1000, the price level is at 1.08 and real GDP is 3000. Calculate the velocity of money.
   b. Assume an output of $Y = 2400$, a velocity of $V = 3$ and M = 1000 in stock of money. What price level is supported by these figures?
   c. Assume an increase in the stock of money to $M = 1100$ while keeping V and Y the same as in b. How is the price level changing?
   d. With a velocity still at $V = 3$ and the price level still at $P = 1.25$, how much money stock is needed to support a real GDP of $Y = 3000$?

2 Revisit the parts b and c of the question above. Calculate the percentage change in money supply and in the price level. Explain your findings with the quantity theory.

3 The relative change in the price level over time t can be written as $\dot{P} = \frac{\frac{dP}{dt}}{P}$ (the inflation rate). If the quantity equation at any point in time t $M(t) \times V(t) = P(t) \times Y(t)$ is written in logarithms it becomes $\ln(M \times V) = \ln(P \times Y) \Leftrightarrow \ln M(t) + \ln V(t) = \ln P(t) + \ln Y(t)$. Use these approaches to show mathematically, that inflation is solely a monetary phenomenon according to the quantity theory as long as the velocity and real GDP remain constant. (i.e. if the velocity remains constant over time, then $\dot{V} = \frac{\frac{dV}{dt}}{V} = 0$).

4 Country A produces 200 products per period. Each product is worth €1. A produces a total intermediate input of 100 products, which are worth €0.5 each. Assume in country A are only coins worth €150 in total.
   a. Calculate the income and transaction velocity.
   b. Now assume that V and Y are constant. The central bank of A increases the amount of coins to €200. What will happen to the price level in A?
   c. Now imagine that the inhabitants of country A want to keep half of the money as cash at home. What has to be the velocity of circulation in this case?
   d. What is the money demand in case c?

5 In the economy of island B there are 5000 coins. The island has a working banking system with a reserve ratio of 5 per cent while the citizens of island B prefer to hold one fifth of the currency as cash. Calculate the total money supply.

PART 13 THE MACROECONOMICS OF OPEN ECONOMIES

29 OPEN ECONOMY MACROECONOMICS: BASIC CONCEPTS

In this chapter we look at domestic and foreign prices and their relationship to the exchange rate, including a consideration of hyperinflation and its effects on the value of a currency. Then we illustrate these relationships using the 'Hamburger Standard.'

FOREIGN AND DOMESTIC PRICES AND THE EXCHANGE RATE

Much of our analysis to this point has focused on the domestic economy, but most nations engage in trade with others. Here we examine the relationship between the price levels of different countries and their respective exchange rates. The exchange rate is the price of foreign money in units of domestic money. Alternatively expressed, it is the price of domestic money in units of foreign currency. This relationship is a key one because the purchase of a foreign good or service necessitates the exchange of domestic currency for foreign currency.

Some goods and services are virtually non-tradable internationally. It is very difficult to sell a haircut abroad, although if a foreigner visits a country and has a haircut whilst there the hairdresser has, in essence, exported that service. However, most goods and services are clearly tradable. We would expect that for these goods and services, the law of one price would apply. A good sold within a country will, ignoring transport costs, have the same price wherever it is sold. If this were not so, arbitrage would take place. Increased demand for the good where it is cheaper will drive up its price, and reduced demand where it is more expensive will lower its price until the goods are exchanging at the same price everywhere. Now consider the situation in two different countries. Exactly the same principle will apply. We expect the good or service to be the same price even if we consider different countries. Arbitrage will take place across international boundaries. However, there is a complication if the two countries concerned use different currencies. Then we would expect the same price, once we convert one price into that of the other country via the exchange rate.

We can gain an insight into these relationships by making some simplifying assumptions. Let's assume that we wish to examine relative prices between the euro area and the US. If we ignore taxes on imported or exported goods or services and ignore transport costs, then the price of good A in the euro area will equal the exchange rate multiplied by the US dollar price of good A. That is:

$$P_{\mathrm{Ah}} = E_R \times P_{\mathrm{Af}}$$

Where:
P_{Ah} = home price, expressed in units of the home currency
P_{Af} = foreign price, expressed in units of the foreign currency
E_R = exchange rate

What is true of one good or service will be true of any good or service if it is produced in both the domestic economy and also in the foreign economy, so in general we would expect that:

$$P_h = E_R \times P_f$$

To illustrate, let us suppose that the home economy is a European economy whose currency is the euro. We will further simplify by assuming that the market for foreign currency is determined by the purchase of goods and services only. We introduce capital movements in the next chapter. Now assume that the foreign economy is the UK, whose currency is the pound sterling. Consider Figure 29.1 which shows the foreign exchange market with the current price of the pound sterling expressed in euro terms and an equilibrium exchange rate of 1.5. That is, one pound sterling can be bought for €1.5. Now suppose that a good is exchanged in the UK for £20. Then the price of the same good in Europe would be:

$$\begin{aligned} P_h &= E_R \times P_f \\ &= 1.5 \times 20 \\ &= 30 \end{aligned}$$

It would sell in Europe at €30.

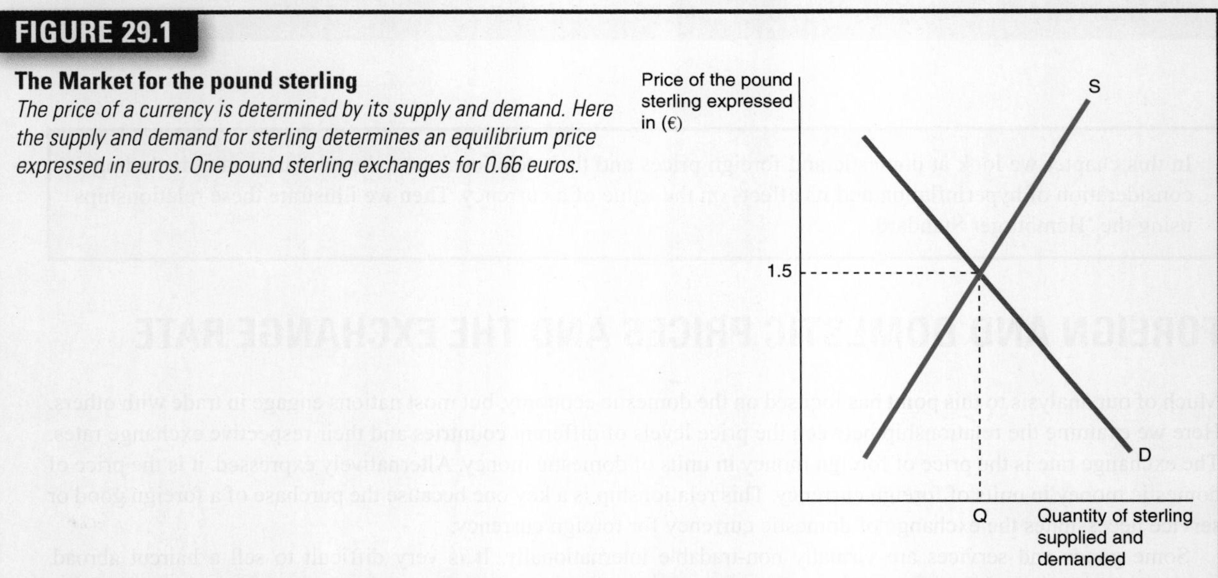

FIGURE 29.1

The Market for the pound sterling

The price of a currency is determined by its supply and demand. Here the supply and demand for sterling determines an equilibrium price expressed in euros. One pound sterling exchanges for 0.66 euros.

Alternatively, we can view the UK as the home market and Europe as the foreign market. The price of the euro in sterling terms must be the inverse of the price of sterling in terms of euros. In Figure 29.1 we showed the sterling exchange rate expressed in euros as €1.5. We show the same market in Figure 29.2 but this time we show the price of the euro expressed in sterling terms. Equilibrium is given as:

$$1/1.5 = 0.66$$

Thus if we now treat the UK as the home country and the country in the euro area as the foreign market we can find the sterling price of the €30 good.

$$\begin{aligned} P_h &= E_R \times P_f \\ &= 0.66 \times 30 \\ &= 20 \end{aligned}$$

It would sell in the UK for £20.

FIGURE 29.2

The Market for the euro

The price of the euro in sterling terms is the inverse of the price of sterling in terms of euros. We show the same market as we showed in Figure 29.1 but here we show the price of the euro expressed in sterling terms. The equilibrium price is 1 / 1.5 = 0.66. That is, one euro exchanges for £0.66.

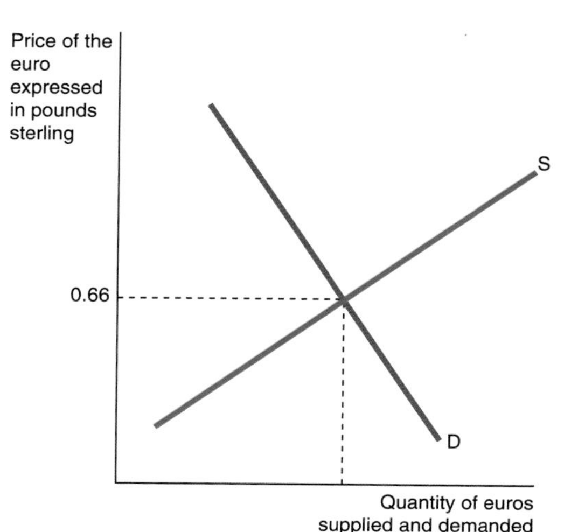

We can use these principles for the price of a good, which is exported, even if it is not produced in the importing country. The price of the good in the home country will equal the price of the good sold in the importing country, ignoring transport costs. Thus if a bar of chocolate is produced in Belgium where it is sold for €3, the home country, and it is also exported to Bulgaria where Belgian chocolate is not produced, we can calculate the price in Bulgaria.

First think of the Bulgaria as the home country, whose currency is the lev. The current price of the lev expressed in euro terms has an equilibrium exchange rate of 2. That is, one euro can be bought for 2 levs. Now suppose that the chocolate bar is sold in Belgium for €3. Then the price of the same good in Bulgaria would be:

$$\begin{aligned} P_h &= E_R \times P_f \\ &= 2 \times 3 \\ &= 6 \end{aligned}$$

It would sell in Bulgaria for 6 levs (BGN 6).

Now let us view Belgium as the home market and Bulgaria as the foreign market. The price of the euro in lev terms must be the inverse of the price of the lev in terms of euros. That is:

$$\frac{1}{2} = 0.5$$

Thus if we think of Belgium as the home country and Bulgaria as the foreign market we can find the euro price of the 6-lev good.

$$\begin{aligned} P_h &= E_R \times P_f \\ &= \frac{1}{2} \times 6 \\ &= 3 \end{aligned}$$

If the chocolate bar is selling in Bulgaria for 6 levs it would, ignoring transport costs, be selling in Belgium for €3.

The Effects of Inflation

It is now possible to see how inflation in the domestic economy affects the exchange rate. If the inflation rate at home exceeds that of the inflation rate in the foreign country, so that P_h rises relative to P_f, the exchange rate will tend to depreciate.

Foreign goods and services become relatively more attractive as they are now cheaper, relative to home-produced goods. Suppose, for example, the European price level rises faster than that of the UK. This causes European consumers to switch out of European goods towards the now relatively cheap UK goods and services. The rise in demand in Europe for UK goods means a rise in demand for sterling. As Figure 29.3 shows, this increases the value of the pound sterling from E_{R1} to E_{R2}. It costs more euros to purchase one pound sterling.

FIGURE 29.3

The Effect of Inflation in the euro Area on the Value of sterling

Inflation in the euro area encourages consumers to switch their demand for goods and services to the now relatively cheap British goods. This shifts the demand curve for sterling from D_1 to D_2, raising the equilibrium price of sterling.

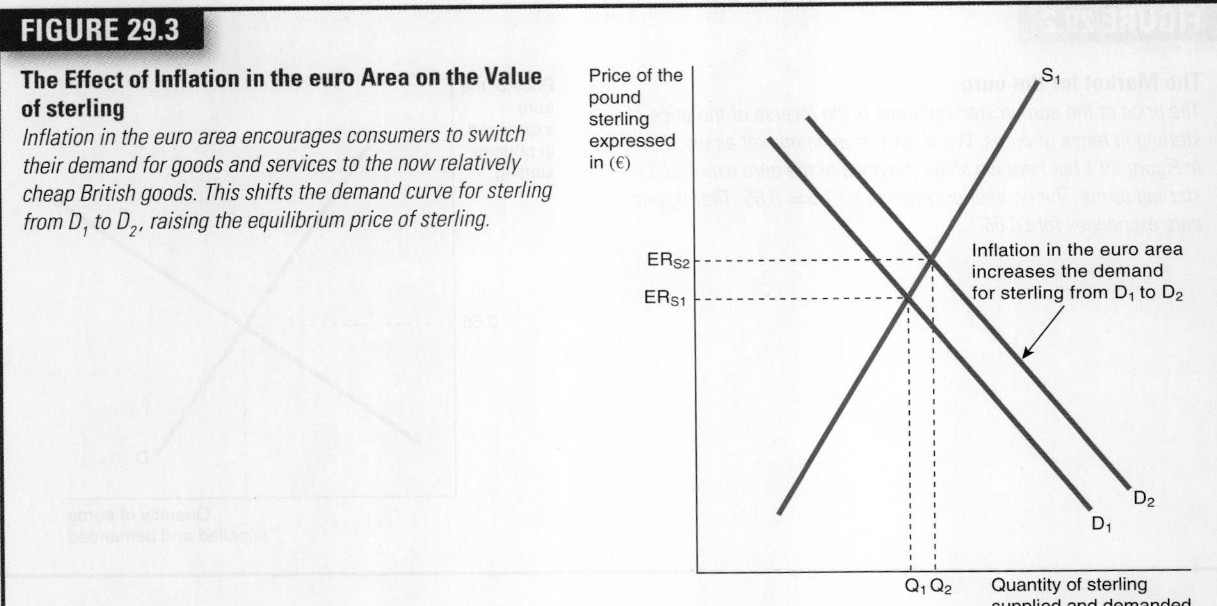

Alternatively, we can show this effect via Figure 29.4. The increase in the demand for sterling means that people are supplying euros in order to purchase that sterling. There is a rightward shift in the supply of euros, depressing its price from ER_{E1} to ER_{E2}.

FIGURE 29.4

The Effect of Inflation in the euro Area on the Value of the euro

Inflation in the euro area encourages consumers to switch their demand for goods and services to the now relatively cheap British goods. This shifts the supply curve for euros to the right from S_1 to S_2 as consumers switch out of euros into sterling. This lowers the equilibrium price of the euro from ER_{E1} to ER_{E2}.

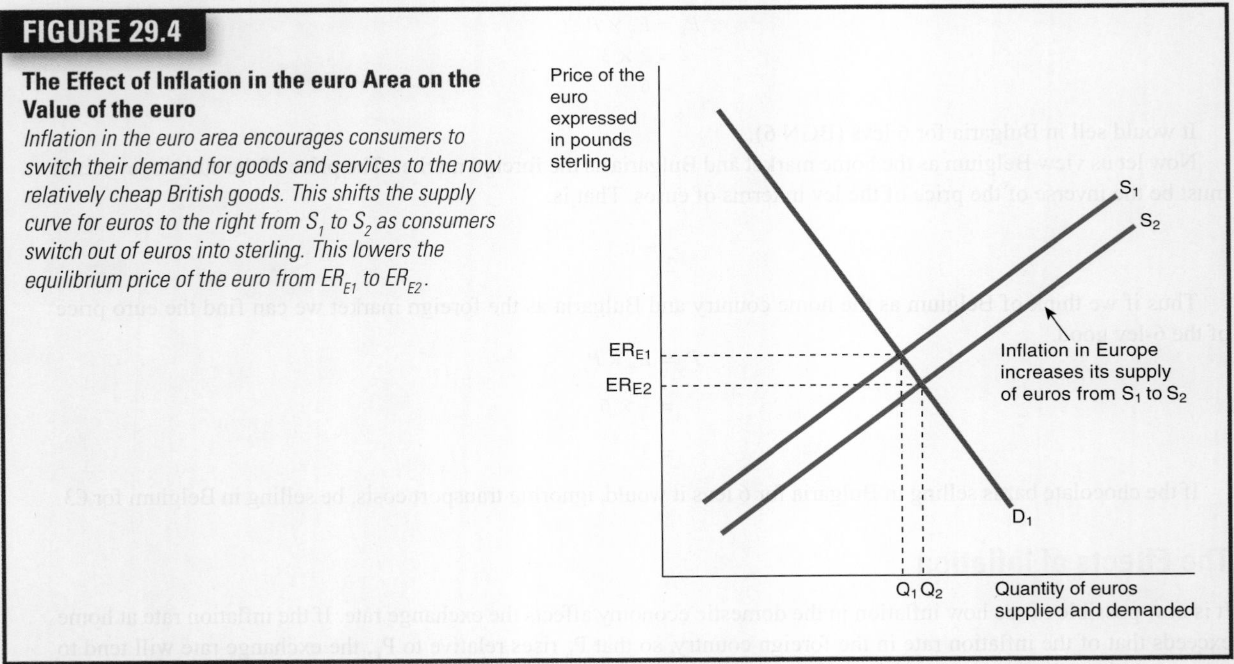

There is a double link between the rate of inflation in a country and its exchange rate. A change in the inflation rate will, *ceteris paribus*, affect the value of the currency. This is illustrated in Figure 29.4. However, a change in the value of the currency will also tend to affect the inflation rate. This is the link that we illustrate now.

If the result is a rise in the sterling exchange rate from, say, 1.5 to 1.7, we can find out the effect on the price of the good in the euro area that had been selling for €30.

$$P_h = E_R \times P_f$$
$$= 1.7 \times 20$$
$$= €34$$

If the sterling exchange rate has risen to 1.7, then the euro exchange rate has fallen from 0.66 to:

$$1/1.7$$
$$= 0.59$$

Hyperinflation in the Weimar Republic

As an extreme example of these principles, let's look at the Weimar Republic that replaced the German Empire in 1919. Over the next few years the money supply increased hugely as the government printed money, in particular to fund demands for reparations following the 1914–18 war.

Column 2 of Table 29.1 gives an indication of the massive increase in the money supply in the Weimar Republic over just a few years. Now look at column 3 which demonstrates the effects on the price level of this monetary expansion. To give a sense of these numbers, what would be the price of a typical good in November of this year if the inflation rate since July were to be the same as that of the Weimar Republic?

TABLE 29.1 German Hyperinflation and the Exchange Rate, 1920–3

Date	German Bank Notes in Circulation (000 000)	German Inflation Rate (Wholesale Prices Index)	US Inflation Rate (%)	Exchange Rate (German Marks to the US Dollar)
Jan, 1920	37 443	12.6	17.0	49.8
Jan, 1922	115 375	36.7	−11.1	186.75
July, 1922	189 794	100.6	−5.1	402
Jan, 1923	1 984 496	2785.0	−0.6	7260
July, 1923	43 594 737	194 000	2.4	160 000
Nov, 1923	400 267 640 301 854	726 000 000 000	3.0	130 000 000 000

Sources: www.inflationdata.com/articles/inflation-consumer-price-index-decade-commentary/inflation-cpi-consumer-price-index-1920-1929/;
https://mises.org[1]
www.wikipedia.org/wiki/Hyperinflation_in_the_Weimar_Republic

Using the principles of index numbers that we examined in Chapter 21:

$$I_{\text{NOVEMBER}} = \frac{\text{Price Index November}}{\text{Price Index July}} \times 100$$
$$= \frac{726\,000\,000\,000}{194\,000} \times 100$$
$$= 374\ 226\ 804$$

By November a weighted average of prices would have increased by 374 226 804 per cent since July. A typical good that you could buy in July for €1 would cost you €374 226 804 in November.

In the meantime, as column 4 shows, the price level in the US was, by comparison, hardly changed. The effect on the exchange rate was as we would expect. The value of the mark rapidly deteriorated. In January 1920 one dollar could be bought with 49.8 marks. By November 1923 it required 130 000 000 000 marks to purchase one dollar. There is a clear causal link here. Expansion of the money supply caused inflation, which in turn depressed the exchange rate.

[1] This is the link to the Mises Institute. The Institute has a wealth of material, including much on the German hyperinflation.

THE HAMBURGER STANDARD AND EXCHANGE RATES

When economists apply the theory of purchasing power parity to explain exchange rates, they need data on the prices of a basket of goods available in different countries. One analysis of this sort is conducted by *The Economist*. This newspaper occasionally collects data on a basket of goods consisting of 'two all-beef patties, special sauce, lettuce, cheese, pickles, onions, on a sesame seed bun.' It's called the 'Big Mac' and is sold by McDonald's around the world.

Once we have the prices of Big Macs in two countries denominated in the local currencies, we can compute the exchange rate predicted by the theory of purchasing power parity. The predicted exchange rate is the one that makes the price of the Big Mac the same in the two countries. For example, assume that the price of a Big Mac in the United States is \$3.57 and in the UK, a Big Mac is £2.29. Purchasing power parity would predict an exchange rate of £1 = \$1.56.

$$\text{PPP£/\$} = \frac{\text{Price in dollars}}{\text{Price in pounds}}$$

$$\text{PPP£/\$} = \frac{3.57}{2.29}$$

$$\text{PPP£/\$} = 1.56 \text{ (rounded up)}$$

If, however, the actual exchange rate quoted on the foreign exchanges was £1 = \$1.60 then the pound would be overvalued – you have to pay 4 cents more to acquire each pound than PPP implies. The extent of the overvaluation can be expressed as a percentage:

$$\%\text{ over or undervaluation} = \frac{\text{Implied PPP rate} - \text{Market rate}}{\text{Market rate}} \times 100$$

$$= \frac{(1.56 - 1.60)}{1.60} \times 100$$

$$= \left(\frac{-0.04}{1.6}\right) \times 100$$

$$= -2.5\%$$

In this example, the pound is overvalued against the dollar by 2.5 per cent and we might expect the pound to depreciate in the future.

If the market exchange rate were to be £1 = \$1.40, then the pound would be undervalued by:

$$\left[\frac{(1.56 - 1.40)}{1.40}\right] \times 100$$

$$= \left(\frac{0.16}{1.4}\right) \times 100$$

$$= 11.43\%$$

In this example, you have to pay 16 cents less than the PPP implies to buy a pound. It might be expected that the pound would appreciate in the future.

How well does purchasing power parity work when applied using Big Mac prices? Here are some examples from January 2016, when the price of a Big Mac was \$4.93 in the United States. The price of a Big Mac in China at this time was yuan 17.6. The implied PPP exchange rate therefore would be \$1 = yuan 3.57 (17.6 / 4.93). The actual exchange rate was \$1 = yuan 6.56 which suggests that the yuan was undervalued by 45.56 per cent. Table 29.2 shows similar information for a range of other countries.

You can see that the predicted and actual exchange rates are not exactly the same. After all, international arbitrage in Big Macs is not easy.

Purchasing power parity is not a precise theory of exchange rates (and Big Mac purchasing power parity even less so) and for some countries it does not always work well. Nevertheless, it often provides a reasonable first approximation.

TABLE 29.2 Purchasing Power Parity Using the Big Mac Index

Country	Price of a Big Mac	Actual exchange rate	Predicted exchange rate	US Dollar under or overvalued
Chile	2100 pesos	715.22 US$/peso	425.96 US$/peso	Undervalued by 40.44%
Britain	£2.89	0.68 US$/pound	0.57 US$/pound	Undervalued by 14.36%
Sweden	45 kronor	8.60 US$/kronor	9.13 US$/kronor	Overvalued by 6.11%
Russia	114 roubles	74.66 US$/roubles	23.12 US$/roubles	Undervalued by 69.03%
Japan	370 yen	118.65 US$/yen	75.05 US$/yen	Undervalued by 36.74%
Mexico	49 pesos	17.44 US$/peso	9.94 US$/pesos	Undervalued by 43%
Norway	46.8 krone	8.97 US$/krone	9.49 US$/krone	Overvalued by 5.77%

Source: *The Economist*, 7 January, 2016

PROBLEMS AND APPLICATIONS

1 In the foreign exchange market the euro is traded against the US dollar. View the euro as the home currency so that the exchange rate (in price notation) is $E_R\left[\frac{€}{\$}\right]$, it tells us how many euros we have to pay to purchase 1 US dollar.

a. The exchange rate $E_R^0 = 0.8\left[\frac{€}{\$}\right]$ moved to $E_R^1 = 1.0\left[\frac{€}{\$}\right]$ over a years' time. Which currency appreciated, which one depreciated and how large is the percentage change in either direction?

b. The euro appreciated by 5 % from the rate $E_R^0 = 0.8\left[\frac{€}{\$}\right]$. What is the exchange rate now?

c. On the foreign exchange market you can buy €1 for $1.5. What is the exchange rate in price notation?

2 The text explained that purchasing power parity demands, that $P_h[€] = E_R\left[\frac{€}{\$}\right] \times P_f[\$]$ prices of the same basket of goods in two countries should be the same, when valued in the same currency.

a. Prices in the foreign economy are at $P_f = 1.25\$$ and the exchange rate is $E_R^0 = 0.8$. What is the price level in the domestic economy?

b. Keep the exchange rate at $E_R^0 = 0.8$. How high are prices in the foreign economy, if the price level at home is at $P_h = €1.80$?

c. Prices abroad are $P_f = \$1.25$ and in the home market they are $P_h = €1.50$. Calculate the exchange rate.

d. What would you expect to happen to the exchange rate if the price level in the home country were to increase by 20% (inflation rate = 20%)?

e. Prices in the home country are at $P_h = €1.50$ and the price level abroad is $P_f = \$2.40$. The exchange rate is $E_R^0 = 0.8$. Is the overvalued or undervalued?

3 The statement of purchasing power parity in the form of $P_h[€] = E_R\left[\frac{€}{\$}\right] \times P_f[\$]$ is very strong. You can rewrite the equation in growth rates as $\dot{P}_h = \dot{E}_R + \dot{P}_f$. What does this mean, if the inflation rate between the home and the foreign country differ? Illustrate your thinking with numeric examples.

30 A MACROECONOMIC THEORY OF THE OPEN ECONOMY

In this chapter we consider the market for loanable funds. Then we show the effects the loanable funds market has on both net capital outflow and upon the market for foreign exchange. This is followed by an illustration of the effect of a government budget deficit on the loanable funds market and the foreign exchange market. Then we examine the effects of an import quota. Finally, we consider the effects of capital flight on these markets.

THE MARKET FOR LOANABLE FUNDS

The market for loanable funds is brought into equilibrium via changes in the real interest rate as highlighted in Figure 30.1. Remember that real interest rates are the nominal, money rates minus the rate of inflation. Here we have an upward sloping supply curve showing that as interest rates rise there is a greater willingness to lend in the market.

FIGURE 30.1

The Market for Loanable Funds

The market for loanable funds determines the quantity of funds exchanged and the rate of interest. The diagram shows an inverse demand function of $r = 13 - \frac{1}{10}Q_D$ *and an inverse supply function of* $r = \frac{1}{20}Q_S + 1$*, with an equilibrium rate of interest of r = 5 per cent. €80 million of loanable funds is exchanged.*

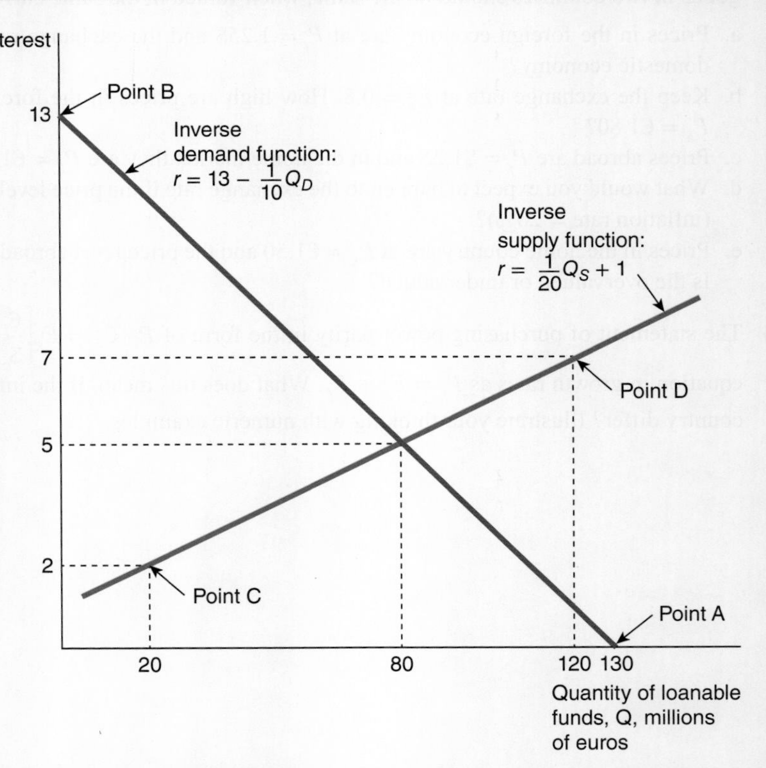

The downward sloping demand curve for loanable funds indicates that when interest rates are lower there is a greater willingness to borrow funds. We can think of the price of loanable funds as the interest rate. We can represent equilibrium in this market as we did for the market for a good.

Let us illustrate the working of the market by assuming that the following equations represent the market at present. The current demand for loanable funds is represented by:

$$Q_D = 130 - 10r$$

Where:

Q_D = the demand for loanable funds in a particular European country, in millions of euros.

r = the real interest rate

The current supply of loanable funds is represented by:

$$Q_S = -20 + 20r$$

Where:

Q_S = the supply for loanable funds in millions of euros in the same country.

Given these functions we can find the equilibrium real interest rate that equates the supply and demand for loanable funds where $Q_S = Q_D$.

$$-20 + 20r = 130 - 10r$$
$$30r = 150$$
$$r = 5$$

The current level of interest rate is 5 per cent. Now we can find the volume of loanable funds exchanged. Using the demand equation and substituting $r = 5$ into it:

$$\begin{aligned} Q_D &= 130 - 10r \\ &= 130 - (10 \times 5) \\ &= 80 \end{aligned}$$

Alternatively, using the supply equation and substituting $r = 5$ into it:

$$\begin{aligned} Q_S &= -20 + 20r \\ Q_S &= -20 + (20 \times 5) \\ &= 80 \end{aligned}$$

The market equilibrium quantity is €80 million per period.

If we wish to graph the market, then as we have seen before, we need to find the inverse demand and inverse supply functions in order to plot them. First let's find the inverse demand function.

$$\begin{aligned} Q_D &= 130 - 10r \\ 10r &= 130 - Q_D \\ r &= 13 - \frac{1}{10}Q_D \end{aligned}$$

Now we find the inverse supply function of loanable funds:

$$\begin{aligned} Q_S &= -20 + 20r \\ 20r &= Q_S + 20 \\ r &= \frac{1}{20}Q_S + 1 \end{aligned}$$

Given that we have straight line functions here, we can find two points on each of the graphs of these functions and join with a straight line. Consider first the inverse demand function. What is the quantity of loanable funds demanded when $r = 0$?

$$r = 13 - \frac{1}{10}Q_D$$

$$0 = 13 - \frac{1}{10}Q_D$$

$$\frac{1}{10}Q_D = 13$$

$$Q_D = 130$$

This point is plotted in Figure 30.1 as point A.

The other point we will find is the value for r at which $Q = 0$.

$$r = 13 - \frac{1}{10}Q_D$$
$$= 13 - 0$$
$$= 13$$

This point is plotted in Figure 30.1 as point B. By joining points A and B we have plotted the inverse demand function. Now we plot the supply function. What is quantity supplied when $r = 2$?

$$r = \frac{1}{20}Q_S + 1$$
$$2 = \frac{1}{20}Q_S + 1$$
$$\frac{1}{20}Q_S = 1$$
$$Q_S = 20$$

This is plotted as point C in Figure 30.1.

What is quantity supplied when $r = 7$?

$$r = \frac{1}{20}Q_S + 1$$
$$7 = \frac{1}{20}Q_S + 1$$
$$\frac{1}{20}Q_S = 6$$
$$Q_S = 120$$

This is plotted as point D in Figure 30.1. We have then joined these two points to give a diagrammatic representation of the supply function. From the diagram, equilibrium can be seen where $r = 5$ and $Q = 80$. We found this point using the demand and supply functions. We could also find it solving for the inverse functions. Thus:

$$r = 13 - \frac{1}{10}Q_D$$
$$r = \frac{1}{20}Q_S + 1$$

In equilibrium:

$$\frac{1}{20}Q_S + 1 = 13 - \frac{1}{10}Q_D$$
$$\frac{3}{20}Q = 12$$
$$\frac{1}{20}Q = 4$$

$Q = 80$ as we found diagrammatically from the demand and supply curves.

Now we can check the value for r when $Q = 80$. Using the inverse demand function:

$$r = 13 - \frac{1}{10}Q_D$$
$$= 13 - \left(\frac{1}{10} \times 80\right)$$
$$= 5$$

Using the inverse supply function:

$$\begin{aligned} r &= \frac{1}{20}Q_S + 1 \\ &= \frac{1}{20} \times 80 + 1 \\ &= 4 + 1 \\ &= 5 \end{aligned}$$

We confirm the equilibrium real interest rate as 5 per cent.

LOANABLE FUNDS, NET CAPITAL OUTFLOW AND THE FOREIGN EXCHANGE MARKET

Now we consider the link between the market for loanable funds and other markets beginning with net capital outflow.

When real interest rates are high, then, *ceteris paribus*, owning the country's assets is more attractive and net capital outflow, NCO, is low. Quite possibly low enough to be negative. However, with low real interest rates, NCO is higher. If we know the NCO function and we know the level of real interest rate given by the market for loanable funds, we can calculate the level of NCO. Let us assume that we have an NCO function of the form:

$$Q_C = 48 - 4r$$

Where:
Q_C = value of the net capital outflow
In inverse form:

$$r = 12 - \frac{1}{4}Q_C$$

This enables us to plot the functional relationship between the real interest and NCO. It also enables us to work out the level of NCO at any rate of real interest determined by the loanable funds market. First we plot the NCO function in Figure 30.2. Depending upon r, NCO might be positive or negative. For example, at $r = 16$ per cent we have:

$$\begin{aligned} Q_C &= 48 - 4 \times 16 \\ &= -16 \end{aligned}$$

We can also get this from the inverse form:

$$\begin{aligned} r &= 12 - \frac{1}{4}Q_C \\ 16 &= 12 - \frac{1}{4}Q_C \\ \frac{1}{4}Q_C &= 12 - 16 \\ Q_C &= -16 \end{aligned}$$

When the real interest rate is 16 per cent, NCO = Q_C = −€16 million per period. Given that we have a negative quantity there is a net capital <u>inflow</u> of €16 million per period.

With r at 5 per cent:

$$\begin{aligned} 5 &= 12 - \frac{1}{4}Q_C \\ \frac{1}{4}Q_C &= 12 - 5 \\ Q_C &= 28 \end{aligned}$$

When the real interest rate is 5 per cent, NCO = Q_C = €28 million per period, that is, there is a net capital <u>outflow</u> of €28 million per period.

At what rate of interest would the NCO be 0?

$$Q_C = 48 - 4r$$

When $Q_C = 0$:

$$0 = 48 - 4r$$
$$r = 12\%$$

These values are shown in Figure 30.2.

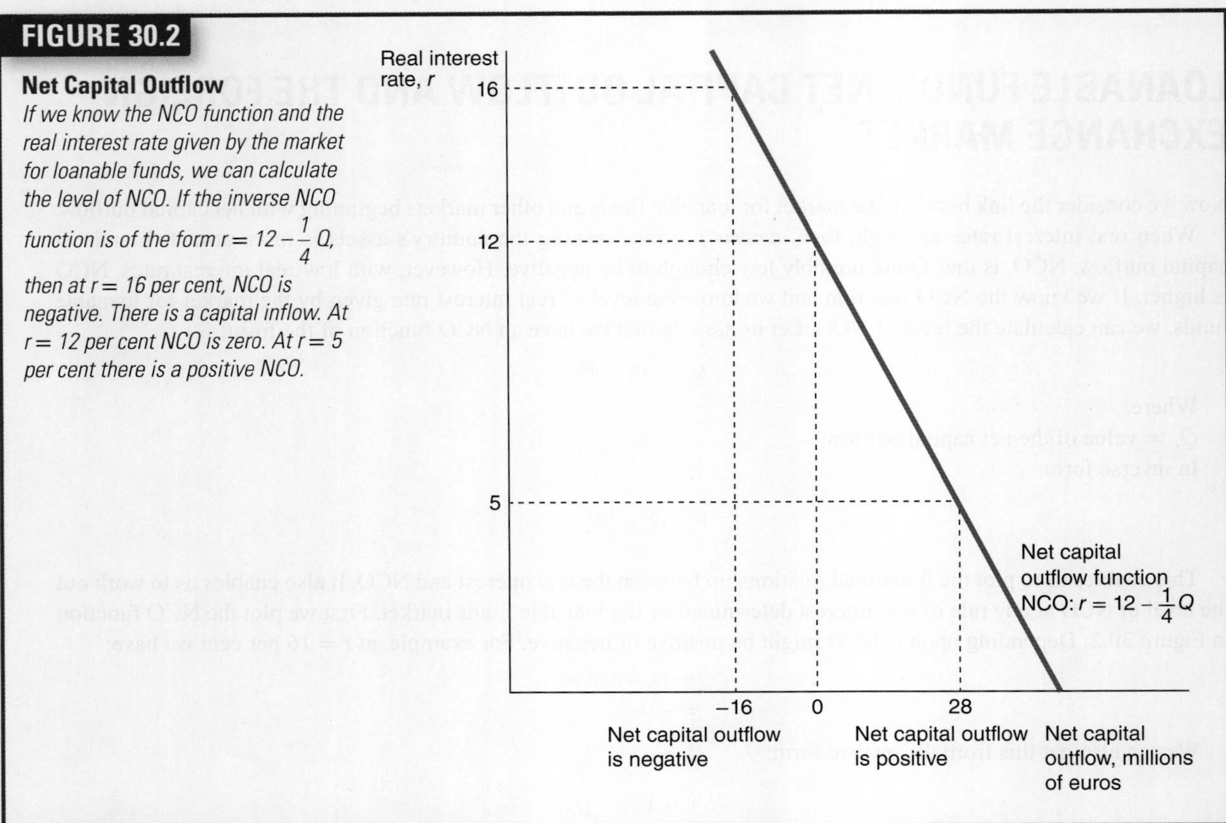

FIGURE 30.2

Net Capital Outflow
If we know the NCO function and the real interest rate given by the market for loanable funds, we can calculate the level of NCO. If the inverse NCO function is of the form $r = 12 - \frac{1}{4}Q$, then at $r = 16$ per cent, NCO is negative. There is a capital inflow. At $r = 12$ per cent NCO is zero. At $r = 5$ per cent there is a positive NCO.

Given that the real interest rate determined in the loanable funds market is 5 per cent we have a value for NCO of €28 million per period for this economy.

The level of NCO helps to determine the value of the exchange rate. This time we present the foreign exchange market in a different form from Chapter 29. There we assumed that there was no capital flow, just the flow of currency related to the purchase of exports and imports. Here we introduce the market with capital flows. Because foreign assets must be bought with foreign currency, the quantity of NCO determines the supply of the currency to be exchanged for foreign currency. The demand for the domestic currency comes from net exports. A depreciation of the real exchange rate increases net exports so the demand for foreign currency is negatively sloped. The market will bring the supply and demand of the domestic currency into equilibrium via an adjustment in the real exchange rate.

We shall assume that this negatively sloped demand function for foreign currency takes the following form:

$$Q_D = 56 - 28E$$

Where E = the exchange rate, the price of the currency in some other currency. In our case we will assume it to be the pound sterling, £.

Or we can find the inverse form:

$$28E = 56 - Q_D$$
$$E = 2 - \frac{1}{28}Q_D$$

Where:

Q_D = Quantity of the euro demanded
E = price of the euro in terms of the pound sterling

The supply of the currency, the euro, is given as €28 million. This amount we established from the market for loanable funds. In equilibrium $Q_S = Q_D$. Hence:

$$28 = 56 - 28E$$
$$28E = 28$$
$$E = 1$$

€1 swaps for £1 in the market for currency.

To summarize, the market for loanable funds determines the real interest rate, which, given our assumed functions for loanable funds demand and supply, gives an equilibrium real interest rate at 5 per cent and a quantity of loanable funds per period of €28 million. This interest rate determines NCO. Given our assumed NCO function, net outflow is €28 million. The NCO of €28 million determines the supply of euros on the foreign exchange market. Given the assumed demand function for euros, this determines the equilibrium real exchange rate of one pound sterling for one euro. This we show diagrammatically in Figure 30.3.

FIGURE 30.3

Simultaneous Equilibrium in Two Markets

The market for loanable funds determines the rate of interest, r, in this case five per cent. This is shown in panel (a). Given the NCO function we can now find the outflow or inflow of capital. In this case there is a net capital outflow of €28 million. This is shown in panel (b). Net capital outflow determines the supply of the currency on the foreign exchange market. Given a demand for euros of $E = 2 - \frac{1}{28}Q_D$, *then one euro will exchange for £1, as shown in panel (c).*

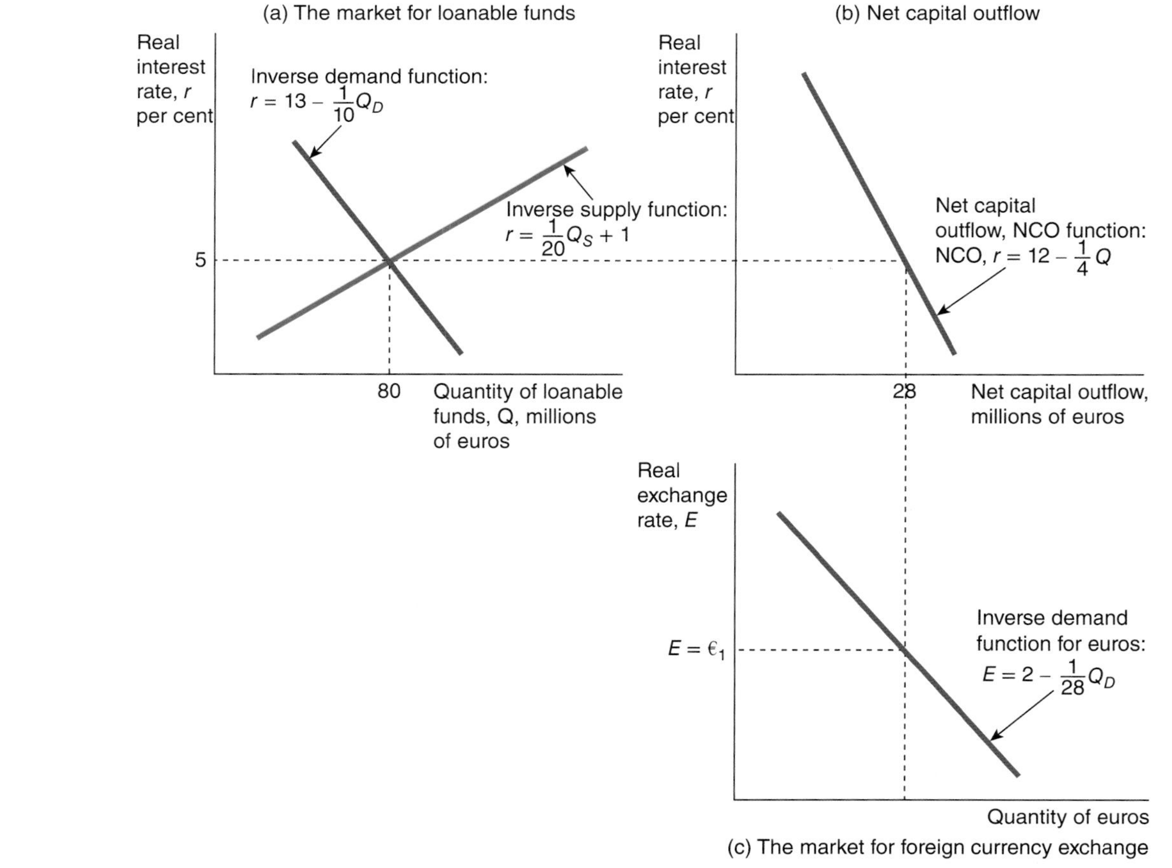

The Effect of a Government Budget Deficit on the Loanable Funds Market

We will now see how a government budget deficit can affect the loanable funds market, NCO and the exchange rate. The first effect will be in the loanable funds market. The budget deficit represents negative public saving. That is, it reduces the supply of loanable funds. Diagrammatically it shifts the supply curve for loanable funds up. We will illustrate this by assuming that the budget deficit changes the supply function for loanable funds to:

$$Q_S = -30 + 20r$$

The inverse supply curve is now:

$$r = Q_S/20 + 30/20$$
$$= (Q_S/20 + 20/20) + 10/20$$

i.e. the old supply curve has been shifted up by 1/2.

Since there is no alteration to the demand function we can now find the new equilibrium real interest rate. The new supply must equal the demand that is unchanged. Thus:

$$-30 + 20r = 130 - 10r$$
$$30r = 160$$
$$r = 5\frac{1}{3}$$

The reduction in the supply of loanable funds means that the level of interest rate has increased from 5 per cent to $5\frac{1}{3}$ per cent. Now we can find the new quantity of loanable funds exchanged. Using the demand equation and substituting $r = 5\frac{1}{3}$ we have:

$$Q_D = 130 - 10r$$
$$= 130 - \left(10 \times 5\frac{1}{3}\right)$$
$$= 76\frac{2}{3}$$

Alternatively, using the supply equation and substituting $r = 5\frac{1}{3}$:

$$Q_S = -30 + 20r$$
$$Q_S = -30 + \left(20 \times 5\frac{1}{3}\right)$$
$$= 76\frac{2}{3}$$

The new market equilibrium quantity is €$76\frac{2}{3}$ million per period.

If we wish to graph this new market equilibrium, then as we have seen before, we need the inverse demand and inverse supply functions in order to plot them. The demand function is unaltered so the inverse function is still:

$$r = 13 - \frac{1}{10}Q_S$$

Now we find the new inverse supply function of loanable funds. With the government budget deficit the supply function has become:

$$Q_S = -30 + 20r$$

Then:

$$20r = Q_S + 30$$
$$r = \frac{1}{20}Q_S + 1\frac{1}{2}$$

This is the new inverse supply schedule, as discussed previously.

Given that we have a straight line function again, we can, as we did earlier in the chapter, find two points on the new supply curve and join them with a straight line. Let us again ask what is the quantity of loanable funds supplied now when $r = 2$ with this new function?

$$r = \frac{1}{20}Q_S + 1\frac{1}{2}$$
$$2 = \frac{1}{20}Q_S + 1\frac{1}{2}$$
$$\frac{1}{20}Q_S = \frac{1}{2}$$
$$Q_S = 10$$

What is now the quantity supplied when $r = 7$?

$$r = \frac{1}{20}Q_S + 1\frac{1}{2}$$
$$7 = \frac{1}{20}Q_S + 1\frac{1}{2}$$
$$\frac{1}{20}Q_S = 5\frac{1}{2}$$
$$Q_S = 110$$

These points are plotted in Figure 30.4.

FIGURE 30.4

The Effect of a Government Budget Deficit on the Market for Loanable Funds

A budget deficit decreases the supply of loanable funds to the market, raising interest rates. With an inverse demand function of $r = 13 - \frac{1}{10}Q_D$ and an inverse supply function of $r = \frac{1}{20}Q_S + 1$, the equilibrium rate of interest is 5 per cent and €80 million of loanable funds is exchanged. With the new inverse demand function of $r = \frac{1}{20}Q_S + 1\frac{1}{2}$, the interest rate rises to $r = 5\frac{1}{2}$ per cent. The value of loanable funds exchanged falls to €76$\frac{2}{3}$ million.

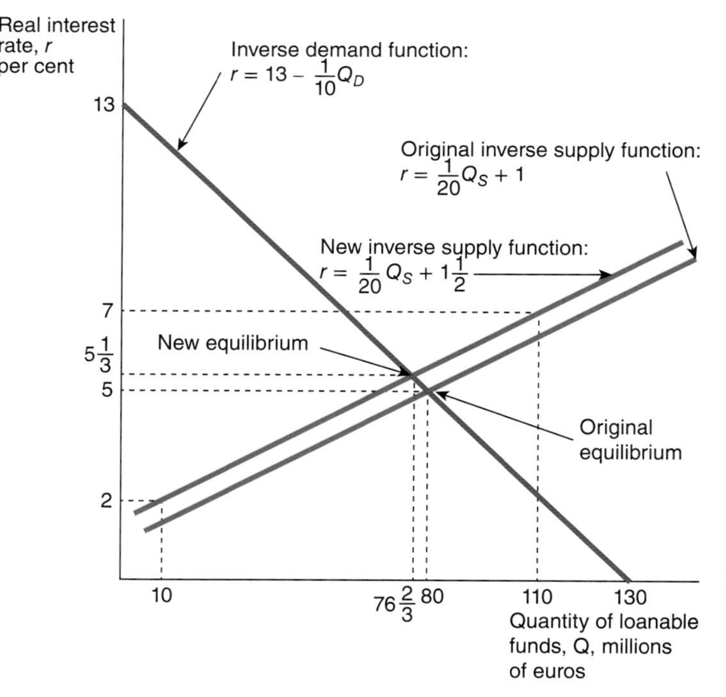

We have joined these two points to give the new supply curve. Figure 30.4 shows the new equilibrium at an interest rate of $5\frac{1}{3}$ per cent with a quantity of $76\frac{2}{3}$ which is what we found mathematically from the demand function and the new supply function. We can confirm this result by finding the new equilibrium from the inverse functions. Quantity demanded will equal quantity supplied. Therefore:

$$r = 13 - \frac{1}{10}Q_D$$

$$r = \frac{1}{20}Q_S + 1\frac{1}{2}$$

In equilibrium:

$$\frac{1}{20}Q_S + 1\frac{1}{2} = 13 - \frac{1}{10}Q_D$$

$$\frac{3}{20}Q = 11\frac{1}{2}$$

$$\frac{1}{20}Q = \frac{11.5 \times 20}{3}$$

$$Q = 76\frac{2}{3}$$

Now we can check the value for r when $Q = 76\frac{2}{3}$. Using the inverse demand function:

$$r = 13 - \frac{1}{10}Q_D$$

$$= 13 - \left(\frac{1}{10} \times 76\frac{2}{3}\right)$$

$$= 5\frac{1}{3}$$

Using the inverse supply function:

$$r = \frac{1}{20}Q_S + 1\frac{1}{2}$$

$$= \left(\frac{1}{20} \times 76\frac{2}{3}\right) + 1\frac{1}{2}$$

$$= 5\frac{1}{3}$$

We confirm the new equilibrium real interest rate as $5\frac{1}{3}$ per cent.

Now we can find out the new level of NCO.

$$Q = 48 - 4r$$

$$= 48 - \left(4 \times 5\frac{1}{3}\right)$$

$$= 26\frac{2}{3}$$

NCO is lower than before as a result of the higher interest rate. However, with our assumed function, it still remains positive at €$26\frac{2}{3}$ million. With this information we can now work out the effect on the exchange rate of the euro against the pound sterling.

The demand function is unchanged:

$$Q_D = 56 - 28E$$

The supply of the currency, the euro, is now $26\frac{2}{3}$. In equilibrium $Q_C = Q_D$. Hence:

$$26\frac{2}{3} = 56 - 28E$$

$$28E = 29\frac{1}{3}$$

$$E = 1.05$$

The reduced supply of euros causes the real exchange rate to appreciate so that now £1.05 exchanges for €1. This new equilibrium is shown in Figure 30.5. The supply curve for loanable funds shifted up, raising the equilibrium real rate of interest. This reduces net capital outflow and causes the exchange rate to appreciate by:

$$0.05/1 \times 100 = 5 \text{ per cent}$$

FIGURE 30.5

The Effect of a Government Budget Deficit in the Foreign Exchange Market

The budget deficit decreases the supply of loanable funds to the market, raising interest rates to $5\frac{1}{2}$ per cent. With an inverse demand function of $r = 13 - \frac{1}{10}Q_D$ and an inverse supply function of $r = \frac{1}{20}Q_S + 1$, the equilibrium rate of interest is 5 per cent and €80 million of loanable funds is exchanged. With the new inverse demand function of $r = \frac{1}{20}Q_S + 1\frac{1}{2}$, the interest rate rises to $5\frac{2}{3}$ per cent, as shown in panel (a). This reduces net capital outflow from €28 million to €$26\frac{2}{3}$ million. This is shown in panel (b). The reduction in NCO raises the real exchange rate of the euro by 5 per cent to £1.05 as shown in panel (c).

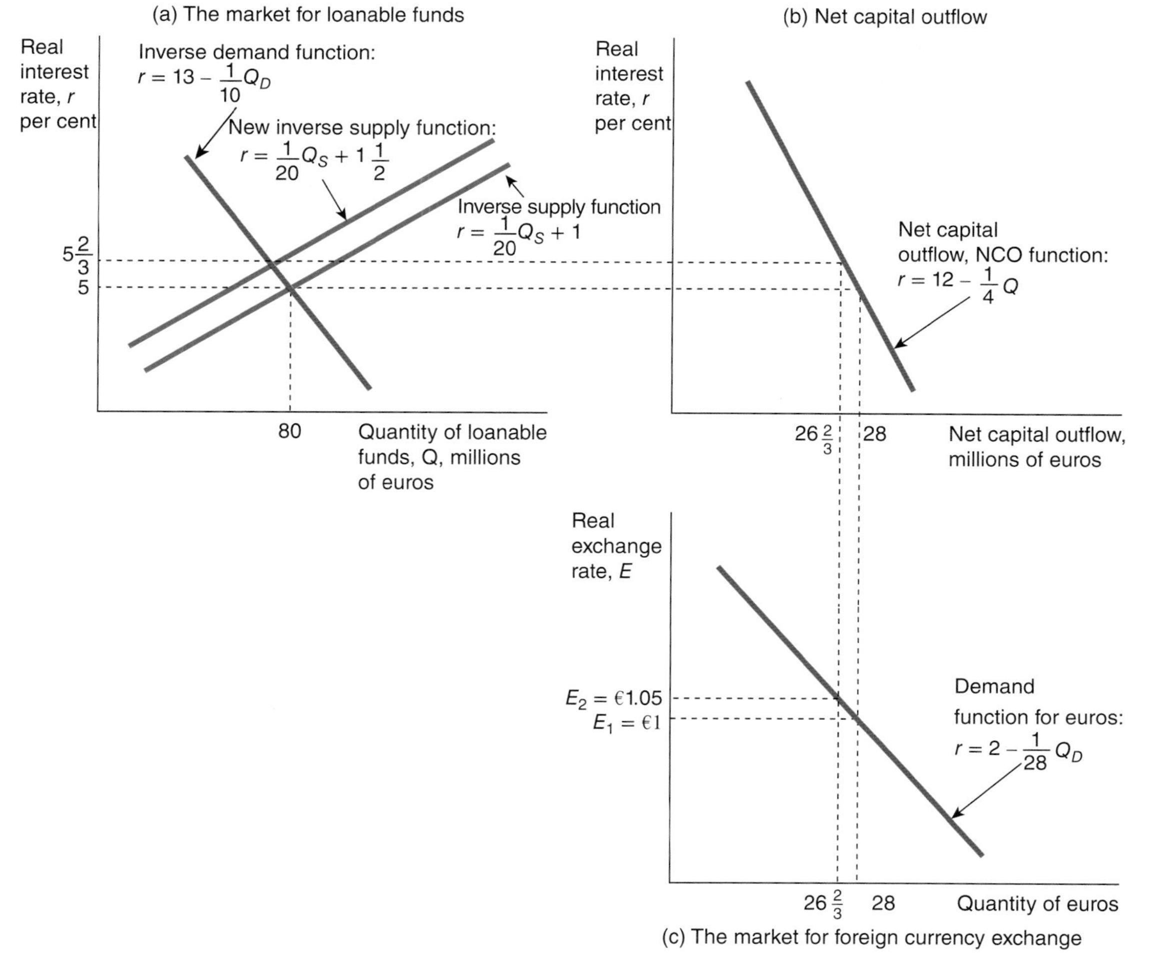

THE EFFECT OF AN IMPORT QUOTA

Next we consider the effect of an import quota by the home country. This has no effect on the market for loanable funds or indeed on net capital outflow. The import restriction reduces imports and therefore net exports increase. Net exports are a source of demand for euros in the foreign exchange market so the demand for euros shifts. Net exports rise for any given exchange rate, increasing the demand function for euros. Let us assume that the change in the demand for euros gives us a new demand function of:

$$Q_D = 63 - 28E$$

Where the supply of the currency, the euro, is given as €28 million. In equilibrium $Q_S = Q_D$. Hence:

$$28 = 63 - 28E$$
$$28E = 35$$
$$E = 1\frac{1}{4}$$

The value of the euro has risen. One euro now swaps for £1.25 in the market for currency. If we wish to show this information graphically we need to find the inverse form of the new demand function:

$$Q_D = 63 - 28E$$
$$28E = 63 - Q_D$$
$$E = 2\frac{1}{4} - \frac{1}{28}Q_D$$

This is shown in Figure 30.6. Notice also that net capital outflow is unaffected and so also is the market for loanable funds. The effect of the import quota on these markets is simply to raise the exchange rate.

The Effects of Capital Flight

Large and sudden movements of financial capital out of a country are referred to as capital flight. Financial investors may lose confidence in an economy and sell their assets there, transferring them to other economies. We now see how such movements affect the markets we have been examining. We shall continue to assume the flight is from a country within the euro area. Clearly, NCO is increased. This is not because of a change in the real interest rate. NCO increases for any given level of interest rate. In other words the NCO function shifts up, which increases the supply of the currency on the foreign exchange market. However, this also affects the market for loanable funds. When NCO increases there is greater demand for loanable funds to finance the purchase of capital assets abroad. That is, the demand curve for loanable funds shifts up. We use our original functions and illustrate how capital flight might bring about a new equilibrium in the markets concerned. Large capital outflows can make substantial changes to market equilibrium as we will now illustrate.

Our original NCO function was:

$$r = 12 - \frac{1}{4}Q$$

A shift of, say, 3 might now be represented by:

$$r = 15 - \frac{1}{4}Q$$

Our original demand for loanable funds function was:

$$Q_D = 130 - 10r$$

The supply of loanable funds was represented by:

$$Q_S = -20 + 20r$$

We found then that:

$$r = 5 \text{ and } Q = 80$$

FIGURE 30.6

The Effect of an Import Quota in the Foreign Exchange Market

The effect of the import quota is to reduce imports and therefore raise net exports, increasing the demand for euros. This raises the real exchange rate, as shown in panel (c). Net capital outflow is unaffected and so also is the market for loanable funds.

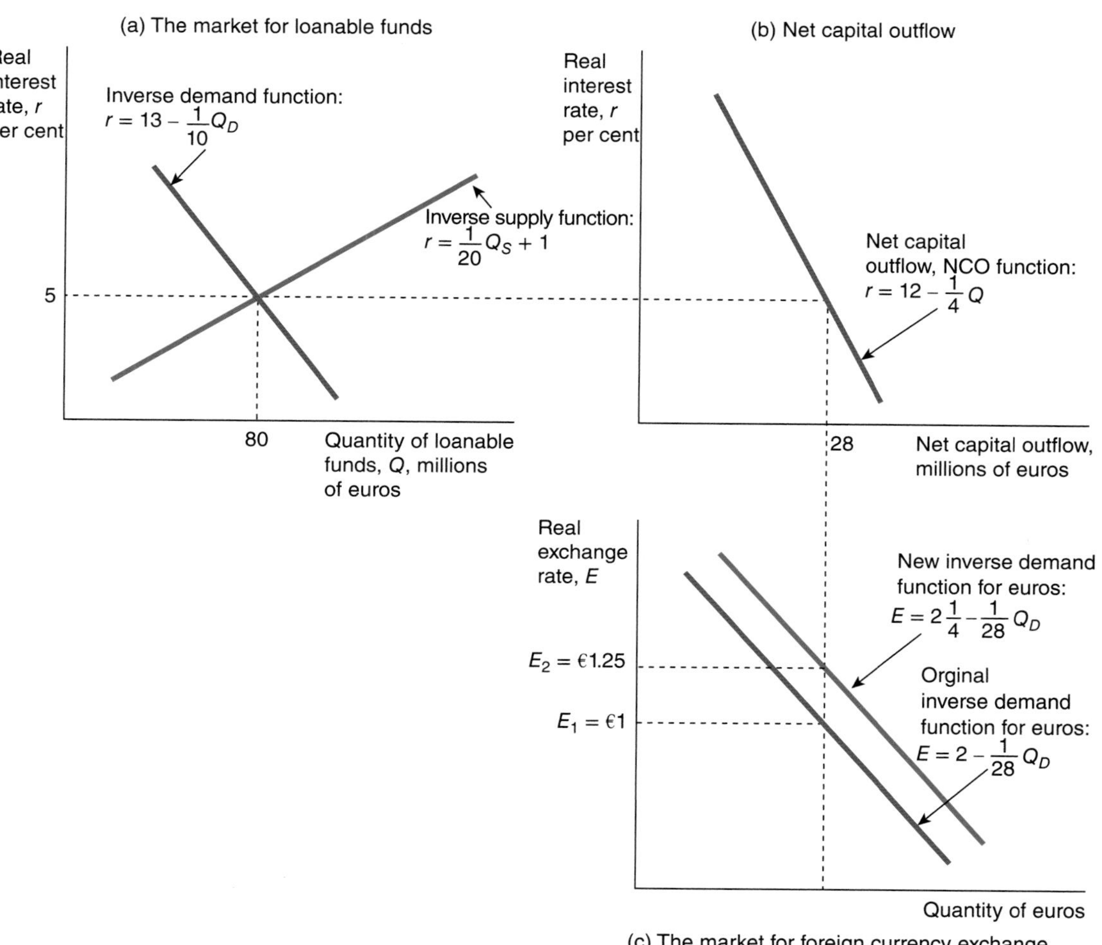

That is, the equilibrium real interest rate is 5 per cent and the market equilibrium quantity is €80 million per period. A shift of the demand function we will now assume to be represented by:

$$Q_D = 190 - 10r$$

The supply of loanable funds is unchanged at:

$$Q_S = -20 + 20r$$

Given these functions we can find the new equilibrium real interest rate that equates the supply and demand for loanable funds.

$$-20 + 20r = 190 - 10r$$
$$30r = 210$$
$$r = 7$$

The level of interest rate is increased from 5 to 7 per cent. Now we can find the new volume of loanable funds exchanged. Using the demand equation and substituting $r = 7$ into it:

$$Q_D = 190 - 10r$$
$$= 190 - (10 \times 7)$$
$$= 120$$

Alternatively, using the supply equation and substituting $r = 7$ into it:

$$Q_S = -20 + 20r$$
$$Q_S = -20 + (20 \times 7)$$
$$= 120$$

The new market equilibrium quantity is €120 million per period, increased from €80 million. If we wish to graph the market, then as we have seen before, we need to find the inverse demand and inverse supply functions in order to plot them. First let's find the inverse demand curve.

$$Q_D = 190 - 10r$$
$$10r = 190 - Q_D$$
$$r = 19 - \frac{1}{10}Q_D$$

The inverse supply curve of loanable funds is unchanged at:

$$r = \frac{1}{20}Q_S + 1$$

We can check our calculations for the new equilibrium quantity by using these inverse functions.

$$\frac{1}{20}Q_S + 1 = 19 - \frac{1}{10}Q_D$$
$$\frac{3}{20}Q = 18$$
$$\frac{1}{20}Q = 6$$
$$Q = 120$$

We confirm that the new equilibrium volume of loanable funds is €120 million per period. Now we check the equilibrium real rate of interest. Using the inverse demand curve:

$$r = 19 - \frac{1}{10}Q_D$$
$$r = 19 - \frac{1}{10} \times 120$$
$$= 19 - 12$$
$$r = 7$$

Using the inverse supply curve:

$$r = \frac{1}{20}Q_S + 1$$
$$= \left(\frac{1}{20} \times 120\right) + 1$$
$$= 7$$

We confirm that the new level of real interest rate is 7 per cent. The new equilibrium interest rate and quantity of loanable funds is shown in panel (a) of Figure 30.7.

The effect of capital flight is to shift the NCO function to the right. We are assuming that it is now:

$$r = 15 - \frac{1}{4}Q$$

FIGURE 30.7

The Effect of Capital Flight in the Foreign Exchange Market

Capital flight from a country changes the NCO function as shown in panel (b). This increases the supply of its currency on the foreign exchange market depressing the exchange rate as shown in panel (c). In this case the price of the euro falls from €1= £1 to €1 = £0.86. It also affects the market for loanable funds. There is now a greater demand for loanable funds to finance the purchase of capital assets abroad, shifting the demand curve for loanable funds. This raises interest rates as can be seen in panel (a). In this case the real interest rate has changed from r = 5 per cent to r = 7 per cent.

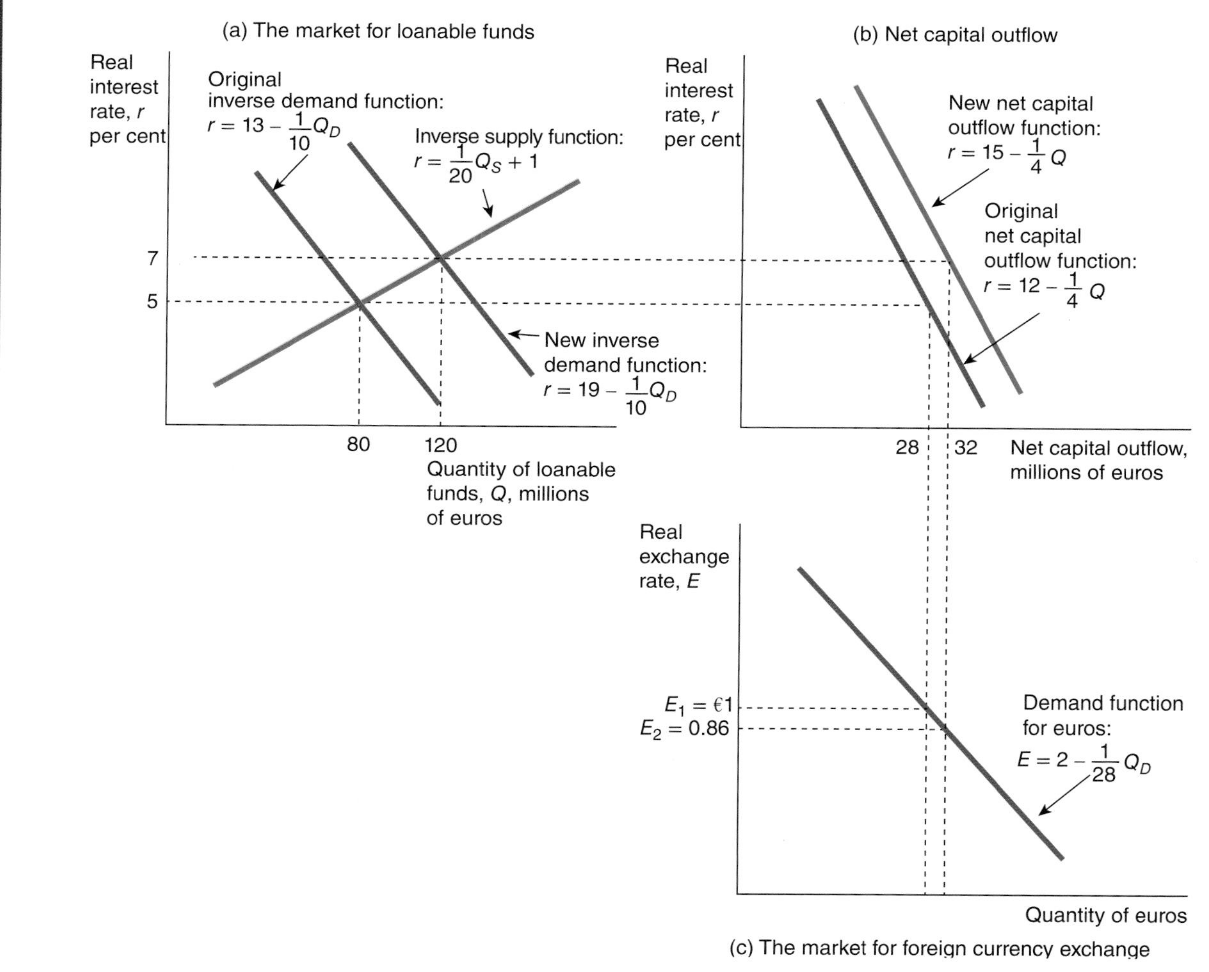

Therefore with a real interest rate of 7 per cent determined in the market for loanable funds the level of NCO is given as:

$$7 = 15 - \frac{1}{4}Q$$

$$\frac{1}{4}Q = 8$$

$$Q = 32$$

The new level of NCO is €32 million per period. We show this in panel (b) of Figure 30.7. We shall assume the negatively sloped demand function for foreign currency is the original one, that is, before the shift from the import quota. So it takes the following form:

$$Q_D = 56 - 28E$$

Where E = the exchange rate, the price of the currency in some other currency. In our case we continue to assume it to be the pound sterling, £.

Or we can find the inverse form:

$$28E = 56 - Q_D$$

$$E = 2 - \frac{1}{28}Q_D$$

Where:

Q_D = quantity of the euro demanded.

E = price of the euro in terms of the pound, sterling.

The supply of the currency, the euro, is now given as €32 million. In equilibrium $S = D$. Hence:

$$E = 2 - \frac{1}{28}Q_d$$

$$= 2 - \frac{1}{28} \times 32$$

$$= 2 - 1.14$$

$$E = 0.86$$

€1 which was originally swapping for £1 in the market for currency, now exchanges for £0.86. Capital flight has reduced the value of the euro.

The Greek Crisis

What we have just described illustrates what has happened in Greece in recent years with substantial capital flight induced by the belief that holders of Greek debt might not be paid at maturity. Real interest rates rose very sharply as our model indicates. The difference between the Greek situation and our model is the value of the euro. Had Greece left the euro area during the period of capital flight, its new currency would indeed have been worth substantially less on the foreign exchange market. However, other euro area countries supported the Greek economy, thus preventing the fall that would have taken place without such European intervention.

PROBLEMS AND APPLICATIONS

1 In Chapter 25 on the time value of money you learned that there is a connection between the interest rate and the decision for investments. Explain the downward sloping demand for loanable funds using this line of reasoning.

2 Describe the market for loanable funds with the demand $Q_D = -100r + 800$ and the supply given by $Q_S = 200r - 400$ as functions of the interest rate r.

a. Find the inverse of the demand and the supply function for loanable funds and show them in a graph.

b. Confirm the equilibrium interest rate r and quantity of loanable funds from the graph with a calculation.

3 In addition to the market for loanable funds you also look at net capital outflows as a function of the interest rate NCO = $-250r + 1000$. Net capital outflows are viewed as the supply of domestic currency in the foreign exchange market, completely inelastic with respect to the exchange rate. The demand for domestic currency $Q_D^€$ in the foreign exchange markets stems from net exports which are assumed to shrink as the price of the domestic currency in terms of foreign currency rises. If you define the exchange rate as the number of US dollars paid per euro $E_Q\left[\frac{\$}{€}\right]$, the demand for euros could be written as $Q_D^€ = 750 - 125E_Q$.

a. Invert the function to show the interest rate dependent on net capital outflows also in a graph.

b. Use your results from Problem 2 to find the equilibrium net capital outflow given the equilibrium interest rate.

c. Transfer the information on net capital outflows into a graph of the foreign exchange market where you have the exchange rate (as defined above) on the vertical axis and the quantity of local currency (€) on the horizontal axis.

d. Find the equilibrium exchange rate where the quantity of euros supplied matches the quantity of euro demanded in the foreign exchange market and check your result in the graph.

4 In this chapter you have developed a model of the loanable funds market, the net capital exports and the foreign exchange market that was represented by these equations:

Demand $Q_D = -100r + 800$ and supply $Q_S = 200r - 400$ in the market for loanable funds.

Net capital outflows: $Q_S^{€} = \text{NCO} = -250r + 1000$ which are equal to the supply of home currency in the foreign exchange market and the demand for euros $Q_D^{€} = 750 - 125E_Q$.

a. Assume an expansion in the supply of loanable funds by 300 units for any level of the interest rate. Write out the new supply function and the inverse.
b. Calculate the new equilibrium in the market for loanable funds.
c. How large is the net capital outflow now?
d. How is the exchange rate affected by the shift in the market for loanable funds?

PART 14 SHORT-RUN ECONOMIC FLUCTUATIONS

31 BUSINESS CYCLES

In this chapter we begin a consideration of the business cycle. Some possible explanations of why this phenomenon occurs will be left until a later chapter. Here we identify the variations in economic activity and show how to measure their size.

INTRODUCTION

A business cycle is the result of fluctuations in GDP that an economy experiences over time. It is an example of a time series, a collection of quantitative observations measured over some given time period. Here we seek to identify and measure the size of these fluctuations. An analysis of the reasons for them we defer to a later chapter. We can identify four elements, namely a long-run (or secular) trend, a seasonal variation, a cyclical variation and an irregular variation. We look briefly at the meaning of these terms.

The long-term trend is an underlying movement in some direction. For most modern economies the GDP trend over time is upwards even though in the short term there may be falls. The upward trend, economic growth, we considered in an earlier chapter. Three possible trends are shown in Panels (a), (b) and (c) of Figure 31.1. Panel (a) describes a linear trend. However, one may observe non-linear trends, for example, in Panel (b), which may indicate an economy where technological improvements are occurring ever more rapidly. On the other hand a different non-linear trend can be seen in Panel (c), which might suggest an economy where the easiest technological advances have been utilized but new discoveries are increasingly harder to achieve.

In principle, we can separate out a number of factors affecting a time series of GDP growth. Most such time series data will have a seasonal variation. This tends to be true for GDP growth where quarterly data shows higher growth rates for some periods of the year than for others. However, since we are interested in a longer term than a year, we shall not analyze these variations.

Cyclical variations are the recurrent variations in a time series usually lasting longer than a year. They can be thought of as what is left after the removal of the other effects. These variations can have considerable economic, social and political consequences and in a later chapter we will briefly examine some possible causes.

Irregular variations are sometimes readily explained. There may be declines, for example, because of a one off event such as a war or a string of bank failures. Others, however, can have far more obscure causes. Our purpose is to discover how to find the trend. As we shall see in this chapter, many governments take account of information about deviations from the trend in conducting economic policy. To summarize, a GDP growth series will usually comprise:

1. a trend
2. seasonal variations
3. cyclical fluctuations
4. irregular variations.

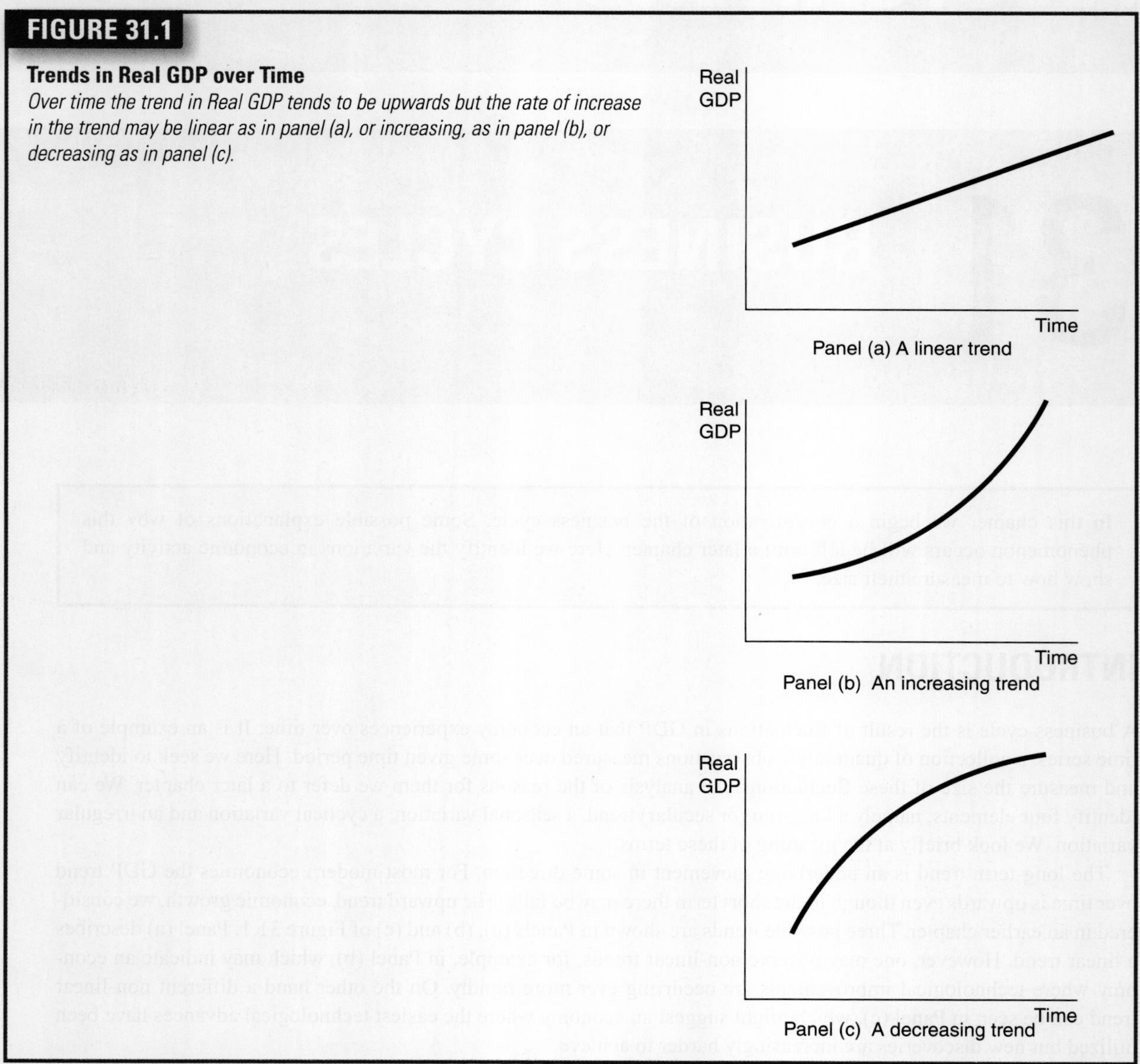

FIGURE 31.1

Trends in Real GDP over Time

Over time the trend in Real GDP tends to be upwards but the rate of increase in the trend may be linear as in panel (a), or increasing, as in panel (b), or decreasing as in panel (c).

THE LONG-TERM LINEAR TREND

We begin with a look at the trend. We can establish the trend in a time series using the principles of regression analysis. In the first instance we will assume that the trend is a linear one.

Finding the linear trend means looking to find the best fit straight line through a series of observations such as those described in Figure 31.2. The best fit is the one that minimizes the sum of the differences between the observations and the trend line after each distance has been squared. It is important to take the square of the differences, for without this the positive and negative differences would cancel each other out and so disappear from the calculations. The commonest trend equation is the 'linear equation in two unknowns' taking the form:

$$y = a + bx + e$$

Where:

y = the variable measured up the vertical axis, in our case GDP
x = the variable along the horizontal axis, in our case time in years
a = the y intercept, that is the value of y when $x = 0$
b = the slope of the trend line
e = the error term, that is, the error in predicting the value of y, given the value of x

This trend line can be found by using a technique called linear regression. It requires that:

$\sum_{i=1}^{n}(y_i - \hat{y}_i)^2$ is minimized

Where:

y_i = each of the n individual observations for y (indexed by i so that the first is $i = 1$, the second $i = 2$ and so on up to $i = n$) $\hat{y}_i$ = the value of the estimates.

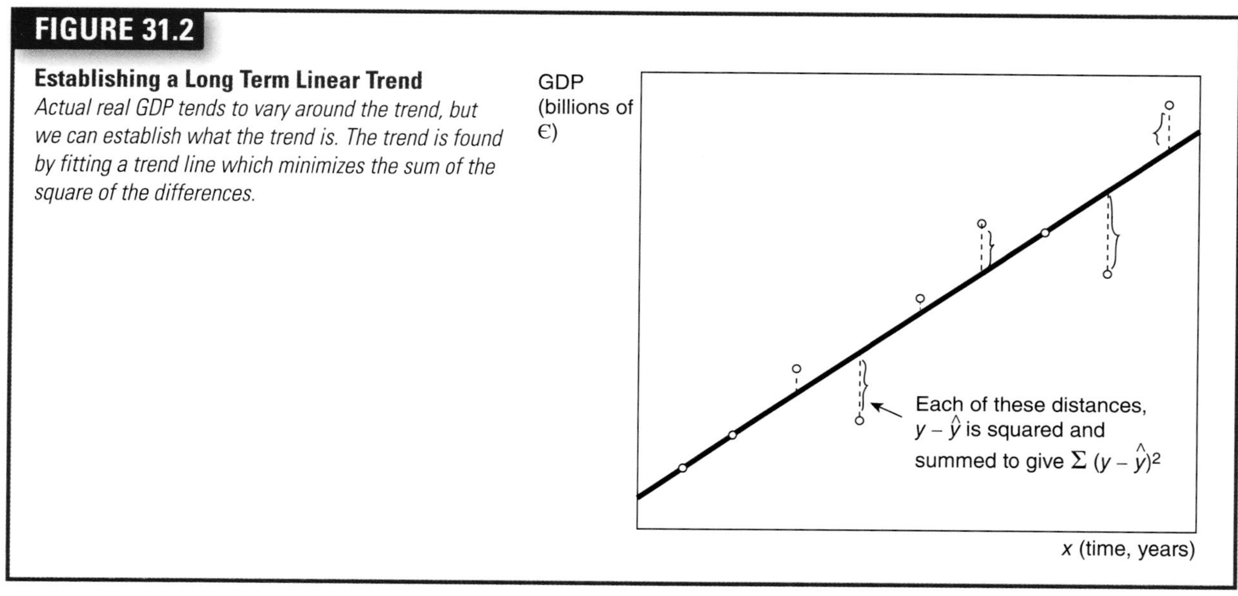
GDP
(billions of
€)
Each of these distances,
$y - \hat{y}$ is squared and
summed to give $\Sigma\ (y - \hat{y})^2$
x (time, years)

FIGURE 31.2

Establishing a Long Term Linear Trend

Actual real GDP tends to vary around the trend, but we can establish what the trend is. The trend is found by fitting a trend line which minimizes the sum of the square of the differences.

Figure 31.2 shows an attempt to describe this best fit where some years GDP is on trend, some years it is below trend and some years above trend. We can now see how we find the trend line with an example. Table 31.1 shows an economy whose long-term growth path is upward but with variations around the trend. How do we calculate the trend output?

The formulae used to find these values are:

$$\sum y = \text{n}a + b\left(\sum x\right) \tag{1}$$

and

$$\sum xy = a\left(\sum x\right) + b\left(\sum x^2\right) \tag{2}$$

Where:

n = number of observations a and b are constants.

Since the x's refer to time periods, in our case it will be years, we can change the scale so that in the new scale the sum of the x's, $\sum x$, becomes zero. This process is called coding. We take the middle value of the period under consideration and assign this x a value of zero. Earlier years are assigned negative value, for example the previous year is assigned a value of -1, the year before that, the value is -2 and so on. Later years are assigned positive values, 1, 2, 3, etc. Since it is the middle observation that takes the value of zero, the sum of these values, $\sum x$, must be zero.

Then from (1) we get:

$$\sum y = na$$

$$a \frac{\sum y}{n}$$

From (2) we get:

$$\sum xy = b\left(\sum x^2\right)$$

$$b = \frac{\sum xy}{\sum x^2}$$

TABLE 31.1 **Illustrative GDP Data over a 9-Year Period**

Year	Annual GDP, billions of euros
2009	12
2010	13.5
2011	13
2012	16
2013	17.5
2014	16
2015	15
2016	17
2017	20

Let's see how we can use this coding process with this particular set of data and so establish the trend line for this country's GDP. To help in this process, Table 31.2 shows the steps in calculating the different values for the formula.

TABLE 31.2 **The Calculation of Trend GDP over a 9-Year Period**

Year	x	Annual GDP, billions of euros (y)	xy	x2
2009	−4	12	−48	16
2010	−3	13.5	−40.5	9
2011	−2	13	−26	4
2012	−1	16	−16	1
2013	0	17.5	0	0
2014	1	16	16	1
2015	2	15	30	4
2016	3	17	51	9
2017	4	20	80	16
Total	**0**	**140**	**46.5**	**60**

Referring to the formulae and Table 31.2 we have:

$$n = 9$$

If we sum all the GDP values from 2009 to 2017 we get 140. In other words:

$$\sum y = 140$$

$$\sum xy = 46.5$$

$$\sum x^2 = 60$$

Now we can find a as follows:

$$a = \frac{\sum y}{n}$$
$$= \frac{140}{9}$$
$$= 15.56$$
$$a = €15.56 \textit{ billion}$$

We find b as follows:

$$b = \frac{\sum xy}{\sum x^2}$$
$$= \frac{46.5}{60}$$
$$= 0.78$$
$$b = €0.78 \text{ billion}$$

Then the trend equation for our economy is:

$$15.56 + 0.78x$$

That is, the trend value for 2013 is €15.56 billion and the annual increment, annual growth, is €0.78 billion. We can now use this equation to discover the trend value for any year by substituting into the equation the appropriate value for x.

For 2009 we can substitute $x = -4$ into our trend equation and we have:

$$\hat{y} = 15.56 + 0.78 \times (-4) = 12.44$$

The trend GDP for 2009 is €12.44 billion.

For 2017 we can substitute $x = 4$ into the equation:

$$\hat{y} = 15.56 + 0.78 \times 4 = 18.68$$

The trend GDP for 2017 is €18.68 billion.

We can plot these two values in Figure 31.2 and join them with a straight line. For any year the deviation from the trend is readily found. For example, for 2017 $\hat{y} = 18.68$ and y = 20. Then the cyclical irregular variation from the trend for that year is:

$$€20 - €18.68 = €1.32 \text{ billion.}$$

In that particular year GDP was above trend.

A Trend with an Even Number of Observations

Should there be an even number of observations, the coding must be modified. There will now be two middle observations with the midpoint of the series falling between them. We then assign $x = 0$ to this midpoint and count in half years. The x's become 1, 3, 5, 7….. for following years and −1, −3, −5, −7…… for the previous years. Thus whether there is an even or an odd number of observations, $\sum x = 0$. Let us illustrate the procedure by calculating the trend equation for the series in Table 31.2 when we have one more observation, namely a value of €20 billion for 2018 GDP. The calculation now becomes as shown in Table 31.3.

Now we have:

$$n = 10$$
$$\sum y = 160$$
$$\sum xy = 133$$
$$\sum x^2 = 330$$

TABLE 31.3 **The Calculation of Trend GDP over a 10-Year Period**

Year	x	Annual GDP, billions of euros (y)	xy	x2
2009	−9	12	−108	81
2010	−7	13.5	−94.5	49
2011	−5	13	−65	25
2012	−3	16	−48	9
2013	−1	17.5	−17.5	1
2014	1	16	16	1
2015	3	15	45	9
2016	5	17	85	25
2017	7	20	140	49
2018	9	20	180	81
Total	**0**	**160**	**133**	**330**

This allows us to find a as follows:

$$a = \frac{\sum y}{n}$$

$$= \frac{160}{10}$$

$$= 16$$

$$a = €16 \textit{ billion}$$

We find b as follows:

$$b = \frac{\sum xy}{\sum x^2}$$

$$= \frac{133}{330}$$

$$= 0.40$$

$$b = €0.40 \textit{ billion}$$

The trend equation for our economy now becomes:

$$16 + 0.40x$$

Notice that the trend equation has changed with the addition of an extra observation. The extent of the change will tend to be less when we have a larger number of observations. It does, however, show that estimates of the trend growth of an economy will have to be changed over time.

Quarterly Data

Whether we have an even or an odd number of observations we may be interested in the GDP figures that are for less than a year. For example, we may wish to analyze quarterly data. We can change our $\hat{y}$ units into quarterly data by dividing the annual figures by 4, that is $\frac{y}{4}$. The quarterly trend equation is found by replacing a with $\frac{a}{4}$, and b with $\frac{b}{4}$. Referring back to our original trend line:

$$\hat{y} = 15.56 + 0.78x$$

This becomes:

$$\hat{y} = 3.89 + 0.195x$$

In this way, a government can see whether GDP for any quarter is above or below trend.

A Non-Linear Trend

It may well be that the trend GDP data is not linear. We will now show how to calculate a non-linear trend of the kind described in Panel (b) of Figure 31.1. For this purpose we will need to use logs. We can use logs to any base but in what follows we will use logs to the base of ten.

The equation we need is of the form:

$$\hat{y} = a \times b^x$$

This gives an exponential curve since the term x appears as an exponent of b. Taking the log of both sides of the equation we have:

$$\log \hat{y} = \log a + x \times \log b$$

We can now proceed in a similar way as before except that the y values are in log form. If we now use coding as before, then $\sum x = 0$, enabling us to find the appropriate values for a and b.

Thus:

$$\log a = \frac{\sum \log y}{n}$$

and:

$$\log b = \frac{\sum (x \times \log y)}{\sum x^2}$$

Let us see how this works for an economy with an exponential GDP trend. The data we will assume is given in Table 31.4.

TABLE 31.4 **GDP Data Exhibiting an Exponential Trend**

Year	GDP, billions of euros, annually
2009	18
2010	23
2011	27
2012	36
2013	45
2014	58
2015	75
2016	80
2017	100

To find the exponential trend for this economy we calculate the value in Table 31.5. This is the same basic procedure that we have already used for the linear trend except that we are now using log ŷ.

Now we calculate both log a and log b.

$$\log a = \frac{14.798}{9}$$
$$= 1.644$$

TABLE 31.5 **The Calculation of GDP with an Exponential Trend**

Year	x	GDP, billions of euros, annually (y)	log y	x × log y	x2
2009	−4	18	1.255	−5.020	16
2010	−3	23	1.362	−4.086	9
2011	−2	27	1.431	−2.862	4
2012	−1	36	1.556	−1.556	1
2013	0	45	1.653	0	0
2014	1	58	1.763	1.763	1
2015	2	75	1.875	3.750	4
2016	3	80	1.903	5.709	9
2017	4	100	2.000	8.000	16
Total	**0**		**14.798**	**5.698**	**60**

$$\log b = \frac{5.698}{60}$$
$$= 0.095$$

Then our exponential trend equation in log form is:

$$\log \hat{y} = 1.644 + 0.095x$$

Now we can find the trend value by taking the anti-log of 1.644 and the anti-log of 0.095. The anti-log is the inverse log calculation. If we know the log of a number, we can find the value of the number itself by taking the anti-log. The logarithm is the exponent. The anti-log means going backwards from that exponent and getting the regular number. If you don't have a calculator with this function you can find one online[1].

In our case the values are 44.06 and 1.25 respectively. Note that taking the antilog we use the rules of powers here. In this example:

$$10^{1.644+0.095x} = 10^{1.644} \times 10^{0.095x} = 10^{1.644} \times (10^{0.095})^x$$

In our case the values are $10^{1.644} = 44.06$ and $10^{0.095} = 1.25$ approximately. Make sure you can do this on your calculator – depending on the make it will probably be the following key sequence: 1.644 INV LOG and 0.095 INV LOG.

We can now write the equation for our exponential trend as:

$$\hat{y} = 44.06 \times (1.25)^x$$

44.06 is the trend value for 2012, the middle year in our series and 1.25 is 1 plus the average GDP growth over the period. That is, GDP growth per annum is 0.25 or 25 per cent.

Alternatively, we can make use of the log form of the equation itself. We can use this to find the trend value for any year we choose. Suppose, for example, we wish to know the trend value of GDP outside of our period of observation. We have data until 2017. What is the trend value of GDP for 2018?

$$\log \hat{y} = 1.644 + 0.095x$$

Thus for 2018 we write:

$$\log \hat{y} = 1.644 + 0.095 \times 5$$
$$= 2.119$$

The anti log of 2.119 = 131.52.

Therefore the trend value for GDP in 2018 is €131.52 billion.

[1] There are online calculators for logarithmic functions that you can find with as suitable search engine.

Output Gaps

The output gap measures the difference between actual output and potential output. If we assume that the trend gives a measure of potential output the divergence from that trend gives us the output gap.

If we wish, we can find the percentage GDP gap. This is the actual GDP minus the potential GDP, divided by the potential GDP. That is:

$$Percentage\ GDP\ gap = \frac{GDP\ actual - GDP\ potential}{GDP\ potential} \times 100$$

By potential output we do not mean full capacity output. At full capacity output there will be severe inflationary pressures. Potential output can be thought of as the maximum output possible without creating inflation.

There are various ways of measuring an economy's output gap. One way is to construct a production function, based on the level of a country's capital stock, labour force and productivity. This gives an alternative estimate of potential output from the one that we have considered. Sometimes governments seek information about output gaps by conducting surveys of business. However it is done, it can provide a guide for government in the conduct of economic policy. If the economy's output is below trend it suggests unemployed resources and may indicate that the government should expand aggregate demand. If the actual output is above trend it suggests that there is excess demand which may cause unwanted inflation, indicating that the government might wish to reduce aggregate demand. Establishing the output gap as we have done in this chapter can be a useful tool of economic policy.

PROBLEMS AND APPLICATIONS

1 Figure 31.3 below shows the worldwide turnover with semiconductors as a monthly time series. (The data are provided by the Semiconductor Industry Association. Shown is the total amount of sales in $1000 that was billed in each month (billings history) www.semiconductors.org).

a. Can you identify a trend in the industry's sales value?
b. Describe the (business) cycles of the industry.
c. Would you suspect a seasonal pattern in the sales values for this series?
d. Are there any obvious irregular variations?

FIGURE 31.3

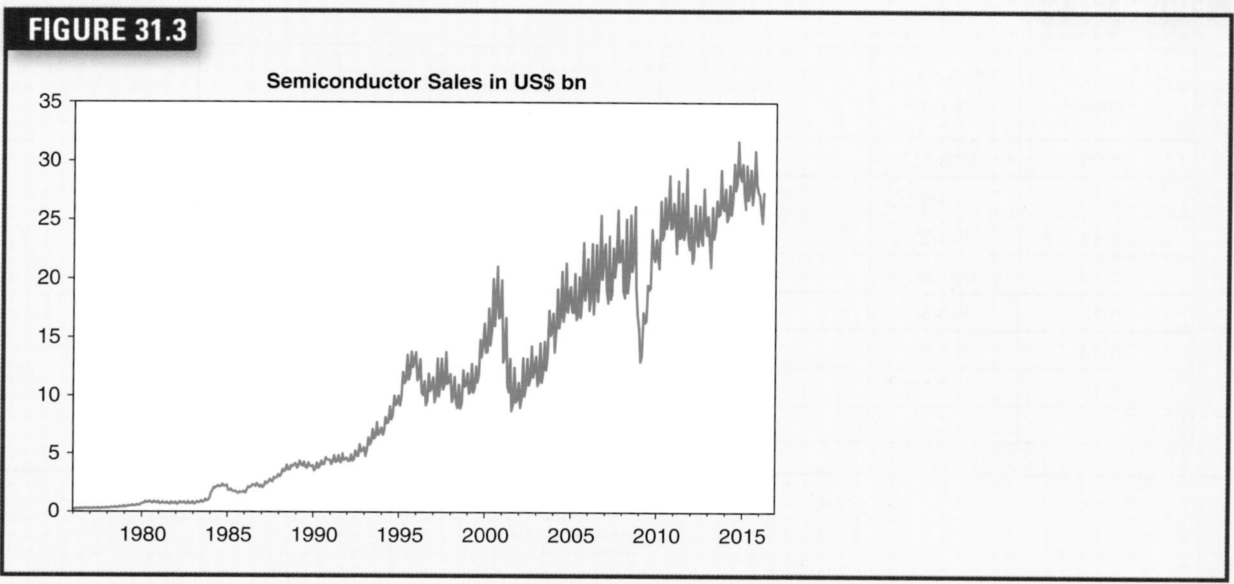

2 The data series in Figure 31.4 shows the growth in the value of worldwide semiconductor sales. (Percentage changes are calculated year on year in decimal numbers, i.e. the peak in January of 2010 tells you that sales were 70 per cent higher than in January 2009.)

a. Describe the nature of the trend in semiconductor sales values and explain your reasoning.
b. Are you able to see the (business) cycles more clearly now? If so, why?

FIGURE 31.4

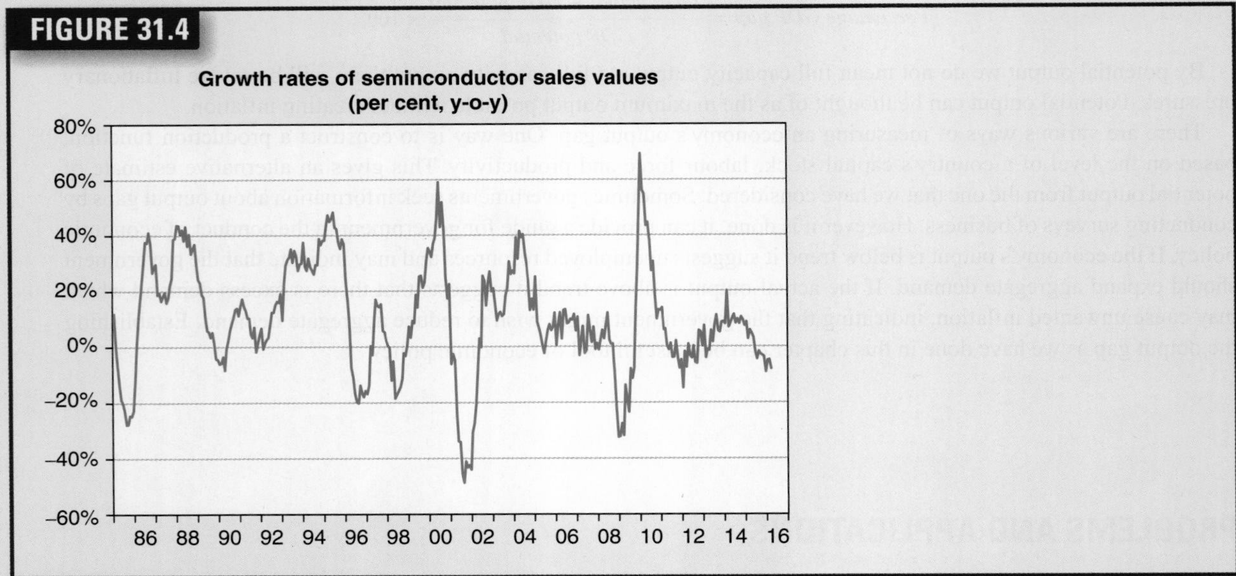

3 Figure 31.5 contains annual values for the worldwide semiconductor sales for seven years, in billions of US dollars.

a. Assume a linear trend. Calculate the regression line.
b. Estimate the turnover values based on your regression equation for the years from 2009 to 2015.
c. Forecast the value for 2016.

FIGURE 31.5

Year	Turnover ($ bn)				
2009	226.31				
2010	298.32				
2011	299.52				
2012	291.56				
2013	305.58				
2014	335.84				
2015	335.17				

4 Figure 31.6 contains annual values for the worldwide semiconductor sales in billions of US dollars; however, you are now looking at older data from 1990 onwards. Assume an exponential trend.

a. Calculate the regression line in logarithms and convert the parameter values with the anti log function.
b. Show your estimated turnover values.
c. Forecast the value for 1997.

FIGURE 31.6

Year	Turnover ($ bn)			
1990	50.52			
1991	54.61			
1992	59.86			
1993	77.31			
1994	101.88			
1995	144.40			
1996	131.97			

32 KEYNESIAN ECONOMICS AND IS–LM ANALYSIS

In this chapter we will explain the basic multiplier. Then we will use the Keynesian cross model to consider some effects of government use of the multiplier. We look at the tax multiplier, then the balanced budget multiplier. We will then consider the accelerator principle and its possible relationship to the multiplier and to the business cycle. Finally, we will illustrate equilibrium using IS–LM analysis.

THE DETERMINATION OF THE MULTIPLIER

In this chapter we will focus on changes in national output. To follow the logic of the chapter it is essential that you are clear about the national income identities that we discussed in Chapter 20. Recall that since gross national income, GNI, is defined as income earned in producing the gross national output, GNP, and gross national expenditure, GNE, is defined as expenditure on the national output, $GNI \equiv GNP \equiv GNE$. We will be using Y to refer to the level of national income, output and expenditure.

The multiplier is a Keynesian concept arguing that when there is a rise in autonomous demand output will eventually rise by some multiple of that demand increase. Begin with the assumption that there is a closed economy (there is no international trade) and no government sector. Thus in equilibrium output must equal the sum of demands made upon it.

$$Y = C + I$$

Where:
Y = aggregate output
C = planned consumption
I = planned investment

In this economy output must be sufficient to meet demands from consumers plus firms' plans to invest. Now assume that planned investment is autonomous, that is, it is independent of the level of income, and that consumers always consume some proportion, c, of income. Then:

$$C = cY$$

Hence:

$$Y = cY + I$$

Or:

$$Y(1 - c) = I$$

Rearranging gives:

$$\frac{Y}{I} = \frac{1}{1 - c}$$

If this is true for levels of national income, then it will be true for changes also, i.e.:

$$\frac{\Delta Y}{\Delta I} = \frac{1}{1 - c}$$

All income is either spent or saved, so that $c + s = 1$, where s is the proportion of income that consumers wish to save. Hence:

$$\frac{\Delta Y}{\Delta I} = \frac{1}{s}$$

However, in an open economy with a government sector saving is not the only withdrawal from the circular flow of income. Households pay a proportion of their additional income in taxes, t, and spend a proportion of their additional income on imports, m. Then:

$$\frac{\Delta Y}{\Delta I} = \frac{1}{s + t + m} \text{ or } \frac{1}{w}$$

Where:
w = the marginal propensity to withdraw from the circular flow. This is the basic multiplier.

To illustrate, assume an economy where $s = \frac{1}{10}$, $t = \frac{2}{10}$, and $m = \frac{2}{10}$. Thus:

$$\begin{aligned} w &= \frac{1}{10} + \frac{2}{10} + \frac{2}{10} \\ &= \frac{1}{2} \end{aligned}$$

Then:

$$\begin{aligned} \frac{\Delta Y}{\Delta I} &= \frac{1}{\frac{1}{10} + \frac{2}{10} + \frac{2}{10}} \\ &= \frac{1}{\frac{1}{2}} \\ &= 2 \end{aligned}$$

The multiplier is 2. Output will rise by twice the increase in autonomous expenditure.

To elaborate, suppose a government increases expenditure by €1 million on a new hospital. Output, in the form of the hospital, rises by that amount. Some households' income now rises by €1 million, because output = income. Of that income increase, one tenth of it is saved, two-tenths of it is taxed, and two-tenths of it is spent on imports. The other half, is spent, raising output in some part of the economy by a further €0.5 million. This raises output and therefore household incomes by a further €0.5 million, of which half is spent, raising output and therefore incomes rise by a further €0.25 million euros. The process continues with output rising in a series:

$$1 + \frac{1}{2} + \frac{1}{4} + \dots\dots\dots\dots\dots\dots$$

Recall from Chapter 27 that if a geometric progression, GP, is less than one, each successive term is smaller. Such a progression is said to be convergent.

When GPs have a common ratio of less than one, if we are adding more and more terms of the series we get a more accurate value of the total but never quite reach it. We referred to this as the limit of the process. If $r < 1$ the progression converges to the value:

$$\frac{a}{1 - r}$$

Where:
a = the first term in the series
r = the common ratio

Our multiplier series has a common ratio of 1/2 and the first term is 1. So we have:

$$\frac{1}{1-\frac{1}{2}}$$

$$= 2$$

The multiplier is 2 so that a €1 million increase in government expenditure on the hospital eventually increases output by €2 million.

The Marginal and Average Propensities to Consume

We must distinguish between the average propensity to consume and the marginal propensity to consume. The proportion of income spent by households on domestic output is called the average propensity to consume, APC. The proportion of additional income spent by households is called the marginal propensity to consume, MPC. We can define the average propensity to consume as:

$$APC = \frac{C}{Y}$$

And the marginal propensity to consume as:

$$MPC = \frac{\Delta C}{\Delta Y}$$

When there is no autonomous consumption, then $MPC = APC$. Consider the information in Table 32.1 Consumption is a proportion of income, here assumed to be 3/4. At all levels of income MPC and APC = 3/4.

TABLE 32.1 **Average and Marginal Propensities to Consume, Autonomous Consumption**

Income, *Y*	Consumption, *C*	*APC*, *C*/*Y*	*MPC*, $\frac{\Delta C}{\Delta Y}$
1000	750	3/4	3/4
2000	1500	3/4	3/4
3000	2250	3/4	3/4

Now assume that the consumption function is partly autonomous and partly induced as shown in Table 32.2. From Table 32.2 we see that:

$$C = 100 + \frac{3}{4}Y$$

TABLE 32.2 **Average and Marginal Propensities to Consume, with Consumption Partly Induced**

Income, *Y*	Consumption, *C*	*APC*, *C*/*Y*	*MPC*, $\frac{\Delta C}{\Delta Y}$
1000	850	85/100	3/4
2000	1600	80/100	3/4
3000	2350	78/100	3/4

Consumers always spend 100, regardless of income. This is called autonomous consumption. They also spend 3/4 of their income. The part of consumption that is dependent upon income is called induced consumption. As you can see, MPC is constant but APC changes with income. When we consider multiplier effects we are considering the effect of changes in autonomous demand on income and therefore we use the MPC. For example, we might consider the effect on national output if consumption becomes, say, 200 plus 3/4 of income.

The principles we are considering apply to any element of demand. For example, suppose import demand is partly autonomous and partly induced, then the relevant concept for calculating multiplier effects is what happens if there is a change in the autonomous element of import demand. Thus we focus, not on the average, but on the marginal propensity to import.

The consumption functions above are linear. If we have a non-linear form we may want to use a more precise definition of MPC, which we can do by differentiation. A consumption function might take the form:

$$C = a + bY - cY^2$$

Where:

a, *b*, and *c* are constants.

The MPC, the rate of change of consumption, is:

$$MPC = \frac{dC}{dY}$$
$$= b - 2cY$$

Although b and c are both constants, the value of the term $2cY$ will vary with income. To illustrate, suppose that an economy's consumption function has been estimated at:

$$C = 100 + \frac{95}{100}Y - \frac{1}{2000}Y^2$$

Then:

$$MPC = \frac{95}{100} - \frac{1}{1000}Y$$

MPC, when income is 100, will be:

$$\frac{95}{100} - \frac{1}{10}$$
$$= \frac{85}{100}$$

When income is 200, MPC is:

$$\frac{95}{100} - \frac{2}{10}$$
$$= \frac{75}{100}$$

As income increases, consumption increases but MPC decreases.

THE KEYNESIAN CROSS AND GOVERNMENT USE OF THE MULTIPLIER

We now consider the economy of the mythical republic of Microtheria and illustrate some possible benefits and costs of macro policy using the multiplier. All values are in billions of Microtherian roubles.

In Microtheria there is some unemployment which the government wishes to address. The economy at full employment would produce 2400 per year. Currently Microtherians spend three quarters of their disposable incomes and the government has a flat tax of 20 per cent on household incomes. The government's annual expenditure is on currently produced goods and services at 400. It makes no investment. There are no other taxes and the government has no transfer incomes to pay. All investment is done by the private sector and is always 400. There are no undistributed profits. Exports are 400 per year. Imports are always one fifth of national income. We will now work out the current level of national income and then consider government multiplier policy to raise output to the full employment level. We begin by finding the current unemployment equilibrium national income. In equilibrium national output will be sufficient to meet all demands upon it. Thus:

$$Y_e = C + I + G + NX$$

Where:
Y_e = national output / income
C = consumption
I = investment
G = government current spending
NX = the trade balance
It will be convenient here to separate out exports and imports so that:
$NX = X - M$
Where:
X = exports
M = imports
The sum of these terms C, I, G and NX is planned aggregate expenditure. We can now find equilibrium Y for this economy.

Since the government takes 20 per cent of income in tax and consumers spend 3/4 of what remains:

$$C = \left(\frac{3}{4} \times \frac{8}{10}\right) Y$$
$$= \frac{3}{5} Y$$

Then:

$$Y_e = \frac{3}{5}Y + 400 + 400 + 400 - \frac{1}{5}Y$$
$$= \frac{2}{5}Y + 1200$$
$$Y - \frac{2}{5}Y = 1200$$
$$\frac{3}{5}Y = 1200$$
$$Y_e = 2000$$

The economy is in equilibrium in the sense that output is sufficient to meet all the planned demands upon it. However, 2000 is not necessarily the level of output at which all the economy's resources are fully employed. The economy may, for example, be capable of producing, say, 2400. The economy at 2000 has an 'unemployment equilibrium'.

The market will always adjust so that the level of output is equal to planned aggregate expenditure. If planned expenditure exceeds the level of output that firms currently produce, firms will see their stocks decline and will step up production to meet demand, raising national output. If planned expenditure is less than current output, stocks are rising so firms will cut production, lowering national output. For example, if output is currently at 1600 planned expenditure will be:

$$C + I + G + NX$$

$$\frac{3}{5}Y + 400 + 400 + 400 - \frac{1}{5}Y$$
$$= \frac{2}{5}Y + 1200$$
$$= 640 + 1200$$
$$= 1840$$

When planned expenditure exceeds output, the difference is referred to as an inflationary gap. Here the size of the inflationary gap is:

$$1840 - 1600 = 240$$

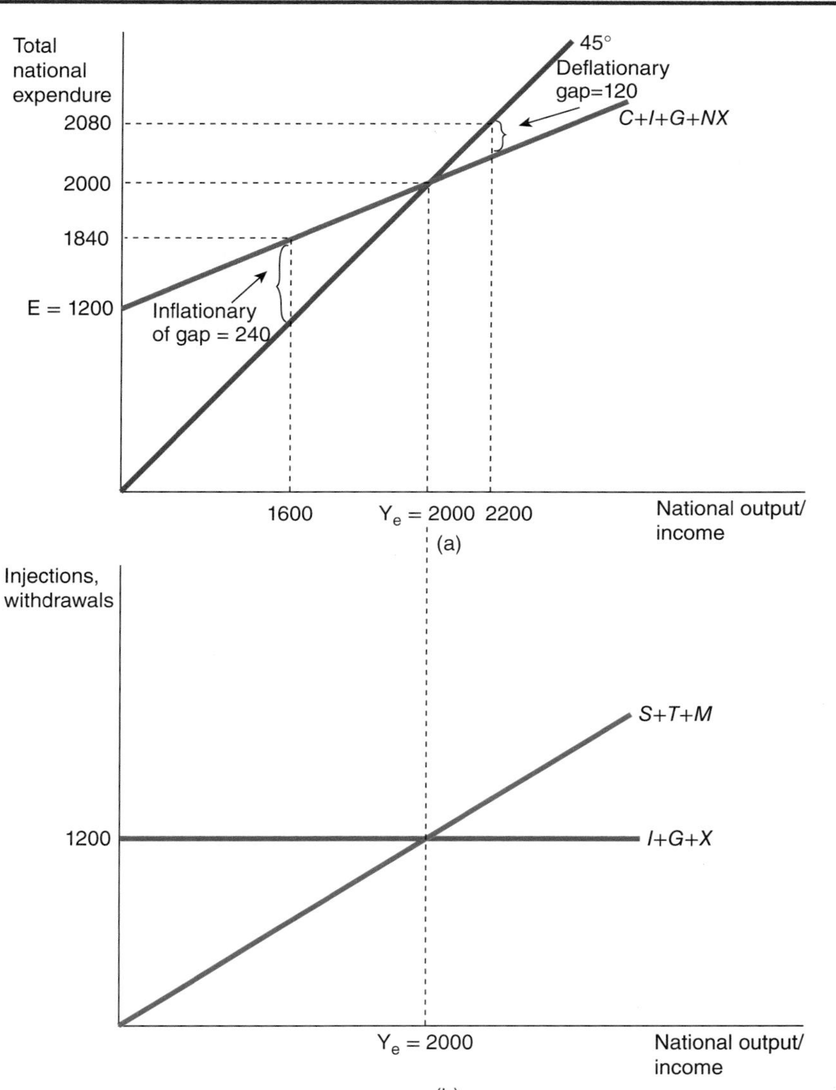

FIGURE 32.1

Equilibrium National Output

The economy is in equilibrium where planned demand = actual output, in this case 2000. If current output is less, for example at 1600, then an inflationary gap exists. Firms experience an unplanned fall in stocks and respond by increasing output. If output is currently in excess of 2000, say, 2200, a deflationary gap exists. Firms' unplanned stocks rise so firms reduce output. This is shown in panel (a). An alternative presentation of the economy is given in panel (b). Equilibrium is shown as the output at which injections into the circular flow are equal to withdrawals from it.

However, if output is currently at 2200, planned expenditure will be:

$$C + I + G + NX$$

$$\frac{3}{5}Y + 400 + 400 + 400 - \frac{1}{5}Y$$

$$= \frac{2}{5}Y + 1200$$

$$= 880 + 1200$$

$$= 2080$$

When planned expenditure is less than current output, the difference is referred to as a deflationary gap. Here it is:

$$2200 - 2080 = 120$$

A diagrammatic presentation of this is shown in Panel (a) of Figure 32.1. An alternative way of saying this is that planned injections into the circular flow of income must, in equilibrium, be equal to planned withdrawals:

$$I + G + X = S + T + M$$

At the equilibrium output of 2000 in Microtheria we have:

$$400 + 400 + 400 = \frac{1}{5}Y + \frac{1}{5}Y + \frac{1}{5}Y$$
$$1200 = 1200$$

This alternative presentation of equilibrium is shown in Panel (b) of Figure 32.1.

At the equilibrium level of output for Microtheria what is the government account?

It has an annual expenditure of 400 regardless of the level of income. That is, G is autonomous. Its current income is 20 per cent of national income. Twenty per cent of 2000 is 400. The government account is in balance.

Now consider the balance of payments account. Exports are 400. Imports are 20 per cent of national income so at present this amounts to 400. The balance of payments account is also in balance.

To deal with the unemployment problem the government plans to increase government current spending. What is the appropriate increase in its expenditure? It is not 400. There will be a multiplier effect of its expenditure so output would rise by more than 400. It might seem that this is impossible since it cannot produce more than 2400 anyway. However, although it cannot produce more than 2400 in real terms, it can produce the full employment output multiplied by a higher price level. In other words, if it expands demand too much it will create inflation. We can calculate the appropriate increase in government expenditure in two ways. First, we can use our national income equation and find G as the unknown. Thus:

$$Y = 3Y + 400 + G + 400 \frac{1}{5}Y$$

$$2400 = \frac{3}{5} \times 2400 + 400 + G + 400 - \frac{1}{5} \times 2400$$

$$2400 = 1440 + 400 + G + 400 - 480$$

$$2400 = 1760 + G$$
$$G = 640$$

Since G was originally 400, the government needs to increase current spending by 240. Through the multiplier effect this will eventually increase Y to the full employment 2400.

Alternatively we can find the same answer by finding Microtheria's multiplier.

$$\frac{\Delta Y}{\Delta I} = \frac{1}{s + t + m} \text{ or } \frac{1}{w}$$

Here $t = 1/5$ and $m = 1/5$, but what is s?

As explained above, consumers spend 3/5 of Y, but they spend 3/4 of their disposable incomes, the income left after payment of taxes. That means they must be saving 1/4 of it. They save 1/4 of 4/5 Y since the government has taken 1/5 in taxes. Thus:

$$S = \left(\frac{1}{4} \times \frac{4}{5}\right) Y = \frac{1}{5}Y$$

Thus:

$$w = \frac{1}{5} + \frac{1}{5} + \frac{1}{5}$$
$$= \frac{3}{5}$$

Then:

$$\frac{\Delta Y}{\Delta I} = \frac{1}{\frac{3}{5}}$$
$$= 1\frac{2}{3}$$

The multiplier is $1\frac{2}{3}$. Output will rise by $1\frac{2}{3}$ the increase in autonomous expenditure. We need Y to increase by 400. So:

$$\frac{400}{\Delta G} = \frac{1}{\frac{3}{5}}$$

$$\Delta G = \frac{400}{1\frac{2}{3}}$$

$$= 240$$

We confirm that the appropriate increase in G is 240 when the intention is to raise Y by 400. We show this in Panel (a) of Figure 32.2 where ΔY is $1\frac{2}{3} \times \Delta G$. Notice that in Panel (b) of Figure 32. 2, injections once more equal withdrawals.

At the new equilibrium output of 2400 in Microtheria we have:

$$(I + G + X)' = (S + T + M)'$$

$$400 + 640 + 400 = \frac{1}{5}Y + \frac{1}{5}Y + \frac{1}{5}Y$$

$$1440 = 1440$$

However, the government's actions have effects both upon the government account and upon the balance of payments account. Let us begin with the government account. Government expenditure has increased by 240 but the deficit this creates is less than that. The increased G has increased national income by 400 of which the government takes 20 per cent as a tax. Thus the government budget deficit is the new level of expenditure less the new level of tax income:

$$640 - \left(\frac{1}{5} \times 2400\right)$$

$$= 160$$

Now we consider the effect on the balance of payments account, NX. Exports are autonomous so they remain at 400. However, the increased national income raises imports. There is now a deficit of:

$$NX = 400 - \left(\frac{1}{5} \times 2400\right)$$

$$= -80$$

Changes in government expenditure affect output, employment, the government account and net exports.

The Tax Multiplier

The simple tax multiplier is the ratio of the change in national output to an autonomous change, this time in tax, when consumption is the only induced expenditure and all other expenditures are autonomous. An autonomous change in tax also creates a multiplier effect. The tax reduces household income, leading to reduced expenditure. This lowers national output and therefore income, causing a further reduction in expenditure and so on. The formula for the simple tax multiplier, which we will call stm, is:

$$stm = -MPC \times \frac{1}{MPS}$$

$$= -\frac{MPC}{MPS}$$

Where:

MPC = marginal propensity to consume

MPS = marginal propensity to save

FIGURE 32.2

The Effect of an Increase in Autonomous Expenditure

If equilibrium output is at 2000 and full employment equilibrium is at 2400, the government may stimulate the economy by increasing government expenditure, G. Output will rise by more than the increase in G because of a multiplier effect. Here an increase of 240 increases output from 2000 to the full employment level of 2400. This process is shown in both panel (a) and also in panel (b).

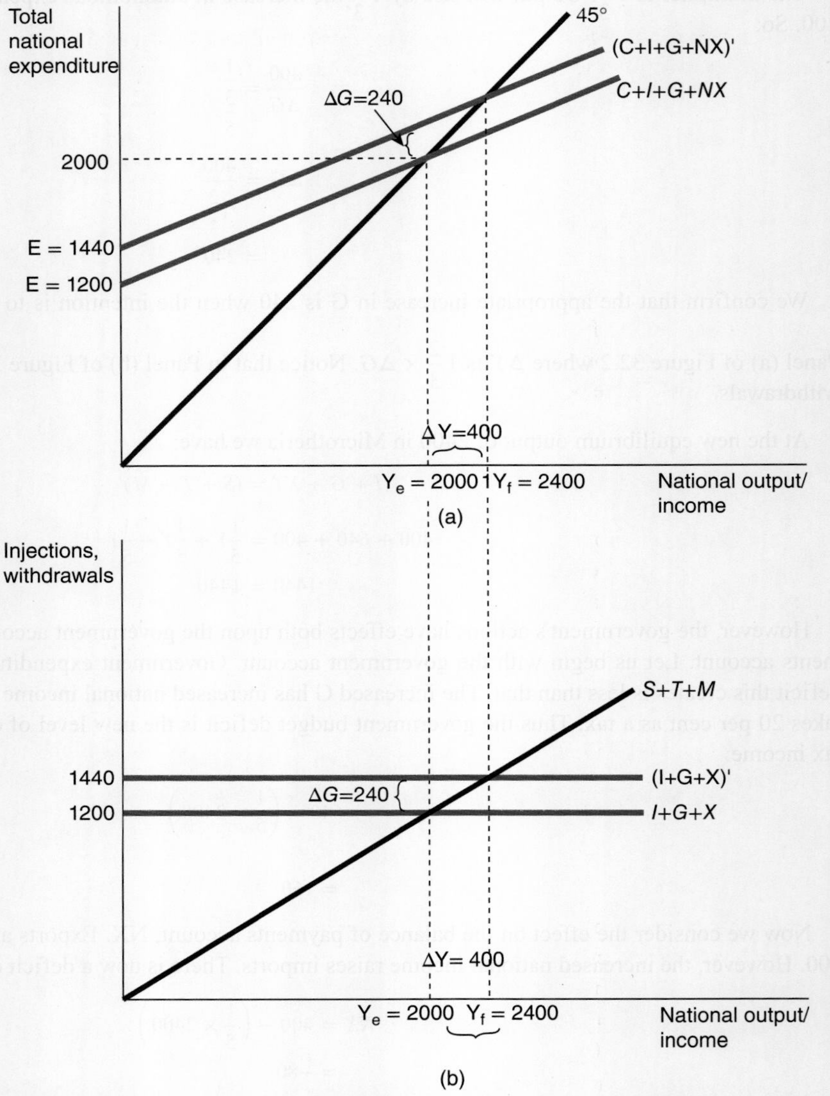

The simple tax multiplier is always negative. Suppose, for example, that MPC $= \frac{4}{5}$ and therefore MPS $= \frac{1}{5}$.

$$\text{stm} = -\frac{\frac{4}{5}}{\frac{1}{5}}$$

$$= -4$$

An autonomous cut in tax of €1 million will produce an increase in national output of €4 million and an autonomous rise in tax of the same amount will lead to a €4 million fall in national output. There are close similarities between the multiplier and the simple tax multiplier but there is also an important difference. When seeking to raise national output, ignoring incentive effects, a rise in government expenditure is more effective than an equal cut in taxation. Given this MPC of 0.8, a €1 million increase in G begins the multiplier process. In contrast, a €1 million cut in T means that only 80 per cent of the €1 million sets off the multiplier process. This important distinction is the basis of the other multiplier we look at, the balanced budget multiplier.

The Balanced Budget Multiplier

What happens to aggregate expenditure if the government increases spending and at the same time increases taxes by the same amount, so as to leave its own position unaltered?

$$\Delta G - \Delta C = \textit{initial impact of balanced budget increase}$$

Where:

$$\Delta G = \textit{increase in government spending}$$

$$\Delta C = \textit{decrease in consumption as a result of the tax increase}$$

The initial impact of the balanced budget increase is the increase in government demand, less the decrease in consumption resulting from the tax increase that is being used to pay for the increase in government spending. The decrease in consumption, ΔC is equal to the tax change, ΔT, multiplied by the proportion of that household loss of income that would have been spent.

$$\Delta C = \Delta T \times c$$

Where:
ΔT = volume of tax being raised
c = proportion of household income now not spent
The net change is $\Delta G - (\Delta T \times c)$
When we have a balanced budget change, such that $\Delta G = \Delta T$, we can substitute ΔG for ΔT to give:

$$\Delta G - (\Delta G \times c)$$
$$= \Delta G(1 - c)$$

Now recall that $c + s = 1$. All the income is either saved or spent. So $1 - c$ can be replaced with s. Then the initial increase in expenditure is $\Delta G \times s$ but the total increase is this, multiplied by the multiplier, where the multiplier is $1/s$. Thus:

$$\Delta Y = \Delta G \times s \times \frac{1}{s}$$

$$\Delta Y = \Delta G$$

If the government increases government spending and increases taxes just enough to pay for it, output will rise, and it will rise by whatever is the change in government spending. The balanced budget multiplier is one. Output rises by the increase in G. This is regardless of the size of the terms c and s.

In terms of our hospital example the increase in G was 240. Through the multiplier this eventually increased Y to the full employment 2400. Had the government raised T by 240 at the same time then output would have risen by 240 to 2240, so that some unemployment remains. It could have achieved the full employment level of output by raising G by 400 and increasing T by 400 also.

The Accelerator and its Interaction with the Multiplier

The accelerator principle, in its simple form, assumes that firms attempt to maintain a constant capital to output ratio. The value of the capital stock will be several times larger than the size of national income, so that an increase in income requires new investment of several times that amount. Similarly, a fall in national income will cause a contraction in the demand for investment several times the fall in income. Indeed, as we shall see, investment demand may fall to zero. The accelerator effect is given as:

$$I_N = a\Delta Y$$

Where:

I_N = net investment, or 'induced investment', the amount of investment in excess of what is necessary to replace the worn out capital stock.

ΔY = the change in income

a = the 'accelerator coefficient'. This is a constant whose size is determined by the extent to which induced investment will rise in response to a change in Y. For example, if a €100 million rise in income leads to a €300 million rise in net investment, the accelerator coefficient is 3.

What determines the size of a? It is determined by the size of the marginal capital–output ratio, $\frac{\Delta K}{\Delta Y}$. If an increase in the capital stock of €100 million is needed to increase national output by €300 million, $a = 3$. If we assume $\frac{K}{Y}$ to be constant, $\frac{\Delta K}{\Delta Y}$ will be the same. Normally, we can expect the accelerator coefficient and the marginal capital to output ratio to be the same.

We will now illustrate the working of the accelerator principle to show how investment can fluctuate with small changes in national income. We assume an economy whose national income has for some while been constant at €1000 million. All values used in this example are in millions of euros per year. Any unit of capital needs replacing after five years. We assume that the capital stock has been built up evenly, so that throughout the period under consideration replacement investment will be 20 per cent of the 3000 capital stock, that is 600. There is a capital–output ratio of 3, so that:

$$I_N = 3\Delta Y$$

Table 32.3 presents an illustration of the accelerator principle.

TABLE 32.3 **An illustration of the Accelerator Principle**

Year	National Income (€millions)	Required Capital Stock	Replacement Investment (€millions)	Induced Investment (€millions of)	Total Investment (€millions of)
1	1000	3000	600	0	600
2	1200	3600	600	600	1200
3	1300	3900	600	300	900
4	1100	3300	600	−600	0

In year 1 we show Y as 1000. The required capital stock is 3000, that is, 3Y. Replacement of 20 per cent of the 3000 capital stock is 600. There is no induced investment because Y has not been changing. Total investment is the sum of net investment plus induced investment, in our case 600 + 0 = 600. Now in year 2 we assume that national income rises to 1200. The required capital stock is therefore 1200 × 3 = 3600. Twenty per cent of the current capital stock needs replacing: 3000 × 20% = 600. The rise in national income of 200 produces induced investment of 3 × 200 = 600. That is:

$$I_N = 3 \times 200$$
$$= 600$$

Total investment in year 2 is 600 + 600 = 1200.

Now assume that in year 3 Y rises to 1300. National income rises but at a reduced rate. Total investment will now decline. The required capital stock is 3900 and replacement investment is again 600 and induced investment is:

$$I_N = 3 \times 100$$
$$= 300$$

Total investment is 900, a fall from year 2 even though national income is rising. When the rate of increase in Y declines, investment falls.

Finally, consider year 4 where Y has fallen to 1100. The required capital stock is 3 × 1100 = 3300. To replace the now worn out capital stock requires an investment of 600. Induced investment is:

$$I_N = 3 \times (-200)$$
$$= -600$$

Total investment is zero. There is no need to replace worn out capital. The current capital stock is sufficient to meet demand requirements.

The accelerator hypothesis can be argued to explain why changes in investment levels are much greater than changes in income. However, there are assumptions to the model which seem to be somewhat unrealistic. For example, machinery can often be continued to be used beyond any assumed time period. Furthermore, replacement investment need not be as definitive as the model suggests. Business may not respond to increase in income as fast as the model assumes. For example, a one year rise in income can be met by working the existing capital harder and waiting for a further period to see if the rise in income is permanent or temporary.

THE ACCELERATOR, THE MULTIPLIER AND THE BUSINESS CYCLE

Attempts have been made to use the multiplier and the accelerator to help to explain business cycles. The multiplier suggests that changes in autonomous demand change income. The accelerator suggests that changes in income cause changes in demand through changes in investment demand. Thus:

$$\underbrace{\Delta I \longrightarrow k}_{\text{multiplier}} \quad \longrightarrow \quad \underbrace{\Delta Y \longrightarrow a}_{\text{accelerator}} \quad \longrightarrow \quad \underbrace{\Delta I \longrightarrow k}_{\text{multiplier}} \longrightarrow \ldots\ldots$$

Where:
k = the multiplier
a = the marginal capital–output ratio

These interactions can produce business cycles. Differences in the values of k and a can cause differences in the nature of the cycle. Any of the four described in Figure 32.3 are possible.

THE IS–LM MODEL

The IS–LM model is a way of explaining how both the goods market and the money market can be in general equilibrium. The link between the two sectors is the real interest rate. The IS curve is the investment/savings curve which shows all the combinations of national income and real interest rate at which the goods market is in equilibrium. The LM is the liquidity preference/money supply curve shows all the combinations of national income and real interest rate at which the money market can be in equilibrium. We use the term liquidity preference to indicate the extent to which people prefer to hold their wealth in a liquid form, such as cash rather than a relatively illiquid form, such as bonds.

The model argues that there is only one level of national income and one real interest rate at which both sectors can be in equilibrium simultaneously. First we examine the goods market, the IS part of the model. In Microtheria we had a model of income determination where investment was autonomous. Now we argue that it is more realistic that investment depends, at least in part, on the real interest rate. The lower the real rate of interest, r, the higher will be the volume of investment, since it would be easier to satisfy the investment criterion that the IRR > r, as we saw in Chapter 25. Thus a lowering of interest rates raises aggregate expenditure and leads to a higher level of national income. We can find all the combinations of national income and interest rates that give equilibrium in the goods market. We shall do so for the kingdom of Macrotheria which has many similarities to but a few differences from Microtheria. Equilibrium output is given as:

$$Y = C + I + G + NX$$

Where:

$$C = 50 + \frac{1}{2}Y$$

$$I = 210 - 12r$$

Where r = the rate of interest

$$G = 300$$

$$X = 100$$

$$M = \frac{1}{10}Y$$

FIGURE 32.3

Possible Multiplier/Accelerator Effects on the Business Cycle

The interaction of the accelerator and the multiplier can produce different effects on an economy. It may produce explosive growth as in panel (a), or dampened growth as in panel (b). Alternatively it may create growth cycles, either explosive cycles, as in panel (c), or dampened cycles as in panel (d).

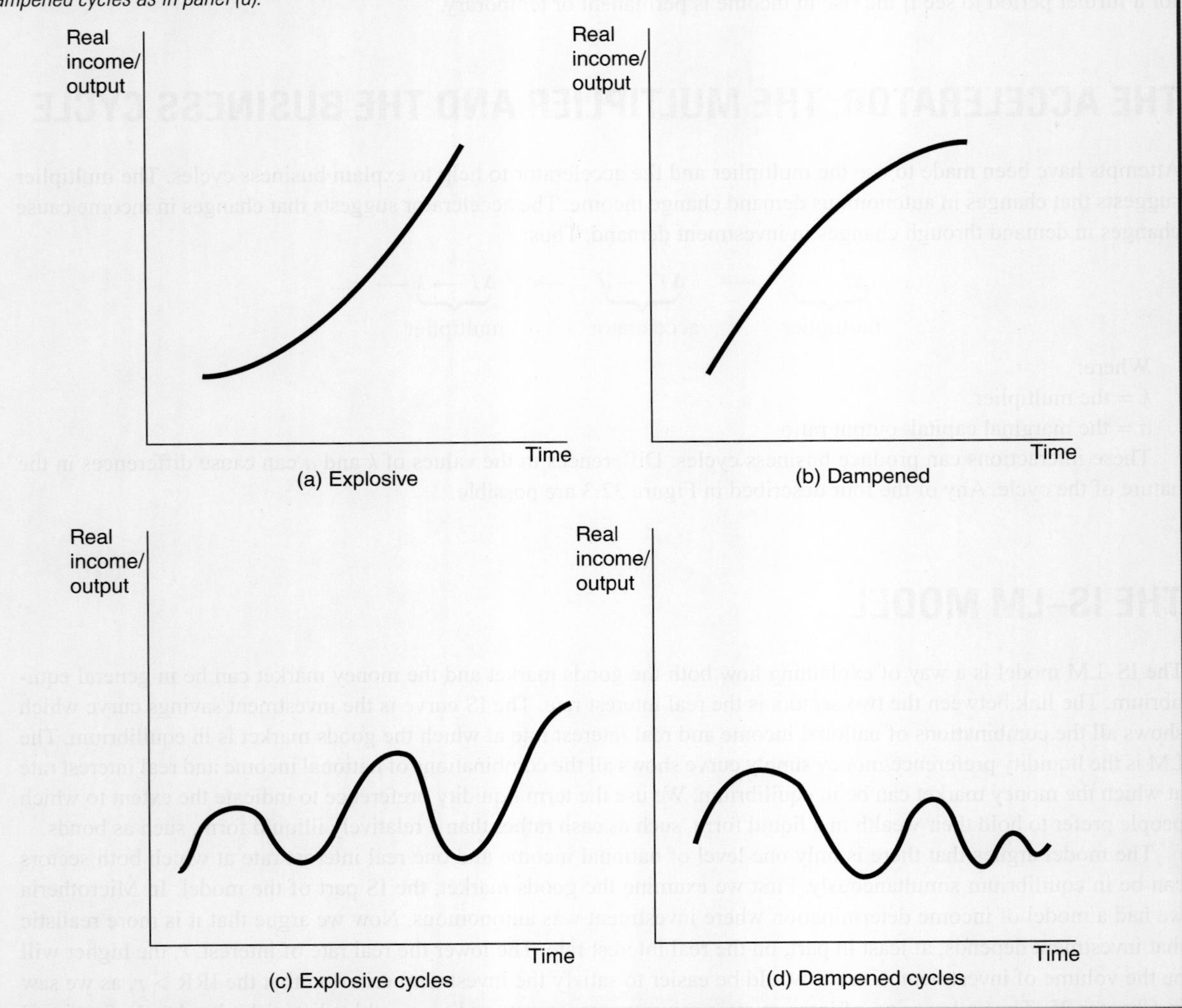

All values are in millions of Macrotherian dollars. Thus:

$$Y = 50 + \frac{1}{2}Y + (210 - 12r) + 300 + 100 - \frac{1}{10}Y$$

$$= 660 + \frac{1}{2}Y - \frac{1}{10}Y - 12r$$

$$= 660 + \frac{4}{10}Y - 12r$$

$$Y - \frac{4}{10}Y = 660 - 12r$$

$$\frac{6}{10}Y = 660 - 12r$$

$$\frac{1}{10}Y = 110 - 2r$$

$$Y = 1100 - 20r$$

This is the IS function. The equilibrium level of national income varies according to the interest rate. We can plot on a diagram but to do this we need r on the left-hand side of the equation.

$$Y = 1100 - 20r$$
$$20r = 1100 - Y$$
$$r = \frac{1100}{20} - \frac{Y}{20}$$
$$r = 55 - \frac{1}{20}Y$$

The IS curve is a straight line function. We find two points on the curve and join these points.
When $Y = 0$, $r = 55$
When $r = 0$, we have:

$$0 = 55 - \frac{1}{20}Y$$
$$\frac{1}{20}Y = 55$$
$$Y = 1100$$

The IS curve is shown in Figure 32.4. We also show one equilibrium combination of interest rate and national income, that of which $r = 10$ per cent:

$$Y = 1100 - 20r$$
$$= 1100 - (20 \times 10)$$
$$= 1100 - 200$$
$$= 900$$
$$Y = 900 \text{ when } r = 10 \textit{ per cent.}$$

Now we consider equilibrium in the money market. This occurs where the demand for money is equal to its supply. However, the demand for money is a function of both the interest rate and the level of national income. Thus there are different combinations of interest rate and national income where there will be money market equilibrium.

First consider the demand for money. It is partly a function of income, Y, and partly a function of the real interest rate, r. However, it also depends upon the real value of money. Real money demand is the nominal amount of money demanded divided by the price level, P. For Macrotheria the money demand equation is:

$$\left(\frac{M}{P}\right)^d = Y - 100r$$

Where:

$$\left(\frac{M}{P}\right)^d = \textit{real money demand}$$

The nominal money supply is 1000 and the price level is 2. The price level, P, is an index showing the weighted average of all prices, where the base year can be thought of as taking the value of 1. So the real money supply is given as:

$$\frac{MS}{P} = \frac{1000}{2} = 500$$

In equilibrium the money supply equals the money demand. Hence:

$$500 = Y - 100r$$

Or:

$$Y = 500 + 100r$$

Rearranging to find the value of r we have:

$$Y = 500 + 100r$$

$$100r = Y - 500$$

FIGURE 32.4

The IS Curve: Equilibrium in the Goods Market

The IS curve is negatively sloped. It shows combinations national income and interest rates at which the goods market is in equilibrium. Here the IS curve is given as $r = 55 - \frac{1}{20}Y$. Then one combination of output and interest rate at which this economy is in equilibrium is $Y = 900$ and $r = 10$ per cent.

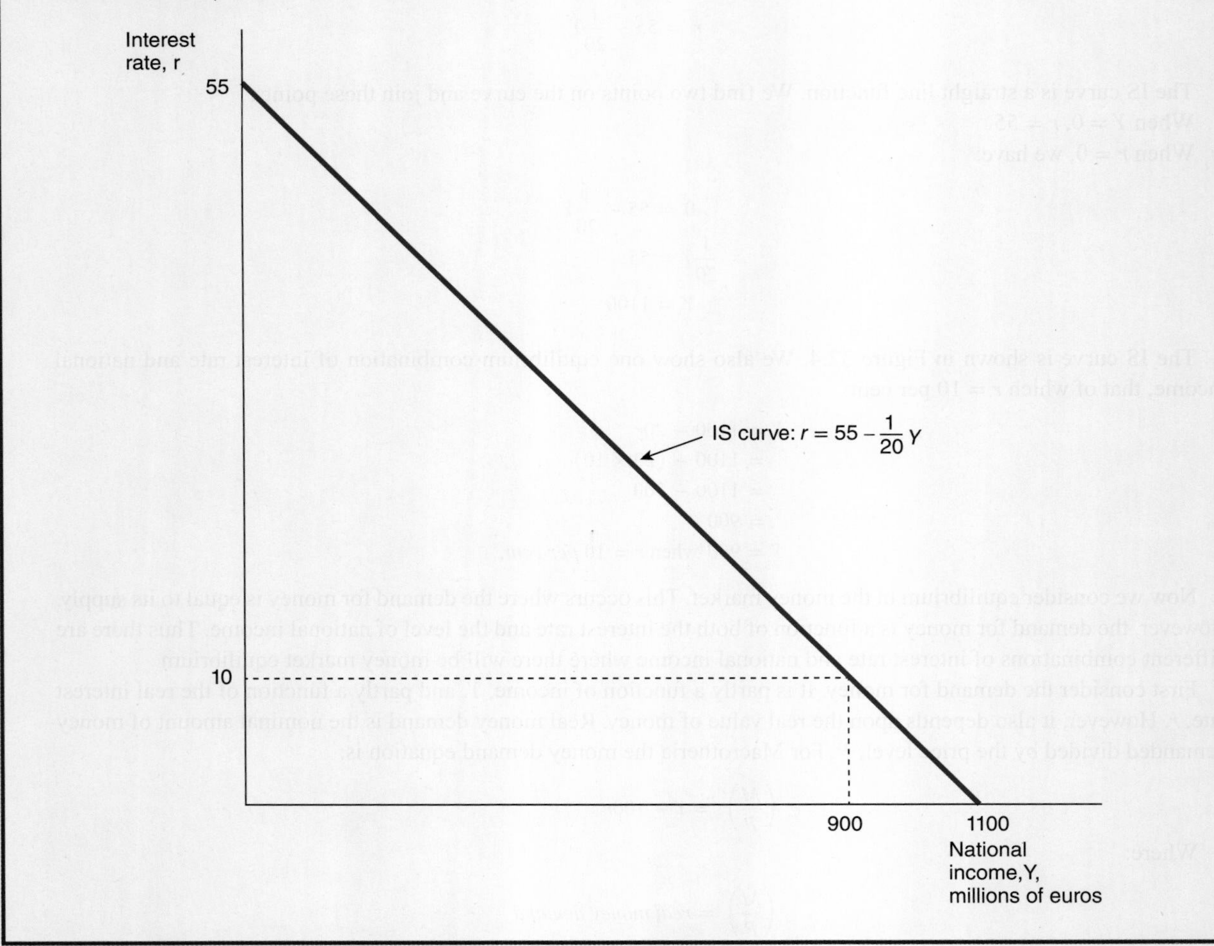

$$r = \frac{Y}{100} - 5$$

$$r = \frac{1}{100}Y - 5$$

This is a form of the LM function. This relationship is plotted in Figure 32.5. Establishing two points on this linear function, we can find that when $r = 0$:

$$0 = \frac{1}{100}Y - 5$$

$$\frac{1}{100}Y = 5$$

$$Y = 500$$

Then we take another value for r, e.g. $r = 10$ and we have:

$$r = \frac{1}{100}Y - 5$$
$$10 = \frac{1}{100}Y - 5$$
$$\frac{1}{100}Y = 15$$
$$Y = 1500$$

These two points establish the straight line LM curve in Figure 32.5.

FIGURE 32.5

The LM Curve: Equilibrium in the Money Market

The LM curve is positively sloped. It shows combinations of national income and interest rates at which the money market is in equilibrium. One combination of output and interest rate, at which the money market is in equilibrium, is Y = 1500 and r = 10 per cent.

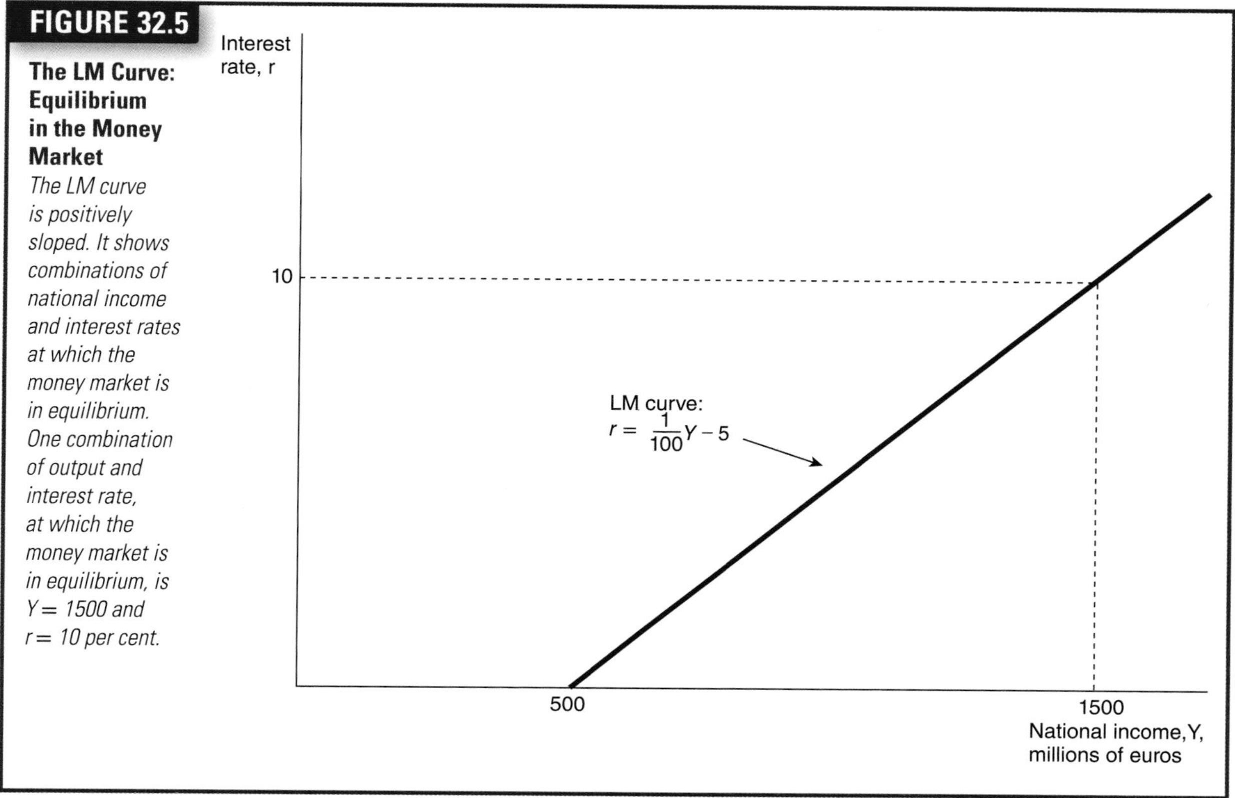

General Equilibrium

General equilibrium requires simultaneous equilibrium in the money market and in the goods market. That is:

$$LM = IS$$
$$L: r = \frac{1}{100}Y - 5$$
$$IS: r = 55 - \frac{1}{20}Y$$
$$\frac{1}{100}Y - 5 = 55 - \frac{1}{20}Y$$
$$\frac{1}{100}Y + \frac{1}{20}Y = 55 + 5$$
$$\frac{6}{100}Y = 60$$
$$Y = 1000$$

We can now find the general equilibrium value for r when $Y = 1000$ using either the LM or the IS equation. Where both the goods and the money market are in equilibrium we refer to this as general equilibrium. Using the IS equation gives:

$$r = 55 - \frac{1}{20}Y$$
$$= 55 - \frac{1}{20} \times 1000$$
$$= 5$$

Using the LM equation we have:

$$r = \frac{1}{100}Y - 5$$
$$= \left(\frac{1}{100} \times 1000\right) - 5$$
$$= 5$$

General equilibrium is found where $Y = 1000$ and $r = 5$ per cent. We show this diagrammatically in Figure 32.6. There are many combinations of r and Y which give equilibrium in the money market. These are shown by the LM curve. There are many combinations of r and Y which give equilibrium in the goods market. These are shown by the IS curve. There is one combination of r and Y that gives equilibrium simultaneously in both markets. Given the functions for Macrotheria, this is where $Y = 1000$ and $r = 5$ per cent.

FIGURE 32.6

The IS and LM Curves: General Equilibrium

There are many combinations of r and Y where the goods market is in equilibrium. There are many combinations of r and Y where the money market is in equilibrium. However, there is a single unique combination of r and Y which gives simultaneous equilibrium in the goods market and money market. With an LM function of $r = \frac{1}{100}Y - 5$ *and an IS curve of* $r = 55 - \frac{1}{20}Y$*, equilibrium r = 5 per cent and equilibrium Y = 1000.*

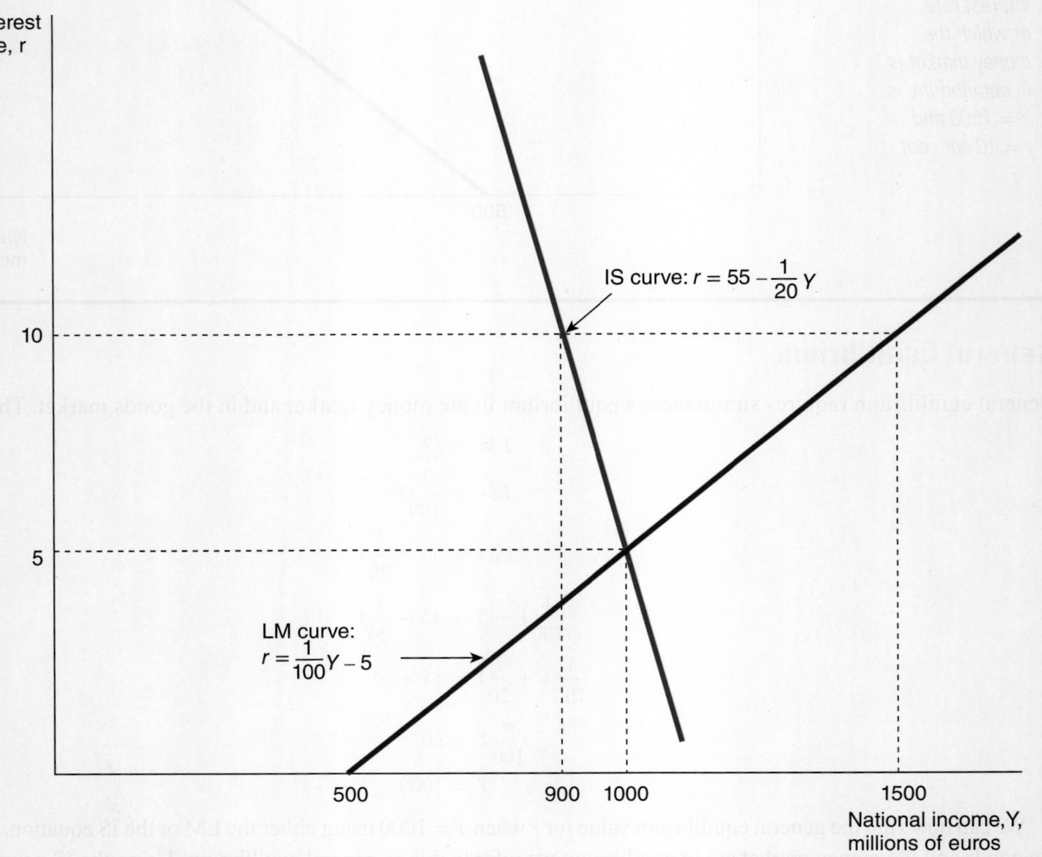

PROBLEMS AND APPLICATIONS

1 In an open economy with a government sector $Y = C + I + G + X - M$. People consume out of their disposable income (after taxes) $Y_d = (1 - t)Y$ with taxes proportional to gross income Y, so that $T = tY$. Assume a fixed ratio c_d of disposable income (Y_d) goes into consumption and a part m of gross income is spent on imports. All other components of GDP are autonomous in the sense that they do not depend on income (Y).

a. Write the expenditure equation of GDP as a function of income (Y).

b. Use your results from a) to derive the multiplier for a change in the "autonomous" components of GDP.

c. Use $c_d = 0.75$, a tax rate of $t = 25$ per cent, and a marginal propensity to import of $m = 20$ per cent. How much of an expansion in GDP will be caused by an increase of €20 billion in investment ($\Delta I = 20$)?

2 Define private savings as $S = S_{pr} = Y - T - C$, public savings as $S_{pub} = T - G$ and total savings in an economy $S_{tot} = S_{pr} + S_{pub} = Y - T - C + T - G = Y - C - G$. However, from $Y = C + I + G + X - M$ you immediately get: $Y - T - C = S_{pr} = I + G - T + X - M$ and therefore $S_{pr} + T + M = I + G + X$. Assume the autonomous components are I = 100, G = 200 and X = 200.

a. Assume the ratios from Problem 32.1 still hold, so the marginal propensity to consume out of the disposable income is $c = 0.75$ and the tax rate is $t = 25$ per cent. What is the marginal propensity for consumption out of total (gross) income and how high is the private sector savings rate in disposable and in gross income?

b. How high is total planned expenditure at an income level of 1000. Is there an inflationary or a deflationary gap?

c. Start from $S_{pr} + T + M = I + G + X$ or the multiplier approach to calculate the equilibrium GDP.

d. Is the government budget balanced at the equilibrium level of income?

e. Assuming exports remain at 200, is the country a net exporter or a net importer?

f. How much additional government expenditure will be needed to reach an equilibrium income level of 800?

3 Remember $Y = C + I + G + X - M$ to develop an IS curve with the following specifications: $C = C_o + cY = C_n + C_d(Y - T)$ and taxes $T = T_0 + tY$, so that: $C = C_n + c_d(Y - T_0 - tY) = C_n + c_d(1 - t)Y - c_dT_0$

Where:

$$C_0 = C_n - c_dT_0 \text{ and } c = c_d(1 - t)$$
$$M = M_0 + mY$$
$$I = I_0 - inv \times r.$$

4 Assume the autonomous components in the demand for GDP are $G = 100$ and $X = 150$; $C = 30 + 0.7Y$ (from a marginal rate of consumption out of disposable income of 0.8 and the tax rate of 12.5% on income); $M = 25 + 0.2Y$; and investment is a downward sloping function in the interest rate r: $I = 25 - 20 \times r$.

a. Derive the IS function and show it in the graph.

b. What happens to the IS curve if foreign demand increases autonomous exports by 50 units ?

5 Real money demand is given by $\left(\frac{M}{P}\right)^d = aY - br = 12.5Y - 400r$.

a. Show the interest rate as a function of income and money demand for (real) money.

b. For a giving nominal supply of money (M^S) of €125 and a price level of 1.25, calculate the LM function and graph it.

c. Assume the IS function is given by IS: $r = 10 - 0.02Y$, calculate the equilibrium level of the interest rate and national income.

d. How does the equilibrium change with an expansion of the nominal supply of money to €89 375?

33 AGGREGATE DEMAND AND AGGREGATE SUPPLY

In this chapter we consider the model of aggregate demand and aggregate supply. We begin with a consideration of an aggregate demand function, then shifts in aggregate demand. Then we consider long-run aggregate supply and general equilibrium in the long run. We then focus on short-run aggregate supply and short-run equilibrium followed by the effects of shifts in the aggregate supply function and how governments might accommodate such shifts. Finally, we examine how changes in the level of aggregate demand can have an effect on the individual components of aggregate demand.

INTRODUCTION

In this chapter we analyze short-run fluctuations in economic activity by using the model of aggregate demand and aggregate supply. In order to make things manageable we will assume linear functions. In some chapters we have used fractions rather than decimals but here it will be more convenient to use decimals. We begin with aggregate demand.

THE AGGREGATE DEMAND CURVE

The aggregate demand curve tells us the quantity of all goods and services demanded in the economy at any given price level. It is a negative relationship. There are three reasons why a fall in the price level will lead to a greater volume of aggregate demand. First, there is a wealth effect. With a given amount of money income a lower price level enables more goods and services to be bought. The wealth effect is felt primarily on consumption demand. Second, there is an interest rate effect. At a lower price level households are less willing to hold a liquid asset such as money. The reduction in the demand for money lowers interest rates and therefore increases investment demand. Third, there is the exchange rate effect. A fall in the price level makes imports relatively more expensive, causing a fall in imports and a rise in exports. This expands NX and therefore causes a rise in aggregate demand. All three of these effects we can see in our aggregate demand curve for the economy of the fictional country of Statistica. The components of aggregate demand are outlined below.

Consumption, C

Our consumption function is as follows. Consumers spend $0.75Y_D$, where Y_D = disposable income. The government takes a tax of 20 per cent of all factor incomes. Thus $C = 0.75x(0.8Y_D) = 0.6Y$, but their decisions are also dependent upon the price level (P) such that a lower price level raises consumption. Then our consumption function is:

$$C = 0.6Y - 25P$$

Investment, I

Investment is also influenced by the price level. However, there is a link between private investment and interest rates, as we saw in Chapter 25. Here, for simplicity, we focus on the relationship between investment and the price level. We will assume an investment function of:

$$I = 400 - 15P$$

Government current spending, G

We assume this to be autonomous and unaffected by the price level. We will assume that government expenditure G = 400.

The trade balance NX

As we have seen, there is an exchange rate effect through the price level so we build it into our model of Statistica:

$$NX = 400 - 0.1Y - 10P$$

The sum of these terms C, I, G and NX gives us planned aggregate expenditure. We can now find the relationship between planned aggregate expenditure and the price level, *P* which is the aggregate demand function for this economy.

$$\begin{aligned} Y &= 0.6Y - 25P + (400 - 15P) + 400 + (400 - 0.1Y - 10P) \\ &= 1200 + 0.5Y - 50P \\ Y - 0.5Y &= 1200 - 50P \\ 0.5Y &= 1200 - 50P \\ Y &= 2400 - 100P \end{aligned}$$

A one-unit rise in the price level, P, causes a 100-unit decline in *Y*. Making *P* the subject of the equation:

$$\begin{aligned} 100P &= 2400 - Y \\ P &= 24 - \frac{1}{100}Y \end{aligned}$$

This is the aggregate demand function.

We show this relationship diagrammatically in Figure 33.1.

If $P = 0$ then we can find *Y* as follows:

$$\begin{aligned} 0 &= 24 - \frac{1}{100}Y \\ \frac{1}{100}Y &= 24 \\ Y &= 2400 \end{aligned}$$

FIGURE 33.1

The Aggregate Demand Function

The aggregate demand function tells us the aggregate quantity of goods demanded at different price levels. The relationship has a negative slope.

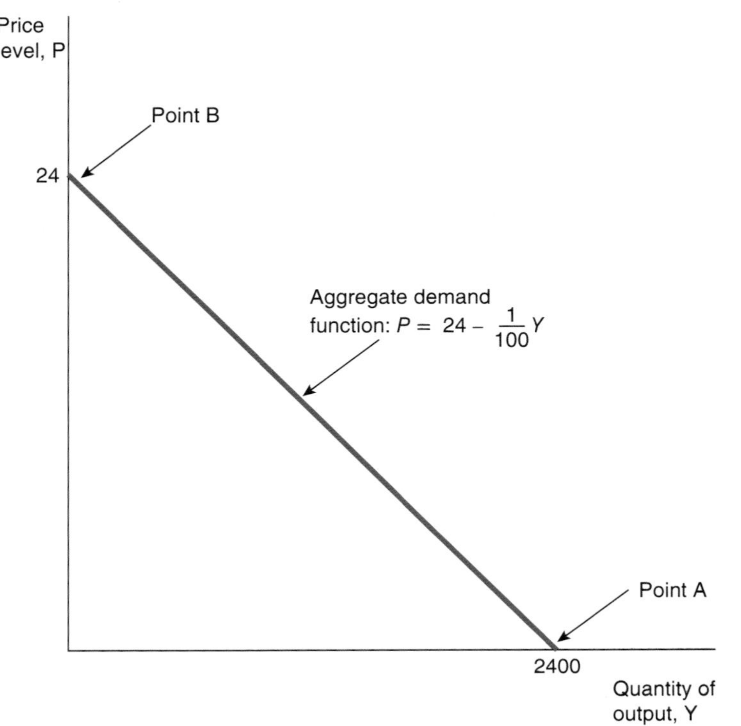

This is shown as point A in Figure 33.1.
If Y = 0:

$$P = 24 - 0$$
$$= 24$$

This is shown as point B in Figure 33.1.

Shifts in the Aggregate Demand Function

There are many factors that can change the whole relationship, shifting the aggregate demand curve. Any change in the components of aggregate demand can do this. We illustrate with one change, that of government expenditure, *G*. Assume the government raises *G* from 400 to 600 but there is no change in the other elements of aggregate demand. Then we can find the new aggregate demand curve. Note this is not a movement along the existing curve. It is not *P* that is changing:

$$Y = 0.6Y - 25P + (400 - 15P) + 600 + (400 - 0.1Y - 10P)$$
$$= 1400 + 0.5Y - 50P$$
$$0.5Y = 1400 - 50P$$
$$Y = 2800 - 100P$$

Or, making P the subject of the equation:

$$100P = 2800 - Y$$
$$P = 28 - \frac{1}{100}Y$$

We plot this relationship in Figure 33.2, which shows the shift in AD.

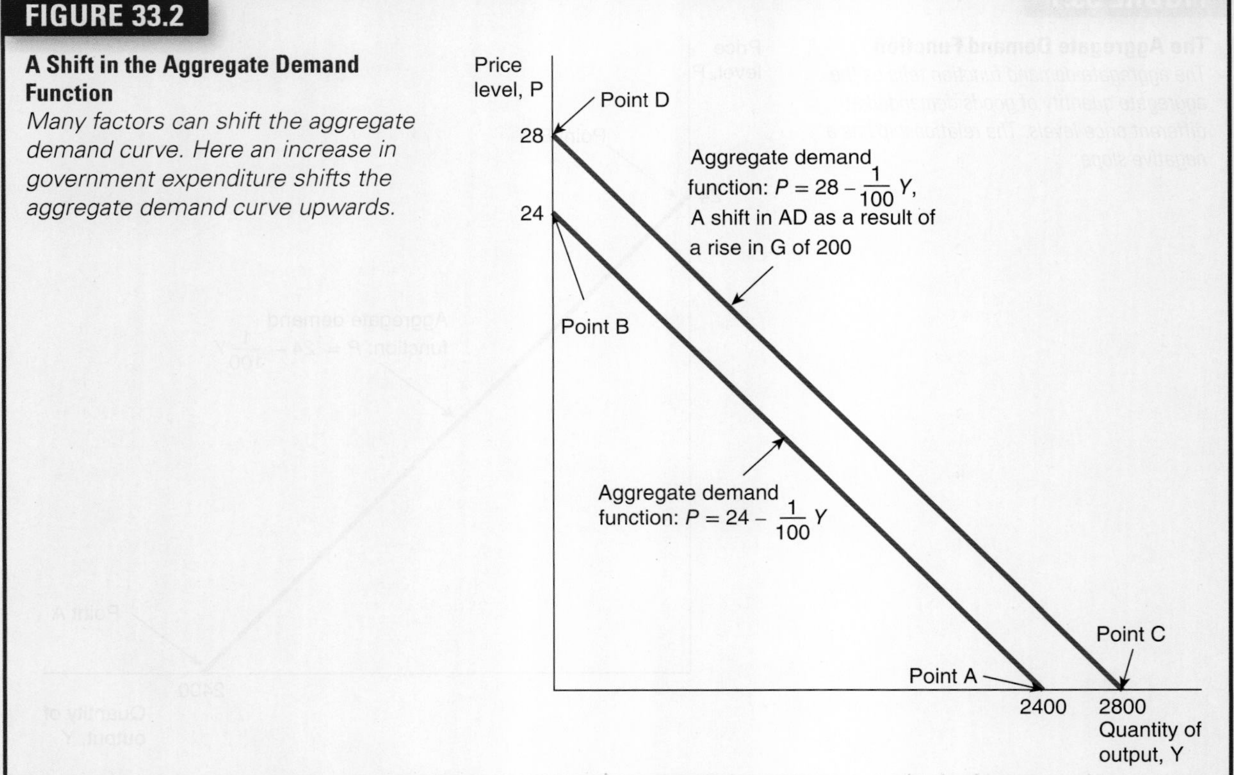

FIGURE 33.2

A Shift in the Aggregate Demand Function

Many factors can shift the aggregate demand curve. Here an increase in government expenditure shifts the aggregate demand curve upwards.

If $P = 0$ then we find Y:

$$0 = 28 - \frac{1}{100}Y$$
$$\frac{1}{100}Y = 28$$
$$Y = 2800$$

This is shown as point C in Figure 33.2.
If $Y = 0$

$$P = 28 - 0$$
$$= 28$$

This is shown as point D in Figure 33.2.

THE LONG–RUN AGGREGATE SUPPLY CURVE

Aggregate supply depends upon its supplies of labour, capital and natural resources, and on the available technology used to turn these factors of production into goods and services. The price level does not affect these long-run determinants of GDP. So in the long run the aggregate supply curve is vertical. If we know this 'natural rate of output' and the aggregate demand function we can find equilibrium for the economy.

First, however, we need to recognize that the long-run aggregate supply curve can shift to the right over time. This occurs if the labour supply expands, for example through immigration, increases in the capital stock or increases in the volume of natural resources, for example the discovery of new oil fields. The curve also shifts right if technological knowledge increases. We now illustrate how long-run equilibrium can be found for an economy and illustrate how rightward shifts in the AS curve can be expected to affect Y and P.

General Equilibrium in the Long Run

Using the aggregate demand function we have considered already we can find general equilibrium in the long run if we have knowledge of the natural rate of output. The AD function is:

$$Y = 2400 - 100P$$

Let's assume the AS function is:

$$Y = 1875$$

Then in equilibrium since $AS = AD$:

$$1875 = 2400 - 100P$$
$$100P = 525$$
$$P = 5.25$$

Long run general equilibrium is where output is 1875 and the index of the price level stands at 5.25. This is shown diagrammatically in Figure 33.3. If over time the AS function shifts right and the AD function stays the same, then as output increases, the price level will decline. For example, if the AS function becomes $Y = 2000$, then in equilibrium since $AS = AD$:

$$2000 = 2400 - 100P$$
$$100P = 400$$
$$P = 4$$

Given the AD function a rise in the natural rate of output reduces the price level.

FIGURE 33.3

General Equilibrium in the Long Run
In the long run the aggregate demand curve is vertical. If aggregate supply is 1875 and the aggregate demand function is $P = 24 - \frac{1}{100}Y$, then the price level is 5.25. If the long-run aggregate supply curve increases to 2000 and there is no change in aggregate demand, then the price level will fall to 4.

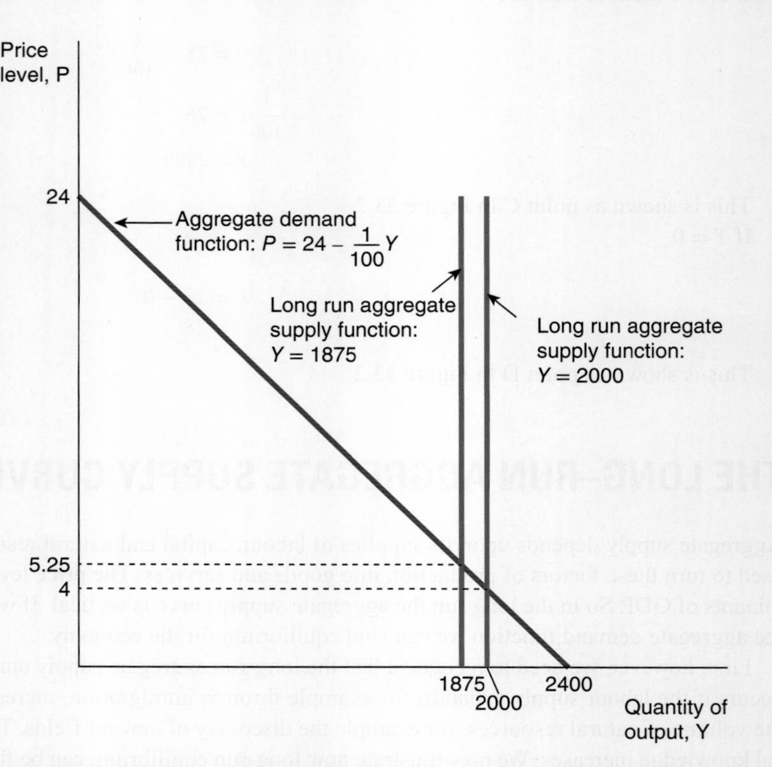

The Short Run Aggregate Supply Curve and Short Run Equilibrium

In the short run the quantity of output supplied deviates from the long-run or 'natural' level that people expect to prevail. When the price level rises above the expected level, output rises above its natural rate, and when the price level falls below the expected level, output falls below its natural rate. So although the long-run AS curve is vertical it is usually assumed that the short-run AS curve has a positive slope.

Let's illustrate with an assumed AS function. We will assume a short-run relationship such that, given the AD function we have been using, the combination of the equilibrium price level and the output level are the same for both short and long run. We assume a short-run AS function of:

$$P = 1.5 + 0.002Y$$

Then in short-run equilibrium since $AS = AD$:

$$\begin{aligned} Y &= 2400 - 100(1.5 + 0.002Y) \\ &= 2400 - 150 - 0.2Y \\ 1.2Y &= 2250 \\ Y &= 1875 \end{aligned}$$

We can now find P by substituting the value for Y into the AS equation. If we use the inverse form, we have:

$$\begin{aligned} P &= 1.5 + 0.002Y \\ &= 1.5 + 0.002 \times 1875 \\ &= 1.5 + 3.75 \\ &= 5.25 \end{aligned}$$

Figure 33.4 shows this equilibrium position for the economy and also shows the long-run equilibrium output, assumed to be 1875.

FIGURE 33.4

Equilibrium in the Short Run

Although the long-run AS curve is vertical, the short-run AS curve slopes upwards. Here the short-run AS function is $P = 1.5 + 0.002Y$, so that, for example, an output level of $Y = 3000$ would be associated with a price level of $P = 7.5$. At 1875 this economy, given its aggregate demand function, is in short-run equilibrium and also in long-run equilibrium.

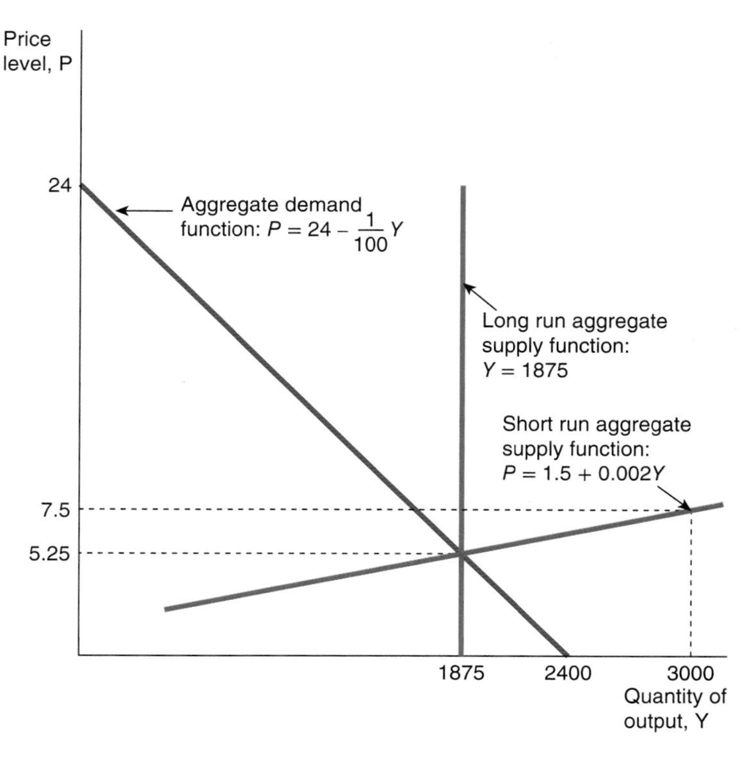

The short run equilibrium output is 1875 and the price level is 5.25. We plotted the short-run AS function as follows. It is a straight line function. We established that at 1875 $P = 5.25$. At an output level of, say, $Y = 3000$:

$$\begin{aligned} P &= 1.5 + 0.002 \times 3000 \\ &= 1.5 + 6 \\ &= 7.5 \end{aligned}$$

The Effects of a Shift in Aggregate Supply

Many things can cause the short-run AS curve to shift. Some of them are positive, some are negative. The positive things would include reduced union power and advances in technology. The negative things are often called adverse shocks and might be increased oil prices or severe weather conditions that lead to reduced crop production. Let us consider an adverse shock caused by a rise in oil prices. Oil prices can have a significant effect on the costs of many firms. In recent years oil prices have often risen quickly. At other times oil prices have fallen sharply. Here we consider an increase. The effects of an oil price fall will simply shift the aggregate supply curve in the opposite direction. Less will be supplied at each price level. Let us begin with the economy represented in Figure 33.4 so that the natural rate of Y is 1875 and $P = 5.25$.

Now the inverse AS shifts and becomes:

$$P = 6 + 0.002Y$$

The AD curve has not shifted. It remains as:

$$Y = 2400 - 100P$$

The new equilibrium with this reduced aggregate supply will now be where the AD function is equal to the new AS function:

$$\begin{aligned} Y &= 2400 - 100(6 + 0.002Y) \\ &= 2400 - 600 - 0.2Y \\ 1.2Y &= 1800 \\ Y &= 1500 \end{aligned}$$

We can find P by substituting the value for Y into the AS equation. Using the inverse form we have:

$$\begin{aligned} P &= 6 + 0.002Y \\ &= 6 + (0.002 \times 1500) \\ &= 6 + 3 \\ &= 9 \end{aligned}$$

We have a new equilibrium where output is 1500 and the price level is 9. The effect of the short-run AS illustrates stagflation – a higher price level and an output below its long-run equilibrium. This is shown in Figure 33.5.

FIGURE 33.5

An Adverse Shift in Aggregate Supply

If there is an adverse shift in the aggregate supply curve the economy's output will fall and the price level will rise. In this case output falls to 1500 and price level increases to 9. Output is now below the long-run equilibrium of 1875. The government can wait for the market to restore long-run equilibrium or intervene by stimulating aggregate demand.

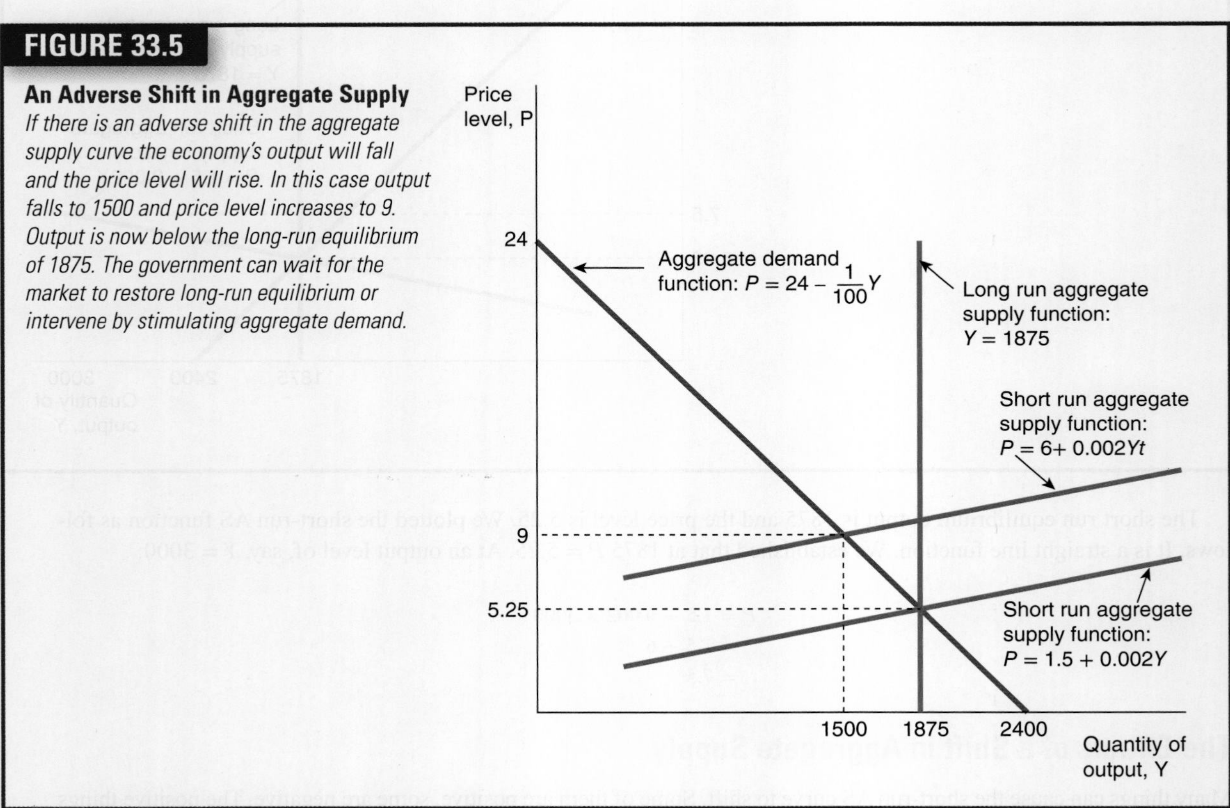

Accommodating an Adverse Shift in Aggregate Supply

The economy can be expected, over time, to return to its long-run equilibrium output. An output level below equilibrium results in increased unemployment, which in turn exerts a downward pressure on wages, causing aggregate supply to increase again. However, the government may be unwilling to wait for the labour market to adjust in this way. It may decide to stimulate aggregate demand and shift the AD curve upwards. Notice, though, as well as raising output to 1875, it will also raise the price level:

$$\begin{aligned} P &= 6 + 0.002Y \\ &= 6 + (0.002 \times 1875) \\ &= 6 + 3.75 \\ &= 9.75 \end{aligned}$$

The economy has returned to its natural rate but at the cost of a higher price level.

Changes in the Components of Aggregate Demand

When governments change the AD function, they change not only the volume of demand but also the size of the individual components of demand. We will illustrate this by assuming an economy where government increases AD by raising government current expenditure, G. We will find the equilibrium output, Y and the price level in the long run as a result of the change in AD. We will then compare the size of the components of AD in each of the equilibrium states we have found.

Earlier in the chapter we considered an economy with elements of aggregate demand as follows:

$$C = 0.6Y - 25P$$
$$I = 400 - 15P$$
$$G = 400$$
$$NX = 400 - 0.1Y - 10P$$

This gave us an AD function of:

$$Y = 2400 - 100P$$

We assumed that the AS function is:

$$Y = 1875.$$

In long-run equilibrium this gave $Y = 1875$ and $P = 5.25$.

Now look at the size of these individual components in equilibrium.

$$C = (0.6 \times 1875) - (25 \times 5.25) = 993.75$$
$$I = 400 - (15 \times 5.25) = 321.25$$
$$G = 400$$
$$NX = 400 - (0.1 \times 1875) - (10 \times 5.25) = 160$$

As a check, these individual components of AD must sum to 1875:

$$993.75 + 321.25 + 400 + 160 = 1875$$

We also looked at the new AD function when the government increases G from 400 to 600. That is:

$$Y = 0.6Y - 25P + (400 - 15P) + 600 + (400 - 0.1Y - 10P)$$

So that the new AD function became:

$$Y = 2800 - 100P$$

If the long-run AS function is unchanged, then the new long-run equilibrium will remain at 1875 but P will change:

$$Y = 2800 - 100P$$
$$1875 = 2800 - 100P$$
$$100P = 2800 - 1875$$
$$P = 9.25$$

Now we can calculate the individual components of AD at the new equilibrium:

$$C = (0.6 \times 1875) - (25 \times 9.25) = 893.75$$
$$I = 400 - (15 \times 9.25) = 261.25$$
$$G = 600$$
$$NX = 400 - (0.1 \times 1875) - (10 \times 9.25) = 120$$

As a check, these individual components of AD must sum to 1875:

$$893.75 + 261.25 + 600 + 120 = 1875$$

Table 33.1 summarizes the effects on individual components of AD as a result of the change in AD brought about by the increase in G.

Our model suggests that an increase in government spending will leave the long-run equilibrium level of output unchanged. However, it will raise the price level. The rise in the price level affects consumption, investment and net exports, all of which are reduced.

TABLE 33.1 **Changes in Components of Aggregate Demand through Increased Government Expenditure**

Component	Original Equilibrium	New Equilibrium	Change in size of component
Consumption, C	993.75	893.75	−100
Investment, I	321.25	261.25	−60
Government, G	400	600	200
Net exports, NX	160	120	−40
Total AD	1875	1875	0

PROBLEMS AND APPLICATIONS

1 Assume a country where consumption is $C = C_0 + c_d(1 - t)Y + c_P P$ with $C_0 = 0$, $c_d = 0.9$ and a tax rate of $t = 0.25$ of income Y. Consumption is a falling function of the price level P, so that $c_P = -550$ is negative. Investment has an autonomous component (I_0) but is also negatively dependant on the price level with $I = I_0 + I_P P = 5000 - 250P$. Government expenditure $G_0 = 4250$ is autonomous of income (Y) and prices (P). The external contribution to income from net exports falls with higher income and also with higher prices $NX = NX_0 + nx_Y Y + nx_P P$, with net autonomous exports of $NX_0 = 5000$, a marginal rate of change with respect to income of $nx_Y = -0.15$ and of $nx_P = -150$ with respect to the price level P. Long-term aggregate supply (the natural rate of output) is at $Y^S = 20\,000$.

a. Specify the aggregate demand Y as a function of the price level with the numerical values given above.
b. Write the inverse aggregate demand function P as a function of the level of income.
c. Use the variables I_0, G, NX_0,…, c_d, c_P, I_P, … to derive the aggregate demand function in general terms.
d. Find the long-term equilibrium price level with the parameters given above.
e. What change in the price level is induced over the long term by an increase in the level of autonomous investment to $I_1 = 8325$ ($\Delta I_0 = 3325$)?
f. Aggregate demand in the short term is given by $P = P_0 + as_Y Y \Leftrightarrow Y = 5000 + 5000P$. Find the parameters P_0 and as_Y to write out the inverse short-term aggregate demand function.
g. Calculate the short-term equilibrium price and demand for the model developed so far.
h. Recalculate the short-term equilibrium with the higher autonomous investment $I_1 = 8325$ from e).
i. Calculate the changes of investment, consumption and net exports following from the increase in autonomous investment.
j. Innovations in production technology shift the natural rate of output to $Y^S_1 = 28\,000$. What happens to the price level in the long term?

2 Look again at the model set up in the previous problem.

a. Change the model to allow for an autonomous component in consumption C_0.
b. How does the long- and short-term equilibrium change if $C_0 = 1900$?
c. What happens to the AD function if the tax rate (t) increases?

34 THE INFLUENCE OF MONETARY AND FISCAL POLICY ON AGGREGATE DEMAND

In this chapter we briefly review the concept of money market equilibrium and then link the money market to aggregate demand. We do this assuming a linear demand for money function. We then consider money market equilibrium with a non-linear money demand function. Finally, we consider the demand elasticity of the non-linear money demand curve.

MONEY MARKET EQUILIBRIUM

Equilibrium in the money market occurs where the quantity of money demanded is equal to the quantity of money supplied. The adjustment process occurs via changes in the interest rate.

The supply curve for money is assumed to be perfectly inelastic, with the stock of money determined by the central bank. The demand for money will be assumed to be linear for now. Later in the chapter we will drop this assumption. The 'price' of money is the rate of interest.

What is the mechanism by which the interest rate adjusts if there is disequilibrium? To illustrate the principle, assume that all wealth is held as money or bonds. An interest rate above equilibrium means an excess supply of money, and therefore an excess demand for bonds. Therefore, the price of bonds rises. Given the inverse relationship between interest rates and bond prices, interest rates will fall. Similarly, an interest rate below equilibrium means an excess demand for money, and therefore an excess supply of bonds. As a result, the price of bonds falls and interest rates rise.

We will now link this money market to the real sector by examining the link between the money market and aggregate demand.

The Money Market and Aggregate Demand

The demand for money is a function of several variables. These are the interest rate, the price level and the level of national income. As interest rates increase, the opportunity cost of money rises so we expect a negative relationship between money demand and interest rates. As the price level rises, people demand more money to engage in transactions which now cost more so we expect an upward shift of the demand for money function when the price level rises. Finally, consider national income. As income rises, people spend more so they demand more money for this purpose. Then we expect an upward shift in the demand for money function when national income increases.

In the light of this, assume a country's demand for money equation to be:

$$Q_D = -\frac{1}{2}r + 2P + \frac{1}{2}Y$$

Where:

Q_D = the demand for money in millions of euros

r = interest rate

P = price level

Y = national income

We assume an aggregate demand function of:

$$Y = 40 - P$$

Now assume further that we have some index of the current price level.[1] In this case we will assume the index to be 5. Then the current demand for money is:

$$Q_D = -\frac{1}{2}r + 2 \times 5 + \frac{1}{2}(40 - P)$$
$$= -\frac{1}{2}r + 10 + \frac{1}{2} \times 35$$
$$= -\frac{1}{2}r + 27\frac{1}{2}$$

Now suppose the government sets the money supply at $Q_S = 25$ (million euros). In equilibrium $Q_S = Q_D$:

$$25 = -\frac{1}{2}r + 27\frac{1}{2}$$
$$\frac{1}{2}r = 2\frac{1}{2}$$
$$r = 5$$

By choosing to set the money supply at 25, the interest rate will be 5 per cent. Since the aggregate demand curve is:

$$Y = 40 - P$$

And by assumption $P = 5$:

$$Y = 40 - 5$$
$$= 35$$

With interest rate at 5 per cent and a price level of 5, national income is 35. In this instance, then, both the price level and the interest rate currently have a value of 5.

If we show this diagrammatically we must find the inverse aggregate demand function:

$$Y = 40 - P$$
$$P = 40 - Y$$

We can find two points on this straight line demand function and join them.

If $Y = 0$:

$$0 = 40 - P$$
$$P = 40$$

If $P = 0$:

$$0 = 40 - Y$$
$$Y = 40$$

This is plotted in Panel (b) of Figure 34.1. We also show the current level of output at 35 and the current price level, P, at 5.

To plot the demand for money function we need the inverse demand for this market also.

$$Q_D = -\frac{1}{2}r + 27\frac{1}{2}$$
$$\frac{1}{2}r = 27\frac{1}{2} - Q_D$$
$$r = 55 - 2Q_D$$

We can find two points on this straight line demand function to plot the demand for money curve.

If $r = 0$:

$$0 = 55 - 2Q_D$$
$$Q_D = 27\frac{1}{2}$$

If $Q_D = 0$:

$$r = 55 - 0$$
$$= 55$$

We have plotted just a part of this demand for money curve in Panel (a) of Figure 34.1.

[1] We represent the price level by an index number. Normally, an index number will have a base of 100 but sometimes it has a base of 1. This is what we are using here. The price level in the base year was 1 and in our example is currently five times higher at 5.

FIGURE 34.1

The Money Market and the Aggregate Demand Curve

Panel (b) shows the economy's aggregate demand curve, $P = 40 - Y$. We assume that currently $P = 5$ and Y is therefore 35. Equilibrium in the money market is shown in panel. Given the supply function of $Q_S = 25$ and the demand for money function of $r = 55 - 2Q_D$, the interest rate is 5 per cent where the quantity of money supplied is equal to the quantity of money demanded.

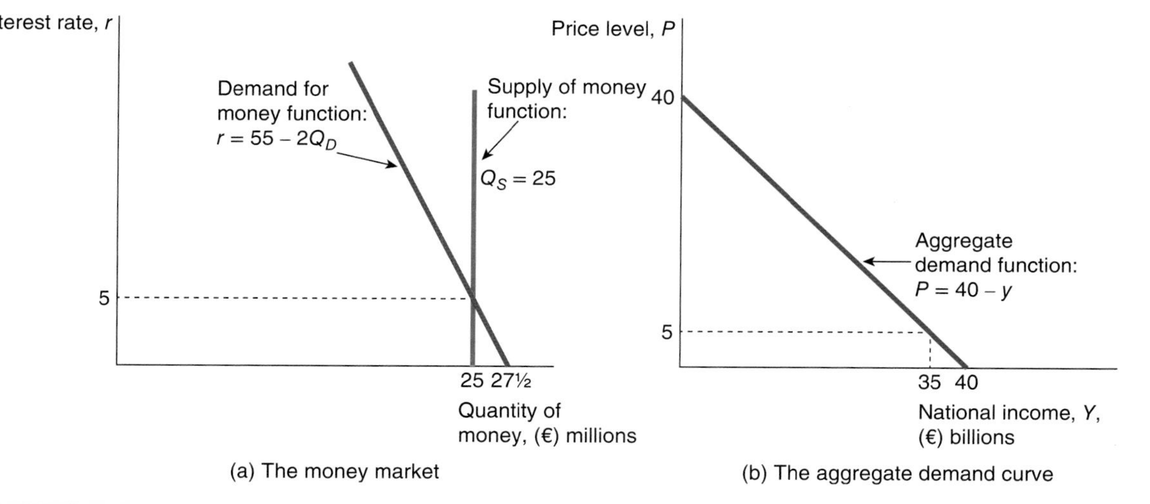

Now consider the effect of a 20 per cent rise in price from 5 to 6.

The rise in the price level affects the money market. With a higher price level of 6 there is a greater demand for money for transactions purposes. We have a new demand for money function. Let us suppose that it is now:

$$\begin{aligned} Q_D &= -\frac{1}{2}r + 2P + \frac{1}{2}Y \\ &= -\frac{1}{2}r + 12 + 17 \\ &= -\frac{1}{2}r + 29 \end{aligned}$$

With no change in the money supply we will have a new equilibrium interest rate.

$$\begin{aligned} Q_S &= Q_D \\ Q_S &= 25 \\ 25 &= -\frac{1}{2}r + 29 \\ \frac{1}{2}r &= 4 \\ r &= 8 \end{aligned}$$

Given a new demand for money function and no change in the money supply, interest rates rise from 5 to 8 per cent.

Diagrammatically, we show the effect by plotting the new demand for money curve, which has given rise to the higher equilibrium rate of interest. To do this we find the new inverse demand function.

$$\begin{aligned} Q_D &= -\frac{1}{2}r + 29 \\ \frac{1}{2}r &= 29 - Q_D \\ r &= 58 - 2Q_D \end{aligned}$$

This is the new inverse demand function. Finding two points on this new demand curve will enable us to plot it. If $r = 0$:

$$0 = 58 - 2Q_D$$
$$Q_D = 29$$

If $Q_D = 0$:

$$r = 58$$

Again, we have plotted just part of this function. As you can see in Figure 34.2 the shift upwards of the money demand curve raises the interest rate to 8 per cent.

Returning now to the aggregate demand function, national output, Y, at the new price level of $P = 6$ will now be:

$$Y = 40 - 6$$
$$= 34$$

National output falls to 34.

We show the new equilibrium diagrammatically in panel (b) of Figure 34.2. Because of the higher interest rate the economy has contracted along the AD function to the lower level of $Y = 34$.

FIGURE 34.2

The Money Market and the Aggregate Demand Curve Following a Rise in the Price Level

If the price level rises to P = 6, the money demand function changes. The new equilibrium in the money market is shown in panel (a) as 8 per cent. The higher interest rate causes a reduction in national output to 34 as shown in panel (b).

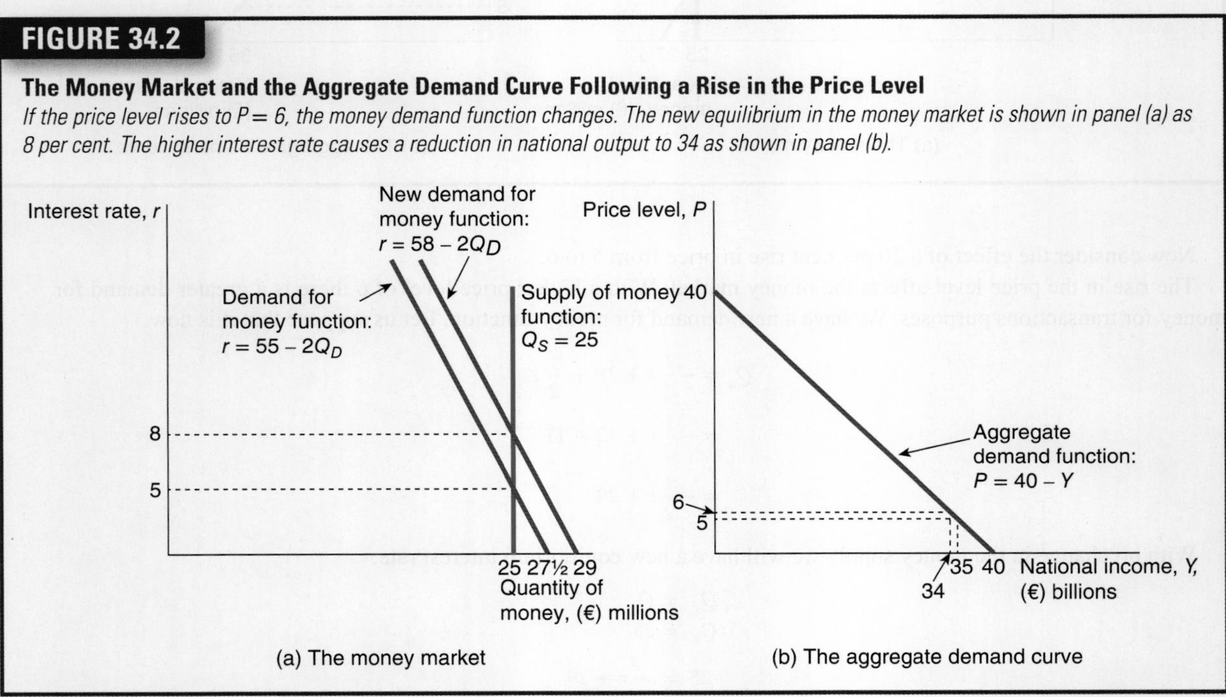

Note that the central bank does not have to accept the rise in the interest rate. It cannot directly control the demand for money function but it can control the money supply. If it increases the money supply sufficiently, it can, if it chooses, keep interest rates at 5 per cent.

To do this we need:

$$Q_S = Q_D = -\frac{1}{2}r + 29$$

And $r = 5$:

$$Q_D = -\frac{1}{2} \times (5) + 29$$
$$= 26\frac{1}{2}$$

The central bank must increase the money supply from 25 to $26\frac{1}{2}$. We show this in Figure 34.3.

FIGURE 34.3

Increasing the Money Supply to Accommodate Changes in Money Demand

If the central bank does not wish to see a rise in interest rates following the rise in the price level and in the demand for money, it can increase the money supply, shifting the money supply curve from 25 to 26½. Money market equilibrium remains at 5 per cent instead of rising to 8 per cent.

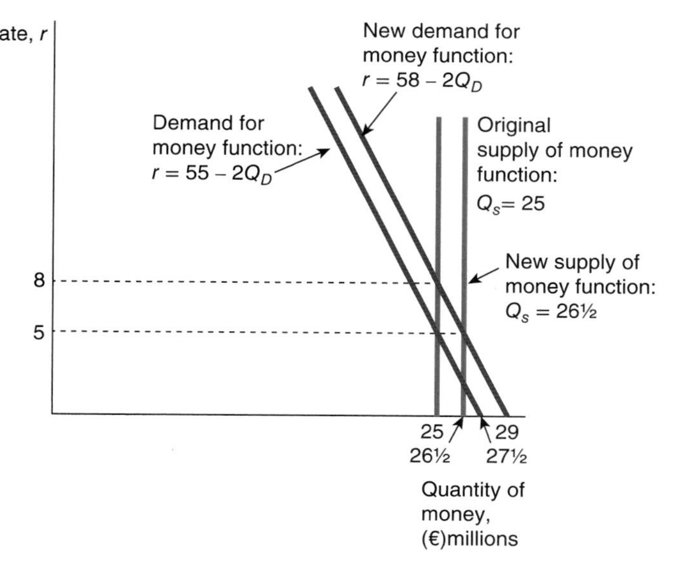

Money Market Equilibrium with a Non-Linear Money Demand Function

The demand for money function is often thought to be non-linear so in this section we find money market equilibrium using such a non-linear demand curve.

Assume that in a small European economy, the demand for money is given as:[2]

$$Q_D = ar^{-b}$$

Where:

Q_D = quantity of money demanded in millions of euros

r = the 'price' of money, the interest rate

a and b are positive constants, so that Q_D is a positive but decreasing function of r.

To illustrate, let's assume that $b = 2$ and $a = 1000$.

Then:

$$\begin{aligned} Q_D &= ar^{-b} \\ &= a \times \frac{1}{r^2} \\ &= 1000 \times \frac{1}{r^2} \end{aligned}$$

If the interest rate, r, is (say) 5 per cent, then:

$$\begin{aligned} Q_D &= 1000 \times \frac{1}{5^2} \\ &= 1000 \times \frac{1}{25} \\ &= 40 \end{aligned}$$

[2] When n is positive y^n is n times y, i.e. $\underbrace{y \times y \times y \ldots \times y}_{n \text{ times}}$. For negative exponents $y^{-n} = \frac{1}{y^n}$

The quantity of money demanded is €40 million when the interest rate is 5 per cent.

Suppose now the interest rate rises to 10 per cent. Then:

$$Q_D = 1000 \times \frac{1}{10^2}$$
$$= 1000 \times \frac{1}{100}$$
$$= 10$$

The quantity of money demanded is €10 million when the interest rate is 10 per cent. The higher rate of interest has led to a fall in the quantity of money demanded.

To plot this information as a demand curve we need the inverse form. Rearranging to get r on the left-hand side we have:

$$Q_D = ar^{-b}$$
$$= a \times \frac{1}{r^b}$$
$$r^b = \frac{a}{Q_D}$$
$$r = \sqrt[b]{\frac{a}{Q_D}}$$

Here we are taking the bth root. For $b = 2$ this is the square root, $b = 3$ the cube root etc. On your calculator you may need to use the x^y button where $x = \frac{a}{Q_D}$ and $y = \frac{1}{b}$. If we assume, as before, that $b = 2$ and $a = 1000$, then:

$$r = \sqrt{\frac{1000}{Q_D}}$$

If $Q_D = 40$:

$$r = \sqrt{\frac{1000}{40}}$$
$$= \sqrt{25}$$
$$= 5$$

We have confirmed that one point on the demand for money function is that when the interest rate is 5 per cent, the quantity of money demanded is €40 million. We can confirm the other point on the curve that we calculated, where $Q_D = 10$.

$$r = \sqrt{\frac{1000}{10}}$$
$$= 10$$

At an interest rate of 10 per cent, the quantity of money demanded is indeed €10 million.

We have sketched this non-linear function in Figure 34.4.

Let's suppose now that, as before, the central bank can fix the money supply at whatever level it chooses. Suppose this is set at €62.5 million. What will now be the equilibrium rate of interest in the money market?

$$Q_S = Q_D$$
$$62.5 = 1000 \times \frac{1}{r^2}$$
$$\frac{62.5}{1000} = \frac{1}{r^2}$$
$$r^2 = \frac{1000}{62.5}$$
$$r^2 = 16$$
$$r = \sqrt{16}$$
$$r = 4$$

FIGURE 34.4

Money Market Equilibrium with a Non-Linear Demand for Money Function
The demand for money function may well be non-linear. Here it is given as $Q_D = ar^{-b}$, where $b = 2$ and $a = 1000$. Combinations of interest rate and quantity of money demanded are shown. For example if $r = 5$ per cent, then $Q = 40$. If the central bank fixes the money supply at €62.5 million the equilibrium value of $r = 4$ per cent.

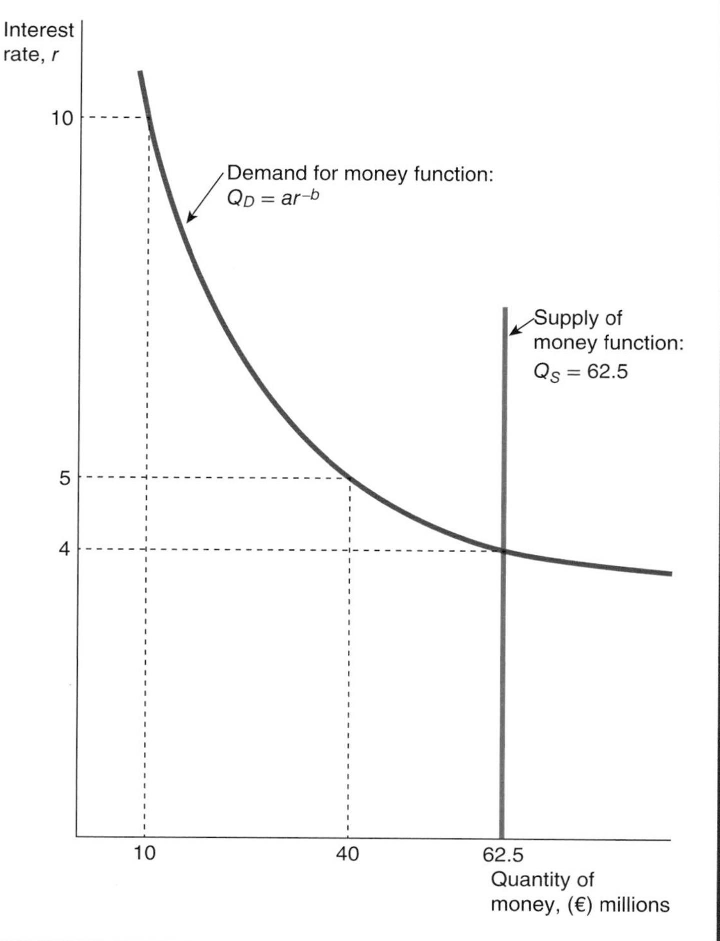

The equilibrium rate of interest is 4 per cent. The money supply and the equilibrium rate of interest are shown in Figure 34.4.

As we showed earlier with a linear demand function, the central bank can choose a level of money supply and then the market will determine the interest rate. Alternatively, the central bank can choose an appropriate level of interest but it will then have to supply the market with whatever money is demanded at that rate. The central bank can choose a money supply or an interest rate, but not both.

Demand Elasticity of the Non Linear Money Demand Curve

A negatively sloped linear demand curve varies in elasticity across its length. However, it is possible for a non-linear demand curve to have a constant elasticity. We demonstrate this by using our assumed demand for money equation.

$$Q_D = ar^{-b} \quad (1)$$

Differentiating this function gives:

$$\frac{dQ_d}{dr} = -bar^{-(b+1)} \quad (2)$$

We found (2) by following the standard rules of differentiation, reducing the power term by one. For example, if $b = 3$, we have:

$$Q_D = ar^{-3}$$
$$\frac{dQ_d}{dr} = -3ar^{-(3+1)}$$

The formula for point elasticity of demand is:

$$E = \frac{dQ_d}{dP} \times \frac{P}{Q_d}$$

Where:
E = elasticity of demand
P = the 'price' of money, the interest rate
Given that the price of money is the interest rate, we can use P and r interchangeably. This means that we can write the formula for elasticity like this:

$$E = \frac{dQ_d}{dr} \times \frac{r}{Q_d}$$

Replacing the first item with (2) and Q_D with (1) we have:

$$E = -bar^{-(b+1)} \times \frac{r}{ar^{-b}}$$
$$= -bar^{-b}r^{-1} \times \frac{r}{ar^{-b}}$$
$$= -bar^{-b} \times \frac{1}{r} \times \frac{r}{ar^{-b}}$$

Cancelling out the terms gives:

$$E = -b$$

In the special case when the demand function is $Q = ar^{-1}$ i.e. $b = 1$ the elasticity equal to -1 over its whole length.

If we have any money demand function where at low interest rates the curve becomes near horizontal, whether it is because $b = 1$ or more generally, it will require substantial increases in the money supply to lower it still further. This is because to further lower interest rates the money supply curve needs to be shifted to the right. Shifting the money supply curve to the right with a near horizontal money demand curve will have small effects on the equilibrium rate of interest.

PROBLEMS AND APPLICATIONS

1 Consider an economy in which consumption is a function of income and the price level in addition to autonomous consumption of $C_0 = 100$, so that $C = C_0 + c_Y Y + c_P P = 100 + 0.64Y - 20P$. Net exports of $NX = NX_0 = 150$ and government expenditure $G_0 = 220$ are considered to be independent of both income (Y) and the price level (P). However, investment has a component influenced by the price level in addition to an autonomous component: $I = I_0 + I_P P = 250 - 16P$. Demand for money is a linear function in the interest rate, prices and income. To avoid confusion with real output or other quantity variables money demand is written as $MD = md_r r + md_P P + md_Y Y = -20r + 40P + 0.25Y$.

a. Derive the appropriate aggregate demand function $Y = Y(P)$ and the inverse $P = P(Y)$.
b. Rearrange terms to show the (inverse) money demand function with the interest rate on the left-hand side of the equation as a function of prices, income and money on the right-hand side.
c. Use the aggregate demand function to rewrite the inverse money demand as a function of the price level and the quantity of money demand only.
d. Show the money supply function in a graph together with the money demand function for a price level of $P = 8$.

e. Assume the money supply is $MS^0 = 300$. Calculate the equilibrium interest rate in the money market at a given price level of $P = 8$.
f. What happens to the interest rate and income if the price level falls to $P = 6$?
g. Assume the price level to remain at $P = 8$ but a contraction in monetary policy reduces the supply of money to $MS^1 = 240$. Find the new equilibrium levels of the interest rate and income.

2 Aggregate demand is given by $Y = 20 - \frac{1}{100}P$. Demand for money is an upward sloping function in the price level and income. With increasing interest rates less money is demand. The money demand function is specified by $MD = \text{md}_a r^{\text{md}_r} + \text{md}_P P + \text{md}_Y Y = 500r^{-\frac{6}{5}} + 40P + 0.1Y$.

a. How large is the demand for money given a price level of $P = 3$ and an interest rate of $r = 2$?
b. Find the inverse of the money demand function which shows the interest rate as a function of the price level and MD.
c. Calculate income at the price level of $P = 3$ and at $P = 1.5$.
d. Use your results from c) to find the equilibrium interest rate in the money market with a money supply of $MS^0 = 350$ at the price levels of $P = 3$ and at $P = 1.5$. Check your calculation with Figure 34.5 below.
e. How does the equilibrium interest rate change if at $P = 3$ the money supply is expanded to $MS^1 = 450$?
f. Calculate the first derivative of the money demand function with respect to the interest rate.
g. How elastic is money demand for a given percentage change in the interest rate? Use $P = 3$ to find a specific value.

FIGURE 34.5

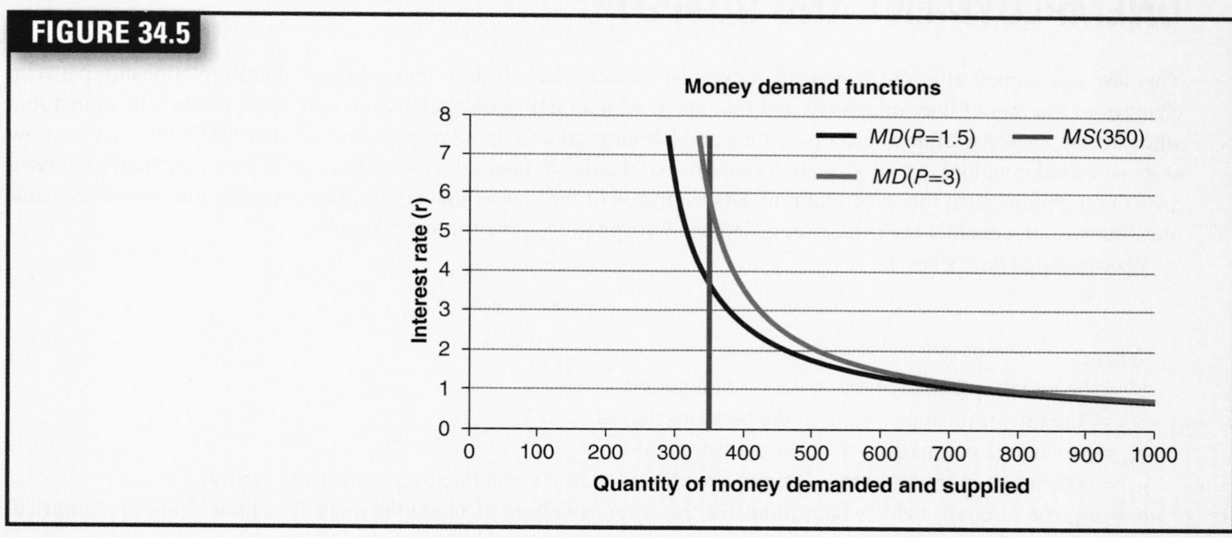

35 THE SHORT-RUN TRADE-OFF BETWEEN INFLATION AND UNEMPLOYMENT

We begin this chapter by considering the relationship between unemployment and output. We do this by looking at Okun's Law. Then we consider the relationship between unemployment and inflation. We do this by looking at the Phillips curve. We then use Okun's Law and the Phillips curve combined to examine the relationship between inflation and output. Finally, we look at the possible cost of controlling inflation via the 'sacrifice ratio'.

OKUN'S LAW: THE RELATIONSHIP BETWEEN UNEMPLOYMENT AND OUTPUT

This law was named after the American economist Arthur Okun. It describes a rule of thumb relationship between changes in the rate of unemployment and the rate at which GDP grows relative to potential growth. He argued that since the labour force tends to grow over time and labour productivity increase over time also, GDP will have to grow at its so-called potential rate of growth in order to avoid a rise in unemployment. To reduce unemployment requires a growth rate higher than this potential rate. His estimates of the size of this relationship were for the American economy, but we can consider the principle, which can be argued to apply for any economy.

We can state Okun's law as:

$$U_t - U_{t-1} = -\beta(g_{Yt} - \bar{g}_Y)$$

Where:

U_t = the rate of unemployment in the current period

U_{t-1} = the rate of unemployment in the previous period

g_{Yt} = percentage output growth in the current period

$\bar{g}_Y$ = percentage 'normal' or trend output growth, taken as a mean rate over some time period

β = a positive coefficient, which indicates the responsiveness of unemployment to output changes. Empirical testing indicates that its value is less than one.

Okun's law is an example of a difference equation that describes behaviour at discrete time intervals, say every year. For continuous time we would need a differential equation. The equation shows that when output growth in a given year is equal to the trend growth, the rate of unemployment will be stable. As an illustration suppose unemployment last period, say, a year ago, was 5 per cent. The normal growth rate for this economy is 3 per cent. Suppose also that the rate of growth of output this year is also 3 per cent. Then:

$$U_t - 5 = -\beta(3 - 3)$$

$$U_t = 5 - \beta(3 - 3)$$

So that whatever the value of β, $U_t = 5$

The unemployment rate stays at 5 per cent. The economy is growing but because it is only growing at the trend rate, unemployment has not fallen.

Unemployment can even increase with a growing economy. This time suppose that unemployment last period was again 5 per cent and the trend rate of growth is again 3 per cent. Now suppose that the actual growth rate is 1 per cent and the value of β is 1/2. We now have:

$$U_t - 5 = -\frac{1}{2}(1 - 3)$$
$$= 1$$
$$U_t = 6$$

The unemployment rate has increased from 5 to 6 per cent in a growing economy. The equation shows that unemployment will only fall if growth is above trend. For example, suppose we use the same economy as above but this time the actual growth rate is 5 per cent. Now:

$$U_t - 5 = -\frac{1}{2}(5 - 3)$$
$$= -\frac{1}{2} \times 2$$
$$U_t = 4$$

The economy is growing at a rate above trend and in this case the rate of unemployment has fallen from 5 to 4 per cent. The extent of the change in unemployment depends partly on the difference between actual and potential growth but partly on the coefficient β. It is to be expected that the value of this coefficient will be different in different economies and at different periods in the same economy. To find the value of β is a matter of empirical testing.

THE PHILLIPS CURVE: THE RELATIONSHIP BETWEEN UNEMPLOYMENT AND INFLATION

We need to consider both the short and the long run. First we think about the short run. The Phillips curve represents the argument that there exists a trade-off between unemployment and inflation. When unemployment is high, inflation will be low and vice versa. We can present the basic idea in the form of an equation:

$$\pi_t = \pi_e - \alpha U_t$$

Where:

π_t = inflation in the current period, *t*

π_e = the expected rate of inflation

U_t = the unemployment rate in the current period, *t*

α = a coefficient expressing the degree to which these variables are related

This says that inflation in the current period depends upon the current employment rate and upon the expected rate of inflation. When unemployment is high, employers are more able to resist inflationary wage demands from employees. Conversely, when unemployment is low, competition among employers for the limited supply of labour bids up wages and thus cost. This leads to a higher price level. The expected price level affects the wages and prices that economic agents set.

Let us illustrate the use of the formula. Suppose that it is expected that the rate of inflation will be 5 per cent, that unemployment is currently 4 per cent and that the value of the coefficient, α, is 1/2. Then we have:

$$\pi_t = 5 - \frac{1}{2} \times 4$$
$$= 3$$

Under these circumstances the Philips relationship suggests an inflation rate of 3 per cent. Now suppose that inflation is expected to be 8 per cent, *ceteris paribus*, then:

$$\pi_t = 8 - \frac{1}{2} \times 4$$
$$= 6$$

Under these circumstances the Philips relationship suggests an inflation rate of 6 per cent. The most natural assumption would be that the higher expected inflation rate has caused employers and employees to agree higher wages and employers to set higher prices. Now, finally, suppose that, reverting to the original situation, we just change the unemployment rate to 8 per cent. Then we have:

$$\pi_t = 5 - \frac{1}{2} \times 8$$
$$= 1$$

The higher unemployment rate leads, *ceteris paribus*, to a lower rate of inflation.

The Phillips Curve and the Long Run

In order to understand the long-run Phillips curve we need to be clear about the meaning of the natural rate of unemployment. It is argued that the natural rate of unemployment is the normal rate of unemployment around which the unemployment rate fluctuates. In the long run the market for labour tends towards this level of unemployment. We think of it as the rate which means there is no pressure in the labour market for real wages to move upwards beyond what is the result of increased productivity. At this natural rate, the rate of inflation will stay unchanged. That is why it is sometimes called the 'NAIRU', the non-accelerating inflation rate of unemployment. Inflation only increases as the labour market tightens and unemployment falls below this level. Thus, the long-run Phillips equation can be expressed as:

$$\pi_t - \pi_{t-1} = -\alpha(U_t - U_n)$$

Where:
π_t = inflation in the current period, t
π_{t-1} = the rate of inflation one period ago
U_t = the unemployment rate in the current period, t
U_n = the natural rate of unemployment
α = a coefficient expressing the degree to which these variables are related

To illustrate, suppose that the economy has a current unemployment rate of 7 per cent which is also its NAIRU. Then:

$$\pi_t - \pi_{t-1} = -\alpha(7 - 7)$$

Then whatever the value of α:

$$\pi_t - \pi_{t-1} = 0$$

The inflation rate will not change.

Suppose now this same economy has a current unemployment rate of 3 per cent, a rate below the NAIRU. To estimate the effect on the inflation rate we must know the value of α. Let us suppose that it is 1/4. Then:

$$\pi_t - \pi_{t-1} = -\frac{1}{4}(3 - 7)$$
$$= 1$$

We expect a positive 1 per cent change in the inflation rate.

If the economy had a different value for α, but the same unemployment rate and the same NAIRU, we can calculate the effect on the inflation rate. For example, if $\alpha = 3/4$, then:

$$\pi_t - \pi_{t-1} = -\frac{3}{4}(3 - 7)$$
$$= 3$$

We expect a 3 per cent increase in the inflation rate.

Finally, we take an example where current unemployment is above the NAIRU. With a NAIRU at 7 per cent but a current unemployment rate of 10 per cent and a value for α of 1/4, we can expect to see a fall in the inflation rate:

$$\pi_t - \pi_{t-1} = -\frac{1}{4}(10 - 7)$$
$$= -\frac{3}{4}$$

The fall in the inflation rate is three quarters of 1 per cent.

COMBINING OKUN'S LAW AND THE PHILLIPS CURVE: THE RELATIONSHIP BETWEEN INFLATION AND OUTPUT

We can now combine the Philips curve with Okun's law to see how inflation is affected by both unemployment and the rate of growth of output.

The Phillips curve relationship can, as we have seen, be described by:

$$\pi_t - \pi_{t-1} = -\alpha(U_t - U_n)$$

Okun's law suggests that:

$$U_t - U_{t-1} = -\beta(g_{Yt} - \bar{g}_Y)$$

Which we can rearrange by moving U_{t-1} to the right-hand side of the equation which gives:

$$U_t = U_{t-1} - \beta(g_{Yt} - \bar{g}_Y)$$

Now we restate the Philips equation, incorporating the Okun equation by replacing U_t in the Philips equation from the rearranged Okun equation. Thus:

$$\pi_t - \pi_{t-1} = -\alpha(U_{t-1} - \beta(g_{Yt} - \bar{g}_Y) - U_n)$$

To illustrate, suppose an economy had an unemployment rate of 8 per cent last year and its natural rate is 4 per cent. Suppose further that the natural (or trend) rate of growth is 3 per cent but the current growth rate is zero. Now let's assume that α takes a value of 1/3 and β takes a value of 1/2. Then we have:

$$\begin{aligned}\pi_t - \pi_{t-1} &= \frac{1}{3}\left(8 - \frac{1}{2}(0 - 3) - 4\right)\\ &= \frac{1}{3}\left(8 + \frac{3}{2} - 4\right)\\ &= \frac{1}{3}\left(4 + \frac{3}{2}\right)\\ &= \frac{1}{3} \times \frac{11}{2}\\ &= \frac{11}{6}\end{aligned}$$

We expect a change in the inflation rate of just under 2 per cent. Inflation is a function of both unemployment and economic growth.

We have now considered the relationship between unemployment and output via Okun's law and the relationship between unemployment and inflation via the Phillips curve. Finally we have considered the relationship between inflation and output by combining Okun's law with the Phillips curve.

THE SACRIFICE RATIO

Linked to the short-run Phillips curve relationship is the concept of 'sacrifice ratio'. This measures the costs in terms of lower output as a percentage of the change in the inflation rate. One can express the lost output as a value or as a percentage of output. If we express it as a value then the formula can be given as:

$$SR = \frac{YL}{\Delta\pi}$$

Where:
SR = sacrifice ratio
YL = value in euros of lost output
$\Delta\pi$ = change in inflation rate

Suppose that aggregate demand falls and the economy contracts. As a consequence, output has fallen by €6 million. Suppose further that the reduction in demand has reduced the inflation rate by 3 per cent. Then:

$$\begin{aligned}SR &= \frac{6\,000\,000}{3}\\ &= €2\,000\,000\end{aligned}$$

The sacrifice ratio is €2 000 000. That is, the cost of a reduction in the inflation rate is a loss of €2 000 000 worth of output for every 1 per cent fall in the inflation rate. If we express the lost output as a percentage, then a typical value is found to be in the range of 3–5 per cent of output.

A government wishing to control inflation can use the sacrifice ratio to determine the short-run costs and benefits of its policy. Since the economy can be argued to return in the long run to its natural rate of unemployment and output, the sacrifice ratio is usually thought of as a short-run consideration only.

PROBLEMS AND APPLICATIONS

1 Fill in the missing values from Okun's law: $U_t - U_{t-1} = -\beta(g_{Yt} - \bar{g}_Y)$

Okuns Law

	U_t	U_{t-1}	$-\beta$	g_{Yt}	$\bar{g}_Y$
a)		4.00	0.50	1.00	2.50
b)		7.00	0.70	4.00	2.50
c)	5.00		0.70	1.00	2.00
d)	6.10	5.30		1.00	2.00
e)	9.20	7.00	0.80		2.00
f)	3.00	4.00	0.80	2.50	

2 Show the formula for the calculation of the expected inflation rate π_e if you have all other information in the short-term Phillips curve $\pi_t = \pi_e - \alpha U_t$.

3 The short-term Phillips curve represents a relationship between the unemployment rate and the deviation of the inflation rate from the inflation rate its expected value. Pick a different, non-linear functional form, which could express this negative relationship.

4 An economy has a NAIRU = U_n of 5.5 per cent. Will inflation be accelerating if the unemployment rate is at 7 per cent or at 4 per cent. Explain using the long-run Phillips curve $\Delta\pi_t = \pi_t - \pi_{t-1} = -\alpha(U_t - U_n)$.

5 According to the text, combining the long-term Phillips curve and Okun's law results in $\pi_t - \pi_{t-1} = -\alpha(U_{t-1} - \beta(g_{Yt} - \bar{g}_Y) - U_n)$. Assume $U_n = 5.5\%$, $\alpha = 1/2$, $\beta = 3/5$, when the trend growth rate of output is $\bar{g}_Y$ is 2 per cent.

a. How strongly does inflation accelerate if last year's unemployment was at $U_{t-1} = 6\%$ and the current growth is at 3 per cent?

b. Which change in the inflation rate do you get for each percentage point in last year's rate of unemployment (U_{t-1})?

c. How sensitive does the inflation rate react to a change in the current rate of output growth?

36 SUPPLY SIDE POLICIES

Taxation policy affects aggregate demand but it may also affect aggregate supply. In this chapter we focus on one particular aspect of taxation policy, income tax. We consider how income tax rates might affect GDP and also how these rates might affect government revenue. Central to this discussion is the concept of the Laffer curve.

INTRODUCTION: THE LAFFER CURVE

One day in 1974, rumour has it, the American economist, Arthur Laffer, sat in a Washington restaurant with some prominent journalists and politicians. He took out a napkin and drew a figure on it to show how tax rates affect tax revenue. It looked like that shown in Figure 36.1.

At a zero tax rate the government gets no revenue. As the tax rate rises, the government's revenue rises also but at a slower rate. With higher tax rates people have less incentive to work and some substitute leisure for work. Output, and therefore income, falls and this affects tax on that income. At some point this effect becomes so strong that an increase in the tax rate decreases the tax take. Arthur Laffer then suggested that the United States was on the downwards sloping side of this curve. Tax rates were so high, he argued, that reducing them would actually raise tax revenue. The curve in Figure 36.1 has become known as the Laffer curve.

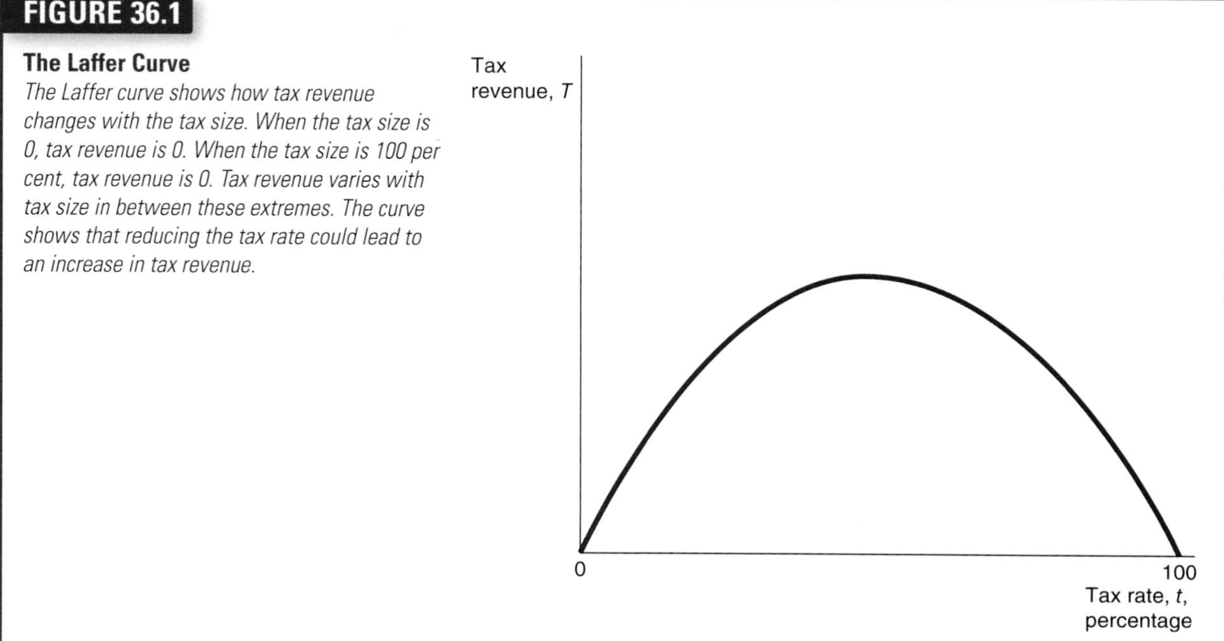

FIGURE 36.1

The Laffer Curve

The Laffer curve shows how tax revenue changes with the tax size. When the tax size is 0, tax revenue is 0. When the tax size is 100 per cent, tax revenue is 0. Tax revenue varies with tax size in between these extremes. The curve shows that reducing the tax rate could lead to an increase in tax revenue.

The idea that a cut in tax rates could raise tax revenue must be correct at some tax rate. Yet there was little evidence for Laffer's view that tax rates – in the United States or in most other economies – had in fact reached such levels. Most studies suggest that most countries are on the rising part of the Laffer curve.[1]

There is certainly no reason to think that the top of the Laffer curve will be at a tax rate of 50 per cent. It might be more or less. It is a matter for empirical study. Interestingly, a recent study of the US economy by Romer and Romer (2010) supports the view that the US is on the downward sloping part of the curve.[2] However, before we look at this evidence a number of things need to be clear. Although in principle the Laffer curve argument can be applied to any tax, our interest here is only in the effects of income tax. Furthermore, there are two related but distinct relationships to be considered. We need to consider the effect of the tax rate on the level of GDP. We will do this first. We also need to consider the effect of the tax rate on government revenue. The last thing to be clear about is that the Romers do not state directly where they believe the top of the Laffer curve to be, but with a little mathematics we can draw from their analysis a conclusion about where their data suggests that it is.

We begin the analysis with the relationship between the tax rate and GDP. We have sketched in Figure 36.2 the kind of relationship suggested by the Romer evidence.

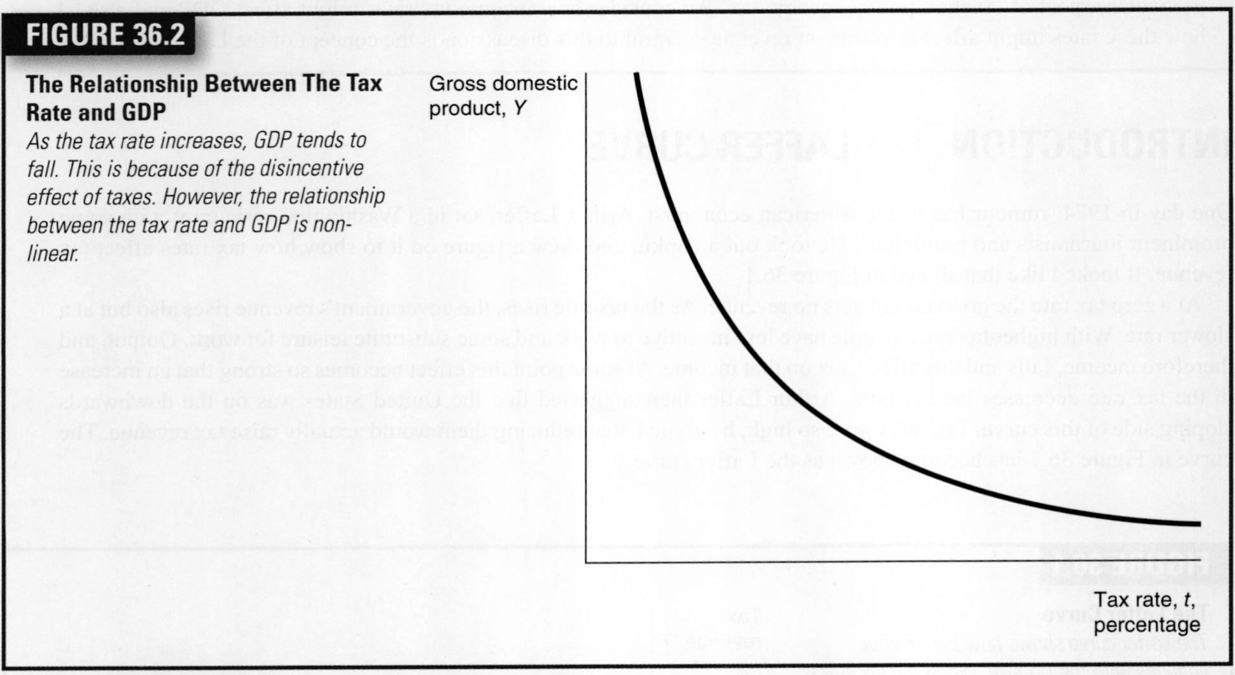

FIGURE 36.2

The Relationship Between The Tax Rate and GDP

As the tax rate increases, GDP tends to fall. This is because of the disincentive effect of taxes. However, the relationship between the tax rate and GDP is non-linear.

As the tax rate increases, the disincentive effect causes GDP to fall. Note that it doesn't fall at a constant rate. It is a non-linear relationship. When the tax rate increases by a small amount GDP declines by a constant *factor*. At larger tax rates, GDP is smaller so the absolute fall in GDP is less than at lower tax rates. Since GDP is the same as Gross Domestic Income we have labelled the vertical axis Y for income. The label on the horizontal axis is the tax rate, or t. The total tax take, government revenue, we shall label T. If we further assume that government revenue comes only from direct tax and that the government takes a given proportion of all income then the tax take is $T = t \times GDP$ or $T = tY$.

Some Evidence from the US

We begin with the relationship between a change in the tax rate and its effect on GDP. A key piece of the evidence from Romer and Romer (2010) is that over a large range of tax rates a 1 per cent increase in the tax rate decreases

[1] For example, Pecorino, P. (1995) 'Tax rates and tax revenues in a model of growth through human capital accumulation.' *Journal of Monetary Economics* 36 **(3)**: 527; and Trabandt, M. and Uhlig, H. (2009) 'How Far Are We From The Slippery Slope? The Laffer Curve Revisited.' *NBER Working Paper No. 15343*, European Central Bank.

[2] Romer D.D. and Romer, D. H. (2010) 'The Macroeconomic Effects of Tax Changes: Estimates Based on a new Measure of Fiscal Shocks.' *American Economic Review*, 100 **(3)**: 763–801.

GDP by 3 per cent of its value at that point on the curve. That is, a 1 per cent increase in the tax rate reduces GDP by a factor of 0.97. Then we know that at any point on the curve of Figure 36.2, the slope of the curve can be found as:

$$\frac{dY}{dt} = -3Y$$

Where:

$$Y = GDP$$

$$t = \textit{the tax rate}$$

This is known as an ordinary differential equation that governs the continuous change in Y with time (compare this with the difference equation for discrete time periods that we met, for example, in Chapter 35). If we assume that this evidence is correct we can find the top of the Laffer curve, which shows the relationship between a change in the tax rate and *government revenue*. That is, we can find t_{max} in Figure 36.3, where the rate of change of the function is zero, that is:

$$\frac{dT}{dt} = 0$$

Since tY is the level of GDP, Y, multiplied by the tax rate, t, we can express this relationship as:

$$\frac{d(tY)}{dt} = 0$$

Now by the product rule for differentiation:[3]

$$\frac{d(tY)}{dt} = t\frac{dY}{dt} + Y$$

We need the tax rate at which:

$$t\frac{dY}{dt} + Y = 0$$

The Romer and Romer 2010 result suggests that:

$$\frac{dY}{dt} = -3Y$$

Then substituting this into our previous expression we have:

$$0 = -3tY + Y$$

Thus:

$$-3t + 1 = 0$$

$$3t = 1$$

$$t = \frac{1}{3}$$

The tax rate, t, which maximizes government revenue, T, is therefore 1/3 or $33\frac{1}{3}$ per cent.

We began with evidence of the relationship between changes in the tax rate and GDP. We used this evidence to imply the relationship between changes in the tax rate and the tax revenue generated. Specifically, we used differentiation to find the top of the Laffer curve where the rate of change of government revenue for a small change of tax rate is zero.

[3] The product rule states that to differentiate a function of the kind:

$$\frac{d(uv)}{dt}$$

Where u and v are both functions of t, we can differentiate each of the terms u and v separately and combine them. Thus:

$$\frac{d(uv)}{dt} = u\frac{dv}{dt} + v\frac{du}{dt}$$

FIGURE 36.3

Finding The Top of The Laffer Curve

The tax rate t_{max} shows the percentage tax rate at which tax revenue is maximized. At this rate a small change in the tax rate has no effect on government revenue.

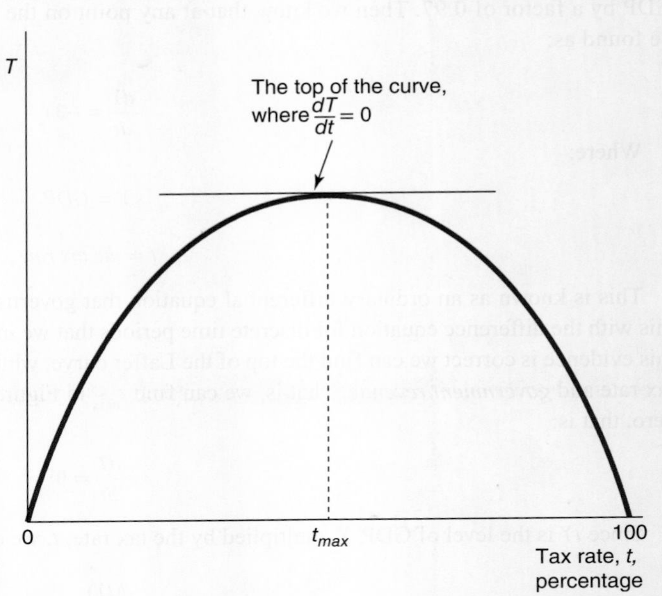

The Value of Laffer Curve Evidence

The Romer and Romer (2010) evidence is clearly of interest, and if it is correct it points to some important conclusions. Reductions in tax may increase government income as well as GDP. It also suggests that the way to get higher income earners to pay more tax is to reduce the rate of tax they are charged.

However, it is possible that what is true of the US may not be true of other economies. Other people's preferences as between income and leisure may be different. Furthermore, a change in the tax rate may only increase GDP and government revenue if we make a *ceteris paribus* assumption. A change in the tax rate may well not be independent of whether the tax rate is changing elsewhere. For example, the European Union comprises many countries with a significant degree of movement of capital and labour. The effects of a decision, say, to reduce tax rates in Germany, is unlikely to be independent of whether a similar cut occurs in Austria and the Netherlands. An increase in the tax rate in the Czech Republic will be greatly affected by the response of such a decision in Slovakia where culture and language are similar and where capital and labour movements are relatively easy.

The main value of studying the Romer and Romer (2010) evidence, however, is that we can see how a little mathematics can allow us to draw conclusions from available evidence.

PROBLEMS AND APPLICATIONS

1 Is there also a tax rate that would maximize tax revenues if the evidence suggested that increasing the income tax rate by one percentage point will reduce taxable income by 2 per cent $\left(\frac{dY}{Y}\Big/_{dt} = 2\%\right)$? If so, what is the maximum tax rate?

PART 15 INTERNATIONAL MACROECONOMICS

37 COMMON CURRENCY AREAS AND MONETARY UNION

The economic effects of a common currency are the same for its member countries as those of a permanently fixed exchange rate. In this chapter we analyze how, with intervention in the foreign exchange market, governments can fix their exchange rate, either as a macro policy in itself or as part of a policy of moving towards full currency union.

INTRODUCTION

Currency values are determined by supply and demand. Supply and demand conditions vary so that market exchange rates alter frequently. However, sometimes governments wish to fix their exchange rate at a rate different from that which markets would give. One reason for this desire is the wish for their economy to become part of a common currency area. For example, to join the European Union's euro area requires a government to fix its exchange rate against the euro for a period. If successful, the country may then be able to give up its currency for the permanently fixed exchange rate of the common currency area.

In this chapter we explore a major way of fixing the exchange rate. We will illustrate this by assuming that the UK government wishes to fix its currency, the pound sterling (£), against the euro.

The Market for Foreign Exchange

We will assume that the market for sterling is determined by a demand curve and a supply curve for sterling where the price of sterling is in euros. The demand curve we will assume is given by the function:

$$Q_D = 95\,000 - 12\,000P_e$$

Where:

Q_D = the quantity of sterling demanded daily, in millions

P_e = the price of sterling measured in euros
The supply curve is given by the function:

$$Q_S = 67\,000 - 8000P_e$$

Where:
Q_s = the quantity of sterling supplied daily in millions
Assuming no government attempt to affect the market, the equilibrium price will be where $Q_S = Q_D$.

$$\begin{aligned} 67\,000 + 8000P_e &= 95\,000 - 12\,000P_e \\ 20\,000P_e &= 28\,000 \\ P_e &= €1.4 \end{aligned}$$

£1 exchanges for €1.4. This is currently the market equilibrium rate.

If we wish to know the volume of currency exchanged we can substitute this value into either the supply or demand function to find it. Using the demand function:

$$\begin{aligned} Q_D &= 95\,000 - 12\,000P_e \\ &= 95\,000 - (12\,000 \times 1.4) \\ &= £78\,200 \end{aligned}$$

Using the supply equation:

$$\begin{aligned} Q_S &= 67\,000 + 8000P_e \\ &= 67\,000 + (8000 \times 1.4) \\ &= £78\,200 \end{aligned}$$

The quantity of sterling exchanged is £78 200 million. This is currently the market equilibrium quantity.

If this rate is commensurate with government policy there is no need for any government intervention. Suppose now that the demand for sterling falls, perhaps because foreign consumers switch their preferences away from UK goods and therefore require less sterling. As a result there is a new demand curve for sterling. We will assume that it is now:

$$Q_D = 91\,000 - 12\,000P_e$$

The supply curve is unchanged at:

$$Q_S = 67\,000 + 8000P_e$$

Then with no government attempt to affect the market the equilibrium price will be changed:

$$\begin{aligned} 67\,000 + 8000P_e &= 91\,000 - 12\,000P_e \\ 20\,000P_e &= 24\,000 \\ P_e &= €1.2 \end{aligned}$$

One pound sterling now exchanges for €1.2. This is now the new market equilibrium rate. The value of the pound against the euro has fallen from its previous level of €1.4.

If we wish to know the volume of currency now exchanged we can substitute this new value into either the supply function or into the new demand function to find it. Using the demand function:

$$\begin{aligned} Q_D &= 91\,000 - 12\,000P_e \\ &= 91\,000 - (12\,000 \times 1.2) \\ &= £76\,600 \end{aligned}$$

Using the supply function:

$$\begin{aligned} Q_S &= 67\,000 + 8000P_e \\ &= 67\,000 + (8000 \times 1.2) \\ &= £76\,600 \end{aligned}$$

The daily quantity of sterling exchanged is £76 600 million. This is now the new market equilibrium quantity. The fall in demand for sterling results in a fall in the price of sterling and a reduction in the quantity exchanged in the market.

It will be helpful at this point to show the market for sterling diagrammatically, but to do so we will need to find the inverse demand and supply functions. First let's find the inverse form of the original demand curve.

$$Q_D = 95000 - 12000P_e$$
$$12000P_e = 95000 - Q_D$$
$$P_e = 7.92 - \frac{1}{12000}Q_D$$

This is the inverse demand curve shown in Figure 37.1. We already found one point on the demand curve. We know that when $P_e = 1.4$, $Q_D = 78\ 000$. When $P_e = 0$, then:

$$O = 7.92 - \frac{1}{12000}Q_D$$
$$Q_D = 7.92 \times 12000$$
$$Q_D = £95040$$

It would be £95 000 without the rounding error so we have plotted it as £95 000.

FIGURE 37.1

Equilibrium in the Market for Sterling

The exchange rate is determined by the demand and supply for the currency in the foreign exchange market. With a demand function of $P_e = 7.92 - \frac{1}{12\ 000}Q_D$ and a supply function of $P_e = \frac{1}{8000}Q_S - 8.38$, £1 sterling exchanges for €1.4 when the market is in equilibrium.

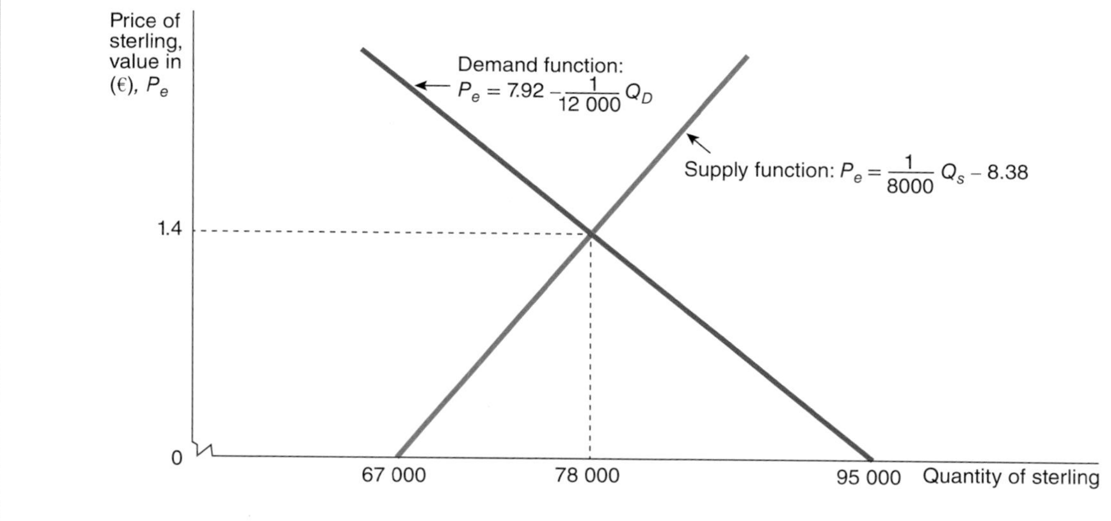

These two points define the straight line inverse demand curve. Now we can find the inverse supply function:

$$Q_S = 67000 + 8000P_e$$
$$8000P_e = Q_s - 67000$$
$$P_e = \frac{1}{8000}Q_S - 8.38$$

This is the inverse supply curve also shown in Figure 37.1. We already found one point on the supply curve. We know that when $P_e = 1.4$, $Q_S = 78\ 000$. When $P_e = 0$, then:

$$0 = \frac{1}{8000}Q_S - 8.38$$
$$Q_S = 8.38 \times 8000$$
$$Q_S = £67040$$

It would be £67 000 without the rounding error so we have plotted it as £67 000. Figure 37.1 shows the equilibrium price of sterling, which is €1.4, and the quantity of sterling demanded and supplied at that price.

We now find the new inverse demand curve that is the result of a decline in demand for sterling.

$$Q_D = 91000 - 12000P_e$$
$$12000P_e = 91000 - Q_D$$
$$P_e = 7.58 - \frac{1}{12000}Q_D$$

Figure 37.2 incorporates the original diagram but with the addition of the new inverse demand curve.

FIGURE 37.2

The Effect of a Fall in the Demand for Sterling

A fall in the demand for sterling is shown as a downward shift in the demand curve for sterling. With an unchanged supply of sterling function the new equilibrium price of sterling is €1.2.

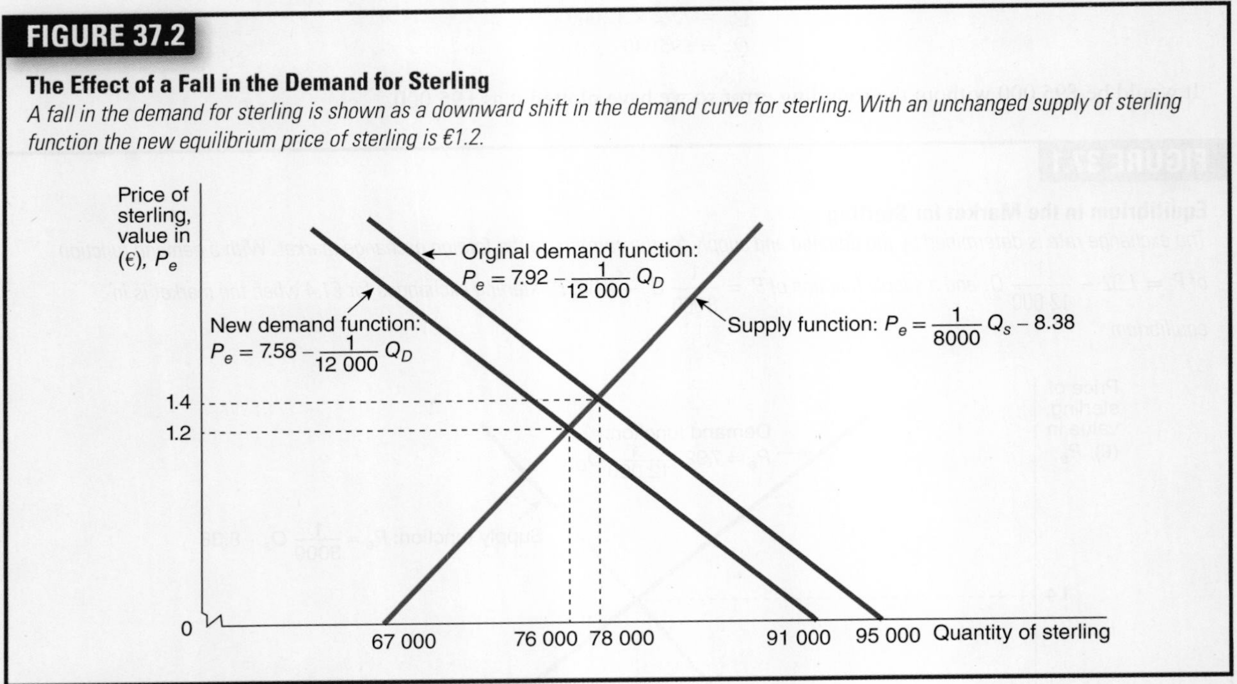

We already found one point on the demand curve. We know that when $P_e = 1.2$, $Q_D = £76\,600$. *When* $P_e = 0$, then:

$$0 = 7.58 - \frac{1}{12000}Q_D$$
$$Q_D = 7.58 \times 12000$$
$$Q_D = £90960$$

It would be 91 000 without the rounding error so we have plotted it as £91 000 in Figure 37.2. These two points define the new straight line inverse demand curve. The new equilibrium price and quantity are also shown.

Government Intervention in the Market for Foreign Exchange

Now we consider what happens if the government wishes to have its currency at an exchange rate different from the free market equilibrium rate. Let's assume that it is the UK government wanting the pound sterling to remain at £1 = €1.4 when the market equilibrium rate is £1 = €1.2. One possibility is to raise the sterling interest rate, making it more attractive for people to hold sterling. This will shift the demand curve for sterling upwards until equilibrium at the desired rate is reached. However, this may conflict with the interest rate needed for internal balance. For example a higher interest rate may discourage investment at home.

The option we will consider here is that of intervention in the foreign exchange market whereby the government acts as a buyer or seller of foreign currency. Using as an example the market we have been describing, how can the UK government (through the Bank of England) intervene in the foreign exchange market to ensure the exchange rate is at the desired level?

At a rate of £1 = €1.4 we know the supply of sterling to be £78 000 per day. However, at that rate the quantity demanded is:

$$\begin{aligned} Q_D &= 91\,000 - 12\,000P_e \\ &= 91\,000 - (12\,000 \times 1.4) \\ &= 91\,000 - 16\,800 \\ &= £74\,200 \end{aligned}$$

Now subtract quantity demanded from quantity supplied:

$$78\,000 - 74\,200 = £3800$$

The amount of sterling appearing on the foreign exchange market without a buyer is £3800 million. It is this quantity that the Bank of England will have to purchase each day to keep the rate at the desired level of £1 = €1.4.

The cost to the government is price multiplied by quantity.

$$3800 \times 1.4 = €5320$$

The central bank must find €5320 million each day that this surplus of sterling exists with which to purchase its own currency. We show this in Figure 37.3.

FIGURE 37.3

Government Intervention in the Market for Sterling

A government may choose to maintain a price of its currency above its equilibrium value by purchasing its own currency. In this example, to maintain a value of sterling of €1.4 it must purchase the excess supply of 78 000 – 74 200 = £3800 per period. This amount must be purchased a price of £1 = €1.4. So the exchange cost is 3800 x 1.4 = €5320 per period. This is shown as the green shaded area.

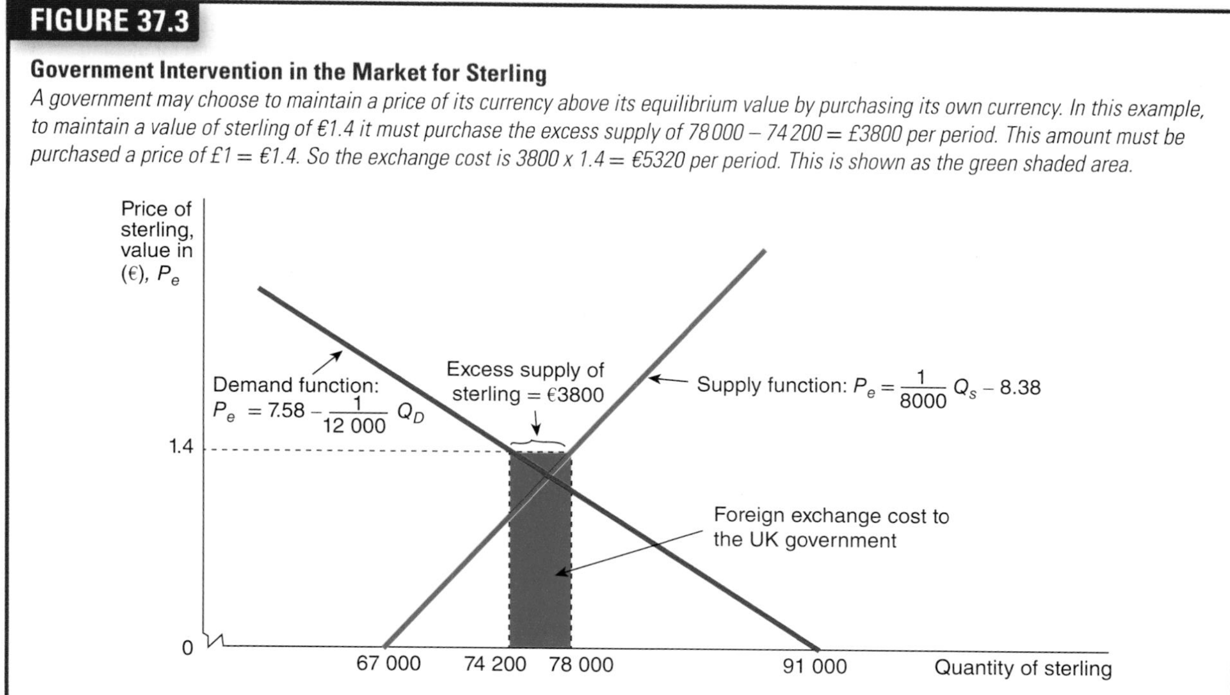

The effect of a change in interest rate to fix the exchange rate and the effect of support price buying will not look the same diagrammatically. Consider first an interest rate policy. If an interest rate policy is used, then the whole demand curve for sterling shifts. It shifts upwards with a rate rise and downwards with a rate fall. An interest rate rise to raise the price of sterling is shown in Panel (a) of Figure 37.4. At every price of sterling the higher rate of interest increases demand. If the market rate without central bank intervention is at P_{e1}, then a successful interest rate increase can push the exchange rate to P_{e2}, by shifting sterling demand from D_1 to D_2. The equilibrium quantity exchanged increases from Q_{e1} to Q_{e2}.

Now consider a support price buying policy, shown in Panel (b) of Figure 37.4. The demand curve doesn't move. It changes shape. If the price is above the desired rate of P_{e2} then central bank intervention is nil. The demand curve is not affected. However, to prevent the exchange rate falling below P_{e2} the central bank must buy up whatever excess supply is on the market. The demand curve becomes perfectly elastic at P_{e2}. The whole demand curve is described by ABCE. Bank of England daily purchases of sterling are shown as the distance between Q_{e2} and Q_{e3}.

FIGURE 37.4

Comparing Interest Rate Policy with Support Price Buying

One way for a government to create an exchange rate above its market equilibrium is to raise interest rates, shifting the demand curve for its currency upwards. In panel (a) this is seen to raise the exchange rate from P_{e1} to P_{e2}. An alternative is to a support price buying policy, shown in Panel (b). The government purchases its own currency in whatever quantity is necessary to achieve its exchange rate goal. Here it changes the demand curve to ABCE, purchasing a volume of sterling of $Q_{e2} - Q_{e3}$.

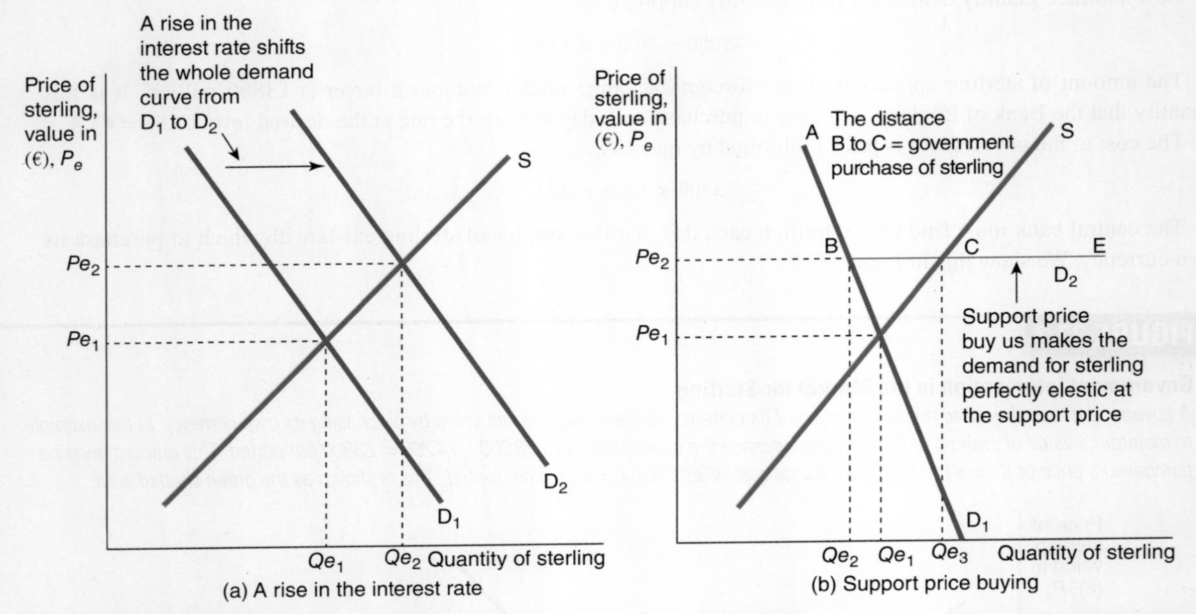

One might draw a parallel between this 'support price buying' and the government purchase of commodities that we examined in Chapter 9. However, there is an important difference. The government there was buying a flow of goods from a flow of tax receipts. Here it is instructing the central bank to buy a flow of currency with a stock of foreign currency reserves. If the reserves are exhausted the policy cannot continue unless foreign governments or some other international body such as the International Monetary Fund will lend it the funds to do so.

Other 'Fixed' Systems

We have considered two possibilities, a floating, market determined exchange rate, or a fixed exchange rate. There are other possibilities. We mention two. One possibility is the use of a target zone. Here the government uses foreign exchange reserves to fix a rate within a band. The currency is allowed only to float within a small target zone. This is a possibility used by the UK in the past. It has also been used by countries in the process of planning to join the euro area. A further possibility is the 'crawling peg'. The exchange rate is allowed to change over time but the government instructs the central bank to intervene in the market so that it only changes at some predetermined rate.

PROBLEMS AND APPLICATIONS

1 In the foreign exchange market the Pantera Peso is traded against the Moraroi Mogu. The exchange rate e is measured in Pesos per Mogu $\left[\frac{Peso}{Mogu\ 1}\right]$. The demand function for Mogus is $Q_D{}^0 = 9600 - 200e$. The supply is given by $Q_S{}^0 = -1200 + 400e$.

a. Calculate the inverse demand and supply functions and show them in a graph.

b. Find the equilibrium exchange rate.

c. Assume the demand for export products of Moraroi is falling and therefore the demand function for the economy's currency Mogu is shifting to $Q_D^1 = 7200 - 200e$. Determine the new inverse demand function and enter it into the graph.

d. If the two currencies have a flexible exchange rate, what would it be now?

e. Pantera and Moraroi are connected through a fixed exchange rate of $e^{fix} = 15\left[\frac{Peso}{Mogu\ 1}\right]$. How much excess supply or demand for the Mogu is there with the original supply Q_S^0 and demand Q_D^0 functions?

f. What does your result from e) imply for central bank interventions, the necessary outlays in the foreign exchange market and for the stance of monetary policy?

g. How does the shift to $Q_D^1 = 7200 - 200e$ affect Pantera's interventions in the foreign exchange market?

h. Return to Q_D^0 and consider a change in the supply of foreign currency to $Q_S^1 = -2400 + 400e$. Calculate the exchange rate in a flexible exchange rate system.

i. What does Pantera's central bank need to do to maintain the fixed exchange rate at $e^{fix} = 15\left[\frac{Peso}{Mogu\ 1}\right]$?

j. Please combine Q_D^1 with Q_S^1 to find the necessary amount of interventions under the fixed exchange rate system.

38 THE FINANCIAL CRISIS AND SOVEREIGN DEBT

In this chapter we conclude our studies with some thoughts about mathematics for economics and, in particular, the role of mathematics as it relates to the financial crisis that much of the world experienced recently. We considered the financial crisis in Chapter 26.

INTRODUCTION

If you have reached this point in your study of economics and mathematics, then congratulations, you have come a long way.

When you began your study of economics, you quickly discovered that it really was necessary to study some mathematics as well. You may well have begun your studies confident that you could handle the maths, but on the other hand you may well have thought any or all of the following:

1. I want to study economics but not mathematics.
2. Economics is interesting because it is about people, but mathematics is not.
3. Mathematics is frightening.
4. Mathematics is more than I can cope with.
5. Mathematics will just make the learning of economics harder.
6. Mathematics as applied to economics seems to be far removed from reality.
7. Mathematics in economics implies a precision that doesn't exist in the real world.

We hope that you are now convinced that none of these things is so.

1. '*I want to study economics but not mathematics*.'
Economics has, for good reason, been called the Queen of the Social Sciences. However, we are confident that you have found that, in order to appreciate its value, you needed some mathematics to make sense of economics. Some want to study poetry and then discover that it is impossible to do so properly without studying the English language. Some want to study astronomy but find they cannot do so in isolation from physics. Some want to study economics but find it impossible properly to appreciate its value without some mathematics. This is what we hope you have discovered for yourself.

2. '*Economics is interesting because it is about people, but mathematics is not*.'
Economics, as you have discovered, is indeed about people and how they behave. However, people are interesting collectively, not just on an individual basis. If we are to understand human behaviour on an aggregate basis, to study what the majority of people are likely to do in any given circumstance, we need to analyze their behaviour with the tools of both mathematics and indeed statistics. You have probably found that in some things you are not like most people. You cannot generalize from your own experience, or even those of your friends, to how society at large behaves. However, differences between people tend to cancel each other out in large populations. For example, some people are rich and others are poor. Thus, collectively, the situation is more stable and less sporadic than your own experience might suggest. Economics, mathematics and statistics all have a part to play in understanding human society at an aggregate level.

3. '*Mathematics is frightening.*'
   This has been the conviction of thousands of students of economics before you. However, we hope that you have found by taking each step, one at a time, you have built up an understanding of a mathematical argument and reached a conclusion that would otherwise have been very challenging previously. Think, for example, of your knowledge and understanding of investment behaviour of firms. How could you have understood this without the basic mathematical rules of discounting? It may have started out as fairly daunting but hopefully, as your confidence grew, you understood the basic mathematical concepts. Then by trying some problems and working through to the solutions your confidence grew further. What once seemed very challenging became quite manageable. We hope that your study through this book has taught you that mathematics is nowhere near as scary as you once thought.

4. '*Mathematics is more than I can cope with.*'
   Well it wasn't! You got to the end. You may still feel you didn't understand everything fully, that there are gaps in your understanding. Don't worry. Few understand it all. You may feel that you will forget some of the things you learned. You probably will. However, we hope that you understood sufficiently to progress through 37 chapters and arrive at a point where you can feel a sense of real achievement and an understanding that you may well have thought improbable.

5. *Mathematics will just make the learning of economics harder.*
   Our aim was to show that mathematics can help make the learning easier. The world is incredibly complex. If we are to understand the essence of its exchange relationships, we need every tool at our disposal to simplify without being unrealistic. Mathematics is a powerful tool to do just this. For example, it is often essential to know how sensitive a variable is to the change in the value of another. An understanding of elasticity would be difficult without some mathematical insights. Moreover, economics requires rigorous thinking to get from assumptions to conclusions. Mathematics will help you to do this. Of course many economic ideas can be understood without mathematics, but think of economic understanding as a jewel that is best seen from many different angles. One angle is history, another is politics, another is geography, still another technology, but an angle that gives a unique perspective is that of mathematics.

6. *Maths as applied to economics seems to be far removed from reality.*
   We hope that we have shown that this is not so. Even when we make apparently unrealistic assumptions we discover insights into human behaviour. Recall our analysis of perfect competition. Even though its combination of assumptions will be found together relatively rarely, it can prove valuable in understanding and even predicting economic behaviour.

7. *Maths in economics implies precision that doesn't exist in the real world.*
   This is believed to be true by many. We can now consider an illustration of this argument with reference to recent economic events. Mathematics has been at the heart of the world's quite recent financial crisis that in many ways has been bigger than anything the world has ever seen previously, a crisis whose effects have been so substantial that they continue to be felt today. To some this is a demonstration of how the use of mathematics is responsible for considerable human suffering as so many people have been caught up in this crisis. Let's examine the role of mathematics here.

The Role of Mathematics in the Financial Crisis Following 2008

Understanding the financial crisis requires an understanding of financial instruments, including 'futures', 'options' and 'derivatives'. Let's remind ourselves of the meaning of these terms.

A future is a contract for an asset, most commonly shares, commodities or foreign currency, bought at an agreed price but not delivered and paid for until a specified future time. Let us take an example of a futures contract in the foreign exchange market. If I am the owner of a European company making a machine to sell abroad in six months' time for \$10 000, I don't know what these dollars will be worth to me in euros when I receive payment. I can fix a price in euros now for the \$10 000 in order to avoid the risk of a movement in the currency price that might cause me to lose out.

An option is a contract giving a buyer the right to buy or sell an underlying financial instrument at a specified price on or before a specified date. The buyer has the right but not the obligation if he/she subsequently chooses not to exercise the right. A company needing to buy copper for its business can take out a contract that enables it to buy the copper in six months' time at a price agreed now. Again the idea is to eliminate uncertainty. The uncertainty is transferred to the seller of the option, who will hope to profit from the deal in the same way that an insurance company takes on risk for potential gain.

A derivative is a more generalized term for any asset whose price is derived from one or more underlying assets. This derivative is in essence a contract between the parties based upon that asset.

What is the price that will be agreed for such contracts? What is the price that a trader in such financial instruments can offer that will be acceptable to the buyer and that will give a good chance of a profit to the trader? The answer is that it is calculated using complex mathematical formulae of which the best known is Black–Scholes equation, published in 1973.[1] It is a complex formula that you don't need to know for introductory economics but will certainly know at some stage if you go on to study finance.

It was not the only formula. Many other mathematical models and techniques were developed from this one. At first they seemed very successful for the traders that used them. By 2007 the value of trade in derivatives worldwide was one thousand million million US dollars. To put this into context it is around 10 times the world's total production of goods throughout history.

Reliance on these mathematical models played a huge part in the crash that followed in 2008. As we saw in Chapter 26, valuations of these financial instruments were far out of line with the underlying worth of the assets. When this finally became obvious the crash came and traders lost large sums. Financial institutions went bankrupt. Lending to firms was restricted and the real economy suffered.

Should we blame mathematics for the financial crisis? The answer is certainly not. It is a powerful argument for all we have been trying to show you through the book. Maths needs to be *understood* so that it can be used properly to illuminate.

The mathematical model was based on certain assumptions. As we have seen many times throughout the book, we must make some assumptions to produce a model of reality. A crucial assumption for the Black–Scholes equation is that if a market experiences steady growth then the value of the asset underlying a derivative has a constant volatility so that it can be known how erratically its price will fluctuate. This proved to be a correct assumption for some time. However, when it finally failed, panic set in, traders tried to sell heavily and prices crashed.

It is important to realize that the assumptions of the model had been clearly spelt out by the authors. Traders chose to ignore their experience and common sense, entering values into spreadsheets based on the model. They simply applied the model uncritically until the crash came. The mathematics gave insights which those who used the maths chose to ignore.

Summary

Rather than demonstrating a failure of mathematics, the financial crisis demonstrated something crucial. Mathematics is enormously powerful. Studying it and utilizing its insights enables us to know its value … and its limitations.

PROBLEMS AND APPLICATIONS

1 You have entered into a futures contract to buy £10 000 in three month's time at an exchange rate of $e^f_£ = 1.5\left[\frac{€}{£\,1}\right]$.

a. At the day the trade is actually carried out, you could have bought the £10 000 at a current exchange rate of $e^s_£ = 1.2\left[\frac{€}{£\,1}\right]$ in the so called spot market. How much are you winning or losing through your futures contract (compare with how much you would net to spend if you purchase in the spot market)?

b. Now, assume you have purchased a 'call'-option that gives you the right to purchase the £10 000 at the exchange rate of $e^f_£ = 1.5\left[\frac{€}{£\,1}\right]$. Under the contract you have the right to demand delivery of the pounds but

[1] Black, F. and Scholes, M. (1973) The Pricing of Options and Corporate Liabilities. *The Journal of Political Economy* 81 **(3)** 637–54.

you do not have to exercise the right; instead you can just let the contract lapse. Would you demand delivery from the option seller?

c. You have purchased the option from an option seller for a premium payment. Does the premium payment influence your (rational) behaviour on the day the contract matures?

d. You can combine a spot market transaction and a futures market transaction into a swap contract. This would mean, that you i.e. buy €15 000 at an exchange rate of $e^{f}_{£} = 1.4\left[\frac{€}{£\ 1}\right]$ now in the spot market from your contract partner and you also commit to selling the euros back to your contract partner against £ at a futures exchange rate $e^{f}_{£} = 1.5\left[\frac{€}{£\ 1}\right]$ in three months. How do interest rates in £ ($i_{£}$) and € ($i_{€}$) enter into your calculation of profits from this contract?

2 'Human behaviour cannot be captured in mathematical equations and to even try this is amoral.' Would it be better if you tried to explain markets and economics without the use of formula?

APPENDIX

Here are two ways to arrive at the answer to the oranges problem that we introduced in the Preface. In this particular case it might be quicker and easier if you tried to solve it by using trial and error but here we present you with the formal solution. If you find a neater solution, we would be interested to hear through Cengage (please contact EMEAMankiw@cengage.com).

SUGGESTED SOLUTION ONE

We start by assuming that the number of oranges that the fruit seller had at the start was x. So if the first customer bought half of that number plus half an orange, we can show this like that:

$$\frac{x}{2}+\frac{1}{2} \tag{1}$$

Then the second customer purchased half of what was left and half an orange. What was left was:

$$x-\left(\frac{x}{2}+\frac{1}{2}\right)$$

Now we need to divide that by two and add half an orange. So we get:

$$\frac{x-\left(\frac{x}{2}+\frac{1}{2}\right)}{2}+\frac{1}{2} \tag{2}$$

The third customer bought half of what was now left and half an orange. What was left was x minus what the first customer bought, minus what the second one bought. So that is:

$$x-\left(\frac{x}{2}+\frac{1}{2}\right)=\left(\frac{x-\left(\frac{x}{2}+\frac{1}{2}\right)}{2}+\frac{1}{2}\right)$$

Now, as before, we need to divide this in half and add half an orange:

$$\frac{x-\left(\frac{x}{2}+\frac{1}{2}\right)-\left(\frac{x-\left(\frac{x}{2}+\frac{1}{2}\right)}{2}+\frac{1}{2}\right)}{2}+\frac{1}{2} \tag{3}$$

It looks complicated but what we now have is three expressions that give us what the first, second and third customer each bought. If we add them together we must get the entire number of oranges x, because we know that at the end the seller had nothing left and had not cut or torn andy oranges.

So 1 + 2 + 3 must equal x.

Here it is:

$$\frac{x}{2}+\frac{1}{2}+\frac{x-\left(\frac{x}{2}+\frac{1}{2}\right)}{2}+\frac{1}{2}+\frac{x-\left(\frac{x}{2}+\frac{1}{2}\right)-\left(\frac{x-\left(\frac{x}{2}+\frac{1}{2}\right)}{2}+\frac{1}{2}\right)}{2}+\frac{1}{2}=x$$

We can multiply both sides by 2 and, being very careful with the plus and minus signs, we get:

$$x + 1 + x - \frac{x}{2} - \frac{1}{2} + 1 + x - \frac{x}{2} - \frac{1}{2} - \left(\frac{x - \left(\frac{x}{2} + \frac{1}{2}\right)}{2} + \frac{1}{2} \right) + 1 = 2x$$

We multiply both sides by 2 again:

$$2x + 2 + 2x - x - 1 + 2 + 2x - x - 1 - x + \frac{x}{2} + \frac{1}{2} - 1 + 2 = 4x$$

We multiply the two sides of the equation by 2 one last time:

$$4x + 4 + 4x - 2x - 2 + 4 + 4x - 2x - 2 - 2x + x + 1 - 2 + 4 = 8x$$

$$x = 7$$

The fruit seller must have had 7 oranges to start with. If you want, you can check your answer.

The first buyer purchases half the oranges plus half an orange. That is:

$$\frac{7}{2} + \frac{1}{2} = 4$$

Then there are 3 oranges left and the second customer buys half of that, which is 1.5 orange plus half an orange, that is, 2 oranges.

All that is left is one orange and indeed the last buyer wants half of that plus half an orange which makes exactly one orange.

SUGGESTED SOLUTION TWO

You can also approach the problem backwards. This time we begin with the final customer:

Customer 3 is looking at z oranges and so leaves:

$$z - \left(\frac{z}{2} + \frac{1}{2}\right) = 0$$

$$z - \frac{z}{2} = \frac{1}{2}$$

$$2z - z = 1$$

So

$$z = 1$$

Customer 2 is looking at y oranges and so leaves:

$$y - \left(\frac{y}{2} + \frac{1}{2}\right) = z$$

But $z = 1$ (from above)

So

$$y - \left(\frac{y}{2} + \frac{1}{2}\right) = 1$$

$$y - \frac{y}{2} = 1 + \frac{1}{2}$$

$$2y - y = 2 + 1$$

$$y = 3$$

Customer 3 is looking at x oranges and so leaves:

$$x - \left(\frac{x}{2} + \frac{1}{2}\right) = y$$

But $y = 3$ (from above)

So

$$x - \left(\frac{x}{2} + \frac{1}{2}\right) = 3$$

$$x - \frac{x}{2} = 3 + \frac{1}{2}$$

$$2x - x = 6 + 1$$

$$x = 7$$

The fruit seller started with 7 oranges. You can see that this solution looks easier and neater.

As is often the case with solving problems, there is more than one way to get the answer. Some ways may be more elegant or efficient. However, the most important thing is to find your way to the correct answer. The nice thing about solving a problem in more than one way is that it adds to your confidence that you have found the correct solution.

INDEX